DATE DUE

DEMCO 38-296

MASTERPLOTS II

SHORT STORY
SERIES

MASTERPLOTS II

SHORT STORY
SERIES
SUPPLEMENT

7

A-Fat

Edited by
FRANK N. MAGILL

Consulting Editor
CHARLES E. MAY
CALIFORNIA STATE UNIVERSITY, LONG BEACH

SALEM PRESS

Pasadena, California   Englewood Cliffs, New Jersey

Library of Congress Cataloging-in-Publication Data
Masterplots II: Short story series.
  Bibliography: p.
  Includes index.
  Summary: Examines the theme, characters, plot,
style and technique of more than 1,200 nineteenth- and
twentieth-century works by prominent authors from
around the world.
    1. Fiction—19th century—Stories, plots, etc. 2. Fic-
tion—19th century—History and criticism. 3. Fiction—
20th century—Stories, plots, etc. 4. Fiction—20th cen-
tury—History and criticism. 5. Short story. [1. Short
stories—Stories, plots, etc. 2. Short story] I. Magill,
Frank Northen, 1907-   . II. Title: Masterplots 2. III.
Title: Masterplots two.
PN3326.M27   1986   809.3   86-22025
Supplement.
ISBN 0-89356-769-8 (set)
ISBN 0-89356-770-1 (volume 7)

PUBLISHER'S NOTE

Masterplots II: Short Story Series Supplement contains entirely fresh critical evaluations of 511 outstanding short stories by 173 different world authors, who represent the full history of the short-story form: from the early nineteenth century through the late twentieth century. Its four volumes follow the six volumes of *Masterplots II: Short Story Series* (1986), continuing their pagination and volume-number sequence. Essays in the combined ten volumes contain more than 1,750,000 words of text, bringing the total coverage to 1,243 stories and 448 authors.

As in the original series, the format is uniform throughout. Essays are arranged alphabetically by story title. Each essay has ready-reference headings listing the name and vital dates of the author, the type and time of the story's plot, its locale, the date of its first publication, and a list of principal characters with brief identifications. Following this top matter, each essay is divided into three sections: *The Story*, which summarizes the narrative; *Themes and Meanings*; and *Style and Technique*.

The appendices and indexes in this set encompass all ten volumes of the combined series and offer several new features. In addition to comprehensive indexes of titles and authors' names, there are lists of titles by dates of publication and by key words, and an index to authors by country. The key word list should prove especially valuable for finding translated stories, which often are published under more than one title in English.

In the decade that has passed since *Masterplots II: Short Story Series* appeared, the short-story form has continued to enjoy a revival so strong that it has been dubbed a "renaissance." In a heartening reversal of the earlier trend away from short fiction, new writers have been increasingly encouraged by a number of American magazines and creative writing programs. In a reaction against experimental, self-reflexive, postmodern short fiction, a new kind of short fiction has found a particularly suitable home in the short-story form. The names for this new fiction are as varied and original as the fiction itself: "new realism," "minimalism," "pop realism," "dirty realism," "K-Mart realism," and even "post-alcoholic blue-collar minimalist hyperrealism"—a term coined by John Barth. These new forms are best represented by the work of such writers as Raymond Carver, Ann Beattie, Mary Robison, Bobbie Ann Mason, Richard Ford, Barry Hannah, Amy Hempel, Joy Williams, and Tobias Wolff—all of whom are well represented in these supplemental volumes. Among these writers, the focus is typically on working-class characters. Carver and Wolff, for example, tend to write on the Northwest; Mason on the South; Ford, Hannah, and Hempel on the West; and Beattie on the East.

In addition to incorporating essays on writers who represent the new experimental trends in short fiction, this set addresses another vigorous trend: the rapidly growing appreciation in American literature curricula of the riches of the nation's different cultures. A fifth of the new essays in these volumes discuss stories by more than sixty-five Latino, African American, Asian American, and Native American writers. *Masterplots II: Short Story Series Supplement* also follows the original series in recognizing the richness of the cultures of other countries. A third of the new essays examine stories by writers from outside the United States. The bulk of these stories are written by British, Irish, and European authors, but the set also contains numerous titles by authors from Canada, Latin America, Africa, and other parts of the world.

Essays on the stories of well-known African American writers were an important part of the original volumes. This supplement extends that coverage with new essays on works by James Baldwin, Toni Cade Bambara, Charles Waddell Chesnutt, Ralph Ellison, Ernest J. Gaines, Zora Neal Hurston, Jamaica Kincaid, and others. Among the thirteen additional African American writers covered here are Maya Angelou, Amiri Baraka, Nikki Giovanni, Charles Johnson, and Ann Petry.

The increase in representation of Asian Americans is dramatic, with eleven of twelve Asian American authors being represented for the first time. These include Mei Mei Evans, Sui Sin Far, Kim Yong Ik, Maxine Hong Kingston, and Amy Tan. The representation of Latino writers shows a similarly dramatic increase: Of the twenty Latino authors covered, nineteen are new to the series. These writers include Rudolfo A. Anaya, Denise Chávez, Sandra Cisneros, Judith Ortiz Cofer, Roberta Fernández, Nicholasa Mohr, Mary Helen Ponce, and Helena María Viramontes.

A particularly valuable addition to this supplement is its expanded coverage of Native American authors, most of whom are noted for skillfully incorporating traditional storytelling motifs into their fiction. The supplement contains new essays on stories by Louise Erdrich and Leslie Marmon Silko, and adds essays on Paula Gunn Allen, Michael Dorris, Joy Harjo, Linda Hogan, N. Scott Momaday, Simon J. Ortiz, Greg Sarris, and Gerald Vizenor.

One of the driving forces behind the *Masterplots II* series is the need for reference material that reflects what is actually taught in literature classes. While striving to keep the reference sets up to date, we have been careful not to overlook significant literary works from the past. To this end, readers will find new essays on stories by such familiar American writers as Donald Barthelme, Truman Capote, Ernest Hemingway, Henry James, Norman Mailer, Vladimir Nabokov, Katherine Anne Porter, John Steinbeck, Mark Twain, Kurt Vonnegut, and many others. Familiar British and European writers covered here include Honoré de Balzac, Heinrich Böll, Dino Buzzati, Anton Chekhov, G. K. Chesterton, Joseph Conrad, Fyodor Dostoevski, E. M. Forster, Graham Greene, James Joyce, D. H. Lawrence, Guy de Maupassant, Seán O'Faoláin, and Virginia Woolf.

As with all *Masterplots II* series, the strength of these volumes rests on the expertise brought by our contributing reviewers. The nearly 250 academicians and others who have written for this supplement bring a range of talents as diverse as the authors whom they discuss. A list of their names appears at the beginning of volume 7. We are also indebted to the project's consulting editor, Professor Charles E. May of California State University, Long Beach, whose outstanding knowledge in this field is matched by his patient cheerfulness.

CONTRIBUTING REVIEWERS

McCrea Adams
Independent Scholar

Michael Adams
Fairleigh Dickinson University

Amy Adelstein
Independent Scholar

Yasuko Akiyama
Carleton College

Betty Alldredge
Angelo State University

Stanley Archer
Texas A&M University

Gerald S. Argetsinger
Rochester Institute of Technology

Charles F. Bahmueller
Center for Civic Education

Barbara J. Bair
Independent Scholar

Jim Baird
University of North Texas

James Barbour
Arizona State University

H. J. Baron
Calvin College

Melissa E. Barth
Appalachian State University

Margaret D. Bauer
Texas A&M University

L. Elisabeth Beattie
Elizabethtown Community College

Cynthia S. Becerra
Humphreys College

Carol F. Bender
Alma College

Robert Bensen
Hartwick College

Joe Benson
*North Carolina Agricultural and Technical
State University*

Dorothy M. Betz
Georgetown University

Cynthia A. Bily
Adrian College

Margaret Boe Birns
New School for Social Research

Robert G. Blake
Elon College

Pegge Bochynski
Salem State College

Brinda Bose
Boston University

J. H. Bowden
Indiana University, Southeast

Kevin Boyle
Elon College

Gerhard Brand
California State University, Los Angeles

Stephen G. Brown
University of South Florida

Faith Hickman Brynie
Independent Scholar

Jeffrey L. Buller
Georgia Southern University

Judith Callarman
Cisco Junior College

Edmund J. Campion
University of Tennessee, Knoxville

Warren J. Carson
University of South Carolina at Spartanburg

Thomas Cassidy
South Carolina State University

Cida S. Chase
Oklahoma State University

Allan Chavkin
Southwest Texas State University

Laura Chavkin
Independent Scholar

C. L. Chua
California State University, Fresno

vii

Julian W. Connolly
University of Virginia

Chella Courington
Huntingdon College

Virginia M. Crane
California State University, Los Angeles

Susan Jaye Dauer
University of Texas at Austin

Jo Culbertson Davis
Williams Baptist College

Frank Day
Clemson University

Bill Delaney
Independent Scholar

James E. Devlin
State University of New York College at Oneonta

Carolyn F. Dickinson
Columbia College

Rosanne Fraine Donahue
University of Massachusetts at Boston

Sarah Smith Ducksworth
Kean College of New Jersey

Joyce Duncan
East Tennessee State University

Margaret V. Ekstrom
St. John Fisher College

Janet M. Ellerby
University of North Carolina at Wilmington

James Feast
Baruch College of the City University of New York

John W. Fiero
University of Southwestern Louisiana

Edward Fiorelli
St. John's University, New York

Gustavo Pérez Firmat
Duke University

Bonnie Flaig
Kalamazoo Valley Community College

Thomas C. Foster
University of Michigan, Flint

Robert J. Frail
Centenary College, New Jersey

Carol Franks
Portland State University

Thomas B. Frazier
Cumberland College

Mary Pierce Frost
Santa Rosa Junior College

Patricia H. Fulbright
Clark College

Kelly Fuller
Independent Scholar

Constance M. Fulmer
Pepperdine University

Robert L. Gale
University of Pittsburgh

Ann D. Garbett
Averett College

Marshall Bruce Gentry
University of Indianapolis

Jill B. Gidmark
University of Minnesota

Howard Giskin
Appalachian State University

Beaird Glover
Independent Scholar

Marc Goldstein
Independent Scholar

Linda Silverstein Gordon
Worcester State College

James Green
Arizona State University

John L. Grigsby
Tennessee Technological University

L. M. Grow
Broward Community College

M. A. Grubbs
University of Kentucky

Angela Hague
Middle Tennessee State University

Elsie Galbreath Haley
Metropolitan State College of Denver

Cynthia Whitney Hallett
St. Mary's University
Halifax, Nova Scotia, Canada

CONTRIBUTING REVIEWERS

Barbara J. Hampton
The College of Wooster

Natalie Harper
Simon's Rock of Bard College

Gregory Harris
Independent Scholar

Sandra Hanby Harris
Tidewater Community College

Stephen M. Hart
University of Kentucky

John C. Hawley
Santa Clara University

Margaret Hawthorne
Independent Scholar

David M. Heaton
Ohio University

Peter B. Heller
Manhattan College

Terry Heller
Coe College

Roseanne L. Hoefel
Alma College

Dennis Hoilman
Ball State University

W. Kenneth Holditch
Independent Scholar

John R. Holmes
Franciscan University of Steubenville

Glenn Hopp
Howard Payne University

Eric Howard
Independent Scholar

Susan Hwang
Independent Scholar

Jeffry Jensen
Independent Scholar

Jeff Johnson
Brevard Community College

Sheila Golburgh Johnson
Independent Scholar

Michelle Jones
Muskingum College

Myra H. Jones
Manatee Community College

Michael Scott Joseph
Rutgers University

Tina Kane
Independent Scholar

Cynthia Lee Katona
Ohlone College

Susan E. Keegan
Mendocino College

Richard Keenan
University of Maryland, Eastern Shore

Richard Kelly
University of Tennessee, Knoxville

W. P. Kenney
Manhattan College

Susan S. Kissel
Northern Kentucky University

Grove Koger
Boise Public Library

Tom Koontz
Ball State University

James Kurtzleben
University of Northern Iowa

Linda L. Labin
Husson College

Marvin Lachman
Independent Scholar

Eugene Larson
Pierce College, Los Angeles

Jon Lavieri
Independent Scholar

Linda Ledford-Miller
University of Scranton

L. L. Lee
Western Washington University

Leon Lewis
Appalachian State University

Anna Lillios
University of Central Florida

Paul R. Lilly, Jr.
*State University of New York
College at Oneonta*

Laurie Lisa
Arizona State University

Janet McCann
Texas A&M University

Joanne McCarthy
Tacoma Community College

Andrew Macdonald
Loyola University of New Orleans

Gina Macdonald
Loyola University of New Orleans

Ron McFarland
University of Idaho

Edythe M. McGovern
West Los Angeles College

S. Thomas Mack
University of South Carolina at Aiken

Joseph McLaren
Hofstra University

A. L. McLeod
Rider University

Jennifer McLeod
California State University, Chico

Marian B. McLeod
Trenton State College

Jim McWilliams
Southern Illinois University at Carbondale

David W. Madden
California State University, Sacramento

Maria Theresa Maggi
University of Idaho

Edward A. Malone
University of Missouri, Rolla

Lois A. Marchino
University of Texas at El Paso

Peter Markus
Independent Scholar

William Matta
University of Guam

Charles E. May
California State University, Long Beach

Patrick Meanor
*State University of New York
  College at Oneonta*

Vasa D. Mihailovich
University of North Carolina

Paula M. Miller
Biola University

Robert A. Morace
Daemen College

Gregory L. Morris
*Pennsylvania State University, Erie
  Behrend College*

Toni J. Morris
University of Indianapolis

Sherry Morton-Mollo
Claremont Graduate School

Roark Mulligan
Christopher Newport University

C. Lynn Munro
Independent Scholar

Anna B. Nelson
Saint Peter's College

Terry Nienhuis
Western Carolina University

Gisela Norat
Agnes Scott College

Emma Coburn Norris
Troy State University

George T. Novotny
University of South Florida

Rafael Ocasio
Agnes Scott College

Bruce Olsen
Independent Scholar

Joyce M. Parks
Independent Scholar

Jay Paul
Christopher Newport University

D. G. Paz
Clemson University

Thomas R. Peake
King College

David Peck
California State University, Long Beach

Leslie Maile Pendleton
Independent Scholar

CONTRIBUTING REVIEWERS

Marion Boyle Petrillo
Bloomsburg University

Lela Phillips
Andrew College

Karen A. Pinter
Sauk Valley Community College

Cliff Prewencki
Independent Scholar

Victoria Price
Lamar University

Norman Prinsky
Augusta College

Charles Pullen
Queen's University
Kingston, Ontario, Canada

Josephine Raburn
Cameron University

R. Kent Rasmussen
Independent Scholar

Abe C. Ravitz
California State University, Dominguez Hills

Rosemary M. Canfield Reisman
Independent Scholar

Janine Rider
Mesa State College

Claire J. Robinson
Independent Scholar

Susan M. Rochette-Crawley
University of Northern Iowa

Kim Dickson Rogers
Independent Scholar

Mary Rohrberger
University of Northern Iowa

Carl Rollyson
Baruch College of the City University of New York

Paul Rosefeldt
Delgado Community College

Sidney Rosenfeld
Oberlin College

Grigory Roytman
Appalachian State University

Murray Sachs
Brandeis University

Chaman L. Sahni
Boise State University

Victor A. Santi
University of New Orleans

Kenneth Seib
Heartland Community College

John Sekora
North Carolina Central University

Constance Sherak
Connecticut College

Agnes A. Shields
Chestnut Hill College

Wilma J. Shires
Cisco Junior College

R. Baird Shuman
University of Illinois at Urbana-Champaign

Charles L. P. Silet
Iowa State University

Rennie Simson
State University of New York
College of Agriculture and Technology at Morrisville
Syracuse University

Carl Singleton
Fort Hays State University

Silvio Sirias
Appalachian State University

Jan Sjåvik
University of Washington

Genevieve Slomski
Independent Scholar

Nick David Smart
New York University

Marjorie Smelstor
University of Wisconsin—Eau Claire

Pamela J. Olubunmi Smith
University of Nebraska at Omaha

Jean M. Snook
Memorial University of Newfoundland

Stephen Soitos
University of Massachusetts at Amherst

George Soule
Carleton College

Scott M. Sprenger
Brigham Young University

Brian Stableford
Independent Scholar

James A. Stanger
University of California, Riverside

Isabel B. Stanley
East Tennessee State University

Judith L. Steininger
Milwaukee School of Engineering

Louise M. Stone
Bloomsburg University

Gerald H. Strauss
Bloomsburg University

Irene Struthers
Independent Scholar

James Sullivan
California State University, Los Angeles

David Sundstrand
Independent Scholar

Roy Arthur Swanson
University of Wisconsin—Milwaukee

Susan Elizabeth Sweeney
College of the Holy Cross

Terry Theodore
University of North Carolina at Wilmington

Julie Thompson
Independent Scholar

Lou Thompson
Texas Woman's University

Jonathan L. Thorndike
Lakeland College

Tiffany Elizabeth Thraves
Randolph-Macon Woman's College

Richard Tuerk
East Texas State University

Constance Vidor
Baltimore County Public Schools

Mary E. Virginia
Independent Scholar

Ka Ying Vu
California State University, Fresno

Qun Wang
California State University, Monterey Bay

Gladys J. Washington
Texas Southern University

Thomas Whissen
Wright State University

Thomas Willard
University of Arizona

Donna Glee Williams
North Carolina Center for the Advancment of Teaching

Tyrone Williams
Xavier University

Judith Barton Williamson
Sauk Valley Community College

Michael Witkoski
Independent Scholar

Susan Wladaver-Morgan
Independent Scholar

Pat M. Wong
Independent Scholar

Robert E. Yahnke
University of Minnesota

Clifton K. Yearley
State University of New York College at Buffalo

Mary Young
The College of Wooster

Laura M. Zaidman
University of South Carolina at Sumter

Weihua Zhang
State University of New York at Albany

Laura Weiss Zlogar
University of Wisconsin—River Falls

LIST OF TITLES IN VOLUME 7

LIST OF TITLES IN VOLUME 7

MASTERPLOTS II

SHORT STORY
SERIES

ACCEPTANCE OF THEIR WAYS

Author: Mavis Gallant (1922-   )
Type of plot: Domestic realism
Time of plot: The late 1950's
Locale: Italian Riviera
First published: 1960

> *Principal characters:*
> LILY LITTEL, a middle-aged English woman living abroad
> VANESSA FREEPORT, her landlady, a widow
> EDITH GARNETT, Freeport's relative and guest, also a widow

The Story

Lily Littel is a rather wilted "Lily-girl" from London, with champagne taste on a ginger-ale budget. Although her name and accent betray humble social origins, she aspires to live like the aristocracy. She lost her working-class husband, Cliff, during World War II, or perhaps simply lost interest in him, and began calling herself "Miss" Littel. She served for eight years as the paid companion of an elderly lady and received a modest bequest in the lady's will. She now spends most of the year in a pensione on the Italian Riviera, which is all that her ginger-ale budget will allow. When her quarterly dividend arrives, however, she goes to Nice on the more fashionable French Riviera to indulge her taste for champagne—indeed any sort of alcohol—because she is a binge drinker. As the story begins, her latest check is in the mail and she looks forward to another getaway. She will pretend to lavish her time and money on a poor sister and will enjoy being missed for a few days.

Mrs. Freeport has been running the small pensione for thirteen years, perhaps to be near the cemetery where her husband is buried. Among her annual paying guests is Mrs. Garnett, a cousin's widow, who is the oldest and wealthiest of the three characters. When Mrs. Garnett requests an Italian meal for the last night of her stay, Mrs. Freeport grudgingly sets the Christmas leftovers to one side. She even serves the wine undiluted. She orders Lily about like a serving girl, and Lily complies. The dinner is a disaster, nevertheless. Mrs. Garnett nibbles at her food and declines the main course. Mrs. Freeport takes offense and accuses her guest of secret eating, which is as bad in their book as secret drinking. She keeps up the insults until Mrs. Garnett faints and must be carried to bed.

After Mrs. Garnett leaves the next morning, Mrs. Freeport breaks into tears, lamenting that she will never see her dear old friend again. Lily replies, quite sensibly, that this sort of behavior has never kept Mrs. Garnett away in the past. Reassured, Mrs. Freeport begins to plan for the next tourist season, when she will make better provisions for her friend. Lily announces her plan to visit her sister and Mrs. Freeport responds politely, but both are too shaken by the day's events to speak more.

Themes and Meanings

Like most British citizens of the period in which this story is set, the three characters are intensely conscious of their social status. The seasonal guest, Mrs. Garnett, gives orders to the landlady, Mrs. Freeport, who in turn gives orders to her regular lodger, Lily. Each follows orders from another, but only grudgingly. Mrs. Freeport thinks her late cousin was crazy to indulge his wife, Mrs. Garnett, even to take her for a wife. Lily, meanwhile, thinks that the aristocratic life is her future; she no more wants to go back to work than she wants to go back to Mr. Littel. She is a shrewd observer of the upper class, well aware of its moral shortcomings but not about to let moral shortcomings get in her way. She is learning how to be a subtle cheapskate, just like the other characters.

It is Lily, above all, who makes the "Acceptance of Their Ways" in watching the richer widows and seeing through their ruses, but still wanting to share their way of life. Each woman seems to realize that she needs the others: Lily cannot afford Nice for more than a few days each year; Mrs. Freeport cannot afford a servant; and Mrs. Garnett does not have better prospects for the next Christmas season. Each woman also has her secrets. Lily has her diary and her drinking habit; Mrs. Freeport has the gravesite to visit; and Mrs. Garnett has a book on optimism to which she turns when others would engage in conversation. Yet they need one another in subtle ways, and so must be accepting.

What these women cannot accept are the ways of the Italian people among whom they live at the moment. Mrs. Garnett is regularly offended by bus drivers and others who try to serve her, and she is constantly offensive in turn. She wants new travel options and is annoyed that the Suez Crisis of 1956 has made travel to Egypt out of the question. Mrs. Freeport hates Italian cuisine, and Lily is more comfortable with the English way of life. Their expatriate world is a narrow world, but as narrow worlds go, it seems a pleasant enough place in which to exist.

Style and Technique

The story begins and ends with Lily, and although narrated in the third person, is told from her point of view. Lily is a shrewd woman, easily the most interesting. Her observations of the others range from envy to scorn and say as much about her as about them. When she forgets about the dinner arrangements for a moment and imagines how much she will be missed when she goes away to Nice, she thinks about the dresses that her landlady will fondly examine in her room and the diary that will be discreetly removed, so that her landlady cannot read its pointed remarks. Mavis Gallant says much about both characters in this brief scene, and more about their relationship; it is typical of her economy with words that all these nuances of character description and dialogue are contained in such a brief story. Like many of Gallant's stories, "Acceptance of Their Ways" first appeared in *The New Yorker*, where it covered four pages with room left for cartoons; it was reprinted in Gallant's collection *An Unmarried Man's Summer: Eight Stories and a Short Novel* (1965).

With her ironic outlook and terse style, Gallant is especially attracted to the oxymoron or contradiction in terms. Lily's past as a paid companion and her present position as a paying guest cast doubt on the companionship and hospitality by placing them within the cash nexus. Lily's manner is characterized at once by bullying and servility, showing her ambivalence toward the other characters. Her eyes look kind when she is plotting mischief. She is generous by nature, but her generosity is overshadowed by an envious admiration for superior women. The very name she goes by, "Miss Littel," reveals some duplicity, for it combines her married surname and her claim to be a spinster, not a widow.

Meanwhile, Mrs. Freeport's pensione smells of "regularly aired decay." The very name "Freeport" is contradictory, since her port is not free. Indeed, her name recalls that of Sir Andrew Freeport, the archetypal capitalist in Joseph Addison and Richard Steele's *Spectator* (1711-1712). The ugly evening gets reduced, the next day, to the yogurt affair, because Mrs. Garnett prefers fresh yogurt to the old cheese that Lily passes, and because Mrs. Freeport is such a stingy hostess that she quickly takes offense. In her nasty fit, she accuses her guest of making a mess on her plate and leaving a wreck of lettuce.

Along with the economy of phrase, there is an economy of scene and action. The story's first half takes place as a series of thoughts occurring to Lily in the time that it takes her to follow Mrs. Freeport's opening request and serve the cheese. The rest is a consequence. When Mrs. Garnett prefers yogurt to the moldy cheese, Mrs. Freeport takes offense.

As an expatriate writing about expatriates, Gallant describes a provisional life, defined in many ways by absent men: Cliff Littel, Mr. Freeport, and William Henry Garnett. In the brief ending, on the morning of Mrs. Garnett's departure, the remaining characters think for a moment about a world that is not a repetition of the same things. Mrs. Garnett, who looks skeletal when tears wash away her makeup, will die. Miss Littel will move to Nice in order to care for her "sister." Although Lily relished the thought of being missed in this way, she cannot bear the prospect now. She now does the most familiar of tasks to reassert her old position in the house: She straightens the lily on Mrs. Freeport's hat.

Thomas Willard

ACROSS THE BRIDGE

Author: Heinrich Böll (1917-1985)
Type of plot: Social realism
Time of plot: Immediately after World War II
Locale: Germany
First published: "Über die Brücke," 1950 (English translation, 1956)

> *Principal character:*
> GRABOWSKI, the narrator and protagonist, a German who
> has survived the war

The Story

As the narrator Grabowski rides across the railway bridge that was part of his regular three-day-a-week routine ten years before the war, he recalls his earlier life. At that time he worked as a messenger for the Reich Gun Dog and Retriever Association. He had little education, knew nothing about dogs, and had only to transport urgent correspondence, money, and a large manila folder of "Pending Cases" between the Königstadt head office and the Gründerheim branch office.

The trip required crossing the Rhine River at one of its widest points. Although he crossed on a wide four-track railway bridge, the crossing always frightened him. With nothing able to convince him that the bridge was safe, he fixated on the first house on solid ground on the far side, a two-story house just before the town of Kahlenkatten.

On his regular trips to Gründerheim on Mondays, Wednesdays, and Saturdays, he always saw the same woman scrubbing the floor by the windows on his left side. When it was not raining, a young girl would be sitting on the front steps holding a large clean doll, frowning at the train. On his return trips from Gründerheim, he saw the woman washing the windows in the rear of the house, always in a certain order.

Gradually Grabowski became obsessed wondering which windows the woman washed on Tuesdays, Thursdays, and Fridays, when he did not ride past her house. He drew up a cleaning timetable for the week, and from what he had observed on three mornings, tried to fill in the other three mornings and all the afternoons.

So preoccupied was he with the house-cleaning schedule that on one occasion he forgot to deliver the "Pending Cases" folder and was duly admonished. At first the district manager threatened to fire him, then suddenly became human and instead gave him a day off to sort out his troubles. On that day, a Thursday, Grabowski rode the usual train route four times in each direction, from 8:00 A.M. to 6:00 P.M., and worked out the woman's whole Thursday timetable, which included cleaning the front steps. On his last trip, he also saw a stooped man humbly digging in the garden, watched by the little girl.

The remainder of the story takes place after the war. Passenger cars have been replaced by boxcars, the four-track bridge has been reduced to a one-track temporary bridge that wobbles dangerously. Whereas previously only the narrator feared the crossing, now everyone is afraid, and car after car of passengers falls silent as they leave firm ground and head precariously out over the Rhine.

Only after his car has safely made the crossing does Grabowski suddenly realize that he is on his old familiar route. He wonders if the house is still standing. It is, and is still very clean. Gripped by an indefinable emotion as thoughts of the past rage within him, Grabowski sees a woman washing the steps of the house. It is not the mother now, but the daughter, and it is in fact Thursday.

Themes and Meanings

"Across the Bridge" has attracted little critical notice and makes an unostentatious beginning to the twenty-five stories that Heinrich Böll published in 1950 as *Wanderer, kommst du nach Spa* (*Traveller, If You Come to Spa*, 1956). Indeed his narrator introduces the story with the remark that "maybe it isn't really a story at all." Böll offers no interpretive guidelines for the reader. He does not even say precisely what it is that Grabowski feels so intensely: "an indefinable emotion." If indeed "it isn't really a story at all," one is left with an account of a coincidence. Authors frequently have their narrators utter such disclaimers, however. The reader is expected to have more insight into their circumstances than the narrators do, and thus participates in the act of fiction by supplying the ending and its rationale.

If one regards "Across the Bridge" as primarily a contrast of things great and small, then one may see that by taking a second snapshot ten tears later, Böll cleverly inverts their relative positions. Much goes without saying. Reference to the Reich Gun Dog and Retriever Association, for example, suffices to conjure up all that was associated with the Third Reich—which Adolf Hitler claimed would last a thousand years. Böll can afford to understate the irony. Everyone knows the Germans lost the war.

Böll was as disinterested in National Socialism as Grabowski is in the contents of the "Pending Cases" folder that he carries. Böll was the only student in his class who chose not to join the Hitler Youth. From the start, he seemed to understand that the systems thought out by philosophers and politicians and struggled for by armies are transient, and any hope or expectation of a better future that one invests in such works is futile. To Böll the machineries of history and the dicta of those who would change it are ephemeral, treacherous, and capricious. By contrast, a humble house that is occupied continuously by successive generations of the same family has its own rules. The simple acts of sweeping the steps and digging the garden and the daily maintenance of a home and family embody the only values that truly last a thousand years.

Postwar German literature has been dubbed *Trümmerliteratur*, or "Rubble Literature," because it shows how, with almost everything in ruins, it took an extreme effort just to survive, to get food every day, and to keep from freezing in the winters. Against that backdrop, the intact Kahlenkatten house and family in "Across the Bridge" seems to be a miracle.

In 1952 Böll wrote an essay titled "In Defense of 'Rubble Literature,'" which argues that "it is our task to remind the world that a human being exists for something more than to be bureaucratized." "Across the Bridge" does just that. The narrator's obsessive interest is necessary to highlight the small and ordinary tasks and rituals that make up human lives and have more durability than the mightiest empire.

Style and Technique

Böll was able to write in the late 1940's only because his wife's income as an English teacher was enough to support their family. He was aware that he was working with a radically changed language. It was *Stunde null*, the "zero hour." He had to work without and around all the words whose meanings had been changed by Nazi propaganda. Hence his relatively simple, straightforward language and conversational tone. The voice that he uses is that of the common man, and his viewpoint is that of private, personal experience. He narrates in the first person without interpreting. He portrays without preaching. He is kindly. This style and attitude greatly impressed his fellow writers in the Group of 47, although he neither feared their criticism nor sought to win their favor. As a result, he won their prize in 1951, the first of many.

One distinctive feature of Böll's style that is much in evidence in "Across the Bridge" is his tendency to end paragraphs with ellipses. He avoids going into more detail than is necessary, leaving open multiple meanings that may or may not contribute to the advancement of his story. For example, after mentioning the large manila folder of "Pending Cases," Böll ends his second paragraph with the sentence: "Being only a messenger, of course, I never was told what was in the folder. . . ." This ellipsis serves both to characterize Grabowski as uninterested in the Third Reich's bureaucracy, and to let the reader engage briefly in historically based tangential speculations of a more sinister nature.

Although Grabowski's reaction to seeing the familiar house still standing and the girl cleaning its steps is one of positive relief, Böll stops short of making a virtue out of German cleanliness. "It was a clean and yet unwelcoming house." At the end of the story, in fact, the cleaner is given a decidedly negative description. Grabowski recognizes the girl by her "pinched, spidery, frowning face, and in the expression on her face something rather sour, something disagreeably sour like stale salad. . . ." It is ironic that someone who has more than most should seem so dissatisfied and that so mundane a scene should elicit so emotional a response. This is early Böll, who went on to become a superb satirist.

Finally, the title of this story is an important key to its interpretation. Despite Grabowski's fears, he not only safely crosses the Rhine repeatedly before the war, but also gets across unscathed after the war, when the makeshift bridge seems no stronger than a thread. Although there are literally two bridges in this story, the bridge of the title is figuratively neither of these structures, but rather the ten years that span Grabowski's past and present. Grabowski is one of the Germans fortunate enough to have made it across that bridge. He has reason to rejoice.

Jean M. Snook

ACROSS THE BRIDGE

Author: Mavis Gallant (1922-   )
Type of plot: Domestic realism
Time of plot: Around 1950
Locale: Paris
First published: 1991

Principal characters:
SYLVIE CASTELLI, the narrator and protagonist, a young woman
who has not yet left her parents' home
MADAME CASTELLI, her mother
MONSIEUR CASTELLI, her father
ARNAUD PONS, her fiancé
MONSIEUR PONS, her fiancé's father
BERNARD BRUNELLE, a young man with whom Sylvie Castelli has
been corresponding
MONSIEUR BRUNELLE, the father of Bernard

The Story

Sylvie Castelli recalls the time when she and her mother walked together near the Place de la Concorde in Paris. As they cross a bridge, Sylvie shocks her mother by saying that she does not love her fiancé, Arnaud Pons, and that she would rather marry another man, Bernard Brunelle. Madame Castelli questions her daughter, and is misled by Sylvie's vague, diffident answers, which convince her that Bernard Brunelle has written Sylvie a letter proposing marriage. Believing that Sylvie can marry Bernard instead of Arnaud, Madame Castelli impulsively dumps her daughter's wedding invitations into the Seine River.

As Sylvie dreams about a perfect, enchanted life with Bernard, her parents cancel her scheduled wedding and break her engagement to Arnaud. Sylvie's fantasies suddenly collapse, however, when Bernard's father states emphatically in a letter that Bernard has not promised to marry Sylvie and that Bernard has no interest in Sylvie. When Madame Castelli demands that Sylvie show her the letter in which Bernard promises marriage, she realizes that the proposal existed only in Sylvie's vivid imagination. Furious with his daughter, Monsieur Castelli blames his wife for the family's humiliation. He and his wife both believe that they have allowed Sylvie too much freedom, and that had Sylvie been restricted as daughters were a generation earlier, the "fiasco" would never have occurred.

Uncertain what to do next, Sylvie considers putting aside the idea of marriage and going to work instead. There are few career opportunities for women at this time, however, and Sylvie does not know how properly to pursue permanent employment. She drifts through the days until her mother persuades her to have her hair cut and to buy some new clothes. With short hair for women once again fashionable, Madame Castelli thinks that a make-over will make it easier for Sylvie to find a husband.

Madame and Monsieur Castelli approach the Pons family, hoping that Sylvie's former fiancé might mend the broken engagement. Arnaud, who has been working in the city of Rennes, agrees to meet Sylvie for lunch in Paris, where he calmly tells her that he is no longer possessed by passionate feelings of love, but still wishes to marry her.

Afterward Arnaud and Sylvie walk together back to the train that will return Arnaud to Rennes. Arnaud, who is conservative with money, wants Sylvie to work after they are married, as his own mother did. He also suggests that after they have children, he will tend the children during the summers, so that Sylvie, an amateur artist, will have time free to paint (an offer which is extraordinary for the time). Shocked at the idea of a man's taking care of children, Sylvie says nothing but thinks slightly the less of Arnaud.

After Arnaud's train leaves, Sylvie decides to walk home, going far out of her way in order to arrive at approximately the same time that Arnaud reaches Rennes. In her mind this binds her to Arnaud. For the first time she begins to think of herself as part of a couple and as an adult woman. In deciding not to tell her parents why she is so late returning home, she subtly but symbolically breaks with her parents.

Themes and Meanings

Of several "bridges" that are crossed by the story's characters, the most important is the bridge between childhood dependence on parents and the adult realm of independent action—a crossing that Sylvie makes at the end of the story. She moves toward adulthood by rebelling against her parents, first by refusing to marry Arnaud and then by choosing Bernard. After she makes clear her preference for Bernard, she avoids showing her mother the letter from Bernard which supposedly contains a promise of marriage. She does this because she does not want to "share" Bernard with her family. In contrast to Arnaud, the son of a family friend, Bernard is someone whom she has met on her own. By rejecting Arnaud and keeping Bernard to herself, Sylvie has a taste of adult independence.

For a female child, the crossing into adulthood also means joining the company of mothers and wives. Some months after her original engagement is broken, Sylvie realizes that mothers conspire to control events. Her mother reveals that she has been privately seeing Madame Pons, who admits that she still wants Arnaud to marry Sylvie. The implication is that the two mothers will subtly pressure their children to reconcile. This conspiracy between women to achieve goals mutually beneficial to their families is necessary because social conditions in postwar France limit their ability to act more openly and directly. Sylvie says that she is ignorant of world events, because her father does "not like to see young women reading newspapers." Her family wants her to have a small collection of accomplishments that will increase her desirability as a potential bride—such as the ability to paint attractive watercolor copies of famous artworks. At the same time, her accomplishments should not be too impressive, lest they make her appear needy or plain. Older married women are subject to other restrictions. Madame Castelli, for example, must ask her husband for money, because she cannot legally have her own bank account or sign checks without her husband's consent. This legally mandated dependence of women on their husbands makes Sylvie's choice of husband vitally important to her future happiness.

Style and Technique

"Across the Bridge" looks back on the events that lead to Sylvie's marriage. The story is constructed out of her memories, which are surprisingly uncolored by emotion, given the circumstances of her engagement. Sylvie describes what she has thought and done, but her feelings are expressed only in the actions that they motivate. For example, when she is berated by her mother for Bernard's nonexistent proposal, Sylvie remembers that "I put my napkin over my face and began to bawl"; her strong underlying emotions are not otherwise described. The absence of feelings accentuates Sylvie's passivity as a young woman. This passivity makes her not entirely sympathetic as a character; the reader waits for her to take charge, to do something. Ultimately, however, dissatisfaction with Sylvie's inaction distances her from the reader. Such distance is a primary characteristic of Mavis Gallant's fiction, and has been both praised and condemned by critics.

In addition, the veracity of Sylvie's story is suspect, because it is reconstructed out of memory. Sylvie tries to assemble a smooth coherent story from her past, and some memories trouble her because she does not know either where to place them or if they are entirely true. She hints that she has pared away the memories that do not connect well with others. Truth in a person's life is not always neat and well contained, however, so Sylvie's story will necessarily be false in places. The combination of the inherent "falseness" of her story together with her highly subjective viewpoint make Sylvie an unreliable narrator.

The story is also a reinvention of the Sleeping Beauty fairy tale, in which the heroine is awakened from a deep slumber that resembles death by a prince who will take her away from the life that she knew as a child. After Sylvie is rejected by Bernard, she feels ashamed and falls into a kind of sleep, drifting through life seemingly without real desire or purpose. In one of the few places in which Gallant provides Sylvie with the memory of actual feelings, Sylvie says that she was waiting for her "true life" to reveal itself. She longs for it passionately, but does not see it as something that she can create through her own thoughts or actions. Ultimately this "true life" is provided indirectly by Arnaud, who plays the role of the fairy-tale prince waking the sleeping maiden when he agrees to become re-engaged to Sylvie. It is important to note, however, that this "true life" is something that Sylvie holds inside her, and not a direct gift from Arnaud, even though his action precipitates the internal processes that allow Sylvie to find it. Ironically, this "true life" with Arnaud can only properly begin when both he and Sylvie put aside romantic dreams and fairy tales. Gallant suggests that they can do this at the end of the story, when Sylvie acknowledges the present, and implies that she has had a happy life with Arnaud.

Kelly Fuller

ACROSS THE BRIDGE

Author: Graham Greene (1904-1991)
Type of plot: Psychological realism
Time of plot: The 1950's
Locale: A Mexican village on the U.S. border
First published: 1949

> *Principal characters:*
> JOSEPH CALLOWAY, an English millionaire wanted on charges of
> investment fraud
> THE NARRATOR, an unnamed foreigner who waits in a Mexican
> town for a lift to the Yucatán
> TWO ENGLISH DETECTIVES, who are trying to catch Calloway

The Story

Joseph Calloway, a rich Englishman indicted on investment fraud charges in his own country, has led authorities on a chase through several Latin American countries. He is now taking refuge in Mexico, hoping that its disordered government will make it easier for him to dodge officials. The narrator, an aimless drifter who is passing through a small border town where Calloway is hiding, sympathizes with the tedious boredom that Calloway feels, with nothing to do but sit in the dismal town's square all day.

Each day, Calloway strolls to the bridge that joins the Mexican town with a U.S. town and wistfully looks across the river. On one occasion, he expresses the idea that life begins on the other side; however, the narrator mocks Calloway's view that the other town has more life and excitement than the Mexican town. He knows that it is the same thing over again. The American town even has the same layout; it differs only in having paved streets and taller hotels and in being a little cleaner and much more expensive. On his way back from his walks to the bridge, Calloway routinely kicks the dog that has accompanied him from England as if he is venting some private frustration. Everyone in the town sees everything that Calloway does and knows his entire story, but he is unaware of this.

When two foreign detectives come to the town searching for Calloway, everyone but Calloway knows who they are. People anxiously gather at the town square, watching in amazement as the detectives—who carry only an outdated photograph of their suspect—chat amiably with Calloway over drinks. They all get along well and speak familiarly of their mutual homeland. After the detectives learn that Calloway is the man whom they are chasing, he and they go to Mexico City. The detectives seek an extradition order so that they can arrest Calloway, who wants government protection. Although Calloway is a criminal, the narrator suspects that Mexico has admitted him to the country because his millions have made him a celebrity in this part of the world.

Calloway returns to the northern village on a train; as he rides in a first-class car, the detectives ride in second class. The detectives have not obtained the extradition order that they want, so they try to lure Calloway out of Mexico. They kidnap his dog and take it to the American town, expecting Calloway to come looking for it. The narrator follows the detectives across the bridge to the American town, where he sees Calloway strolling around. It is not clear whether Calloway is looking for his dog or is merely fulfilling his desire to see what lies across the bridge. Unaware of Calloway's proximity, the two detectives chat with the narrator in a nearby store, where he learns that one of them is a dog-lover.

When the dog sees Calloway heading toward the bridge, he bounds after him. The detectives get into their car and chase the dog, which ends up in the middle of the road, dangerously close to the speeding car. The driver—the detective who loves dogs— swerves to avoid the animal and hits Calloway. The mortally injured man throws his arm toward the dog then dies of shock and a weak heart. The detectives believe that Calloway's gesture was a caress, but the narrator thinks it was meant to be a blow.

Themes and Meanings

Typical of Graham Greene's fiction, "Across the Bridge" examines human motives and desires under a surface political intrigue. Like many of his works, Greene infuses this story with a deep sense of religion and morality. In Greene's world, the worst kind of person one can be is the kind that Calloway is: neither truly good nor truly evil, but merely petty. Throughout the story, a reader can have little sympathy for Calloway's life or even his death. Although he is a criminal, he does not strike one as evil. His crime is a white-collar crime—merely a manipulation on paper done by a mild-mannered man behind a desk. Calloway is far from being good and generous either. His feelings for his loyal dog can scarcely be called love, as his habit of daily kicking the animal reveals. His ambiguous gesture at the end of the story symbolizes the essence of his character. The detectives like to believe that his thrust of his arm is a loving gesture toward his pet, but the narrator sees it as a hard, spiteful blow. Very likely, the gesture is neither; it is Calloway's very lack of good or evil conviction that makes him so pathetic. His story is laughable when it should be tragic.

The story consistently depicts Calloway as a hapless old man who is easily taken advantage of by a Mexican boy, who cleans his shoes several times a day for money. The fact that everyone in the town but Calloway knows what is going on is another example of his pathetic quality. He appears at his worst, however, when he kicks his dog, "not in anger," the narrator points out, but as if he "were getting even for some trick it had played him a long while ago." Calloway's pettiness gives the story a comic quality. Several times the narrator comments on Calloway's oddly comic nature; he even goes so far as to say that Calloway's death would not make the story less comic.

Many Greene characters are motivated purely by evil, but their stories involve a fall and salvation. Although he often depicts them as evil incarnate, he also makes them sympathetic, preferring the fervor that they embody to the weak-willed and self-deceiving manner of a character such as Calloway. For Calloway, there is no salvation in his death, not even dignity.

Style and Technique

Greene's stories frequently demonstrate a liberal use of irony, providing both a comic turn and poignant message. The irony in "Across the Bridge" is expressed through the personal observations of the narrator, who knows more than the other characters, thus providing the reader with an informed point of view. Through the narrator, the reader can find irony by contrasting what other characters believe and what is actually true. The reader becomes part of the audience in the story who watches Calloway's story unfold. Comic scenes such as that in which the detectives fail to recognize their suspect are made funnier by the presence of the knowing, incredulous audience in the square, of which the reader is a part.

The narrator also expresses the irony in Calloway's dying gesture: What he may mean as a blow is seen by others as a kind, loving motion to his dog. Calloway, who has habitually kicked his dog, is now the loving master reaching out to hold his loyal pet to his very last breath, even though the dog is the key to Calloway's demise. Readers may believe that they know better, but in the final paragraph, the narrator changes his tone. After having looked skeptically upon Calloway's "caress," he now concedes that this gesture could actually have been a loving one. Here, the narrator assumes a "humble" position, which for Greene symbolizes the limited knowledge that human beings have.

Although the narrator generally seems to know more than other characters, he is not omniscient. He is simply a third-person limited narrator, who is consistent with Greene's religious beliefs that human individuals cannot know everything. In the final paragraph, the narrator pulls away from assuming that he knows Calloway's true motives behind the ambiguous gesture. He lets the reader think that Calloway was going to hit the dog in that movement, but then concludes that it could possibly have been a gesture of love.

This sudden shift in the narrator's view, along with his concluding comments about "a human being's capacity for self-deception," makes the reader aware of an underlying sense of irony that permeates the story. People are self-deceived because they believe that they know or control some part of their future, but this, according to Greene, is laughable in the eyes of God. In the difference between what humans, whether they be ignorant characters or knowing audiences, can know about human life and what only God can know is a comic irony. This larger kind of irony adds a profound religious implication to Greene's story while providing many humorous moments as well.

Susan Hwang

ACT OF FAITH

Author: Irwin Shaw (1913-1984)
Type of plot: Social realism
Time of plot: Summer of 1945, immediately after the surrender of Germany
Locale: France
First published: 1946

> Principal characters:
> NORMAN SEEGER, the protagonist, a twenty-one-year-old Jewish
> sergeant in the U.S. Army
> OLSON and
> WELCH, his friends, both army privates
> SEEGER'S FATHER, an economics professor in Ohio
> CAPTAIN TANEY, Seeger's commanding officer

The Story

The war in Europe is recently over. Sergeant Norman Seeger and his friends, having survived the Normandy invasion at Omaha Beach and the capture of Strasbourg from the Germans, are struggling to collect enough money to enjoy their weekend passes to Paris. Olson and the taciturn Welch hold Seeger in considerable esteem. Seeger has won the Purple Heart at Saint Lo and, despite his youth, Olson affectionately refers to him as *"Mon vieux."* Likewise, both Olson and Welch call him "Sir"; they know that Seeger's noncommissioned status does not warrant the title, but believe that his experience and valor do. A remark by Olson reveals that Seeger has saved the lives of his comrades. When a young second lieutenant who is obviously untested by battle passes the three friends, Olson stares him down and offers no salute. It is thus that the two "kids" in the threesome put their trust in Seeger to get a loan against their late pay from Captain Taney.

When Seeger can only put together two hundred francs, the three men are at a loss to locate adequate funds, until Welch remembers that luger pistols taken from German soldiers are going at nearly premium prices; he can get sixty-five dollars for Seeger's luger if Seeger will part with it. Both young men recognize that Seeger may not want to surrender the pistol, but they cannot appreciate the value of the luger to Seeger, who took it from an SS major whom he killed at close quarters in Coblenz. Seeger has five hours in which to measure the value of the weapon against the importance of going to Paris.

As Seeger struggles to make his decision, he receives a letter from his father, who is anguishing over his other son Jacob's break with reality, brought on not so much by the boy's leg wounds taken at Metz as by Jacob's having recently "devoured . . . concentration camp reports." The father cannot dismiss Jacob's fear that a bazooka-armed mob is coming after Jews. He has been experiencing antagonism toward American Jews and indifference to those brutalized in Europe.

The letter unleashes Seeger's repressed memories of his own experiences with anti-Semitism—which he encountered even as soldiers were hitting the beaches at Normandy for the last great assault on Hitler's armies. Most strikingly, he recalls an old Jewish couple who were amazed that he was both a Jew and powerfully armed in the service of their liberation. These memories and the old couple's belief in him and his Garand rifle magnify the burden of selling his luger. He resolves the dilemma in an ostensibly simple fashion, asking Olson and Welch what they think of Jews. Olson's response and Welch's concurrence end Seeger's turmoil, "Jews? . . . What're they?" This retort helps Seeger to put other memories in perspective, recollections of how his casual pals unhesitatingly put themselves in harm's way for him, risking their lives without question for a friend and comrade in arms. Finally, Seeger gives up the luger with an ease that masks the agonizing he has gone through: "What could I use it for in America?"

Themes and Meanings

At the heart of this story is the struggle of American Jews, at midcentury, to keep faith with their nation and the ideals of the U.S. Constitution in the face of both German death camps and the U.S. national reaction to what is now called the Holocaust. Soon after World War II, it became apparent that the U.S. government had chosen not to confront the conditions of the German concentration camps or to inform the citizenry of Nazi genocide during the course of the war. Into the bargain, anti-Semitism was virulent in the United States both during and after the war. Irwin Shaw is at pains to reveal the spiritual turmoil and agony of American Jews in the wake of these social currents. He accomplishes this especially by showing his readers that Jews bore their share of suffering in the defeat of fascism and also reminds the reader that anyone who fought in Europe was, during the summer of 1945, a candidate for being shipped to the Pacific war zone for more combat. One must remember that Seeger is one of three sons called to service. His brother Leonard has been killed; he and his other brother, Jacob, have been wounded. Such manifest signs of sacrifice should discredit the anti-Semitism that the living sons and their father have so keenly experienced.

At another level, the story reveals how the young among a class of scapegoats in an ostensibly democratic nation, and especially under conditions of extreme trial, must struggle with the antithetical social messages of this society in order to establish bases of trust and confidence. In order to contain his exhaustion and to enhance his infrequent pleasures, Seeger has buried a long list of hateful messages: They concern the naval officer who would not eat with a Jew; the combat engineer who remarked about Jews' profiting from Europe's agony; the soldier in the PX who said their bayonets were going to be used on the "Yids" when the war ended. At the story's climax, it is memories such as these and their many parallels in his father's accounts that Seeger must overcome if he is to keep faith with the commitment that he has made for four harrowing years. Seeger does not turn to the fine ideals of the Bill of Rights for reassurance, but to the clear message of Olson's, Welch's, and Taney's brotherhood with him in combat. His act of faith rests, finally, upon their proven disregard for anything but his humanity. This is the faith proper to confronting the bigotry waiting in Ohio for Seeger. The story thus makes a case that even the rich symbolism of a luger taken from the SS itself is not so powerful as this trust.

Style and Technique

As a conventional slice-of-life story recounted from the third-person point of view, this story has plotting that is adroit but simply linear. The straightforward technique is controlled by the presentation, in evolutionary stages, of the compressed and layered conflict within the protagonist. Shaw plots the story to highlight the subtle texture of this conflict and to embody his theme of faith precisely within its resolution. In so doing, Shaw hooks conflict and theme to several profoundly meaningful objects. Money is entirely positive; it represents nothing more than access to well-deserved pleasure and its enjoyment with genuine friends. It is important that the money stands for something as emotionally and spiritually valuable as the luger. The luger, on the other hand, stands equally for access to that fraternity and for Seeger's sense of ongoing security in the face of the death camps. His view of the war has left him with a commitment never to be victimized by any kind of fascist. His is not a pistol picked up idly at a roadside; it belonged to one of those responsible for the camps, a murderer of Jews who was vanquished by Seeger himself. It thus stands for Seeger's personal and ethnic duty. Through it readers see Seeger as an instrument not only of American national integrity but of Jewish justice. The reader should then see its emblematic affinity with Seeger's rifle, which the old Jewish couple so clearly perceived in terms of their liberation. The sale of the luger is untainted by any interest in financial profit. Rather, it affirms a brotherhood between honorable citizens of a free society and a faith in the capacity of that bond, above even the legitimate use of force, to secure the rights of those endangered in a democracy.

Two complementary objects alluded to in his father's letter serve to increase Seeger's anxiety and the pressure upon his confidence in Olson's and Welch's fidelity. The bazookas of Jacob's fantasy are the traumatic extensions of the luger, the SS, and the death camps into the troubled postwar Jewish-American scene. Jacob's Bronze Star is equally significant; his ambivalent attitude toward it reflects the vacillation within him of hope and despair concerning the meaning of his and his brothers' service to America. The father's despondency and Jacob's tortured relation to these objects push Seeger to the furthest limits of potential disillusionment. It is especially this matter in Ohio that he must set beside Olson and Welch, "who were like his brothers," in the test of his belief in both his service and America's character. His friends have sufficiently more weight in his imagination than his fears of injustice, thus making his choice to sell the luger "an act of faith."

David M. Heaton

ADAM AND EVE AND PINCH ME

Author: A. E. Coppard (1878-1957)
Type of plot: Fantasy
Time of plot: Early twentieth century
Locale: England
First published: 1921

> *Principal characters:*
> GILBERT CANNISTER, a young husband
> MILDRED, his wife
> JAFFA CODLING, the alter ego of Gilbert Cannister in his fantasy
> dream
> GABRIEL, the unborn child of Gilbert and Mildred

The Story

The narrative begins in mid-sentence in the reverie of Jaffa Codling, who walks in the English countryside and remarks on the beautiful light, which reminds him of a euphonic name. He enters his garden and sees three children playing, then goes into his house. Upstairs he hears his wife Mildred speaking affectionately to a man. When he looks into his room, he sees his wife caressing a man in a rocking chair. The artificial scene troubles Codling. Why is his wife kissing another man? Why does he himself feel so disembodied?

As the maid brings something to the couple in the room, Codling tries to communicate with her, but she stares through him. When Codling goes outside, the gardener walks through him. Gradually, he realizes that he is a spirit cut loose from his body. As a writer, he realizes he has often tried to plumb the depths of evil in his writing and has felt cut loose from his true self at these moments. Suddenly he feels happy and declares himself a new Adam in an old Eden.

At this moment his three children, Adam, Eve, and Gabriel, come into his view and pester the gardener with questions. Gabriel has a toy sword that the gardener thinks is dangerous as it can cut a lock of Eve's hair. Codling grows more confused. He throws a flowerpot at the gardener that flies right through him and breaks on the ground. As Codling watches his children play, it becomes clear that the youngest child, Gabriel, can see Codling and the spirit of a fish, which the other children cannot see. After the children run off, Codling is left alone with his dreams until Mildred comes into the garden to call him to dinner. His odd manner frightens her.

He goes into the house and picks up a book with his name, "Gilbert Cannister," in it. Suddenly Jaffa Codling and Gilbert Cannister are fused, soul and body. When Gilbert goes with Mildred to see his sleeping children, he is surprised to see only two, not three, and exclaims, "only two." Mildred then confesses that she is pregnant. Gilbert now realizes that he has met the spirit of his third child, Gabriel, in his own spirit form of Jaffa Codling and tells his wife of this unusual happenstance, declaring that the new baby will be named Gabriel.

Themes and Meanings

"Adam and Eve and Pinch Me" seems to suggest that an immense spirit world surrounds the literal world. Gilbert Cannister is a professional writer who is used to delving into the psyches of his characters. The story describes an out-of-body experience in which he is forced to plumb the depths of his own psyche. He notes his own Jekyll and Hyde nature.

One moment Cannister's alter ego, Jaffa Codling, is noting the beauty of nature and his children, the next he is jealous because he thinks his wife is kissing another man. He mistrusts her and feels enraged. Later he is annoyed at the maid and throws a flowerpot at the gardener. Still later he seems to communicate with the child Gabriel. This mixture of anger, beauty, joy, and jealousy deeply disturbs Codling. In truth the range of emotions in an individual is disturbing indeed, but one's conscious mind often denies the disturbing elements.

Jaffa Codling's world is also a highly symbolic one. The children's names, Adam, Eve, and Gabriel, take one back to the Garden of Eden, while the title of the story recalls the nursery rhyme "Adam and Eve and Pinch Me Tight." Throughout the story, Codling keeps pinching himself trying to understand what is real and what is not. Gabriel's sword is the one that barred Adam and Eve from reentering Eden after the Fall; it is indeed dangerous, just as the gardener warned the little boy Gabriel about his sword. Gabriel is also the biblical messenger who announced the impending birth of Christ to Mary, just as Mildred tells her husband of her own impending delivery at the end of this story. The singular beauty of the countryside and the colors created by the sun recall an Edenic past and the seemingly endless summer of childhood.

As Jaffa Codling journeys through the spirit world, he analyzes his own actions and intentions and finds them to be a "little spurious, counterfeit." When he merges into the body of Gilbert Cannister at the end of the story, the brief conversation between him and his wife seems quite prosaic compared to the extraordinary adventure that has preceded it. Mildred promises to give Gilbert a new baby, "if you are a very good man"—a remark that sounds almost like baby talk. Gilbert retains a glimpse of the spirit world that he has just visited, however, as he begins to tell her about the child Gabriel.

Style and Technique

The style of "Adam and Eve and Pinch Me" owes something to the stream-of-consciousness style made popular by James Joyce and Virginia Woolf during the period when A. E. Coppard wrote this story. Like the fictional characters of Woolf and Joyce, Jaffa Codling flits from image to image in his mind: from Edenic images of Adam and Eve and Gabriel to William Shakespeare's Isabella in *Measure for Measure*; from birds, to fish, to ships, to stars—stars that fall in your hand and burn you and do not leave a mark.

Coppard's story goes a step beyond stream-of-consciousness, however, because Codling the spirit becomes separate from Cannister the physical body. Cannister can speak as well as Codling, however, and Codling can critique Cannister's speech. Codling/Cannister thus has a dual personality.

"Adam and Eve and Pinch Me" also recalls William Wordsworth's "Lucy" poems in which he has "strange fits of passion" and fears that Lucy has come to harm. Codling seems to have irrational fears about his wife's faithfulness. Charles Lamb's early nineteenth century essay, "Dream Children," also comes to mind in connection with Coppard's story. In Lamb's reverie the children are a complete figment of his imagination and sadly vanish from his real world. Although Lamb's reverie is more sentimental than Coppard's, it may be thought of as a forerunner to "Adam and Eve and Pinch Me."

One of A. E. Coppard's great strengths as a writer is his ability to raise many questions in the mind of the reader, answer a few easy ones, and leave the reader to puzzle out the rest. For example, Coppard lets the reader know that Codling is Cannister's spirit and that Gabriel is his unborn child, but the reader never fully understands why Codling has become disembodied, why he is suspicious of his wife, or why he is ecstatically happy one moment and in despair the next. Much of the story revolves around unstated questions about the meaning of these contradictory states.

When Cannister's wife startles him back into a conscious state, he runs up to his room and finds that he can open doors that seemed to be locked when he was a spirit. He is trying to work these contradictions out when Mildred takes him to see the children and tells him of the expected third child. Cannister says that they will name the child Gabriel and tells his wife that he already knows about him. Then Coppard ends the story with the words ". . . and he told her a pleasant little tale." Once again Coppard has planted ambiguity in the reader's mind. If Cannister tells Mildred the whole story, it will not be pleasant; if he glosses over areas less favorable to himself, it will not be the whole truth.

Perhaps the ultimate meaning of "Adam and Eve and Pinch Me" is contained in the manner in which Coppard chooses to write the story. The contradictory emotions felt by Gilbert Cannister when he is separated from his body in the spirit Jaffa Codling show the reader that life itself is contradictory and confused, mean-spirited and light-hearted, and beautiful and rich. Coppard embodies the meaning of his story in his method of writing it.

Isabel B. Stanley

AMANDA

Author: Roberta Fernández
Type of plot: Domestic realism
Time of plot: The 1950's
Locale: South Texas
First published: 1990

Principal characters:
THE NARRATOR
HER MOTHER
AMANDA, the dressmaker

The Story

The narrator recalls moments as a five- or six-year-old girl when she would spend her days watching Amanda work at her sewing machine, transforming cloth into fantastic dresses, and spend her nights thinking about Amanda's creations until she fell asleep. Amanda was her connection to the world of creation, as well as a link to the larger social world that Amanda relayed to her through provocative gossip about the men and women she knew in South Texas.

The narrator is not completely comfortable, however, in Amanda's presence. Although she can speak freely with other people, with Amanda she is rendered almost speechless because she is sure that Amanda is indifferent to her.

The narrator has other apprehensions about Amanda. It is rumored around town that Amanda and her friends Librada and Soledad are associated with magic. Although no one considers Amanda a real enchantress, her special powers make the children, at least, believe that she has little figurines that are exact replicas of everyone who had ever crossed her.

When Librada visits the narrator's house, she leaves behind a slimy substance in which the narrator puts her arm. The narrator and her mother both think the substance is associated with Librada's status as a witch, so the mother takes the substance outside in newspapers and burns it.

The narrator believes that Amanda is part of a complex plot that she cannot figure out. Although out of fear she wears a scapular and blesses herself before she enters Amanda's house, she still is attracted to Amanda because she believes that Amanda is her only link to exciting possibilities that lie beyond the everyday world of others. In order to enter this world of hidden powers, the narrator requests an outfit from Amanda, one that a witch would give her favorite daughter, so horrible that it would enchant everyone. By the time that Amanda gets around to creating the outfit, the narrator has almost forgotten about it.

Eventually, Amanda makes an ankle-length black cape from cat fur, sparrow bones, chicken feathers, and cat paws. The narrator's mother is upset when she sees her daughter wearing the cape, and forbids her to wear it.

One night during a full moon, the narrator puts the cape on and has her moment of transcendence: She gazes at the moon and familiar surroundings that glow luminously, as the chirping of crickets and cicadas reiterates the permanence of everything around her. The mother catches her and again urges her never to wear the cape again. Years after this singular experience of perfection in the universe, the narrator goes to the storeroom and discovers the cape. It is stiff from the dryness of the trunk, but she recognizes that it was made as an expression of love by Amanda.

When the cape is lost as the narrator travels west, no one can understand why she is so upset. It is clear, however, that she mourns the loss of the witch's daughter's cape because of the closeness she felt with Amanda. The narrator confesses that she cannot imagine that anyone would ever again take the time to create something as personal for her as Amanda had done.

Themes and Meanings

In telling the story of a Mexican American girl who grows up in South Texas and moves to California, Roberta Fernández is replaying her own life story. Whether the events of the story are autobiographical or simply imagined, its themes are universal.

The story focuses on the extremes of experience: plenitude and loss, presence and absence, youth and adulthood. The narrator is privileged to have her encounters with Amanda, to be surrounded by the strength and special powers of older women, including her mother, and to have her moment of epiphany beneath the full moon when she recognized the harmony and perfection of the universe. Because the story leaves childhood behind and ends with the narrator far from Texas on the foggy coast of California, it contains elements of sadness. The cloak has been lost, Texas has been abandoned, and the narrator has not seen Amanda in years, but the narrator's memory is keen, and her imagination, kindled by Amanda, is still strong. The past may be unretrievable in reality, but in memory and in storytelling it endures and has power.

Amanda is the narrator's first hero as an artist, the first creator to inspire the narrator to imagine a world separate from the prosaic world of logic and practicality. The story begins: "Transformation was definitely her specialty"—precisely what the artist must learn in order to be successful. Amanda teaches the narrator how to create, transform, believe in the world of the senses mixed with imagination. It is crucial for this artist, this narrator, that the teacher is a woman, because Fernández's search as a writer has been for a feminist aesthetic. The larger work of which "Amanda" is a part, *Intaglio: A Novel in Six Stories* (1990), presents a narrator who, according to critic Nicolás Kanellos, is "trying to piece together her own adult identity by remembering the women who most influenced her." Amanda's genuine love for the narrator is expressed in the cape that she pieces together from cat fur and chicken feathers, and the narrator's love for Amanda is pieced together out of the memories she has stored away over the years.

Style and Technique

The epigraph from Fernández's story comes from the Chilean poet Pablo Neruda. She intentionally leaves the quotation in Spanish, not translating it, and in this way she announces her identity: She will braid together her two traditions, her experiences as a girl in the Mexican American society of South Texas, and her life as a woman in California, where no one can understand her sense of loss when her cape disappears. Roughly translated, the epigraph says, "Where is the child that I was? Does it continue inside of me or has it gone? Why do we spend so much time growing just to sever connections?" These questions are answered dramatically within the story. Fernández's narrator focuses on the past in order to preserve it, in order to keep the child inside alive. The narrator will not accept a world in which the child that she was will disappear, not only because the past contained magical experiences, but also because the past is part of her unique heritage as a Mexican American.

Fernández, who earned her Ph.D. in Romance languages from the University of California, Berkeley, does not turn her back on her past; through her writings she creates connections between herself as a writer and the women of South Texas who were her first models as artists and artisans. If Neruda wonders why one must spend so much time severing connections, Fernández posits a world in which people need to spend time forging connections between the past and the present, between the Latin American and the North American literary traditions, between the role models of childhood and adult heroes. Neruda may be an important poet for Fernández, but the type of character that Amanda is also serves as a significant source of inspiration, an example of how to live in this world that seems to encourage people to cut ties, move forward, and become adults who can function adroitly in a world based almost entirely on reason and consumerism. In "Amanda," alternative models are held up for scrutiny and for applause.

Kevin Boyle

AN AMATEUR'S GUIDE TO THE NIGHT

Author: Mary Robison (1949-)
Type of plot: Domestic realism
Time of plot: The 1970's or 1980's
Locale: Phoenicia, Indiana
First published: 1983

> Principal characters:
> LINDY, the seventeen-year-old narrator
> HARRIET, her mother
> GRANDPA, her grandfather, a retired tailor

The Story

Lindy, a high-school senior about to graduate, has a job waitressing and busing tables at the local Steak Chateau restaurant. An average student and an amateur astronomer, she has a Frankus reflector telescope that she bought with her own money so she can watch the night sky. She enjoys examining Jupiter and the constellations, but notes that on a clear night the stars are so bright that they are swimming in their own light.

Lindy often double-dates with her mother, a young-looking thirty-five-year-old. On these dates, they pass themselves off as sisters, and it is the mother who always gets the best-looking men. Lindy's parents are divorced, and her father has remarried and is living in Toledo. When Lindy wonders aloud what it would be like if her father came back, both her mother and grandfather respond that he had better not. As her grandfather observes dryly, it would cut down on her mother's dating.

The two women share a home with the mother's father, a retired, self-employed tailor. Although he claims that he sometimes forgot to tie off the threads, so that some of the clothes he made fell apart, his business was successful, and he now has enough money to take care of all three of them. Because they are all night owls, the grandfather keeps them informed of the late-night horror movies on television. The grandfather is seldom serious about anything, often resorting to juvenile responses such as "Poof you're an egg" when the girl asks him to make her an egg for breakfast, and "Not I, said the pig" when asked if he has seen something that is missing. He lies, too: He insists that Harriet, Lindy's mother, attended Lindy's graduation ceremony, but sat back in one of the cooler seats, under the trees. The narrator knows that he lied to her and that her mother did not go because "She was scared of the 'going forward into the world' parts of the commencement speeches."

Lindy's mother is one of the fastest comptometer operators in the state, but quits her job because she thinks people at work do not like her. Besides pretending to be her daughter's sister, the mother fantasizes other things; for example, she usually decides after two dates with a man that he must be married or running away from someone. She makes up a story about a ring of thieves stealing cars from the neighborhood; she talks about poison, taking "light pills," and having a brain tumor; and she determines that a stranger on a bus is a police detective on the bus for them. She also tries to have herself admitted to a nearby institution, but the hospital "didn't have space for her, or they didn't think she needed to get in right then." The narrator observes, "The problem I saw was that Mom really needed to keep occupied."

Themes and Meanings

The most important event buried among the seeming trivia of Mary Robison's story and the apparent triviality of its characters' lives is the young narrator's graduation from high school. The quest that begins for each person leaving the protection of school is daunting, even for those well prepared. As the title suggests, the narrator is an amateur (a novice) searching the darkness (night) of the future with much less light (knowledge, direction) to guide her than one her age should have. Not even for her daughter's sake can the childlike mother face this ceremony that represents going forward into the world, for she herself has gone nowhere and is going nowhere. The grandfather—usually a symbol of ancestral knowledge, giving wisdom to his progeny—is hardly more mature than the mother. He is symbolically defined by his loose threads. Neither adult can function as the narrator's guide. The father-figure is totally absent, both from the configuration of the family and from Lindy's special occasion—except for his note, which spells out all too clearly the narrator's plight, "Happy Graduation, Good Luck in Your Future."

Many people look to the stars as a guide to their lives and future. The narrator looks to the stars, the light, for when they are connected, they form patterns or models. Understanding exactly what one sees is difficult, because on a clear night the "stars are too bright . . . swimming in their own illumination"; especially because she is an amateur, the narrator is overwhelmed by the light and cannot make sense of it. Rather than admit ignorance, most often she makes up answers. Who can she ask to help her understand what lies ahead, what is in her stars, her future?

Graduation is a moment of transformation: No longer a student, now what will she be? With a cap and gown and piece of paper, with one stroll across a stage, at the end of this magical ceremony, "Poof you are an —": transformed from child to adult. Within the story, the changes that parallel this idea of transformation are all grotesque: In the horror movies the family watches, the Creeper is half-man, half cat-beast; Zombies are the living dead; a man changes into a werewolf, and the werewolf becomes a person again. The young girl is trying to become an adult, but she admits that she could lie on the couch forever and go nowhere, like her mother and grandfather.

There is a chance, however: She lives in the town of Phoenicia, named for the mythological Egyptian bird that consumed itself by fire and rose, renewed, from its own ashes; the constellation of Phoenix in the Southern Hemisphere looks much like a stork, the symbolic bringer of new life. Like the narrator, all high-school graduates are amateurs in life and can either lie on their parents' couches, going nowhere, or choose to rise like a Phoenix from the ashes of their spent childhood into their own individual lives.

Style and Technique

Mary Robison is most often considered a minimalist. The minimalist style produces deceptively simple and realistic fiction that, at its best, offers a concentrated and uncluttered narrative. Minimalism reflects the major characteristics of the short story, the genre in which it is most often employed. Both minimalism and the short story rely heavily on figures of speech and the baggage of connotation that come with each, especially metonymy, in which one thing symbolizes another with which it is associated. Here, the title of this story is the key to the symbolic connection between the narrator's hobby and her need for direction and answers to puzzling questions about the future.

Some readers may find this story more cluttered than most minimalist fiction, but the clutter of the story represents the clutter that fills these characters' lives, and the trivia with which many people fill their lives so that they can believe they live full lives. The irony is that their lives are empty shells of existence filled with empty echoes of life. Here the mother and grandfather especially are going through the motions of life but at most are only existing.

In addition to the internal connection between the narrator's hobby and her role as a high-school graduate, the story reflects the universal situation of graduates poised on the brink of their futures. It also mirrors the duality of choice, the duality of cause, the duality of change, and the duality of consequences.

This final image of a universal truth reflected in a deceptively simple short narrative is the greatest achievement of the minimalist technique as well as that of the genre of the short story. For both offer what appears to be the simplest of stories. Both offer what appears to be the slightest view—a keyhole. Both offer the appearance of realism, and both use metonymy as the major figure of speech. A single event becomes the symbol for a particular human condition. Both minimalism and the short story create an inverse relationship between a singular event and the universal experience, or the trifling incident and the significant occasion.

Cynthia Whitney Hallett

AMERICAN HISTORY

Author: Judith Ortiz Cofer (1952-   )
Type of plot: Social realism
Time of plot: 1963
Locale: Paterson, New Jersey
First published: 1993

> *Principal characters:*
> SKINNY BONES, the narrator and protagonist, a Puerto Rican
>   teenager
> EUGENE, an Anglo teenager known as the Hick because of his
>   Georgia accent
> SKINNY BONES'S MOTHER, a housewife
> EUGENE'S MOTHER, a nurse

The Story

Skinny Bones is a teenage Puerto Rican girl struggling to adapt to life in a multifamily apartment building in Paterson, New Jersey. She lives in a former Jewish neighborhood that is now inhabited mostly by Puerto Ricans and African Americans. As a loner, Skinny Bones is attracted to marginalized individuals like herself. She finds her soulmate in Eugene, a shy teenager who has recently come from south Georgia. Because of his marked Southern accent he is soon dubbed "the Hick," and he becomes the school's newest object of ridicule, joining Skinny Bones as an outcast. Skinny Bones falls in love with Eugene, and they soon become inseparable, despite their cultural differences. Eugene, a bright student, tutors Skinny Bones in several subjects. Although Skinny Bones is a good student, she is not admitted to advanced courses because English is not her first language.

The story's climax occurs when Skinny Bones accepts Eugene's invitation to a tutorial session at his home, immediately across from her own apartment building. She accepts gladly, since she has been wanting to meet Eugene's family. After having watched his kitchen from her own apartment, Skinny Bones is particularly interested in Eugene's mother, "a red-headed tall woman." Their study date, however, is almost interrupted by the assassination of President John F. Kennedy. Skinny Bones must convince her grieving mother to allow her to go to Eugene's house instead of going to church to pray for the slain president.

At Eugene's house, Skinny Bones encounters another unexpected problem. When Eugene's mother answers her knock at the door, she regards Skinny Bones as one of those "people" who live across the street and immediately dismisses her. The mother also forbids her from studying with Eugene, because he is smart and does not need any help.

Frustrated in what appears to be her first adolescent love, Skinny Bones returns home and tries to "feel the right thing for our dead president." Eventually she cries, but realizes that the tears coming up from a deep source inside are strictly for her.

Themes and Meanings

Puerto Rican American literature has shown a strong attachment to northeastern cities in representing the cultural clash that Puerto Rican immigrants have experienced in the United States. The characters most typically depicted by Puerto Rican authors are adult males—who experience the plight of living in poverty, isolated from the expected American Dream. Judith Ortiz Cofer deals with issues related to the Puerto Rican migration experience, but her characters are usually teenage girls or women, who—like the male characters of other Puerto Rican writers—confront ethnic discrimination. Her female characters also tend to abandon the traditional barrio of Puerto Rican culture and involve themselves in cultures that are foreign to the traditional Puerto Rican Caribbean lifestyle.

"American History" stands out particularly because the theme of cultural isolation and xenophobic attitudes in a large American city is viewed through the fresh eyes of a teenage Puerto Rican girl. During Skinny Bones's early struggles to adapt to life in Paterson, the theme of cultural isolation is explored on various levels. The problems that she has in adapting are geographical (she is unused to the bitter cold of the Northeast), interpersonal (she is still learning about another culture's codes), and familial (she confronts her mother's inability to provide feminine advice in this foreign society). Through narrating her daily-life experiences she discovers that all these issues are related to one another and are intricate parts in the forging of her own personality as a young Puerto Rican woman growing up in the United States.

Skinny Bones's interest in documenting her daily life leads her to create a journal in which she introduces the reader to a number of locales and characters. Her primary focus is her world at "Public School Number 13," the impersonal educational facility where she first experiences racial conflicts with African American students. They give her her nickname—which she loathes—in order to avoid using her real Spanish name, which never appears in the story.

Skinny Bones shows an inclination toward feminine issues, such as the process of becoming a young woman. These issues merge with the story's thematic axis, which revolves around how people from different cultures react to each other and what aspects of their behavior may be viewed as xenophobic. Skinny Bones does not assume a judgmental role even though all the non-Puerto Rican characters represent alien cultures that affect her life. African American teenagers stand out because they represent the struggle by both groups to avoid cultural assimilation into the nondescript American melting pot.

Style and Technique

Ortiz Cofer's commitment to document the Puerto Rican experience of adolescent female characters is evident in "American History." In fact, her female characters, unlike the male characters created by other Puerto Rican writers, move away from the traditional cultural and linguistic separation of life in the barrio, to allow a more direct interaction between the environment and the self. "American History" singles out the development of the feminine psyche of a teenage Puerto Rican in a feminist text that incorporates the young woman's voice into the struggle for racial equality.

As the narrator and protagonist in a story with few characters, Skinny Bones not only represents a transitional Puerto Rican generation, she also determines the literary devices. She narrates in a style that is clearly personal, fashioned after the popular female teenage practice of keeping a journal for careful recording of all of her daily activities. The technique resembles the *Bildungsroman*, a literary chronicle written from the point of view of a young character. As a *Bildungsroman*, "American History" introduces Skinny Bones's personal view as an outcast character of society at large, including her vision of American culture from her perspective as a Puerto Rican teenager. That personal view gives to the text its freshness of expression and its unbiased stands on the subject matter presented.

The authentic testimonial narrative devices of a *Bildungsroman* text reveal Skinny Bones's role as a young reporter of life in the barrio. Although young people are evidently the author's expected audience, both adults and youngsters react positively to her story's direct and austere writing style. That personal style, reflective of a young teenager's daily journal entries, presents issues to be discussed at a personal level—such as Skinny Bones's meditations on her life—inviting that analysis by the reader. Therefore, the reader, without much warning, learns from concrete examples about such controversial issues as racist attitudes among ethnic groups.

The story also offers a political view of popular American history. Skinny Bones's dual roles are evident: As a teenager, she confides to her journal details of her attempt at a romantic relationship outside of her ethnic group; as a historian, she records President John F. Kennedy's assassination. Ortiz Cofer recognizes her political dimension. She has remarked that she does "not know of any intelligent, thinking person, sensitive to what is going on in the world, who is not political. If my stories have serious lives being lived, that is, lives that are not being recounted for the sake of mere entertainment, then I am a writer with political intent."

In style, technique, and content Ortiz Cofer creates a new kind of Puerto Rican short story. The core of the narration is supported by her use of English, instead of Spanish or Spanglish (a mixture of the two languages). That linguistic decision has proved pivotal in bringing together characters of diverse ethnic groups not part of the Puerto Rican barrio.

Rafael Ocasio

THE AMISH FARMER

Author: Vance Bourjaily (1922-   )
Type of plot: Psychological realism
Time of plot: An unspecified modern time
Locale: Indiana
First published: 1980

> *Principal characters:*
> VANCE, the narrator, a university writing teacher
> KATIE JAY, a student in his class
> NOEL BUTLER, his friend during his graduate student days
> DAWN BUTLER, Noel's wife
> DANIEL, the Butlers' Amish landlord

The Story

Vance teaches writing at an Indiana university. He has a student named Katie Jay from whom he tries to elicit a particular response by telling his class a story. He instructs them to pay particular attention to the crucial function of his story's narrative point of view.

Vance's story goes back to a time ten years earlier when one of his fellow graduate students, Noel Butler, called begging to see him because someone had just tried to kill him. As Vance awaited Noel's arrival, he remembered the circumstances under which he had met Butler and his beautiful wife, Dawn. Noel was a competent and popular graduate student who was desperately in love with his wife. Vance had met Dawn at a departmental party, where her sexuality caused him—and most of the other men—to act like a foolish schoolboy. Despite being smitten, however, Vance was aware of Dawn's sexual ploys and instability. Her coquetry went beyond the usual self-aware fun; there was something dangerous about her intimacies—such as her tight gripping of Vance's wrist in seeming desperation.

Earlier, Noel had had to struggle to persuade Dawn to leave Boston to join him in Indiana with her five-year-old son, Jimmer (the son of a famous but cruel choreographer). He arranged for his family to live on an Amish farm, twenty miles—and three centuries—away from his campus. Dawn agreed to live in this remote place because of their previous "interesting experiences" in Boston. As Noel told Vance, the struggle of living through their first harsh winter on the farm made living there worthwhile.

The Butlers' thirty-two-year-old Amish landlord, Daniel, was the youngest and favorite son of an Old Order Amish patriarch. Daniel cared well for his farm, his wife and seven children, and his community of fellow believers. Although the Amish do not use modern technology, he provided the Butlers' cottage with electricity and a telephone.

It was Daniel, Noel told Vance, who tried to kill him. Noel admitted that he had failed to recognize how strongly Dawn and Daniel were attracted to each other until he figured out when they first consummated their relationship. During a treacherous winter storm Noel had had to leave Dawn stranded while he struggled back to the farm to check on Jimmer's well-being and to get help. The only person available to help was Daniel, who violated Amish precepts by driving an old tractor through the storm to rescue Dawn. Vance suspected that the forbidding storm conditions placed Dawn and Daniel into a situation in which they became "the only man and woman in the world," and that their desire for each other became too great to resist.

After drawing this conclusion, Noel accused Dawn of unfaithfulness, but she denied it and mocked both him and Daniel. The following spring, Noel came home early one day and saw Daniel leaving his house. He again accused his wife of unfaithfulness and told her that he was leaving. When Daniel saw them fighting, he attacked Noel with a wrench.

Noel now wanted Vance to go back to the farm with him to help him fetch his belongings. Dawn then called him, asking her husband to talk with Daniel, who was in an agony of shame. Together, they met with the farmer, who asked Noel to forgive him and pray for him. Nevertheless, Dawn, her son, and Daniel moved to northern Indiana, where they still live. Noel finished his graduate studies and later left the state.

Vance asks his class to analyze his story to assess what would change if it were told from another perspective. His students, however, do not believe that anyone but him could tell it. Katie Jay's failure to enter the discussion disappoints Vance, who hoped to hear what she would say about Dawn because of what she has revealed about her own casual attitude toward sex. Vance then lectures that if his story were to be a tragedy, it should be by Daniel's father, who would see the incident as a precursor to the breakdown of his Amish community.

Afterward, Katie does not leave with the rest of the class. When Vance approaches her, she grips his arm—as Dawn did ten years earlier—and tells him haltingly that she needs an Amish farmer herself. Can he not see that?

Themes and Meanings

The theme of this story is seeing, which Vance articulates to his class: "What I am going to try to illustrate is the remarkable power of point of view." The narrator (who shares author Vance Bourjaily's first name) controls his class's perceptions of his characters' situation. Nevertheless, he carefully assures them that they should realize—if they listen attentively—that he is projecting his own point of view on the story when he tells them what he did not observe. "Imagine Daniel knocking then . . ." or "I think an embrace develops out of this . . ." or "Perhaps she touches him. . . ."

Unlike Vance's students, the story's readers not only read his story of the love triangle from his point of view, they also read his rendition of how he tells his story to his class, as well as the story of his interaction with Katie Jay—all from his point of view. Vance asks his class to analyze the point of view of his Amish farmer story; in order to understand its theme the reader must analyze the point of view for its classroom context. The class itself fails to get much beyond what they are given; they either dismiss the possibility of other points of view or trivialize them with stock categories, such as melodrama, romance, or comedy. They are left with Vance's didactic assertion that only if it were told from the point of view of Daniel's patriarchal father would the story become a tragedy because the infidelity of his son foretold the breakdown of his self-contained moral community.

One might ask what would happen to this story if a class member, perhaps Katie Jay, were to tell it. Further, one might ask whether the story gains its power—as one class member suggests—from its narrator revealing how it has affected him. In asking such questions, the reader should ask about the reliability of the story's narrator. Noel tried hard to understand his relationship with Dawn. Did Vance understand his with Katie Jay? Although he was able to mock himself when he told about his first meeting with Dawn, that ironic distance seems lacking in the classroom. The relationship between professor and student is at least as tenuous as the Butlers' marriage, yet there is no evidence for Vance's diversionary counterclaim of Daniel's father's belief that Amish society is decaying.

At the same time, both the class and the readers should ask themselves if even a flawed narrator can reveal truths about life. Katie, for example, learns a crucial truth about the inadequacy of her own sexual attitudes. If her professor cannot tell his story from all points of view, or even from the most important one, it is nevertheless a significant telling for her.

Style and Technique

Vance Bourjaily, a post-World War II American novelist, is associated with the "after the lost generation" writers who use techniques pioneered by post-World War I writers. He is known primarily for his first novel, *The End of My Life* (1947), which explores the effects of the world war on his generation and culture. Although he experiments with style in each of his novels, "The Amish Farmer" is representative of the core of his work in its naturalistic realism and emotional detachment. What one critic said about his novel *Confessions of a Spent Youth* (1960) applies equally to this story: It has a "conversational style that moves easily from quiet humor to unobtrusive lyricism." In a few sure descriptive strokes, Bourjaily brings his varied characters to life. For example, the men who meet Dawn perceive her as "a wave of heat" with "brute magnetism" and "the look of a woman standing her ground and at the same time enticing you to share it with her." Yet something is "missing from the voice despite the smiles and the flicking tongue. . . ." Another significant feature of this story is its strong narrative thrust. It moves ahead, compelling its readers with it; even the asides to describe the Amish worldview move the plot forward. The frame of the classroom for the "story within the story" fits naturally.

This style is particularly appropriate for Bourjaily's theme about the reliability and power of perception. The narrator does not have an omniscient point of view; his flaws as a narrator are highlighted by his flawed students. He sets up an interesting case study that readers can apply to both stories while being forced to confront the limitations of one person's perspective. Bourjaily himself once commented in an interview that "the process of writing fiction is not a matter of describing directly a reality that one sees. It's much more often a matter of re-creating a reality which one recalls perhaps imperfectly which one remembers as having been in some way moving, and one almost has to re-create it in order to discover why it is that it still moves one to think about it."

Barbara J. Hampton

AMY FOSTER

Author: Joseph Conrad (Jósef Teodor Konrad Nałęcz Korzeniowski, 1857-1924)
Type of plot: Psychological realism
Time of plot: Around the 1890's
Locale: East coast of England
First published: 1903

> *Principal characters:*
> YANKO GOORALL, an Eastern European; the sole survivor of a
>   shipwreck
> AMY FOSTER, the Englishwoman whom he marries
> KENNEDY, the country doctor who relates their story to the frame
>   narrator
> SWAFFER, the farmer for whom Yanko works

The Story

An unnamed narrator recalls a time several years earlier, when he was staying with his friend Kennedy, a country doctor in the English coastal village of Colebrook, near Brenzett. One day as he accompanied the doctor on his afternoon rounds, they came upon a dull-looking woman named Amy Foster, who was hanging out her wash. Kennedy asked after her son's health. As he continued his rounds, he told the narrator about this woman's recent life.

Although Kennedy agreed that the woman looked passive and inert, he confided that this same woman once had enough imagination to fall in love. The oldest child of a large family, Amy was put into the service of the Smiths, the tenant family at New Barns Farm, where she worked for four years. Meanwhile, she occasionally made the three-mile walk to her family's cottage to help with their chores. As Kennedy explained, Amy seemed satisfied with this drab life until she unexpectedly fell in love.

After the narrator and Kennedy passed a sullen group of men trudging along the road, Kennedy resumed his story, this time telling about a man who used to walk the village paths with such a jaunty, upright bearing that Kennedy thought he might be a woodland creature. The man was an emigrant from central Europe who had been on his way to America when his ship went down near the coast. He could speak no English, but Kennedy guessed that he had boarded the ship in Hamburg, Germany.

Kennedy then described the railway journey that had carried the German to Hamburg. After riding a train for several days before changing trains in Berlin, he reached the mouth of a river, where he saw a ship for the first time. There he lost contact with the three men who had recruited him to immigrate to America with the promise of his earning three dollars a day there. Using a telegraph, the three men secured passage to America for the man, whose father paid for the passage by selling livestock and part of his farm.

Kennedy again digressed to mention that he had patched this story together from fragments gathered over two or three years. When the castaway first appeared in

Brenzett, his wild language and appearance shocked the town. Taking him for a gypsy, the milk-cart driver lashed him with his whip and boys pelted him with stones. The man ran to New Barns Farm, where he frightened Mrs. Smith. Amy Foster, however, responded with kindness. Though Mr. Smith thought that the man's wild appearance and indecipherable speech proved that he was a lunatic, Amy implored the Smiths not to hurt him.

Several months later, reports of the shipwreck appeared in newspapers. The emigration agents were exposed as confidence men who had cheated people out of land and money. Townsfolk speculated that the German may have floated ashore on a wooden chicken coop. At New Barns, he showed his appreciation for Amy's kindness by tearfully kissing her hand.

The stranger went to work on the farm of the Smiths' neighbors, the Swaffers, who had Kennedy examine the man. Observing the man's verbal and emotional isolation, Kennedy wondered why he did not go mad. The castaway's nightly thoughts returned to Amy Foster, who had treated him kindly. Eventually, the stranger learned a few words of English. One day he rescued Swaffer's infant grandchild from a pond into which she had fallen.

Kennedy could not describe exactly how the stranger made a new life for himself. The villagers still found his customs odd; his favorite songs, his religious habits, and his clothes all marked him as an outsider. He was a mountaineer from the eastern Carpathians whose first name was Yanko. His last name, as best as the locals could tell from his speech, was Goorall. This name, Kennedy recalled, survived in the parish marriage register.

Yanko began his courtship of Amy with a present of a green satin ribbon, and he persisted in spite of the warnings and threats of the townspeople. After Yanko asked for Amy's hand, Mr. Swaffer gave them a cottage and an acre of land—the same land that Kennedy and the narrator passed during their rounds—in gratitude for saving his granddaughter from drowning.

After Amy bore Yanko's son, Yanko told Kennedy about problems that he was having with Amy. One day, for example, she took their boy from his arms when he was singing to him in his own language. She also stopped him from teaching the boy how to pray in his own language. Yanko still believed that Amy had a good heart, but Kennedy wondered if the differences between them would eventually ruin their marriage.

After breaking off this story, Kennedy said that the next time he saw Yanko, the man had serious lung trouble brought on by a harsh winter. When Kennedy treated Yanko, he was lying on a couch downstairs, suffering from fever and muttering in his native tongue. Kennedy asked Amy to move her husband upstairs to get him away from the drafty door, but she refused. Kennedy saw fear in her eyes, but had to leave to treat his other patients. That night Yanko's fever worsened. Perhaps thinking he was speaking in English, he demanded water, but Amy could not understand him. As his demands increased in intensity, she took her child to her family's farm three miles away.

The next day Kennedy found Yanko outside his cottage. He took him inside and called for Amy, but Yanko told him she had fled the night before. Yanko weakly wondered why and then said the word "Merciful!" just before dying of heart failure. Over the years that followed, Amy never mentioned her husband.

Themes and Meanings

The tragedy of Yanko Goorall probes the modernist theme of isolation and alienation. This idea also figures prominently in Joseph Conrad's major works, such as the novels *Lord Jim* (1900), *Heart of Darkness* (1902), and *The Secret Agent* (1907). Yanko is an unwilling loner whose free and easy nature undergoes repeated assaults until even the only person who has offered him love abandons him at the moment of his greatest need. His first ordeal was physical confinement in crowded trains, the boxlike berths aboard a ship, and the dungeonlike lodge at New Barns.

Kennedy senses, however, that Yanko's most painful ordeal is his verbal and psychological confinement. He notes that "an overwhelming loneliness seemed to fall from the leaden sky of that winter without sunshine. He could talk to no one, and had no hope of ever understanding anybody." The story repeatedly contrasts Yanko's nobility with the prejudice and insensibility of the townspeople, whose rejection intensifies his feelings of estrangement. Amy's father, for example, opposed Yanko's marriage partly because he heard him mutter to himself in his native language. Told by Kennedy that Yanko was dead, the father responded with indifference: "I don't know that it isn't for the best."

Like much of Conrad's writing, this story has autobiographical roots. As a Pole, Conrad knew isolation during his years at sea on British ships. He learned English in his twenties, but other problems contributed to his loneliness during his residence in England. In addition to his problems establishing himself as a writer, he had nagging financial worries and a growing emotional distance from his English wife. He personally had an experience similar to that of Yanko in 1896, when he suffered from a fever and rambled incoherently in Polish, frightening his young wife.

Style and Technique

The use of multiple narrators and repeated flashbacks are techniques that Conrad carried to even more complex levels in other works. In "Amy Foster," the technique permits Conrad to minimize the elements of his story that interest him the least (such as melodrama, the sea adventure, and the budding romance), while concentrating on Yanko's isolation, rejection, and personal despair. Conrad's artistic choices, as in many of his other works, break up the linear development of plot in favor of character analysis and psychology. Kennedy's disjointed narrative thus supports Conrad's conscious artistic design. The strategy allows Conrad to emphasize fragments of Yanko's life that lack proper chronological unity but reflect the larger thematic unity. This technique also enables Conrad to introduce brief comments from the other characters whom Kennedy quotes to round out the picture of Yanko.

Kennedy is an ideal narrator to relate Yanko's story. His training as a physician, his analytical mind, and his professional duties in towns outside of Brenzett distance him from other villagers. The unnamed narrator who begins the story introduces Kennedy by remarking that

> the penetrating power of his mind, acting like a corrosive fluid, had destroyed his ambition, I fancy. His intelligence is of a scientific order, of an investigating habit, and of that unappeasable curiosity which believes that there is a particle of a general truth in every mystery.

Such detachment provides Kennedy with a growing appreciation and understanding of Yanko's rejection and anguish, as well as a measure of shared guilt in its outcome.

Glenn Hopp

THE ANATOMY OF DESIRE

Author: John L'Heureux (1934-   )
Type of plot: Fantasy
Time of plot: An apocalyptic future
Locale: Unspecified
First published: 1981

> *Principal characters:*
> HANLEY, a victim of war
> THE NURSE, also known as the saint, who loves Hanley
> THE GENERAL, who orders Hanley's flaying

The Story

Hanley has been flayed by the enemy and is unable to find anyone to love him; not even his wife and children will spend time with him because he is raw, and he will never be any better. Only one nurse, known as the saint, stays with him and applies blood retardant to his flesh. Although he does not find the woman pretty, he does find her saintly. He asks her to love him, to possess him. She says that she will perhaps love him if sometime she finds out that she must.

The narrator recalls how Hanley's flaying occurred. He was sleeping in a trench when soldiers found him and brought him back to their camp to serve as an example of what happens to infiltrators. When Hanley was taken to the general's tent, he captivated the general, who caressed his skin, saying that he had a beautiful face. He apparently performed a sexual act with his prisoner. When Hanley was led out for his punishment, the general told the men who carry the knives to spare Hanley here and there, because he could be his own son. Hanley's face and genitals were spared but the rest of his skin was flayed and hung on the barbed wire. Hanley was left to die, but after the enemy retreated, he was taken by his own unit to the hospital, where he met the nurse.

After some time passes, the nurse agrees to make love with Hanley. While they are in bed, he decides he does not miss his wife and children; in fact, he does not even miss his skin. The nurse, meanwhile, whispers to Hanley that she cannot live without him, after he wakes her to apply some blood retardant on his body.

Hanley soon recognizes that he wants more from the saintly nurse. He is in love and is loved, and wonders why that is not enough. The nurse replies that nothing is ever enough. After making love, Hanley recognizes that even sexual intimacy is not enough; it is only a metaphor for what he wants.

At the close of the war, the general is made mayor of the capital city by the occupying forces, and then he is elected senator and made a trustee of three nuclear arms conglomerates. Despite his achievements, he feels an absence. He longs for Hanley: "I wake in the night and see your face. . . . You could have been my son. . . .

I can endure no more. I am possessed by you."

Hanley finally recognizes what it is that he wants from the saint: He asks for her skin. Feeling resigned, even satisfied, she consents. Hanley, for a brief moment, feels completely fulfilled. Just as the general gazed deeply into his eyes, traced the lines of his eyebrows, and pressed his palms lightly against his forehead before he ordered Hanley's skin to be removed, so too Hanley, wearing the saint's skin, now gazes deeply into her eyes, traces the lines of her eyebrows gently, and presses his palms lightly against her forehead.

Hanley's happiness soon shifts to sadness and tears because he recognizes that despite the love he feels from the saint, there can never be possession, only desire.

Themes and Meanings

In early Aztec society, a ceremony was performed each year to honor the goddess of grain. A young virgin selected from the group became the embodiment of the grain goddess; her reign was brief, however. After a short period of ritual fasting and prayer, the young girl was sacrificed to the goddess, her skin was flayed, her blood sprinkled on the crops, and then the priest who performed the ritual would wear her skin. John L'Heureux offers a similarly gruesome tale in "The Anatomy of Desire," but his story is perhaps even more unsettling than the Aztec ritual because it begins and ends not with purification and hope, but with absurdity and despair.

Hanley is flayed because of some soldiers' absurd notion of duty. Soldiers loyal to the general come across the sleeping Hanley and make an example of him. He is accused of being an infiltrator, but it is clear that he is dragged across the arbitrary demarcation line by the soldiers; he has infiltrated nothing. He is simply a random victim of war, a war whose origin and purpose are never shared with the reader. His sacrifice is related to no larger myths of the society, no purpose.

The French psychoanalyst Jacques Lacan has said that "what is desired is always displaced, always deferred, and reappears endlessly in another guise." L'Heureux's male characters, especially Hanley, seem to reflect Lacan's belief. Happiness and contentment are absent in the story because, as the nurse says, nothing is ever enough. There is always desire, and no matter how arduously one fights for satisfaction, one's desire will always remain, will always be transferred to some other object. Even if one can somehow enter into another person, either metaphorically or by literally wearing the other's skin, one will still feel a need, a lack, or at least Hanley will.

There is an exception, however, to this schema. The nurse perhaps serves as another model. She is neither transfixed by desire as the general is, nor constantly frustrated by her inability to satisfy her longing as Hanley is. She is resigned, even satisfied, when she gives her skin to Hanley. The reader is not given any other glimpse into her mind before the story ends, but she seems to be able to reach some kind of contentment through sacrifice. Perhaps she, as a nurse among soldiers, as a woman among men, is able to achieve a rapprochement with desire; perhaps nothing is ever enough, as she says, but in her own saintly way she is able to find satisfaction, or at least resignation, despite the seemingly unquenchable nature of desire.

Style and Technique

Johanna Kaplan, a critic for *The New York Times*, has called L'Heureux's style "spare, witty and elegant." Those words certainly apply to "The Anatomy of Desire"; it is spare and witty and, despite the gruesomeness of certain scenes, the language remains elevated. Even the saint's flaying is described in an elegant fashion: "Hanley lifted the shroud of skin from her crimson body." This elegance and spareness create a tension within the story simply at the level of style. If fiction needs friction in order to achieve its effects, L'Heureux creates friction by yoking together the understated style with the sensational aspects of the story.

The technique that gives this story added complexity is L'Heureux's use of the double, or counterpart. He avoids relying on the simple dichotomies of good and evil by carefully plotting the story so that the difference between victim and victimizer becomes muted. The villainy of the general is clear: He is a pointlessly cruel powermonger who serves as a trustee for nuclear arms conglomerates. Because his actions are mirrored almost exactly in the actions of his victim, Hanley, the reader can see the general not as an individual with serious faults, but as a type, a representative of humanity. Certainly he is cruel, but he suffers as well. Just as Hanley caresses the face of the nurse whom he has flayed, so too the general caresses Hanley's skin before he orders his flaying. The general and Hanley both yearn for an end to desire, for a level of satisfaction that they never achieve. The general and the soldier, the two enemies, the innocent victim and nasty victimizer are one, it seems, under the skin.

This use of the double allows the character of the saint to stand out in full contrast. Unlike the general and Hanley, who are united by similarities, the saint is shown in relief despite her similarities to Hanley. When she is flayed, her face and genitals are spared, just as Hanley's were. She is caressed by Hanley and told she has a beautiful face, just as Hanley was. She has the blood retardant applied to her skin, just as she applied it to Hanley's. These similarities only suggest the differences between her and Hanley, between her and the general. They are horribly human, desperately human, whereas she is resignedly a saint.

Kevin Boyle

ANOTHER PART OF THE SKY

Author: Nadine Gordimer (1923-   )
Type of plot: Social realism
Time of plot: The 1940's
Locale: Rural South Africa
First published: 1952

> *Principal characters:*
> COLLINS, the white principal of a reformatory for black African youths
> HIS WIFE
> NGUBANE, one of his black assistants
> THE BOY, an inmate who has run away

The Story

The protagonist walks across a compound to his house, considering the appearance of the place for which he is largely responsible. He is Collins, the idealistic white principal of a reformatory for young African men. When he first arrived there, it was surrounded by high walls topped with jagged pieces of glass. Now the walls are gone and the grounds are marked with edged pathways and flower beds. He has had playing fields built and musical instruments brought in, and he has given the inmates more freedom.

The newspapers call Collins "the man who pulled down the prison walls and grew geraniums in their place"; however, he reflects that it was not really geraniums but roses that the boys have planted. Whenever people think that they understand something, there is always a small inaccuracy waiting to be revealed. The world is simply more complicated than most people realize. Collins understands—or thought he did—the complexity of his own position, the benefits and disadvantages of tearing down the prison walls.

Now one of Collins' boys has run away and is suspected of beating and robbing an old woman. During the two days since he has heard of the assault, Collins has tried to convince himself that this boy could not have committed the crime. He reminds himself that to the police all blacks look alike and that the police think that the offender is his boy because they know that he is missing. They do not know, however, the quiet discipline that Collins has imparted; they have not studied boys for nine years as he has.

Collins' worry will not go away. Every minute, he expects to hear the phone ring, the police calling to say that the boy has been arrested. As he worries silently, his wife worries in her own silence. Over the years she has supported his work, stayed in the background, and kept silent. Now, as Collins climbs into bed, he knows that his wife is awake and worrying; however, they do not speak to each other. Both fall asleep, worrying.

In the middle of the night a knock at the door awakens Collins, who immediately thinks that they have come to tell him about the boy; however, the man at the door is Ngubane, one of Collins' assistants. The man is in shock, frightened. Collins thinks that Ngubane is bringing news of the boy. Instead, Ngubane tells him that he and his brother Peter have just spent their day off in Johannesburg, where Peter has been killed in an accident. Collins comforts the grieving man, gives him a sleeping pill, and tells him to take the next day off to arrange for the funeral.

After Ngubane leaves, Collins and his wife go back to bed. In the darkness, just before dropping off to sleep, the wife admits, "I thought he'd come to tell us bad news about the boy." Lying alone and worrying again, Collins suddenly realizes that he was actually relieved when he heard the reason for Ngubane's coming. So focused has he been on his own boys, on his "system," that he has ignored the rest of his life—his very humanity. He did not comfort Ngubane out of compassion, but only mechanically, without feeling any of the man's pain. Furthermore, he has not for years considered his wife as anything more than a part of his work. He may have been a good principal, but he has not been a good man. "If you search one face," he realizes, "you turn your back on another." The epiphany is so devastating that he shuts his eyes against burning tears.

Themes and Meanings

A dominant theme throughout Nadine Gordimer's fiction is the unusual complexity of life and politics in South Africa before it abolished apartheid. In her stories there are no easy solutions to the problems that history created in South Africa. Even though it is clear that the system of apartheid is wrong, there are often no clear moral choices for the whites living under the system.

Collins is in many ways a typical Gordimer protagonist. He tries, in his own way, to offer respect and human kindness to the African boys under his care. He tries to give them more freedom, to teach them discipline and hard work, and to help them become productive. Nevertheless, he cannot escape his own racism. He offers them the best that he knows, but does it in a patronizing way. Once, for example, he stumbles over the brick edging of a pathway and reflects that the boys laid the edging "with all their race's peasant pleasure in simple repetitive patterns." He smiles at their simpleness. Wanting to teach them good values, he turns to his own religion, Christianity, and makes his charges attend weekly church services. He cannot imagine that developing a spiritual life within their own systems of belief would strengthen them and is puzzled every time that a boy runs away. Why should anyone choose to live by a paraffin-tin fire instead of a warm reformatory?

Collins truly wants to help Africans. He mentions no friends, no colleagues, no pleasures or recreations of his own. He has given up his personal life to devote himself to the reformatory. Further, he has taken professional risks by converting the reformatory from a harsh prison to a nearly normal school. However, the only methods that he can imagine are those that will help the boys to become more like him.

Despite Collins' limitations, "Another Part of the Sky" is not about a misguided principal and a saintly boy. The boy, after all, has committed some kind of offense that is the reason for his being in the reformatory in the first place. Eventually the reader comes to realize, as Collins and his wife do, that the boy is in fact the person who has assaulted and robbed the old woman. Clearly, some form of control and some discipline is necessary. This is not a simple case of whites trying to transform innocent Africans.

The prison wall is an important symbol in this story. Gordimer repeatedly states that walls separate people from each other, making real communication impossible. The story demonstrates how walls exist not merely between black and white people, but between a reporter and the truth, between a governing board and a principal, between a man and his loyal wife. While Collins can tear down bricks and broken-glass barriers, he cannot establish real contact with another person.

The story leaves the reader with more questions than answers. Is oppression under a well-meaning and caring master any less oppressive? What is the best treatment for youthful offenders? Can a dominant culture teach without dominating? How can a man care about a community without caring about its individual members? How can people—individually and in groups—reach out to each other? Most important, can a man search one face without turning his back on another?

Style and Technique

Although there are other characters and actions in the story, the focus of "Another Part of the Sky" is internal. To help focus attention on Collins and his thoughts, Gordimer uses a limited third-person narrator who knows nothing that Collins does not know, presenting all the action only as Collins experiences or remembers it.

The reader may begin to question Collins' understanding of the world and his part in it, but the narrator does not push this questioning. No overt judgment is made of Collins—no words such as "patronizing" or "selfish" are allowed. Working within these constraints, Gordimer allows hints about Collins' flaws to emerge subtly from his own reflections, without his even noticing them.

Because the story unfolds late at night when Collins' wife pretends sleep, there is little need for talk in the story. What little speech there is—the governing board's consoling words to Collins, his own conversation with the grieving Ngubane—flows naturally into the paragraphs with neither indentations nor quotation marks. The only objects mentioned are those that Collins sees or touches. Gordimer chooses not to put the reader into the moment, but instead to keep the reader inside Collins' mind, to give only his reflections on a moment.

When the sudden moment of insight comes, it surprises the reader as well as Collins. The realization has to do with Collins' humanity, not just his politics. By filtering every image and speech through the lens of Collins' own mind, the story demands that the reader see Collins as an individual, not merely a representative of his race.

Cynthia A. Bily

ANOTHER TIME

Author: Edna O'Brien (1930-   )
Type of plot: Psychological realism
Time of plot: The 1980's
Locale: An Irish seaside resort
First published: 1988

> *Principal characters:*
> NELLY NUGENT, the protagonist, a former television announcer
> VINCENT, an older teacher whom Nelly recalls having loved
> GERTIE, the sultry young woman who married Vincent
> CAIMIN, a dim-witted hotel waiter

The Story

On the verge of a mental breakdown, Nelly Nugent decides to escape London by vacationing at a small seaside resort some twenty miles from the village where her family lived when she was a child. She fancies that this new place, full of mystery and romance, will lead to some kind of personal "redemption." The dismal reality of the dingy hotel and its provincial inhabitants sets the stage, however, for a series of bitter disappointments that drive her into an even deeper depression.

Nelly's hotel room is both tiny and shabby; instead of looking out on a sweeping ocean expanse, she can see only a sliver of the shoreline. Matters worsen when Nelly's before-dinner drink with her hosts proves awkward; her refusal to have a drink at the local pub with another guest sends the man into a rage, and her solitary candlelight dinner is disturbed by a large crowd of unruly children. After beginning her journey wanting to escape London, Nelly now counts the days until she can escape her vacation site.

When Nelly walks along the seashore the next morning, the peaceful scene revives her until she is recognized by a vacationer as a former television announcer. This encounter forces Nelly into another unpleasant reverie as she recalls that she gave up a promising career to marry a man with a "black heart." Predictably, the marriage ended in divorce and a bitter custody battle for the children, who are now grown and no longer integral parts of Nelly's life.

Having shrunk from all possibilities of human contact, Nelly encounters a young calf that engages her sympathies because it is being driven mad by flies that are swarming into the wounds left by the removal of its horns. She orders its owner to hold the animal while she digs the flies out. After they put the calf in a dark shed away from the flies, the calf's pathetic shrieks make it plain that it prefers the torment of the insects to the isolation of the unlit cell. After taking care of the calf, its lonely owner asks Nelly to marry him. She realizes that the young man is not serious, as he simply wants some company, but pretends that she is married and flees back to her hotel.

At her hotel, Nelly is greeted with the unwelcome news that she has had a visitor named Gertie. The mere mention of Gertie's name forces Nelly to recall a painful event that happened more than thirty years earlier. After getting a sophisticated black dress from an older friend, Nelly mustered the courage to visit a man named Vince, the new teacher at a nearby technical college who had set all the feminine hearts of the village aflutter. Unfortunately, her audacious visit turned into a disaster when Gertie appeared from the kitchen and sensuously claimed her man.

Now, Nelly cannot avoid meeting with the adult Gertie, who generously admits that Nelly has "kept her figure," while she has not. Gertie also confides that Vince, now dead, always bragged about knowing Nelly, especially after she became a television celebrity. For the first time in the story, Nelly reaches out to a fellow human being by inviting Gertie to stay for tea. Unfortunately, Gertie must leave, but she promises to return another time.

Themes and Meanings

Lantern Slides (1990), the story collection in which "Another Time" appears, features a series of lonely older women who have been either widowed or jilted. Most of them have experienced rewarding love affairs, but these affairs are in the past. The present is dreary and the future looks even bleaker. Most attempts at rekindling love end in bitter loneliness. For many of them, loneliness is imposed by family or society; Nelly Nugent's isolation is different—it is self-imposed. During her seaside visit, she spurns the overtures of two men—her neighbor at the hotel and the calf's owner. She even makes Caimin, the dim-witted waiter who likes her, feel like "a dog that knows it has done something wrong." When she walks on the almost deserted beach, she embraces solitude by reveling in "the isolation, the sense of being alone."

When Edna O'Brien enters Nelly's mind, it becomes clear why this former television celebrity is so determined to be alone: All of her relationships have caused intense suffering. Her marriage ended in divorce and a painful custody battle; the departure of her firstborn to boarding school caused a "rupture" resulting in "raw pain"; and her mother's death led to a bitter struggle with her "maggot brother." The past has such a powerful impact on Nelly that she is clearly on the verge of mental collapse. She dreams that one of her children had "stripped her of everything, even her teeth"; her visit to the travel office fills her with "doom"; an invitation to a sing-along causes her to shudder inwardly; and a compliment from poor Caimin makes her feel that she is about to "break down."

Instead of breaking down, Nelly experiences a kind of resurrection. Ironically, it is her former nemesis Gertie who is the catalyst that releases her from her "welter of rage." Gertie's generous admission that her husband Vince had cared about Nelly prompts Nelly to feel "as if doors or windows were swinging open all around her and that she was letting go of some awful affliction." All the pent-up rage that had poisoned her soul and relationships finally appears to be released.

As an epigraph to *Lantern Slides*, O'Brien uses a quote from Thomas Mann: "Each human life must work through all the joys and sorrows, gains and losses, which make up the history of the world." In "Another Time," Nelly Nugent, having been released from the sorrows and losses of her past, is poised to embrace a brighter future. While it is clear that Nelly and Gertie will never meet again, Nelly now has a chance to give meaning back to her life.

Style and Technique

Edna O'Brien's straightforward chronological structure with flashbacks into Nelly's past belies the subtlety of her story's multilayered motifs. The story's most prevalent motif, consisting of both physical and mental cages, reinforces Nelly's desperate mental state. The travel agent's posters depict cities surrounded by walls, the hotel closet hooks remind Nelly of "skewers," and a hotel window's slanted view of the ocean seems like a barred prison window. Reminiscences of her childhood are even more imprisoning, especially when Nelly recalls her brother's padlocking a hall door to keep her out and Gertie's standing in Vince's doorway to shut her off from her would-be lover. Those painful memories of her childhood cause Nelly to "put an iron grille" over her former life as she tries to keep "the weed and bindweed of the past" from pushing "up through the gates of her mind." Neither the present nor the past offers any consolation to Nelly.

Even more subtle are the various motifs that O'Brien uses to hook the present to the past, especially as the past relates to Vince—the love that Nelly never managed to forget. Nelly's selection of a seaside resort—with which she associates happy newlyweds—is the same place where Gertie and Vince were supposed to have honeymooned. The red clothing of the people on the beach stands out, as did Vince's dashing red sweater. The shifting green, blue, and violet of the sea mirror the colors of the "stained-glass fanlight" in Vince's front door.

The third motif, water, is at once the most complicated and most central to O'Brien's theme. While the "liquid silver" stream that young Nelly crossed on her way to pick up the black dress represents a transition from girlhood into womanhood, the sea is both comforting and terrifying. Nelly selects a holiday getaway surrounded by ocean on three sides, but one that maintains a reassuring jetty to the mainland. The sea is by turns "gentle," "bright, like a mirror with the sun dancing on it," and "sulky." After Gertie's visit, Nelly feels "like a river that winds its way back into its first beloved enclave before finally putting out to sea." Although this last line of the story appears to suggest that Nelly has released all of her bitter feelings, her future is not entirely secure. Nelly's attraction to the sea suggests release; however, the sea is also a traditional symbol for death, or at least the unknown.

Sandra Hanby Harris

APPROXIMATIONS

Author: Mona Simpson (1957-   )
Type of plot: Social realism
Time of plot: The 1960's and 1970's
Locale: Illinois, Nevada, and California
First published: 1984

> *Principal characters:*
> MELINDA, the narrator, a Midwestern teenager
> CAROL, her mother
> JOHN, her father, a waiter in California
> JERRY, her stepfather, a professional skater

The Story

Melinda imagines a scene in which her parents are holding each other closely as they dance to music. She has had this same fantasy since she was four years old, when she learned that the man in the black-and-white photograph was her father. She has no real memories of her father, only this fantasy. When Melinda once asked her mother where her father was, her mother replied vaguely, telling her that her father was gone, but would be back sometime. Melinda remembers other people asking about her father, but she has never met him.

Melinda's mother, Carol, refuses to face reality, drifting along, waiting for Melinda's father to return. Melinda and Carol are now used to living alone. On Saturday nights they dress in identical outfits and go ice-skating together. Carol points to the empty seats, telling Melinda that when she is older she can bring boys there to watch her skate so that they will know that she is more than simply another pretty girl, that she can really do something. Carol's advice to her daughter emphasizes physical appearance and the importance of attracting men.

Melinda first hears from her father, John, in 1963, when he calls from Las Vegas to invite her and her mother to join him at Disneyland. When Melinda finally sees him, she finds that he is an ordinary balding man. He works as a waiter in a hotel restaurant and shares an apartment with three roommates. He introduces her to his friends, making Melinda feel that he is proud of her. As he touches her hair, she thinks that she loves him blindly. He gives her a cheap package of headbands, but she is so pleased with this token of her father's love that she does not even open the package.

When Carol asks John when they will go to Disneyland, he replies that he has lost the money "on the tables." This revelation provokes a fight, but they sleep together in the bedroom that night while Melinda sleeps on a couch in the living room.

The next morning Melinda and her father have breakfast at a coffee shop. At his invitation she tastes her father's soft-boiled egg and then tells him how good it is, hoping to share it with him. Instead of sharing the egg, however, her father orders another one for her. He promises that they will visit Disneyland on their next trip. As

Melinda holds his hand tightly, she dreams of other trips so that she can spend time with her father. On the plane ride home Carol notices how much the package of headbands means to Melinda. She then reminds her daughter that while she works to pay for the rent, skating lessons, school, and books, all her father has given her is a seventy-nine-cent package of headbands.

The following year Carol marries Jerry, an ice-skating professional whom she has met during a Saturday night skating session at the rink. Melinda and her mother skate in a few ice shows but eventually drop out, while Jerry continues to go to the rink every day just like any other man going to a job. On one Saturday Carol insists that Melinda accompany Jerry to a Girl Scout father-daughter banquet, telling her that Jerry wants to adopt her. Refusing to attend the event, Melinda goes outside to play. When Melinda sees Jerry dressed up for the dinner in a turtleneck sweater and paisley ascot, she feels sorry for him but does not change her mind about attending. As she rides off on her bicycle, she tells herself that none of the other fathers would be wearing ascots.

When Melinda is ten years old, her natural father asks her to visit him in California by herself, but Carol talks him into sending two airplane tickets so that she and her daughter can make the trip together. She thinks that she can persuade John to buy her a television set that she wants. In California, Carol, Melinda, John, and John's rich new wife tour Disneyland, eating in restaurants and buying souvenirs. Melinda and her father have little to say to each other, and Carol makes no progress in getting John to buy her a television. On their last night in California, Carol coaches Melinda on how to dress and behave in order to get her father to buy the television. The next morning when John buys a candy bar, he asks Melinda if she wants anything. Melinda wants only to stand there eating candy with her father, but knows that this moment will be only a memory next year when her father forgets to write or call her. Instead, she follows her mother's advice and tells John that she is saving up for a television set, realizing as she says this that she is cutting the ties with her father.

After they return home, Carol is still angry with Melinda for failing to get the television and takes out her frustration by telling Melinda that she is ordinary and belongs with the mill workers' children. To escape her mother's yelling, Melinda goes to the ice rink. When she sees Jerry, she runs toward him and throws herself into his arms. She now realizes that while her dream of being reunited with her natural father is gone, Jerry is there for her. The story ends with Jerry teaching Melinda how to do loops on the ice.

Themes and Meanings

As the story's title suggests, the characters' lives are full of approximations. Jerry settles for an "approximation" when he buys the used Cadillac that he can afford instead of the new Lincoln Continental that his wife wants. As a stepfather Jerry is himself an approximation; he is not the perfect father of Melinda's dreams, but a shy steady man who is willing to take care of her. Some of the individual scenes are approximations. At the beginning of the story, for example, Melinda imagines her father holding Carol and closing his hand over her ear. At the end of the story Jerry embraces Melinda and holds his hand over her ear. Melinda's imagined scene of her parents dancing is replaced by a real scene in which Carol and Jerry skate together. As Melinda matures, she gives up her fantasy of a perfect family, and learns to appreciate the "approximations" that are the realities of life.

Melinda fantasizes about her father and so longs to know him that she takes each small gesture of his affection and holds on to it tightly, hoping for a relationship with him. Disneyland is important to her only because it provides an opportunity for her to be with her father. She wants to share an egg with her father in the restaurant, but he prefers not to share. When they walk together hand in hand, it is John who releases Melinda's hand. After a number of disappointments, Melinda realizes that she will never be a part of her father's life.

This is the story of a young girl coming of age in a fragmented family. With an absent father and a critical, self-absorbed mother, Melinda is shut off from a normal family life. In a number of scenes Carol shows a callous disregard for Melinda's feelings. When they go to California in order for Melinda to meet her father for the first time, Carol monopolizes his time, first by fighting with him, later by sleeping with him. When she closes the door, she leaves Melinda alone on the couch. At the skating rink, Carol is so absorbed with Jerry that she forgets to give Melinda the cue to begin skating, and Melinda falls on the ice. This is, however, also a story of survival, and Melinda survives in spite of her mother's selfishness and her father's indifference.

Style and Technique

Through flashbacks and reminiscences provided by a first-person narrator, Mona Simpson shows a character growing from childhood to adolescence. Instead of simply telling a story, she provides scenes as vivid as snapshots. Melinda has only a vague idea of what her father looks like, but when she comes face to face with him, she describes him in realistic detail, noting his bald spot and even the way that his chin sticks out from his face. At times Melinda appears to be taking a mental picture of her father so that she can remember him. She watches him working in the restaurant, balancing dishes on the inside of his arm or standing at the candy counter buying Lifesavers. John's casually dressed roommates form a picture as they lean on the iron banister of the porch to their apartment. These and other scenes are brief but vividly portrayed. Melinda describes how Jerry tries to impress her mother by doing a "t-stop . . . shaving a comet of ice into the air." Jerry and Carol laughing at the stage exit, or skating under the spotlight, Carol twirling in Jerry's arms—in these scenes Melinda is excluded. Taken together these snapshots tell the story of Melinda's life.

Judith Barton Williamson

ARABESQUE—THE MOUSE

Author: A. E. Coppard (1878-1957)
Type of plot: Psychological realism
Time of plot: Early twentieth century
Locale: England
First published: 1921

> *Principal characters:*
> FILIP, a middle-aged man
> HIS MOTHER
> CASSIA, a young woman he met years earlier
> THE MOUSE

The Story

Filip, a middle-aged man, sits in his room on the fourth floor of an old house in the commercial area of a city. He is reading a Russian novel, as is his late-evening habit. After becoming aware of a small mouse scurrying about the room, he baits a trap to catch it. There are many mice in the building; he knows he must try to eradicate them, but feels pity for the bright-eyed rodent. He says, "Mean—so mean, to appeal to the hunger of any living thing just in order to destroy it." This sentence becomes a key to the flashbacks that follow.

Filip remembers having been a sensitive child who was upset at having to carry dead larks, tied by the feet, home for supper. When he got home, his face stained with tears, he discovered his mother expressing breast milk into their fire; she was weaning his baby sister. As his mother allowed him to help squeeze out her milk, he noticed her heart beating, then felt his own heart beat. His mother noted that the heart must beat for one to live. Filip kissed his mother and cried out, "Little mother! Little mother!"

The next day Filip's world changed forever when his mother was knocked down in the street by a horse, and a cart ran over her hands, crushing them. Her hands were amputated and she died shortly thereafter.

Haunted by the image of his handless mother, Filip grew into a questioning man who found justice and sin and property and virtue incompatible. His rebellious spirit was rebuffed by others and he became timid and misanthropic, easily offended by small slights and moved by imagined grievances.

As Filip's awareness of the mouse returns momentarily, his mind flashes back to another moment when he was a young man and met a beautiful young woman named Cassia at the village festival. During their only meeting, Filip and Cassia were exuberant and full of life. They danced and strolled together; then he carried her home. When he set her down on her porch, she put her hand on his heart and remarked on its beating. He cried "Little mother, little mother!"

Hearing a snap, Filip is brought back to the present by the realization that the mouse has sprung the trap. The mouse, however, is not caught; it stares at him mutely. Horrified to see that the trap has amputated both of the mouse's forefeet, Filip picks it up, and it promptly bites him. Uncertain what to do, he flings the mouse out the window. Filled with remorse, he runs outside and searches unsuccessfully for the mouse until he is chilled to the bone. He returns to his room, retrieves the mouse's feet from the trap, throws them into the fire, and rebaits the trap.

Themes and Meanings

The title of A. E. Coppard's story, "Arabesque—the Mouse," is a cue to both its meaning and its style. An arabesque is an ornamental object, such as a rug or mosaic, in which flowers, fruits, animals, and other figures are represented in fancifully combined patterns. Coppard's story is just such an arabesque. Filip's present encounter with the mouse is arranged by his imagination and memory into a pattern of warmth, violence, and loss—which explain his misanthropic personality and constricted life.

The line, "Mean—so mean, to appeal to the hunger of any living thing just in order to destroy it," explains the pattern, or arabesque, his life has formed. Filip was evidently a sensitive, needy child who drew warmth and solace from his mother as a nursing mother. Her warm breast and heart were especially reassuring to a fearful child. This reassurance was snatched from Filip by the unspeakable violence and poignance of his mother's maiming and death.

Filip's brief encounter with Cassia is similarly affirming to him. At that moment he is strong, virile, and seems assured. When Cassia remarks on his heartbeat, however, he is cued to the memory of his mother's discussion of his heartbeat the day before her death. He even repeats the phrase, "Little mother, little mother!" The reader does not learn what broke off his relationship with Cassia, but does learn that they only met one time. Filip's psyche seems to have been warped by his mother's death, and he is unable to connect to others on a permanent basis.

In Filip's fourth-floor room is a color print by the Japanese painter Utamaro of a mother breast-feeding her child in front of a mirror. This picture tells the reader that Filip has chosen objects for his home that reinforce his memories of his mother and of Cassia.

The amputation of the mouse's feet by the mousetrap, recalling Filip's mother's amputated hands, creates a tragic irony almost too great for Filip to bear. He is cut off from others because of his nervous sensibility and critical rectitude about matters of property and justice. His only positive life experiences are connected to his mother and Cassia. The maiming of the mouse seems part of an inexorable pattern in his life.

Filip's relationships deteriorate from a major one with his mother, to a minor one with Cassia, to a minuscule one with the mouse. In like manner, Filip's world has shrunk to a tiny sphere with little human contact. When he goes out into the cold to find the injured mouse, he is trying to reconnect with life; however, his search fails and he returns to his old ways—calmly rebaiting the trap and returning to his Russian novels, which are emblematic of another, far away world.

Style and Technique

The style of "Arabesque—the Mouse" is that of an arabesque, a carefully woven Persian carpet or Byzantine mosaic. By using this technique, Coppard is suggesting that people's lives are patterns of their own weaving made from the circumstances and events that happen to them. The circumstances of Filip's life are not his to choose, but the pattern is his. All memory is selective, and his memory selects warmth followed by loss.

Coppard's style resembles the techniques of James Joyce and Virginia Woolf, who wrote during the period in which Coppard wrote "Arabesque—the Mouse." Joyce and Woolf employed a stream-of-consciousness style, however, which differs from Coppard's work. The arabesque technique uses all materials remembered to form the pattern of the whole; there are no loose threads or unconnected memories as is so often the case with stream-of-consciousness writings.

Coppard's technique leaves many unanswered questions in the mind of the reader. Were there no other nurturing influences in Filip's life? Why did his relationship with Cassia fail? Why does he read Russian novels? Characteristically, Coppard gives the reader some hints about Filip's life but leaves the reader to sort them out and form conclusions about Filip. In his studied stinginess with the reader, Coppard points toward other minimalist writers who succeeded him later in the twentieth century.

At the close of the story, Coppard refers to the mouse twice as "the little philosopher." Is Coppard suggesting that the mouse has something to teach Filip, or does Filip himself see the mouse as a little philosopher? The reader cannot be sure. Filip certainly rushes out to rescue the mouse, but what would he do with it if he found it? It has no forefeet, just as Filip's mother had no hands. Perhaps Coppard uses the many indeterminants in "Arabesque—the Mouse" to show just how precarious the task of building a secure self is. After chance kills Filip's mother, Filip becomes a wounded, maimed person just as she was; however, unlike her, he must live without the metaphorical hands to reach out to others. The incident with the mouse reminds Filip of his own incompleteness. Coppard's arabesque technique makes the tenuous life-maiming events in his story the pattern of Filip's psyche.

Isabel B. Stanley

THE ARGENTINE ANT

Author: Italo Calvino (1923-1985)
Type of plot: Fable
Time of plot: Mid-twentieth century
Locale: A coastal village in Liguria, Italy
First published: "La formica argentina," 1952 (English translation, 1957)

Principal characters:
THE UNNAMED NARRATOR
HIS WIFE and INFANT SON
SIGNORA MAURO, their landlady
SIGNOR REGINAUDO, their neighbor
CAPTAIN BRAUNI, a nearby neighbor
SIGNOR BAUDINO, from the Argentine Ant Control Corporation

The Story

Acting upon the advice of his uncle, a man moves his wife and infant son to a small rented cottage in a Ligurian coastal village in Italy. At first, all seems idyllic, but on their first night, as they prepare for bed, they discover that their kitchen is swarming with ants. "Argentine ants," the narrator informs his wife, and he remembers being told that this is the country of the Argentine ant. After the narrator calms his wife, they retire to bed; they are awakened by the cries of their baby and find his bed is filled with ants.

The next day, the narrator considers the situation, noting that the yard, which he had planned to convert to a garden, is alive with ants. He visits Signor Reginaudo, their nearest neighbor, for advice, and finds that the old man and his wife have used, and found practically useless, every ant spray, poison, and powder available. Still, the Reginaudos are not discouraged and actually laugh at themselves, the ants, and the ridiculous situation. They arm the narrator with a variety of concoctions, carefully chosen to be harmless to the baby, and return him to his family.

The narrator then rushes off to see Captain Brauni, another neighbor with his own way of fighting the ants. Captain Brauni has transformed his house and yard into a maze of ant traps. Some ants are destroyed when they fall off a narrow wire into a can of gasoline; he kills an average of forty ants a minute, Captain Brauni says with almost comic precision. Many other devices are scattered about. Captain Brauni orders his wife to bring out a sack; it is filled with dead ants. His insanely rational plan is to kill enough worker ants so that the queens will begin to starve and leave their nests; only then can the problem be solved. He promises to construct a device for the narrator.

As the days progress, the narrator and his wife discover that neither poisons nor contraptions are effective. One afternoon a strange man comes through their property, leaving small saucers of molasses scattered about. It is Signor Baudino, known as the ant man, from the Argentine Ant Control Corporation. Supposedly he is spreading poison, but most residents agree with Signor Reginaudo that the corporation is actually feeding the ants to keep business thriving.

The narrator and his wife call on Signora Mauro, their landlady, to ask why she failed to mention the ants before they rented the house. Signora Mauro insists that a truly clean house should have no problem with ants; hers certainly does not. As they sit in her large, dark house, they notice that she is subtly moving and twitching; the narrator realizes that ants are crawling under her clothes and that her house is even more thoroughly infested than their own.

When they return to their house, they find an ant has crawled into the baby's ear. It is flushed out with warm oil, but the situation is intolerable for the wife. She rushes down the street with a crowd of women behind her and the narrator tagging along; they arrive at the office of the Argentine Ant Control Corporation and confront the ant man, who first makes general denials and then runs off. There is nothing to be done. That evening, the couple and their baby walk down to the coast, to the sea and a fresh wind, but no ants. They sit and watch the ocean.

Themes and Meanings

Writing about "The Argentine Ant," American author Gore Vidal said that the story "gives us the human condition today. Or the dilemma of modern man. Or the disrupted environment. Or nature's revenge. Or an allegory of grace. Whatever. . . . " A great part of the strength and appeal of Italo Calvino's story is that it can plausibly support each of these interpretations, as well as others. At the same time, the details of setting, characters, and action are so realistically rendered that the story is securely anchored in reality; the reader has the visceral understanding that these events actually happened, or could have happened, in just the way Calvino recounts them, whatever elusive meaning they may possess.

Although the story can be interpreted on several levels, it is clear that it is an allegory of the difficulty for human beings to achieve freedom and choice. As Vidal implies, the world may be defined through a number of approaches: theological, philosophical, artistic, social, economic, or political. For each approach human beings are inherently limited. The Argentine ants can be seen as symbols of those limitations.

For example, some critics have seen the story as a political parable, with the ants representative of the modern conformist trend, a trend that reached its nadir during Calvino's younger years with the triumph of the Fascists in Italy and the Nazis in Germany. Their mindless obedience can easily be traced in the relentless, thoughtless, and unstoppable onslaught of the ants. Calvino fought with the Italian Resistance during World War II against the Fascists and their Nazi allies, and later joined the Italian Communist Party, only to leave it in protest of the brutal suppression of the 1956 Hungarian uprising. He was familiar with the evils of totalitarianism, and the ants in his story may be seen as a symbolic expression of such a political system.

Yet, like the insects that are so important to the story, "The Argentine Ant" refuses to be pinned down. The story could also be interpreted as a satire on modern faith in technology, with the Reginaudos and Captain Brauni compulsively chained to their unworkable powders and sprays and intricate traps, which have no real impact on the problem. On the other hand, "The Argentine Ant" could be about the existential role an individual must play in the contemporary world, with the unnamed narrator caught between an indifferent nature (the ants) and an inauthentic society (his neighbors). There are numerous other interpretations, more or less plausible.

The essential theme of this ambiguous yet realistic story is ambiguity itself. Just as art can have many meanings, Calvino implies, so can life, and vice versa. As Gore Vidal would annotate, "Whatever." The ultimate meaning of "The Argentine Ant" is that "The Argentine Ant" has many different meanings, all plausible, all important.

Style and Technique

"The Argentine Ant" is written in a style of scrupulous realism. Its descriptions are given in precise, simple language that is utterly clear and, in its surface meaning, unambiguous. The reader has no doubts about what is happening; what it means is another matter, and that level of ambiguity is actually reinforced by the clarity of Calvino's presentation. For example, Captain Brauni's activities in building his increasingly intricate ant-trapping devices are easily followed, and even their most complicated workings are clearly presented. It is what Brauni's activities signify that is puzzling: Are they actions for their own sakes, or do they represent something universal in human nature or human society? In a similar fashion, Signor Baudino, the local representative of the Argentine Ant Control Corporation, is described in a short, precise vignette, making him an easily imaginable individual. That description, however, emphasizes his ant-like appearance. Does this mean that Baudino, and perhaps the other characters in the story, has somehow become like the ants? Can this identification be extended to include modern human beings in general? The very simplicity of the prose that suggests such a connection denies an easy answer.

Calvino's deceptively forthright style presents its most subtle considerations in its treatment of the ants, which makes it difficult to understand if they are symbolic and, if so, what they represent. For example, throughout the story they are often compared to sand. Considering the seemingly inevitable onslaught of the tiny creatures, the narrator admits that he was "face to face with an enemy like fog or sand, against which force was useless." Later, when the narrator visits Captain Brauni, the captain has his wife bring out bags filled with ants slaughtered by the captain's devices. As Brauni lifts handfuls of ants from the bag and lets them fall back, they appear "a soft red-black sand of dead ants." At the end of the story, the narrator, his wife, and their child are at the seaside, at last free of the ants, and he gazes on the ocean and thinks "of the infinite grains of soft sand down there at the bottom of the sea where the currents leave white shells washed clean by the waves."

Is the sea a refuge from the ants, or has it, too, become part of their domain? The clear, simple style suggests a response but refuses to answer. From such clarity and subtlety does Calvino fashion "The Argentine Ant."

Michael Witkoski

THE ARTIFICIAL FAMILY

Author: Anne Tyler (1941-   )
Type of plot: Domestic realism
Time of plot: The 1980's
Locale: Baltimore, Maryland
First published: 1975

> *Principal characters:*
> TOBY SCOTT, a graduate student
> MARY GLOVER, an art gallery worker
> SAMANTHA GLOVER, Mary's daughter

The Story

When Toby Scott meets Mary Glover at a party, he is immediately impressed by her long hair and old-fashioned gingham dress. Afraid that he might not see her again, he asks her to dinner immediately. Mary tells the eager bachelor that she has a daughter, but Toby does not know if this means that she is married or is simply unwilling to date.

Samantha Glover, Mary's daughter, is a somber five-year-old who dresses like her mother, in floor-length dresses. The impression that Mary and Samantha make together is that of stoic pioneers riding a wagon train across the prairie.

Samantha accompanies her mother when Toby asks her out. On a trip to the Baltimore zoo, Samantha sits between Toby and Mary as they look at animals. Mary never volunteers any information about her first marriage or Samantha's father. When Toby inquires, Mary refuses to answer any questions, revealing only that she ran away after two years of marriage. Her previous life remains mysterious.

Toby's feelings for Mary and Samantha deepen. When Mary mentions that she has child-care problems, Toby volunteers to watch Samantha himself. Mary works in an art gallery with fixed hours, while Toby can easily adjust his own schedule. Despite Toby's offer to watch Samantha, Mary keeps paying her teenage babysitter. Toby fears losing Mary because his graduate student life spent in classes and laboratories lacks warm human relations.

After knowing each other only five months, Toby and Mary are married. Toby's parents object to his brief courtship and the fact that Toby is acquiring a ready-made daughter. While Toby questions his ability to love his own biological children—were he ever to have them—he finds that he can easily warm to loving Samantha.

Toby envies the resolve with which Mary carried Samantha from her presumably troubled first marriage. She took no clothing, jewelry, or personal belongings of any kind. As if fleeing from a burning building, Mary simply snatched away the only thing that really mattered: Samantha. Toby wonders about the strength of the relationships that he is forming with Mary and Samantha. For some reason, Mary is reluctant to enter compassionately into their marital union. Overly concerned with Toby's privacy, she never even enters his office—the spare bedroom. She even places a no-entry sign above his door, even though he has said that he was always alone at his lab and does not want to be alone at home. Although Toby attempts to bond emotionally with Mary and her daughter, Mary scrupulously avoids close personal contact.

Toby becomes a model father, playing games with Samantha, reading her stories, and giving her piggyback rides each night before bedtime. Samantha returns Toby's affection more readily than Mary does. Every evening she walks to his lab, calling him to dinner. Her attention, smiles, and warmth flatter Toby, who wonders if he would feel differently about her if she were his own daughter.

At Christmas, Toby's parents visit the newlyweds. The four days of their visit seem to drag out forever because of their tactless remarks about Toby's "artificial" family. Not knowing that the topic is forbidden, the Scotts ask many questions about Samantha's father. They also comment on the way that Mary has taken over Toby's life. Toby, Mary, and Samantha form an alliance against the Scotts, seeking refuge together in Toby's study to play dominoes. They even sneak off to the movies together to escape from their intrusive houseguests.

Gradually, Toby's once private study becomes a gathering place for the new family. Toby reads, Mary sews and places her pottery around the room, and Samantha plays on the floor. Finally, the ice thaws and the marriage seems to form strong emotional, spiritual, and physical bonds. Under the influence of Toby's playfulness, Samantha grows unruly with her mother, talking back and roughhousing, in contrast to her former sullenness. Mary complains that Toby's attention is spoiling Samantha. Toby dotes on Samantha, giving her everything she wants. Toby's feelings for her strengthen. On one occasion, Toby becomes angry when Samantha steps into the street without looking; he pulls her back, feeling a deep sense of shock and nervous helplessness.

Toby becomes so confident about his fathering that he asks Mary for another baby. Toby loves Samantha so much that he wants more children to love, but Mary insists that women have less love to give than men because of the demands of housekeeping. Toby and Mary also disagree over Samantha's Easter basket. Toby gives Samantha a big prepackaged basket with chocolate, jellybeans, and candy rabbits, but Mary insists that she and Samantha observe Easter differently, and she resents having to be the parent who says no to treats. Although Samantha enjoys receiving the candy, Toby senses that he has lost the battle. Once again Mary grows distant and emotionless.

After Samantha finishes the first grade in school, Mary leaves Toby for good. The only message that she leaves for him simply says, "I've gone." Devastated, Toby puts his head in his hands and thinks about how he can find his family. After eating a sandwich that Mary has made for him, he runs to Samantha's school, dodging cars. He feels the same kind of grief felt by a parent whose child has died. After Samantha's teacher tells him that she has not been at school, Toby walks home in a daze. He lies down on the sofa without turning on lights. He knows that he will find Mary's and

Samantha's clothes in their closets. Once again, the only things that they have taken away are their gingham dresses and themselves.

Themes and Meanings

The first question that this story poses is exactly what is meant by "artificial" in its title? Toby's desire for a family has an artificial easiness about it. Perhaps he savors the idea of a family more than the reality of complex people with mysterious pasts. Mary's commitment to Toby seems even more clearly artificial and dishonest. She and Samantha appear artificial or unreal; they appear out of nowhere and disappear equally mysteriously. Yet, Mary is overly concerned with the artificial quality of the Easter basket that Toby buys in a store instead of making it himself.

In exploring definitions of love and the struggle for power within a family, "The Artificial Family" addresses the sanctity of marital love—a love that demands willing, imperfect, vulnerable partners engaged in forming a more perfect union. Toby, the character most concerned with his ability to love, seems to exemplify unconditional love and acceptance. His courageous act of saving Samantha from being hit by a car and his grief after her later departure indicate that he has fully entered into the relationship. Toby desires to have more children and unconditionally accepts Samantha despite his own parents' misgivings.

Mary prizes her independence and her ability to abandon a bad marriage without hesitation. Her hardened "survivor" mentality prevents her from displaying vulnerability or showing her true personality. Toby notices that her face seems artificial, like a mask, after they fight over the Easter basket. Mary resists Toby's offer to help with child care and resents depending upon him.

Toby's concern with his ability to love, his high regard for family, and his desire for children—all qualities that are generally regarded as feminine—stand opposite to Mary's masculine independence, unresponsiveness, and refusal to invest in the relationship. Mary seems to lose authority over her daughter because of Toby's abundant attention and lax discipline; her leaving may be read as an attempt to reassert her control. Mary and Toby attempt to love each other, but too many "artificial" impediments bring their marriage to an end.

Style and Technique

Anne Tyler tells this story in a straightforward, realistic, and unsentimental style. "The Artificial Family" avoids both an overtly didactic message or a conclusive, tightly wrapped ending. Instead, readers must guess why Mary leaves Toby. The story leaves many unanswered questions: What is the meaning of Toby's desire for children? Was this experience artificial or real for Toby and Mary? How will Toby cope with his loss? What will Mary and Samantha's new life be like? Will Mary ever be in complete control?

American novelist John Updike once described Anne Tyler as a Southern writer because, like Flannery O'Connor or Carson McCullers, she evokes a solid sense of family, place, and region. Tyler's characters seem isolated from the large currents of change in American culture and evoke nostalgia for an earlier, simpler time. Tyler is preoccupied with character psychology but not corrupted with the modern idiom of clinical psychotherapy. The motives and desires of Toby and Mary are deftly implied and lightly sketched, leaving much room for creative interpretation.

Jonathan L. Thorndike

ASTRONOMER'S WIFE

Author: Kay Boyle (1903-1992)
Type of plot: Domestic realism
Time of plot: A summer around 1930
Locale: A European mountain villa
First published: 1936

> *Principal characters:*
> KATHERINE AMES, the protagonist
> MR. AMES, her husband, an astronomer
> THE PLUMBER

The Story

Early in the morning, Katherine Ames steps quietly out of bed, trying not to disturb her husband—who either is still asleep or pretends to be. Mrs. Ames—as she is called throughout the story—comes "into her own possession" by beginning the day with brief exercises. She will stay busy with household duties, deeply ingrained habits that absent her from her husband's constant, unknowable silence.

Silence is her astronomer husband's dominant characteristic. The couple's relationship is built upon the understanding that he is a man of the mind, who spends his days studying, meditating, contemplating the heavens through his rooftop telescope, or wandering through the mountains. His constant silence informs his wife that she is part of his life only in the sense that man is "the new arching wave, and woman the undertow that suck[s] him back." Mrs. Ames feels chided and shamed by her husband's silence, which constantly reminds her that he is preoccupied with mysterious ideas that she can never comprehend. As a result, she has forgotten her youth; no light shines from her grey eyes.

The serving girl announces the arrival of the plumber, who has come to repair an overflowing toilet. Mrs. Ames discusses the problem with him in a grave, dignified manner. She delicately avoids using the name of the offending appliance, referring to it not as "the wash basin," but as "the other." After studying the situation, the plumber suggests that the pipes are stopped up, rebukingly adding that the problem would not have occurred if there were a valve. During this discussion, Mrs. Ames speaks in nervous, hushed tones, reminding the plumber that her sleeping husband should not be disturbed. She is unsettled by the "relentless eye" of the plumber, who has been looking at her directly. His face softens a bit as he tells her he will check the pipes from the drain opening in the garden.

Suddenly, from behind the closed bedroom door where he has listened to the plumbing conversation, the astronomer's voice rings out (the only time in the story that he speaks): "Katherine! . . . There's a problem worthy of your mettle!" Her only apparent reaction to his scorn is the heightened color of her face, which the plumber notices as they step into the sunlit garden, which is full of a profusion of flowering plants.

For the first few moments in the garden, Mrs. Ames is in despair, still hearing her husband's taunt. She tells herself that a man's mind is concerned with great problems, dreams, and illusions, rather than with tangible things, while for woman, life is like the ocean where she must cling to floating debris for survival. When she looks down she sees the plumber gazing up at her from the trapdoor to the drains. His hair is "as light as gold." He suggests in a bitter voice that perhaps her husband, a man of knowledge, would like to come down into the drains. Confused, Mrs. Ames responds that her husband never goes downward, only up—on rooftops or mountaintops. She notices the plumber's lean, rugged build, his firm, clean, and tanned flesh. She can understand his strong hands holding the trapdoor rings.

Like a star, the plumber's light-gold hair glows from down in the drain. Understanding what this man is saying to her about the stopped-up elbow drain, Mrs. Ames is surprised to be able to comprehend anything that a man says. She sits motionless on the ground trying to make sense of this discovery that some men go "up" and others "down." She concludes that her husband is "the mind," this other man "the meat," of all humankind.

When the plumber emerges from the drain, Mrs. Ames questions him softly, looking up at him as he answers, smiling, that the elbow joint can easily be fixed, as can "everything a-miss." She begins to feel youth and delight as he talks of problems solved, his eyes full of "insolence, or gentleness, or love." Mrs. Ames stands up and calls the servant, telling her to report to Mr. Ames that she has gone "down." Then she enters the earth with the plumber, knowing that what he has said is true.

Themes and Meanings

Kay Boyle is especially well known for her intense psychological portrayals of people who long for meaning and love in a disordered world. In that vein, "Astronomer's Wife" is concerned with the relationships between men and women and the effects of emotional manipulation and control. The important men in Mrs. Ames's life have apparently all been cold and domineering. She assumes that all men are like her husband, who makes her feel that men are strong, intelligent, and important, while women are weak, incompetent, and irritating. When Mr. Ames makes his only utterance, he reaffirms his idea that his wife is spiritually incapable of understanding anything more complicated than a stopped-up drain. This insult has a double effect: It undermines Mrs. Ames's already-shaky self-confidence, thus reinforcing her dependence upon him, and it announces her general inadequacy to the plumber and the servant.

For obvious reasons, Mrs. Ames prefers her husband's usual ominous silence to his actually speaking to her. His silence keeps distance between them and reminds her constantly of his superiority. Her mental and emotional state, as a result, is characterized by confusion, frustration, loneliness, and ineffectualness. The plumber, a man of sensitivity, holds out a metaphoric hand to rescue her. At first, he is brusque in discussing the plumbing problem; however, after hearing Mr. Ames's humiliating remark to his wife, he feels compassion for Mrs. Ames and anger toward her husband.

Initially, when the plumber looks directly at Mrs. Ames, it disturbs her. Gradually, however, she grows more aware of him as a man and realizes that he is entirely different from her husband. When she consciously decides to go down into the drains with the plumber, she frees herself from the bondage that her husband has imposed upon her. Love, hope, and meaning have come back into her life.

Style and Technique

Boyle's short stories are characterized by fluency of language, whose fresh, striking images and metaphors give her characters' lives a sense of immediacy. This story unfolds through a gradual revelation in relation to these metaphors rather than through crises of action. For example, the occupations of the astronomer and the plumber are metaphorically significant. An astronomer is concerned with a study of heavenly bodies, and as such, has his eyes fixed upward. Boyle's astronomer seems completely disconnected, mentally and spiritually, from earthly matters. Furthermore, he keeps himself physically remote from even his wife, seldom speaking to her. Throughout the entire story, he remains behind his bedroom door. Mrs. Ames realizes—and tells the plumber—that her husband only goes "up," never "down."

The plumber's vocation suggests several things about his role. A plumber's attention is fixed, literally, upon the earth—buried pipes and drains and such. This story's plumber, who remains nameless, seems completely at ease with his strong, capable body and with his mission in the cavernous drain. He goes "down" readily into the earth and speaks to Mrs. Ames from within the drain. Amazed, Mrs. Ames sits "down" on the grass, and during a meditative few moments, begins to see the plumber, always "down," as a symbol of the physical body of man, in contrast to her husband, always "up," representing man's mind. Through simple word choice—"up" and "down"— Boyle represents opposing planes of living. As she and the plumber enter the earth together, he has begun, metaphorically, to plumb the depths of her despair and will remedy it as easily as he repairs drains, with simple human love and communication.

Judith Callarman

AUNT CARRIE

Author: Rita Dove (1952-   )
Type of plot: Social realism
Time of plot: Around the mid-twentieth century
Locale: An unnamed city and Fort Myers, Florida
First published: 1985

>   *Principal characters:*
>   THE UNNAMED NARRATOR
>   AUNT CARRIE, her father's sister
>   ERNEST PRICE, her father
>   BELLE PRICE, her mother
>   SAM ROGERS, Aunt Carrie's dead husband
>   EDNA ROGERS, Sam's first wife
>   GRANDMA EVANS, Belle Price's mother

The Story

"Aunt Carrie" is told in two parts, first from the perspective of the narrator as a child and later as the childhood experience is re-evaluated by the narrator as an adult.

The setting for the first portion of the story is a train station. The nine-year-old narrator is excited by her first visit to a train station. She is awed by the dark and noisy trains and by her imaginings of Pittsburgh, the point of departure for her father, whom she, her mother, and her Aunt Carrie have come to meet. Ernest Price has been away attending a convention and is about to return. Before her father's train arrives, the girl is confused by the odd behavior of her mother, who is acting tense and speaking in a weird tone of voice; somewhat inexplicably, she has brought Aunt Carrie along to the station.

The young narrator has difficulty believing that her aunt is just a few years older than her mother although she realizes that Aunt Carrie is not considered physically attractive, and that she seems old and worn. She senses that the older woman wears lipstick to make herself pretty, but that her effort is ineffective. Part of her impressions are formed by offhand negative comments about Aunt Carrie that her mother has made, so her own views of her aunt are not sympathetic.

When her father arrives, the girl runs into his arms. While he holds her, something happens among the adults that she does not understand. Aunt Carrie seems upset; pulling distractedly on a hankie, she is covered by her coat and retreats behind the large pregnant physique of Mrs. Price, where the girl can barely see her. Belle Price confronts her husband, but her words are meaningless to the child. She refers to Aunt Carrie as his "lovely sister" and informs Mr. Price that she once read a letter that Aunt Carrie wrote to him years ago. All three adults are immobilized by this announcement, and the child fears that her parents are about to have an argument. Her father looks like he is about to cry, and Aunt Carrie is actually crying. She decides that it was not nice of her mother to call Aunt Carrie lovely when she is not, and that this must be the source of the tension.

The story then shifts from the vignette at the train station to a moment years later, when the narrator is grown up and living in the same city as Aunt Carrie. She has just asked Aunt Carrie to tea. Their dialogue sheds light on the cryptic scene on the station platform and answers some other questions about her parents that have stayed in the narrator's mind.

Soon after the incident at the station the narrator and her parents moved to Florida, and the narrator has always wondered why. She asks Aunt Carrie if she knows. After some encouragement, Aunt Carrie tells her niece her family history: how her father deserted their family when she was thirteen and how she raised her younger brother Ernest while her mother and the older siblings went out to work. Homely and untalented, she had little status within the family. At seventeen she was married off to an older man and kept house for him until he died. Left a widow without means at nineteen, she moved back into her mother's home. One day while hanging laundry there, she was forcefully attracted to a young man coming down the street.

As she recalls this attraction and the sensuality and sexual consummation that accompanied it, the story is revealed to be a tale of incest, for it is her brother Ernest with whom she became involved. After confessing this secret, she tells her niece that she ended the affair because she realized it was crazy. Ernest went on to meet and marry the narrator's mother and to establish a successful career and family. Carrie then became the caretaker of the neighborhood, babysitting her brother's and other children, and generally being available for people in need. After Carrie and Ernest left the brief incestuous period of their lives behind them, it came to seem as if it had actually happened to other people. When Ernest was away in Pittsburgh, his wife discovered a letter that Carrie had written to him after their first sexual encounter, reassuring him about his worth and encouraging him to hold his head up with pride. All this immediately preceded the encounter at the train station, the move to Florida, and Carrie's ostracism from the family.

The narrator then asks Carrie how she knew the details about her mother's finding her letter. Carrie explains that after the narrator's maternal grandmother, Grandma Evans, was widowed, she called Carrie one day, befriended her, and told her the story. The story of Aunt Carrie ends with the niece and the aunt bonded together and the narrator pledging to see Carrie again in the future.

Themes and Meanings

Rita Dove's story is about the senses and human passions, most especially love, mercy, compassion, anger, and unforgivingness. It is also a story of awakening and memory, of the revision of a childhood incident into a mature adult context, and the breaching of alienation as various characters reach out to one another in different ways. It is a tale of identity, most importantly Aunt Carrie's identity, the perception of which changes markedly from beginning to end.

As in much of her poetical work, Dove takes her themes and meanings from the context of family history. One major theme of "Aunt Carrie" is the passage of knowledge, memory, and respect from one generation to another through oral tradition or the telling of a tale.

Style and Technique

When asked why she uses the details of the everyday and familiar in her writing (in "Aunt Carrie," a cup of tea, the roses on a hankie, the smell of pomade, a bedsheet blowing in the wind, or the touch of a dry palm), Dove has explained that the more specifics you know about someone, the harder it is for you to kill that person. Poetry, she says, springs right out of life and makes you feel more connected. So it is with "Aunt Carrie."

There are two references, one in each part of the story, to the narrator's love of drawing. This is used as a literal and metaphoric device: The picture the girl draws of her father in the first part of the story serves to show that the Ernest that the child knows is a different person from the one with whom Carrie is so familiar. The narrator draws out Aunt Carrie in the second part of the story, gently pleading with her to tell her the truth behind her parents' actions. Indeed, the story is crafted like a drawing— the first part functions as a sketch or framework that is later filled in with detail. The first section is sketched from the "outside," through the astute observations of the child. The true meaning of what she has observed is then revealed through the carefully wrought confessions of Aunt Carrie. As she tells her tale the narrator and the reader learn the specifics of Aunt Carrie's life, its pathos, and its yearnings and losses. In the process Aunt Carrie is transformed. When she first appears, she is an unattractive, cowering figure about whom not much is known and who exists on the fringes of the scene, obscured by the dominant and controlling position of the narrator's mother. In the second part of the story, rather than reacting to others, she is the actor or central figure, and we come to see things from her point of view. Through the details of her life she is sympathetically transfigured into a fully human and humane person whose experience has been tragic. Through the telling of her life some of the exile and ostracism she has experienced at the hands of the narrator's unforgiving mother is healed. Her niece, in effect, takes her back into the family and reverses the invisibility to which she has been subjected by reaching out to her after she has heard her story and telling her she wants to see her again. Identity is revealed and coupled with identification. Similarly, Grandma Evans, widowed and alone, knows of the taboo that has been broken but can identify with Aunt Carrie's loneliness, and befriends her, leaving the past behind them.

Barbara J. Bair

AUNT MOON'S YOUNG MAN

Author: Linda Hogan (1947-   )
Type of plot: Social realism
Time of plot: The early 1950's
Locale: Rural Oklahoma
First published: 1988

Principal characters:
THE NARRATOR, a young Chickasaw woman
AUNT MOON, an older Chickasaw woman who lives alone
ISAAC, a young stranger who becomes involved with Aunt Moon

The Story

On an autumn day in rural Oklahoma a town prepares for its annual fair. The event attracts people from neighboring towns who have goods to sell, thereby breaking the monotony of life in Pickens. Among the new attractions in town is a magnetic young man whom the narrator immediately identifies as a full-blooded Indian. Remarking that most of the people in Pickens are of mixed blood, the narrator explains that she feels somehow inferior to a pure-blood. After the narrator and her mother eye the drifter, the narrator thinks about Aunt Moon, an older woman whom she admires.

Aunt Moon lives alone with her dog, Mister, in a house that her father built on a hill. There is something mysterious about Aunt Moon, who seems to have a special kind of vision, an ancestral wisdom. Aunt Moon dries medicinal herbs, upholding a tribal tradition that most townspeople have discarded. The narrator is attracted to Aunt Moon because the old woman seems more alive than the rest of the people in Pickens.

When the narrator and her cousins visit the fair, they see barnyard oddities such as chickens that lay green eggs. The narrator wants Aunt Moon to look at the strange chickens, but Aunt Moon seems distracted. The narrator realizes that Aunt Moon has spotted the young drifter and is drawn to him. That night the narrator's mother and father dress for a waltz contest. At the dance, the narrator notices that the local women seem especially animated because of the presence of the young man. When Aunt Moon arrives, she dances with the young man, causing the other women to raise their eyebrows and whisper. Soon, the town of Pickens is scandalized by the affair carried on between Aunt Moon and the young stranger. The women shun Aunt Moon in public but go to her in secret to buy her ancient remedies. The narrator's father forbids her from visiting Aunt Moon's house so long as the stranger, Isaac, is there.

At this point, the narrator digresses by telling the reader how she came to call Bess Evening by the name of Aunt Moon. Bess Evening seems to fit her nickname because sometimes she is full of strength and light and at other times seems pale and weak. The narrator's mother tells her the story of the freak accident that took the life of Aunt Moon's daughter. The narrator understands that her friend must cope with the tragedy each day of her life.

Aunt Moon experiences another loss when her dog Mister, frightened by an electrical storm, runs through town twitching and crashing into things. Thinking that Mister has rabies, men shoot him. This new loss devastates Aunt Moon, but Isaac comforts her. By the next fall, Aunt Moon is pregnant and Isaac has disappeared. With Isaac gone, the local women are not jealous; they offer Aunt Moon their sympathy and cluck their tongues over what a snake Isaac has turned out to be. The narrator is looking through Aunt Moon's window, however, when Isaac returns. Aunt Moon and Isaac hold each other like true lovers. The narrator learns that Isaac has escaped from jail, where he was sent for selling illegal herbal remedies.

The story ends as the narrator sets out for Denver, where she will live with her cousins. She hopes to find work and go to school. Carrying a bag filled with Aunt Moon's herbs and an eagle feather wrapped in a scarf, she leaves Pickens not knowing whether she will ever be back.

Themes and Meanings

"Aunt Moon's Young Man" explores the theme of spiritual well-being. The role of storytelling, the importance of ancestry, the nature of relationships among women, and the difficulty of coming of age are all issues in the story that contribute to the narrator's development of inner strength.

Two kinds of storytelling exist side by side. Mean-spirited gossips spread the details of Aunt Moon's questionable parentage. This malicious narration seems to wound the communal spirit. By contrast, the narrator's mother tells stories about Aunt Moon's life that help the younger woman to understand and respect her elder. The narrator's fascination with Aunt Moon is linked to her curiosity about the mostly forgotten ways of her tribe. Aunt Moon inherits from her parents the knowledge of the medicinal value of dried herbs. The narrator seems to understand that, in a quest for identity, one's heritage is an important area of investigation. Healing is not Aunt Moon's only power. She is a strong woman both physically and intellectually: The narrator respects her for her ability to deliver Holstein calves, as well as for her analysis of American culture. The narrator delights in this model of feminine strength. Aunt Moon sets an example that the young woman cannot find in any other person, even her mother.

The narrator's mother is a strong woman in the sense of being a stern authority figure. She seems to read her daughter's mind and rein in her fantasies. In contrast to Aunt Moon, who opens up new worlds, the mother represents restriction. While the narrator may not revere her mother, she at least does not hold her in contempt, as she does the other women of Pickens. The narrator learns to despise the women in town because they are not loyal to one another and do nothing to foster an authentic sense of community. When the gossips turn on Aunt Moon, the narrator lashes out at them.

Estranged from her neighbors, uneasy around her mother, and unsure of her place in Aunt Moon's life now that the old woman has a lover, the narrator feels a sense of isolation in Pickens. She craves new experiences and opportunities—the kind that she hopes to find in Denver. This is the coming-of-age that the narrator is poised to undergo. She lets one of the local boys kiss her, but the experience seems hollow, and pales in comparison to the image of passion she sees between Isaac and Aunt Moon. Her own passage is to be spiritual, not sexual. With her last words the narrator describes the "small, beautiful woman" in her own eyes. This is the emblem of feminine pride and strength that the narrator learned to see by watching Aunt Moon. By telling her own story, the narrator provides a role model for other women in search of self. She passes on the gift that Aunt Moon has given her.

Style and Technique

Linda Hogan is a poet as well as a fiction writer. It is with a poet's sense of imagery that she details the images in "Aunt Moon's Young Man." Description does double duty in this story, creating a tableau that is both earnestly real and deeply symbolic.

From the narrator's first descriptions of Pickens, the reader comes to understand that the Chickasaw are a people with inescapable and uneasy relationships to the land and the forces of nature. The livestock carted to the fair slump in the oppressive Oklahoma heat. Biting flies bring back not-too-distant memories of unpleasant days past. White chicken feathers remind the town of the cotton crop that has all but failed them. The air is still in the wake of a recent tornado, and thunderclouds on the horizon threaten to turn the dusty roads to mud. The environment is stagnant, but expresses the potential for turmoil. The people of Pickens evidence a similarly paradoxical set of attitudes and emotions. They show the strain of monotony, yet seem poised to experience the chaos that the full-blooded drifter will create. Nature serves as an index for human behavior.

This fusion of physical and psychological elements becomes an important motif as the story progresses. One example of this is the description of the women avoiding Aunt Moon on the street. Hogan sends the gossips scurrying "like swallows swooping into their small clay nests." The swooping motion conveys the women's fear of the unique and sometimes powerful Aunt Moon. The small clay nests represent the narrowness of the women's minds and lives. The narrator employs just this sort of metaphor when she gives Bess Evening a name that corresponds to the many emotional phases that the old woman goes through. Linda Hogan's skillful use of poetic imagery lends a remarkable depth and texture to "Aunt Moon's Young Man."

Nick David Smart

AUNT ROSANA'S ROCKER

Author: Nicholasa Mohr (1935-   )
Type of plot: Domestic realism
Time of plot: The 1970's
Locale: New York City's Spanish Harlem
First published: 1985

> *Principal characters:*
> CASTO, a Puerto Rican immigrant
> ZORAIDA, his wife

The Story

Casto and Zoraida, two Puerto Rican immigrants living in New York, have been married for nine years and have four children. For two months, Zoraida has acted as if possessed by a demon lover during her sleep. As she moans and mimics sexual behavior in bed, Casto paces the floor in the next room trying not to hear her passionate sounds and vainly trying not to imagine her lascivious gestures. Casto married Zoraida because she was frail, sickly, and somewhat plain, not loud and coarse like other girls. He now believes that his wife's nightly behavior is lewd and vulgar, not the kind of behavior in which a decent husband and wife should engage. He believes that his wife enjoys her dream sex, and calls her a happy victim, an animal, and a hypocrite.

After telling his parents about how he is being cuckolded by a spirit possessing Zoraida, Casto is urged to take his wife to a spiritualist who can exorcise the demon lover that visits her nightly. Although the spiritualist's incantation works, Zoraida still does not become the kind of wife Casto wishes to have. Although she is a wonderful housekeeper and a devoted mother, serving dinner on time every night and attending to the children without any problem, whenever Casto approaches her for sex, she sits in a rocking chair and stares into space like a zombie. Casto calls another meeting of the family to help him decide what to do next. His mother, Dona Elvira, thinks that her healthy son is too good for the sickly Zoraida, while Dona Clara, Zoraida's mother, thinks that Casto is a brute of a man who does not deserve anyone as delicate as Zoraida.

Purencia, Casto's sister, thinks that it serves her mother right that, since she never thought anyone was good enough for Casto, he now has a sickly wife. She is puzzled about Casto's problems with Zoraida and wonders if Zoraida, whom she calls goody two-shoes, is one of those quiet ones who hide the action. She is curious whether Zoraida is doing something about which nobody knows. Don Isidro, Zoraida's father, can only lament that his daughter still looks like a sickly child. Having been born prematurely, Zoraida was called a miracle baby by the doctors; thus, her parents gave her the middle name of Milagros. Confused by the marital difficulties between Casto and Zoraida, Don Isidro thinks that his daughter is lucky to have found a man that would have her at all.

The rocking chair in which Zoraida sits when Casto wants sex originally belonged to her great-aunt Rosana, who was very beautiful and had many suitors. Part of her family history, the chair reminds Zoraida of Puerto Rico and is the one place where she now feels she can be herself and be free. Her parents decide that to solve Casto's marital problem they will take the chair back home with them. After they leave, Zoraida falls asleep thinking, as if she were her great-aunt Rosana, that she will not be able to sit in the chair any more and meet her suitors. When Casto comes to bed, he feels that a great burden has been lifted from him. He touches Zoraida but, finding her asleep, he turns over, thinking that he can always try again tomorrow.

Themes and Meanings

Stereotypical male expectations of female sexuality is the central subject of Nicholasa Mohr's story of Zoraida and her obsession with her dream lover and her great-aunt's rocking chair. The theme is first suggested by the fact that Casto believes that the kind of sex that Zoraida is having with her demon lover is not the kind of sex in which a decent husband and wife should engage. Although the story does not make explicit what Casto means by normal, healthy sex, it seems clear that it does not include a woman's wanton enjoyment of the sex act. Casto finds Zoraida's total delight in her hallucinatory sex acts disgusting. A hypochondriac who is obsessed with his health and who takes handfuls of vitamins and spoonfuls of tonic every day, Casto justifies his need for sex as necessary to keep him from becoming ill. He feels that he is the master of his home, but he will not touch Zoraida as long as she seems under the control of something unhealthy. Zoraida's enjoyment of sex makes Casto call her a whore and an animal, vulgar and common. When he married her, her shy behavior and ill appearance, like that of a "sick sparrow flirting with death," made him think of her as a lady.

Throughout the story, Casto insists on his rights as a man to have sex when and how he wants. Zoraida's conscious views about sexuality are not made clear in the story, but the fact that she can only take pleasure in sex while she is asleep, and therefore has no conscious control over her behavior, further suggests the stereotype that women are not supposed to enjoy sex, but only to be concerned with what pleasure they give to their husbands. Although this is a common Western stereotype, Mohr suggests that it is particularly prominent in Hispanic cultures.

When Zoraida is denied her dream fantasy sex by the spiritualist, she retreats to the rocking chair every time her husband wants sex, becoming invisible or zombie-like to him. Her mother tells her that women have to humor men, that they are like babies and that sex helps them relax. She recommends that Zoraida pretend that she like sex, for that makes men get it over with very quickly. Only at the end of the story does the reader fully realize that Zoraida has been possessed by the spirit of her great-aunt Rosana, a beautiful woman who had many lovers and who, therefore, embodies the kind of female freedom denied to Zoraida. When Casto comes to bed after the rocking chair has been taken away, he feels that he is once more in control of things. Retreating into her one remaining role, Zoraida tries not to think of the rocker or of Casto; she reassures herself that her children are safe in bed in the next room.

Style and Technique

The focus of "Aunt Rosana's Rocker" is primarily on Casto, but it is clear that the narrator's sympathy is with Zoraida, who is the victim of stereotypes that control her life. The story communicates these stereotypes primarily by focusing on Casto's sense of being treated as less than the man of the house, first by Zoraida's sexual pleasure with a dream lover and second by her retreating into the rocking chair and becoming invisible to him when he wants to have sex. Casto's macho expectations are presented by the narrator as if they are perfectly reasonable, and Zoraida has no right to her own pleasure or her own identity.

Although the story is told in a realistic style, the fact that a spiritualist is called in to exorcise the demon that seemingly has possessed Zoraida and, more important, the fact that the reader learns at the end of the story that Zoraida has somehow been taken over by the spirit of her dead great-aunt Rosana, suggest some of the elements of Magical Realism that characterizes the fiction of such Latin American writers as Isabel Allende. As Zoraida lies in bed at the conclusion of the story, she thinks that without the rocker she will not be able to sit there and meet all of her suitors. She recalls that the last time she sat in the chair she was dancing to a very slow ballad, but without the rocker she cannot remember it, nor can she sit in the rocker again and pick up her memory where she had left off the time before. Mohr purposely leaves the end of the story inconclusive. Although Casto feels confident that he can now have Zoraida sexually any time that he wants, Zoraida's final posture of lying in bed with her back turned toward him indicates that even without the rocking chair, she will continue to be invisible to Casto.

Nicholasa Mohr is one of the few Hispanic women in the United States to overcome the often-closed world of New York publishing to present realistic images of the situation of Hispanic women and children growing up in New York City. "Aunt Rosana's Rocker" is a fine example of Mohr's depiction of the Puerto Rican woman's struggle to overcome stereotypes of race and gender.

Charles E. May

AUTUMN IN THE OAK WOODS

Author: Yuri Pavlovich Kazakov (1927-1983)
Type of plot: Psychological realism
Time of plot: The 1950's
Locale: Northern Russia
First published: "Osen v dubovykh lesakh," 1961 (English translation, 1963)

Principal characters:
THE UNNAMED NARRATOR
HIS GIRLFRIEND

The Story

A young man living in a hut above the Oka River in northern Russia goes down to a makeshift dock, at which he is expecting a woman to arrive. He is apprehensive because he is not sure she will come. After he has waited anxiously for a few moments, the river boat finally docks, and she steps gingerly ashore. They are shy with each other at first as they climb the hill back to the hut, but the initial discomfort goes away as he shows her the beauties of the area even in the darkness, relying mostly on the sounds and smells. Using his lantern, he points out to her the white feathers of the chicken eaten by a fox and the mountain ash berries he uses to make his own vodka. Her reserved reactions reveal that she comes from a different region—that of the White Sea and the frozen tundra.

Back in the hut, the cozy stillness and the crackling fire enable them to deepen the friendship they fleetingly established when they first met in her native town on the North Sea. They are still awkward, however, as shown when she asks him to turn around while she is undressing and not to keep the light on all night. They listen to a jazz melody in English that comes over the radio from an unknown source. He interprets the various instruments as acting out an unknown drama, in a way resembling the quiet drama of their meeting in the oak forest. They talk and reminisce, finally falling asleep at dawn, while the first real snow of the autumn sprinkles the windows.

The day breaks sunny and cheerful, and they go out to explore the surrounding area. He proudly shows her the heifers grazing on the gray winter grain shoots, the hardly faded dandelions, frozen mushrooms, and various kinds of trees. Despite this bravado, it becomes apparent that he is anxious to impress her so she will not be disappointed and leave him. She allays his insecurity by agreeing that it is good there. When a tug appears on the Oka River and goes away—a potential harbinger of her departure—they look at it from above, "quietly, silently, as in a white dream. . . . " They are together at long last, and the rustic beauty around them mirrors their happiness.

Themes and Meanings

Yuri Kazakov was a leading short-story writer in the so-called thaw period in Russian literature from the 1950's through the 1970's when, after decades of strict

Communist Party control, writers felt free to write as they pleased and not follow Party dictates. One group of writers concentrated on village life, presenting the struggle of the peasants to preserve their moral fiber and to survive the intrusion of the urbanites trying to remake their way of life. Another group depicted life in the big cities under the onslaught of political, moral, and technological progress. Kazakov positioned himself in the middle. Although most of his stories deal with urban characters in their city environment, many of them want to escape from urban life and hope to find solace in nature and the countryside. "Autumn in the Oak Woods" is a perfect example of such a balancing act.

It is not clear from the story why the young man, the protagonist and narrator, has chosen to live away from big cities. There are indications that he once lived in a large city or at least had an opportunity to do so, and his female companion comes from a large city. Yet they have come to the pristine environment of the countryside and prefer it to the hustle and bustle of city life. Whether this is a rebellion against the constraints of an urbanized society is not made clear, but judging from the pleasures the two characters derive from their sojourn in the country and by their final decision to stay there, it can be surmised that they are turning their backs on urbanization.

Their determination goes further than that. The characters not only prefer the country life, but also approach the newfound, enjoyable ambience from an almost philosophical position. Their every step, word, and thought makes it clear that they are after something much deeper than making a simple change. That something is a search for a union with nature. They want to be a part of nature, not merely accidental visitors and consumers. The young man enjoys his stay in the hut with every sight and sound he perceives and every happening he witnesses. To him, everything is wonderful. How glorious it is that his friend has arrived, that there is snow to greet her, that they have a little music, and that everything is so promising. He draws hope and strength from the beauty of nature, convinced that when he shows his friend the Oka River, the fields, the hills, the forest, and the ravines, she will conclude that this is the place for both of them to live and be happy.

Such an attitude does not stem from the mere enjoyment of the beauty in nature, however. When he shows his friend the feathers of the chicken devoured by a fox, he is not angry or vengeful and does not think first of killing the fox, as his friend, seemingly logically, suggests. He tacitly admits that a constant struggle for survival is a part of nature, just as the white snow, the blue sky, and the steamy river are. His hut has almost no furniture, only the necessities, just as nature is often frugal and functional. All he needs is a tea kettle, a modest amount of food, a little radio music to keep him in touch with the world, and the warmth of his beloved next to him. Even when he has doubt about whether his friend will stay with him, he trusts nature to convince her, and it turns out that he is right. His actions and gestures appear to be natural, as, for example, when he refuses to kiss his friend upon her arrival in the light of the boat searchlight.

The characters sought the best place under the sun for themselves, and they found it in nature, in the countryside away from big cities.

Style and Technique

Kazakov accomplishes his task and advances his main theme through an accomplished style and technique that have rendered him one of the best short-story writers in Russian literature. He begins his story with, "I took the pail to get water from the spring. I was happy that night because she was coming on the night boat. . . ." He then proceeds, step by step, through the important events of the plot: descending to the river dock, meeting his friend, bringing her back to the hut, and showing her around, while all the time worrying whether he could convince her to stay with him. When it finally is clear that she will stay, the reader feels the satisfaction of a completed story. At the same time, instead of telling everything to the last detail, he allows readers to draw some conclusions on their own.

Sometimes it seems that not much is happening. In this sense, Kazakov often has been compared with the greatest Russian storyteller, Anton Chekhov, who has also been criticized for the fact that not much happens in his stories and plays. The author believes, however, that telling everything explicitly is not necessary. In the same way, it is unnecessary that the story have a clear-cut ending—a hint is enough. Thus, Kazakov does not say that she is staying, he only shows a tug come and leave again without her.

Kazakov is especially adept at creating characters. Slowly and unobtrusively, in an almost impressionistic manner, he completes the portraits. The narrator emerges as a taciturn but strong man, somewhat sentimental and romantic, showing weaknesses but with enough hope to carry him through perhaps the greatest challenge of his life. His friend also is shown as a strong person, "of the sea," as he characterizes her, with a husky voice and a mind of her own. The blending of the characters with their environment is perhaps the strongest artistic point of the story. The two characters emerge at the end as a part of nature, which may have been Kazakov's main goal in writing this story.

Vasa D. Mihailovich

AXOLOTL

Author: Julio Cortázar (1914-1984)
Type of plot: Fantasy
Time of plot: Spring during the 1950's
Locale: Paris, France
First published: 1956 (English translation, 1963)

Principal characters:
THE NARRATOR
AXOLOTL, an aquatic salamander into which the
    narrator metamorphoses

The Story

An unnamed man living in Paris becomes fascinated by an axolotl, a creature that he observes in the aquarium of the Jardin des Plantes. (A salamander noted for its permanent retention of larval features, such as external gills, the axolotl, or axolote, is found in lakes near Mexico City, where it is considered edible.) Despite its association with the everyday, the creature gradually assumes a mysterious quality as the narrator's fascination with the animal intensifies. He visits the exhibit every day and feels a growing affinity between himself and the creature. His description of the axolotl is realistic (the axolotl is like a lizard, about six inches long, with a delicate fish tail and paws), but he adds some eerie details. The creatures have humanlike nails and eyes with unfathomable depth.

After the narrator describes the axolotl in the fourth paragraph of the story, the first hint appears that the affinity between him and the axolotl goes beyond that of a naturalist's love for the object of his study. Suddenly the narrator starts speaking in the first-person plural, as if he himself were an axolotl: "We don't like moving around too much, and the aquarium is so cramped; we hardly move and then we bang our tail or our head into another one of us; then we get problems, fights, tiredness. Time is less oppressive if we stay still." The narrator is projecting himself into the mind of the creature that he is observing; it is the first indication that he is slowly being sucked into the axolotl's universe.

As the narrative continues, it moves—more and more disconcertingly—between the objective eye of the human observer and the internal universe of the axolotl. The narrator goes on to describe his fascination with the creature's eyes, in which he glimpses a "sweet, terrible light" and "an unfathomable depth which made me dizzy." As he becomes intrigued by the idea that the axolotl are, deep down, human, he imagines that their eyes are telling him: "Save us, save us." He visits them religiously every day, behavior so odd as to cause the guard to take notice. The narrator cannot keep his mind off the animals; he starts dreaming about them, feeling that they are devouring him with their eyes.

Then the unthinkable happens. One day, as the narrator is pressing his face against the glass, looking into the eyes of an axolotl, he suddenly turns into one and sees his own, human face pressed against the glass instead of that of an axolotl. At this point the narrative takes a new tack by focusing on the narrator trapped within the body of an axolotl.

The last paragraph of the story is ambiguous; it raises the possibility that the narrator and the axolotl are the same person, leaving the reader wondering who is who. The man visits the aquarium less frequently now, since "the bridges between him and me are broken." The narrator is consoled by the thought that perhaps the man will "write about us, that he will write all this about the axolotls down believing that he is imagining a story."

Themes and Meanings

This story centers on Argentine writer Julio Cortázar's favorite theme: the monstrous, the bestial as mysteriously attached to human destiny. The main meaning of this particular story, "Axolotl," is that it raises the question of the mysterious relationship between the human subject and the animal kingdom. After all, we cannot look into the heads of other creatures; for all we know, they may be thinking about philosophy and are simply unable to express their thoughts. "Axolotl" also explores the question of the empathy between creator and reader; in a sense readers are being sucked into the text. If the story is successful, according to Cortázar's criterion, readers will feel sucked into its plot and arrive at a meeting of minds similar to that between the narrator and the axolotl.

Also present as a theme in this story is the notion of unease with the human body; in an essay on the short story and its environment published in 1969, Cortázar explains how writing serves as an exorcism for him, a way of "casting out invading creatures," and this seems to fit "Axolotl" in the sense that it appears to exorcise a feeling of nausea created by a sense of entrapment within the clumsy heaviness of the human body. "Axolotl" is gripping precisely because it speaks to its readers about a more elemental feeling, that of the soul being trapped within a body, or spirit being trapped within matter. This is an archetypal idea to which many religions, including Christianity and Buddhism, have appealed.

The main reason Cortázar uses the axolotl as a focus for his story is that it is one of the few species in nature that dies before completing its metamorphosis; it reproduces during its larval stage, and thus is a curious example within the natural world of an incomplete life form. (When the Austrian scientist Alexander von Humboldt brought the first specimen from Mexico to Paris in the nineteenth century, the discovery that it could reproduce in its larval stage caused a sensation in the scientific world.) The axolotl's incomplete metamorphosis also makes it appropriate for Cortázar's story: Stunted in its growth, it mirrors the human mind trapped within a body and forced to a basic, "animal" level of existence.

Style and Technique

In an essay on aspects of the short story published in Cuba in 1962, Cortázar defined the short story as "a mysterious brother to poetry" in which fantasy is shown to rule supreme, as opposed to the false empirical realism created by the Western notion of logic and causality. This definition applies to "Axolotl" because the story shows how a fantastic reality bursts into the realm of the everyday. In this short story, as in many others, Cortázar first gains the reader's confidence, putting readers at their ease by creating a normal setting and conventional characters in familiar situations. Soon, however, readers find themselves trapped by a strange, nightmarish turn of events that threatens and ultimately destroys the logical, routine reality described up to this point. Cortázar has also likened the short story to a photograph. Unlike novels and films, which provide abundant details and complete, well-rounded plots, the short story— like a photograph—limits its scope to a single frame, a fragment of reality that forces the reader to supply the missing pieces. One of Cortázar's finest stories, "Axolotl" is elegantly written; it uses suspense well and explores the mysterious boundaries between the human and the animal kingdoms.

Stephen M. Hart

BABETTE'S FEAST

Author: Isak Dinesen (Baroness Karen Blixen-Finecke, 1885-1962)
Type of plot: Domestic realism
Time of plot: 1883
Locale: Berlevaag, Norway
First published: 1950

> *Principal characters:*
> MARTINE and
> PHILIPPA, the adult daughters of the founder of an austere religious sect
> BABETTE, their French servant and cook
> LORENS LOEWENHIELM, an army officer who once fell in love with Martine
> ACHILLE PAPIN, a famous opera singer who once fell in love with Philippa

The Story

This story focuses on a lavish dinner that a French servant woman named Babette prepares for a group of pious ascetics in an isolated Norwegian village on Sunday, December 15, 1883. The events leading up to this feast take many years to develop.

Martine and Philippa's father founded a religious sect respected throughout Norway that strictly denied the value of all earthly things, insisting that charity toward the poor and preparing for heaven were the only meaningful activities on earth. In their small and isolated village, Martine and Philippa adhere to their father's teachings along with a small group of his followers. The two beautiful sisters pass from their childhood into adulthood facing only two earthly temptations: At eighteen Martine is wooed by young Lieutenant Lorens Loewenhielm; a year later, Philippa spurns the advances of the famous opera singer Achille Papin, who meets her while vacationing near their village. Having rejected earthly love in order to maintain their focus on spiritual matters, Martine and Philippa continue to lead the small group of ascetics after their father dies.

Fifteen years after rejecting their suitors, Martine and Philippa are joined by a French woman named Babette, who appears at their doorstep exhausted, wild-eyed, and impoverished after escaping political turmoil in Paris. A letter from Achille Papin states simply that Babette "can cook." For twelve years Babette serves Martine and Philippa without pay, preparing for them and their flock the austerely simple meals that their religion demands.

One day, Babette receives a letter from Paris informing her that she has won ten thousand francs in a lottery. Her news coincides with Martine and Philippa's plan to celebrate the one-hundredth birthday of their father on December 15. Babette makes her first request in twelve years—to prepare a real French dinner for the celebration at her own expense. Although Martine, Philippa, and their followers fear sinful luxury and extravagance in such a meal, they reluctantly accept her offer, secretly vowing among themselves to take little notice of the food and drink.

When the feast day arrives, Lorens Loewenhielm, now an aging general, becomes the twelfth guest. In the village to visit his aunt, an original member of the religious sect, he attends the dinner with her in order to honor Martine and Philippa's father. As a member of the French aristocracy, Loewenhielm is the only guest at the table who appreciates the magnificence of Babette's meal. By its end, he realizes that Babette was once a renowned Parisian chef.

After the feast and the departure of the guests, Martine and Philippa expect Babette to announce her return to Paris, where she can live as a rich woman with her ten thousand francs; however, Babette declares that she will stay with them in Norway. In any case, she has spent all of her winnings on the feast. She explains that as a chef she is an artist and that she is happy to remain as their servant because she has been a great artist one last time.

Themes and Meanings

Well into Babette's sumptuous meal, General Loewenhielm makes a speech that captures the story's main theme. In this celebratory feast, he says, "righteousness and bliss shall kiss one another." By this he seems to mean that spirituality can be achieved in this world as well as in the next and that spirituality may be closely related to human pleasure without lapsing into sinfulness.

In dedicating their lives to spirituality, Martine, Philippa, and the other members of the sect have denied themselves the wonders and delights of this world. For example, both Martine and her sister have forsaken excellent chances for earthly romance. Martine's spurned lover, Loewenhielm, is more than a victim of her rigorous self-denial. According to a legend in his family, another Loewenhielm married "a female mountain spirit of Norway," thereby gaining "second sight." When Loewenhielm met Martine during his youth, she appeared to him to be the embodiment of the family legend and suddenly "there rose before his eyes a sudden, mighty vision of a higher and purer life." Frightened by this possibility, Loewenhielm felt uncharacteristically inadequate in Martine's presence, so he returned to France, where he chose worldly pleasures and advancement over "second sight." He then rose as a military and court figure until his chance return to Norway for the feast in 1883.

Anticipating seeing Martine again, the now aging Loewenhielm is plagued by doubts. Did he make the right choice? He goes to Babette's feast in a combative mood, resolved to dominate where he once felt intimidated, determined to prove that he made the right choice—that "the low rooms, the haddock and the glass of water on the table" that typified Martine's ascetic world "would very soon have become sheer misery." Instead, Loewenhielm finds a wondrous meal produced almost magically in this remote Norwegian village. When he rises to leave, he seizes Martine's hand and tells her "I have been with you every day of my life" and will "be with you every day that is left to me." Babette's feast has taught him that the miraculous can come to one through earthly experiences, that his spiritual kinship with Martine was never lost, diminished though it might have been by their physical separation.

Loewenhielm serves as a foil for the ascetics: They want to achieve spirituality so badly that they deny the world in order to attain it; he wanted spirituality so badly that he ran away from it because it frightened him and instead embraced worldly pleasures. The achievement of spirituality is a compromise between these two positions, symbolized in the willingness of Babette to remain in this Norwegian wilderness, supported by her memory of the one evening when she created a meal fit for the gods.

Style and Technique

Isak Dinesen presents weighty themes with a delightfully subtle sense of humor that surfaces most noticeably during the feast and its aftermath. Appropriate to the main theme, everything works by opposites. The ascetics come to the feast prepared to endure and resist the temptations of the world, but end up getting tipsy and discovering the brotherhood and true spirituality they had been losing. General Loewenhielm comes to the feast determined to prove his superiority to the rustics, but is humbled by the Parisian magnificence of Babette's meal. Although Babette creates the meal only for her own satisfaction (not knowing that Loewenhielm will be a guest), she transforms the lives of many in a single evening.

The comedy during the meal arises from Loewenhielm's wonderment at the fare and the nonchalant responses of the ascetics. Although they do not understand what so excites him, they manage to appear sophisticated in their nonchalance. For example, as Loewenhielm expresses incredulity at being served Blinis Demidoff (a kind of blintz), he looks around at his fellow diners, only to see them all eating their own Blinis Demidoff, "without any sign of either surprise or approval, as if they had been doing so every day for thirty years." Once the ascetics become slightly drunk, they readily accept more drink. They know that what they are drinking is not wine because it sparkles. "It must be some kind of lemonade," they guess. The "lemonade" agrees with "their exalted state of mind and seem[s] to lift them off the ground, into a higher and purer sphere."

Before Babette's meal, the aging ascetics grow so quarrelsome and petty that Martine and Philippa worry about their group's spirituality. During the feast, however, the wine so loosens their tongues and the food so warms their hearts, that by its end they are forgiving old quarrels and building new intimacies. Soon the house is "filled with a heavenly light," as if they have "been given one hour of the millennium." After the dinner the disciples stagger out of the house and stumble together in the snow, giggling and playing like small children in a "kind of celestial second childhood." In a monument to comic understatement, Martine enters the kitchen after the guests depart and says, "It was quite a nice dinner, Babette."

Terry Nienhuis

THE BABYSITTER

Author: Robert Coover (1932-   )
Type of plot: Antistory
Time of plot: The 1960's
Locale: Suburban United States
First published: 1969

> *Principal characters:*
> HARRY TUCKER, a middle-aged man
> DOLLY TUCKER, his overweight wife
> JIMMY TUCKER and
> BITSY, their young children
> THE BABYSITTER, an unnamed schoolgirl
> JACK, her boyfriend
> MARK, Jack's friend

The Story

In just over a hundred paragraphs presenting several different points of view, the story recounts the confusing events of a single evening, between 7:40 and 10:30 P.M. The multiple viewpoints frequently collide and even merge as the story revises itself, offering concurrent and competing plots. In other words, several plots occupy the same time and space and involve the same characters, whose fantasies influence reality. The story seems to ask the question, what would the world be like if everyone's competing fantasies were to come true?

As Harry and Dolly Tucker dress for a cocktail party, the babysitter arrives at their house. Harry imagines that the girl is arching her back, jutting out her pert breasts, and twitching her thighs just for him. After the Tuckers leave, their young children, Jimmy and Bitsy, attack the babysitter playfully, jumping on her and tickling her. Jimmy fantasizes that his babysitter will overpower him and spank him.

Meanwhile, the babysitter's boyfriend, Jack, and his friend Mark are playing pinball in a nearby arcade, discussing the idea of visiting her. Although the boys have carefully studied the pinball machine, they still cannot easily beat it. Jack would like either to collaborate with Mark in the seduction or rape of his girlfriend or protect her from Mark's advances—or possibly both.

The story soon becomes an exercise in multiple choices. Does Mr. Tucker return home to discover the babysitter watching television alone, or has she been having sex with Jack and Mark, or is she giving Jimmy a bath? Does the babysitter spend a quiet evening alone, or is she harassed all night by anonymous phone calls and Peeping Toms? Is she raped and murdered by Jack, or by Jack and Mark, or perhaps by Mr. Tucker? Does the baby choke on a diaper pin or drown in the bathtub? Does everyone die at the end of the story, or does everyone quietly go to bed?

The answer to all these questions is yes. As one critic has pointed out, there are at least five hundred possible plot lines in this story.

Themes and Meanings

In American culture and literature, babysitters have long been the objects of lust and fantasy, especially for middle-aged men. One need only turn to John Irving's novel *The World According to Garp* (1978) and John Cheever's story "The Country Husband" (1954) to find examples of babysitters who have become the targets of lustful married men. Robert Coover's "The Babysitter" explores this fascination. The title character serves as the object of desire for three generations of males: preadolescent Jimmy, teenage Jack, and middle-aged Harry Tucker.

In a role reminiscent of the pot-belly stove in Stephen Crane's 1898 short story "The Blue Hotel," the Tuckers' livingroom television set functions as an extension of the characters. It commands their attention, participates in their activities, and even vies with them for narrative control. The characters regard the television not only as a source of entertainment, but as a reward for obedience, an employment perk (in the babysitter's case), an alibi or excuse, and a companion-protector. So conspicuous is the television's presence and role that "The Babysitter" can be interpreted as an indictment of television for its harmful effects on viewers. In the course of his intentionally confusing narrative, Coover examines television's coupling of sex and violence; its tendency to desensitize people; its tacit encouragement of voyeurism; and its function as a surrogate babysitter.

Not only do the television programs bombard the characters with images of violence (for example, the fighting cowboys in a western), they also couple sex and violence. In one program, a detective stares "down at the body of a half-naked girl" who has been strangled and presumably raped. Coover's characters also link sex with violence. In one plot line, the babysitter experiences an orgasm as she watches a television gunfight. Other characters fantasize about rape or being raped. At times, the television actually participates in the violence and promiscuity of the characters. When Mr. Tucker returns home unexpectedly, he finds the babysitter's "panties hanging like a broken balloon from the rabbit-ear antennae on the TV." As Jack and Mark rape the babysitter, "the television lights flicker and flash over her glossy flesh," as if the television were touching her. During one violent scuffle, in which two figures—perhaps Mark and Jack—try to rape a girl—probably the babysitter—the television set crashes to the floor, ironically becoming a victim of the violence.

Desensitized by years of television viewing, the characters feel little compassion for other people's suffering and tend to dehumanize their objects of desire, as Jack and Mark do when they treat the babysitter as a pinball machine. Possessing short attention spans, they expect "commercials" at intervals and change channels frequently. They engage in voyeurism, spying on the babysitter through the bathroom window or the keyhole in the door. They may not prefer to watch, as Chance does in Jerzy Kosinski's novel *Being There* (1971), but they watch anyway, conditioned by their television experience. Television has an especially tragic effect on children, who are more impressionable than adults and spend more time in front of the television. Since its proliferation in the 1950's, television has indeed earned the epithet "The Great American Babysitter." It is television's role as a surrogate babysitter, which indoctrinates Americans from a young age, that Coover attacks in this story, just as the story is a statement on human sexuality, the art of fiction making, and American culture generally.

Style and Technique

Structurally, "The Babysitter" follows the chronology of a television schedule. It is divided into five sections, each of which corresponds to a program on television. The first section, which covers the time period from 7:40 to 8:00 P.M., is dominated by images and sounds of a musical on television. This section complements Mr. Tucker's "musical" fantasy of the babysitter. In the second section, which corresponds to Jimmy's "spanking" fantasy, a western organizes and informs the events between 8:00 and 8:30. The third section, unified by a spy show, encompasses the period from 8:30 to 9:00 and corresponds to Jack's "spying" fantasy. Between 9:00 and 10:00, the babysitter changes channels constantly, switching back and forth among three programs: a love story, a ball game, and a murder mystery. It is not easy to associate any of these programs with a specific character, but the murder mystery, which receives the most attention in the various plots, seems to parallel the actions of Mark and Jack, while the love story seems to parallel the triangle of Harry, Dolly, and the babysitter. Covering the period from 10:00 to 10:30, the last section repeatedly mentions the news, the only "real" or nonfiction program on the television. Whereas the fictional programs feed the fantasies and influence the actions of the characters, the news program assesses the damage of the Great American Babysitter.

The shifting points of view in the story simulate the changing of channels and television's fragmentation of reality. At the beginning of the story it is relatively easy to identify and distinguish the various points of view. The first paragraph, for example, is probably told from the point of view of the babysitter; the second from that of Mr. Tucker; and the third from that of Jack. Jimmy's point of view is not represented until the fifth paragraph and Mrs. Tucker's not until the eleventh. It is uncertain whether any of the paragraphs represent Mark's, Bitsy's, or the Host's point of view.

Early in the story, Coover uses tag phrases to help the reader link the individual paragraphs to characters. For example, the recurring phrase "light brown hair" identifies Mr. Tucker, while "enough's enough" or "that's enough" identifies Jack. As the story progresses, however, the points of view begin to conflate, frustrating attempts to distinguish among them. By the end of the story, chaos has replaced clarity and coherence. The shifting points of view and the steadily increasing confusion make "The Babysitter" a particularly effective satire on television and justify its classification as an antistory.

Edward A. Malone

THE BALLOON

Author: Donald Barthelme (1931-1989)
Type of plot: Metafiction
Time of plot: 1966
Locale: New York City
First published: 1966

Principal character:
THE UNNAMED NARRATOR

The Story

A seemingly purposeless balloon suddenly appears in New York City. The balloon, which was inflated by the narrator one night while people were sleeping, covers almost the entire southern half of Manhattan—from Fourteenth Street in Greenwich Village to the southern edge of Central Park, near the Plaza Hotel on Fifth Avenue, covering twenty-five blocks on either side of Fifth Avenue. The narrator first refers to the appearance of the balloon as a situation, but then qualifies this idea because, by the narrator's definition, situations imply sets of circumstances that lead to some resolution. This balloon, however, is merely a "concrete particular" passively hanging there.

The balloon provokes a series of reactions from various people in the city, including a flood of original ideas and milestones in the history of inflation. Impressions about the balloon run the gamut of responses from the banal to the creative. The balloon's meaning is disturbingly elusive, and this lack of purpose, of cause, of a fixed reason for the balloon, creates in the authorities a lack of trust, frustration, even hostility. Experts conduct secret tests to determine ways of removing or destroying the balloon, but because the narrator has cleverly hidden his pumps, they decide that nothing can be done.

In contrast to the suspicions of the authorities, the general public responds warmly to the balloon. Children enjoy bouncing on it, while others begin to locate themselves in relation to it. Opinions vary, but even people who are ambivalent toward the balloon experience an "admixture of pleasurable cognition." The balloon affords them a unique opportunity for contemplation, even though the balloon's meaning can never be known absolutely.

Each person's response to the balloon becomes a reflection of his or her general outlook on life. One man thinks the balloon is inferior to the sky, but the narrator concludes that the balloon is actually an improvement on the dark, ugly January weather. Another person considers the balloon to be an unanticipated reward, as if just being in its presence was a gratifying and positive experience. No matter the response, the balloon provides the citizens a reprieve from the ordinary grind of their lives; its shifting forms and malleability are pleasing, especially to those whose lives are rigidly patterned.

Having reviewed the public's and the public officials' reactions, the narrator reveals the reason for having inflated the balloon. The narrator has been romantically involved with a person who has been visiting Norway, and the balloon was the narrator's way of disclosing the unease felt at the partner's absence. When the narrator's partner returns, the narrator decides that the balloon is no longer needed. The balloon is dismantled, awaiting another time that they again feel angry with each other.

Themes and Meanings

"The Balloon" is a good example of metafiction, a postmodern literary movement in which a writer explores the process of writing by writing stories about how stories are written. Critic Patricia Waugh, in her book *Metafiction* (1984), states that the purpose of metafiction is "simultaneously to create a fiction and to make a statement about the creation of that fiction." For a practitioner of metafiction, conventional story forms are exhausted, so new techniques are created in self-conscious narratives— narratives that reveal themselves as narratives per se—exploiting the old conventions to create fresh ways of telling stories.

In a metafictional sense, this is a story about writing stories, while it also explores the relationship between the author and his work, and the public's response to it. The balloon itself is an allegorical representation of the story that contains it, so that the reader is forced to confront and respond to the story in the same way that the citizens of New York City must confront and respond to the balloon. The balloon can represent any artistic creation—a song, a painting, a sculpture—and allusions to the balloon as having a "deliberate lack of finish" and its being a rough draft reinforce the idea that the balloon is an art object designed to provoke public and private reactions.

The balloon, like Donald Barthelme's story, provides the community—and the reader—an opportunity to express several alternative, often contradictory, perspectives regarding its significance. The naïve point of view is represented by the children who accept the balloon at face value, without expecting it to mean anything more than the pleasure it offers them as a plaything, something to be enjoyed simply for what it is. The implication is that art may be enjoyed in its immediacy, without the need to establish any significance other than the fact of the object itself. Other views expressed in the story represent more mature or professional expectations and center on the need for substantial meaning. Although the narrator claims the need for meaning is out of fashion, because we have learned not to insist on meanings, many citizens demand that the balloon have some practical utilitarian value. One response, for example, suggests that the balloon be used as an advertising vehicle. Barthelme remains neutral as to which view is correct, implying that all views are correct and that the importance of art is relative to the expectations of the viewer.

The idea of content-neutral art, which provokes a series of equally valid if contradictory perspectives, corresponds to the precepts of much of modern art. Barthelme, an art critic himself, is suggesting that his balloon, like modern art—with its emphasis on abstract images and nonspecific content—allows imaginative engagement precedence, in terms of meaning, over the need for rational explanations. Modern art, like

Barthelme's balloon, resists analysis, and private reactions are as meaningful as any critical consensus as to its significance. Ironically, "The Balloon" illustrates the common reactions of the public and professional literary critics to Barthelme's stories when they first began to be published in *The New Yorker* magazine.

The only attempt to expose the narrator's purpose for the balloon (and by extension, that of the story), or to ground the reason for the balloon in any personal aspect of the narrator's private life, occurs in the enigmatic last paragraph. The narrator claims that the balloon was inflated simply as an emotional diversion to alleviate stress during the absence of the narrator's partner. In the end, the narrator implies that the purpose of art is ultimately always personal, but private motives have nothing to do with the public's reaction to it.

Style and Technique

In writing "The Balloon," Barthelme intended that readers not familiar with metafiction would duplicate the confusion of the citizens when they first encounter the balloon. Conventional fiction usually relies on a sequence of episodes, sustained by cause and effect, that lead through a series of complications, culminating in a climactic event and resolution of the action. Barthelme deliberately dispenses with these devices to subvert a reader's expectations. In his minimalist approach, he uses a truncated narrative that presents only the essentials of the story with very little comment on the action by the author. By foregrounding the form of the story, he develops a metaphor, a critique of how to read, challenging common assumptions about what constitutes a story.

His style is playful; his plots turn more on chance than design. Details accumulate arbitrarily, composed of what Barthelme has called "drek," the leftover tidbits that litter contemporary life. In an interview with critic Joe David Bellamy, Barthelme states that in using drek he creates a collage that combines unlike things to make a new reality. This collage effect in "The Balloon" is constructed from surface details, advertising slogans, political jargon, and common elliptical phrases, all enhanced with irony. The implausible—the appearance of a huge mysterious balloon in the heart of New York City—is depicted with a calm, detached, matter-of-fact tone that belies the fantastic nature of the event. This ironic treatment of an unrealistic event in a realistic manner underscores Barthelme's attempt to reinvigorate worn-out fictional forms and hackneyed language. By exposing the profound ordinariness of life, Barthelme offers imaginative transcendence through his faith in the creative process of art.

Jeff Johnson

THE BASEBALL GLOVE

Author: Víctor Martínez (1954-   )
Type of plot: Social realism
Time of plot: The 1970's
Locale: Central California
First published: 1993

> *Principal characters:*
> THE NARRATOR, a Chicano teenager
> BERNARDO (NARDO), his brother

The Story

The narrator, remembering when he and his brother Bernardo, or Nardo as the family calls him, were both teenagers, recalls the various jobs that Nardo held one summer: busboy, dishwasher, parking attendant, and short-order cook. Nardo managed to get himself fired from all of them, either for not showing up or showing up too often for a boss that hated him. Nardo's favorite job was working as a busboy for a catering service at the Bonneville Lakes country club, touching elbows with the rich and enjoying free drinks and other perks. He lost this job when, on a dare, he took off his busboy's jacket and asked a girl to dance. Unfortunately, his boss saw him.

There is not much left that summer for Nardo and his brother except the fields, and Nardo does not relish the idea of sweating over clods of dirt in temperatures more than 100 degrees, during one of the hottest summers in the history of California's San Joaquin Valley. Everyone in the family works, however—Nardo's sister Magda sweats in a laundry and Nardo's brother sells fruit door to door—so the pressure is on Nardo to get a job. Naturally lazy by temperament, Nardo is scolded, shamed, and threatened by his parents, especially by his father, but nothing seems to work. After a while everybody gives up on Nardo, who stays home lifting weights, exercising, and primping in front of a mirror.

The narrator, who is not at all like his brother, wants to work. Uncle Louie, with whom he sold fruit door to door, hurt his leg tripping over tree roots in the front yard, and the boy now feels empty without something useful to do. Besides, he needs money for school clothes and supplies. Most of all, he wants a baseball glove that he saw in the window of Duran's Department Store. His fantasies are filled with baseball, and he sees himself making spectacular Willy Mays-like catches with such a glove. When he tries to convince Nardo to go into the field with him to pick chili peppers, Nardo—to everyone's amazement—agrees. Nardo is going to prove to them all that he is not lazy.

At the chili field the next day, the two brothers find that most of the rows have already been taken, because most of the fieldworkers got up while it was still dark, but the foreman agrees to give them a scrawny row that nobody else wants—a row coated with pesticide and thick with exhaust fumes from traffic on the nearby road.

Their job is to fill a can with chili peppers and carry it to a nearby weighing area, where they will receive immediate payment. The weighing area, however, is sheer hell. Older women and young girls, some with handkerchiefs tied around their faces, sift through the peppers, and the scent of freshly broken peppers makes it almost impossible to breathe. At the weighing area is a company-owned vending truck from which workers can purchase snacks and soft drinks. Nardo is angered that he must pay eighty-five cents for a cheap soft drink that has gone flat.

The brothers endure this work, amazed at the Mexican working next to them. With a can in each hand, the man efficiently moves up and down the rows, pouring the cans into sacks he has stationed every twenty feet or so. Suddenly a van approaches, and workers begin to scatter. The brothers quickly realize it is the immigration authorities, come to pick up illegal aliens. Soon the Mexicans are all rounded up and herded onto a bus. The twenty or so workers who are left search the rows for filled sacks, confiscating them for themselves. Nardo claims the sacks belonging to the Mexican who was working the rows next to them; they contain more than the brothers could have picked in two days. Now, Nardo tells his brother, he can buy that baseball mitt.

Looking down at the sacks, the narrator feels weary and wonders how long it would have taken him to pick this many peppers. Then he envisions the baseball glove, clean and smelling of leather, and sees himself standing in the cool, green grass of center field, like the Bonneville Lakes golf course Nardo has told him about. He imagines he is already on the school baseball team with people looking at him with respect and admiration—not the people who pick peppers or those who were rounded up in the vans, but people he has yet to know.

Themes and Meanings

"The Baseball Glove" is not just a story about two brothers; it is also a story about two aspects of the Chicano experience. One involves first- and second-generation Mexican Americans; the other involves illegal immigrants from Mexico who come to the United States to work. The narrator and his brother, Nardo, are at the lower end of the American economic ladder, but at least they can get jobs as busboys, dishwashers, parking lot attendants, and short-order cooks. They dream of moving up someday among the rich at such places as Bonneville Lakes, and the narrator even dreams of success in that most American of all sports, baseball. The baseball glove embodies that dream; purchasing it represents for the narrator the beginning of his dreams of American success, which he intends to achieve by the usual American qualities of hard work, thrift, and rugged individualism.

Nardo, on the other hand, has been reared in the United States long enough to take it for granted. He casually loses job after job, loafs about the house, and sponges off his industrious family. Only as a last resort does Nardo undertake the most menial of jobs, picking chili peppers in the unbearably hot fields of the San Joaquin Valley—a job in which many Mexican Americans and illegal aliens are employed. The brothers discover in just a few hours what is a lifelong reality for many workers: The job is backbreaking, the wages are low, the conditions are terrible, and the company owns everything, even the burrito truck that sells snacks and soft drinks at exorbitant prices.

In contrast to the two brothers are the Mexican workers in the same field. They are not only capable workers, they are exemplary ones—fast, efficient, and uncomplaining. Although they earn less than minimum wage in the United States, they earn much more than they would make in Mexico and are among the few people in the United States willing to do such exacting labor. The chili growers, in fact, could not survive without them. When they are rounded up by the immigration authorities, the legal workers, rationalizing that the others do not live in the United States, confiscate the Mexicans' filled chili sacks for themselves, exploiting them just as badly as their employers do.

Although the narrator finds himself sympathizing with the illegals, hoping that they will get away, he, too, succumbs to the false dreams of American success. He ends up not thinking about the people carried away by the authorities, but of the people he has yet to know, those who will admire him as he stands in center field, the center of attention. The implicit reality of the story, however, is that he and Nardo have few valuable skills, and that in an exploitative culture they may never get much beyond the chili fields, let alone onto cool, green baseball fields. The glove behind the window of Duran's Department Store may remain, like the American Dream of success for such boys, forever partitioned off, just beyond their reach.

Style and Technique

Víctor Martínez tells his story by suggesting much, but declaring little. Although Nardo seems a lazy slacker at first, a little thought suggests that he is the victim of a society that offers him only dead-end jobs while enticing him with visions of unattainable society girls, golf courses, and opulent parties. While Nardo has dropped out of the American Dream, his brother still fosters notions of conventional success: Someday he will be much admired, the focus of everyone's attention, a gifted baseball player. Although such things are possible in the United States, they are unlikely for Mexican American boys such as the narrator, who must rise above discrimination and his working-class background to attain anything at all. At the end of the story, he still retains his dreams, but the experience with the illegal workers has clearly unsettled him, perhaps even changed him.

Martínez tells his story with economical prose containing occasional figurative language, such as, "my weariness stretched as wide as the horizon," and poetic descriptions. The narrator gives the reader an account from inside the Chicano experience, forcing one to see his people as he does—with sympathy, humor, and affection—and that his dreams are the same as those of any teenage American boy. In the case of Nardo and his brother, however, Martínez makes it abundantly clear that those dreams will be exceptionally hard to achieve.

Kenneth Seib

BATTLE ROYAL

Author: Ralph Ellison (1914-1994)
Type of plot: Social realism
Time of plot: 1947 and the late 1920's
Locale: Unnamed rural area in the American South
First published: 1947

Principal characters:
THE NARRATOR, an African American man
HIS GRANDFATHER
THE SCHOOL SUPERINTENDENT
TATLOCK, a young man whom the narrator fights

The Story

The story consists of a frame in which the mature narrator remembers the advice that his dying grandfather gave to his son (the narrator's father) and his remembrance of a cruel betrayal that confirms the grandfather's advice.

The grandfather tells his son to "keep up the good fight," to continue the black people's war by guerrilla tactics, to be a traitor and spy in the enemy's country as he himself has been. He tells his son: "Live with your head in the lion's mouth. I want you to overcome 'em with yeses, undermine 'em with grins, agree 'em to death and destruction." The narrator and his alarmed family puzzle over the old man's last words, especially since the narrator has been praised by the town's powerful white men for his meekness and cooperativeness. He is secretly concerned that without meaning to he is already somehow carrying out his grandfather's advice.

The battle royal episode begins when white leaders ask the narrator to deliver a high school graduation speech on the virtues of humility to a gathering of leading white citizens, a "triumph" for the black community. The event, held in the ballroom of a leading hotel, turns out to be a "smoker," a male-only affair involving whiskey, cigars, and smutty entertainment. The latter begins with the battle royal of the title, a free-for-all boxing match in which blindfolded combatants punch at each other wildly. Because the boxers are all high school classmates of the narrator, he is recruited to take part.

Before the boxing match begins, a drunk woman does a nude dance before the equally drunk men, who try to grab her. After she escapes, the narrator and nine other African American high school boys are blindfolded and pushed into a ring, where they pound at each other to the blood-thirsty screams of the audience. By pushing his blindfold partly free, the sweaty and bloody narrator escapes some blows. He sees the other boys leaving the ring and realizes that he is being left alone with the biggest fighter, Tatlock. Since the custom is for the last two boxers to fight to the finish, the narrator tries to bribe Tatlock to take a dive, but he fails and is knocked out. Afterward, he and the other boys are invited to collect gold coins scattered on a rug for their payment, but the rug is electrified so they must endure shocks as they entertain the white men. The coins turn out to be brass advertising tokens.

Finally, the other boys are paid off and sent home while the narrator is told to give his speech—which is a florid and conventional appeal to African Americans to be friendly toward whites and to accept the status quo. After gagging on blood from a cut in his mouth caused by a punch, the narrator inadvertently utters the phrase "social equality" instead of "social responsibility." The room goes quiet until he corrects himself. His return to meekness and humility is rewarded with thunderous applause, a calfskin briefcase, and a scholarship to the state college for Negroes. His family and neighbors are delighted, but he himself dreams about his grandfather, who shows him a message deposited in his briefcase: "Keep This Nigger-Boy Running." He awakens remembering the sound of the old man's ironic laughter.

Themes and Meanings

"Battle Royal" was first published as a short story in *Horizon* in 1947 under the title "Invisible Man." It later became the first chapter of Ralph Ellison's only novel, *Invisible Man* (1952), whose title comes from a phrase at the beginning of the story: "But first I had to discover that I am an invisible man!" "Battle Royal" provides a fascinating window into the creative forces that produced *Invisible Man*, which is recognized as one of the great American novels of our time, as well as a masterwork of the burgeoning black literature movement of the second half of the twentieth century. Grandfather episodes provide the thematic motor that drives much of the novel, which is a study of a naive young man who is wounded by racism but unsure how to respond. He wants to be a good member of his family and community, but fails to understand the poisonous effect that Southern race relations have on even such simple acts as delivering a harmless graduation speech. The story makes clear just what the narrator will face in his maturity.

The battle royal episode itself introduces many of the themes with which the narrator deals later in his life in the novel. These include social Darwinism, which metaphorically encourages individuals to fight to the finish in order to receive rewards; the ways in which the black community's strongest and wiliest members take advantage of their fellows, refusing to cooperate against the common white enemy just as Tatlock refuses to fake defeat; the corrupting influence of prizes and praise on the narrator himself; and the need for the white establishment to maintain symbolic as well as literal power over the black community. If *Invisible Man* defines many African American responses to racism and politics, "Battle Royal" provides a capsule version of the thematic crux of the larger work, how to respond to the cruelty of racism while retaining one's decency and humanity.

Ellison involves the reader so deeply in the experiences of his narrator that one shares both his pain and his confusion and uncertainty. The innocence and decency of the narrator, who is simply trying to do the right thing, are so effectively conveyed that readers of all races and cultures can understand the special problems that he faces.

Style and Technique

One of this story's greatest achievements is successfully rendering the narrator's dreamlike and emotional memories, although these are often abstract in their lack of full detail—in contrast to the sharp, cinematic depiction of the "reality" of the battle royal experience, yet with each style reinforcing the idea of the other. The narrator's recollections tend to be simple declarative sentences using the first-person pronoun: "I was naive. I was looking for myself. . . ." Through this highly personal medium the reader learns of the narrator's guilt and confusion about his grandfather's advice and his innocent lack of understanding of the mean-spirited intentions of the white establishment.

By contrast, the battle royal descriptions contain minute specificity, with details creating a word picture of place and setting: "It was a large room with a high ceiling. Chairs were arranged in neat rows around three sides of a portable boxing ring. The fourth side was clear, revealing a gleaming space of polished floor." Such straightforward description alternates with metaphors and similes that suggest the bizarre and exotic nature of what is happening: The blindfolded boys grope about "like blind, cautious crabs," their fists "testing the air like the knobbed feelers of hypersensitive snails." The nude dancer has yellow hair of "a circus kewpie doll," her breasts are "round as the domes of East Indian temples." The scenes in the boxing ring are especially effective, with visually descriptive phrases cutting quickly from image to image to convey the chaos of the blindfolded match: "The room spun round me, a swirl of lights, smoke, sweating bodies surrounded by tense white faces." The overly rhetorical style of the graduation speech slyly makes fun of the overwrought prose of that genre: "We of the younger generation extol the wisdom of that great leader and educator who first spoke these flaming words of wisdom. . . ."

Throughout, Ellison matches style and content, his medium conveying his message. Ellison's interest in and knowledge of jazz improvisation (he was a professional-level musician) is evident in the rhythms of his prose, which soars with a free exuberance yet still retains a tough-minded discipline. Even long after they were written, his verbal improvisations retain a freshness and newness assuring that this short story and the novel that grew out of it will remain essential reading.

Andrew Macdonald

THE BATTLER

Author: Ernest Hemingway (1899-1961)
Type of plot: Psychological realism
Time of plot: The 1910's
Locale: Michigan
First published: 1925

Principal characters:

NICK ADAMS, a young roustabout
AD (ADOLPH) FRANCIS, a punched-out former boxer
BUGS, an African American former trainer who looks after Ad
A RAILROAD BRAKEMAN

The Story

Nick Adams has been riding the rails in Michigan. Essentially innocent and by his own admission not tough, he falls for the ploy of a railroad brakeman on the freight train upon which he has hitched a ride. The brakeman spies Nick and tells him to come close because he has something for him. The something that the brakeman has for Nick is a hefty punch that catapults him off the moving train to the earth below. Nursing a black eye, Nick washes up in a nearby tamarack swamp, then makes his way along the roadbed toward Mancelona, some three or four miles distant. As he walks along the tracks he sees a small fire in the distance and heads toward it.

Nick approaches the fire cautiously, hidden by the night and by the beechwood forest in which he lurks. Seeing a man beside the fire, he approaches stealthily. When he gets closer, he greets the man, who looks up and asks him where he got his shiner. Nick then unfolds his story. The hobo has a badly mutilated face and has lost one ear. Nick stares at him so hard that he asks Nick whether he likes his face. Introducing himself as Ad—and later as Adolph Francis, a former lightweight champion of whom Nick has heard—he invites Nick to eat with him. He also announces that he is crazy and that he has a heart that beats only forty times a minute—which he insists on having Nick verify by taking his pulse as he counts to sixty.

Just as this ritual ends, a third man, Bugs, stumbles down the railroad embankment. Ad's erstwhile friend, Bugs, is black. Ad insists that Bugs is crazy too, and Bugs does not deny it. After verifying that Nick neither is nor ever was crazy and that he comes from Chicago, Bugs begins cooking ham and eggs in a skillet. Ad asks to use Nick's knife to cut the bread, but Bugs intervenes, warning Nick not to give his knife to Ad. Instead, Nick cuts six pieces of bread for the three of them.

After they eat, Ad becomes pensive and goes off into a world of his own. Bugs addresses him but elicits no response. Suddenly, Ad turns on Nick, demanding to know who the hell Nick thinks he is to come and eat his food and then get snotty when asked to lend his knife. Ad challenges Nick to a fight, which Nick tries to avert. Ad is determined, however, and is on the brink of punching Nick when Bugs approaches him from behind and knocks him out with a blackjack wrapped in cloth.

Bugs then explains that he looks after the punch-drunk ex-boxer, whose career ended when he and his female manager—to whom he bore a striking resemblance—got married, causing all sorts of speculation about incest. Ever since, Ad has lived the hobo life with Bugs nearby to save him from disaster. His former wife sends him money for his subsistence.

Bugs advises Nick that he can revive Ad whenever he wishes, but that it would be best if he were not around when Ad regains consciousness. Giving Nick a sandwich to take with him, Bugs bids him farewell and revives Ad, giving him a cup of hot coffee to help him wake up.

Themes and Meanings

Superficially, little happens in "The Battler," which was initially titled "A Great Little Fighting Machine." Although the story is little more than a vignette, it is touching in its simplicity and is remarkably psychologically sensitive and penetrating. Three unremarkable people come together by accident. Out of this brief chance encounter emerges a touching story of loyalty and camaraderie similar to John Steinbeck's *Of Mice and Men* (1937), in which George takes care of the retarded Lenny. Ad is not retarded; rather he is addled by the injuries he sustained in his fighting career. The character is based on two prizefighters whom Hemingway knew—Ad Wolgast and Bat Nelson. Bugs is based on Wolgast's black trainer.

"The Battler" is one of the many Nick Adams stories for which Hemingway gained early recognition. In these stories, Nick is consistently a catalyst rather than a central figure. He enters a situation, causes something to happen, observes it, then departs relatively unchanged. The story unfolding in "The Battler" belongs to Ad and Bugs. The basic conflict is that of a man, Ad, against the world. Life has not dealt him the best hand, yet his salvation comes from the loyal devotion of his friend, a sensitive, courteous, genuinely caring person. Bugs is unfailingly patient, yet he knows the limits that he must impose upon Ad to save him from himself.

"The Battler" demonstrates how two men, each bearing his own burdens, can form a symbiotic relationship that enables both to survive. Bugs is called "nigger" and has undoubtedly suffered the humiliation of racial discrimination. Hemingway shows subtly that Bugs understands his place in a society that discriminates against him solely on the basis of his pigmentation. Hemingway always has Bugs refer to the other two characters in the story as "Mr. Francis" and "Mr. Adams," not as "Ad" and "Nick." Although Ad is the former prizefighter, Bugs is the story's strong character. Without him it is doubtful that Ad could continue his hobo existence. It is also possible that if Bugs were not burdened by the responsibility that he has accepted for Ad, he might have a better life for himself. Nevertheless, Bugs is committed to Ad for the long haul. He is uncomplaining, although he is realistic in dealing with Ad.

Nick Adams merely passes through a situation. He stumbles into it without planning to do so, is briefly engaged in it, then, having observed its dynamics, he departs at the appropriate time. The story is thematically tight. Hemingway wastes no words in its telling. He shows more than he tells, revealing character convincingly yet almost incidentally. The result is a story that has remarkable thematic and structural coherence. In this story, as in the other Nick Adams stories, the central character is one of society's rejects. Society has used and discarded Ad Francis. This is the fate, seemingly, of those who battle against society. Ad's descent began presumably because he passed his manager off as his sister. His eventual marriage to her evoked a public outcry that destroyed the marriage and essentially ended Ad's career. Outraged at the injustice of what happened to him, Ad then became uncontrollably violent, picking fights and eventually ending up in jail. Upon his release, Bugs rescued him and has devoted himself to controlling him to spare him further difficulties, yet coddling him like a dependent child.

Style and Technique

Known for his clipped, direct style, uncomplicated sentence structure, and simple vocabulary, Ernest Hemingway demonstrates in "The Battler" the effectiveness and appropriateness of depicting characters on the social fringe, essentially antiheroes, as unostentatiously as he can. Few of his sentences exceed ten or twelve words. Simple sentences predominate and, when Hemingway uses a compound sentence, it is usually held together by a simple "and."

During his post-World War I residence in Paris, Hemingway learned a great deal about style from Gertrude Stein, with whom he had a close friendship in the early 1920's. Stein, a careful observer of how ordinary people actually use language, experimented with dialogue and, especially in her experimental novel *Three Lives* (1909), captured the authentic means by which common, working-class people communicate. In so doing, she presented endless repetitions, often to the point of exasperating her readers. Hemingway's "The Battler" uses similar techniques. For example, Bugs tells Nick that Ad's wife "Looked enough like him to be twins," then, within half a page, repeats this information in almost the same words. Some authors would intrude upon the actual language and would refine the dialogue to eliminate the repetition. Hemingway, however, prefers to allow his characters to speak the way real people speak, even if they repeat themselves.

In shaping his dialogue, Hemingway often avoids forms of the verb "to say." Rather, he uses such verbs as "advised," "warned," "finished," "asked," "smiled," or "came out." He draws attention to his most significant dialogue by using this device, reserving phrases such as "he said" for the more ordinary dialogue.

Ernest Hemingway developed a style unique among American writers, one easily distinguishable by its economy and directness. This style, an amalgamation of much that he learned from Gertrude Stein and of his experience as a journalist, has had a significant impact upon more recent novelists, many of whom have striven to imitate Hemingway's controlled rhetorical simplicity.

R. Baird Shuman

THE BEACH UMBRELLA

Author: Cyrus Colter (1910-   )
Type of plot: Domestic realism
Time of plot: A late summer day around 1963
Locale: Chicago
First published: 1963

> *Principal characters:*
> ELIJAH, a forty-one-year-old warehouse worker
> MYRTLE, his wife
> RANDALL, his twelve-year-old son, who works at odd jobs to earn
>   spending money
> MRS. GREEN, a young mother at the beach with her sons

The Story

On a hot Saturday in late summer, Elijah lolls in the sun on a Lake Michigan beach, like many others out to have a good time. Unlike them, however, he is alone and does not have a beach umbrella. Enchanted by the crowd of frolickers, he comes to the beach almost every Saturday, but his family has stayed home, where his wife is growing upset about his lack of ambition for his family. When she scolds him about getting a "real job," such as a high-paying job in a steel mill, he thinks of her as being "money-crazy."

Watching the smoke rising from a mill across the lake, Elijah ponders his job at the warehouse. After working hard there for nine years, he holds a position of responsibility. He wears a white shirt and a tie. The pay might be better, but he likes almost everything else about his job. And his pay would be enough, he thinks, if Myrtle did not want so much. A blue-collar job in the mill would be undignified and would leave him exhausted every night.

Feeling lonely and rejected by the groups of bathers, Elijah observes that beach umbrellas attract people to them—men and women who have come to the beach to have fun with others like themselves. Suddenly he feels that he must buy a flashy colorful umbrella.

By Monday evening Elijah has found an umbrella that would fulfill his dream, but he has less than half of the money that it costs. After dinner, his son Randy goes back to work at a store, and Myrtle again berates Elijah for not earning more money. The children, she tells him, will soon need clothes for school. Through the evening Elijah stares at the television, feeling oppressed by his alienation from his family. When Randy comes home, he avoids conversation by going to bed. Later, while Myrtle works in the kitchen, Elijah awakens his son and borrows fifteen dollars, telling Randy that he should not say anything to his mother about the loan.

On the next Saturday the sky is cloudy, but an anxiously hopeful Elijah carefully selects a spot on the beach where he raises his new red and white umbrella. When the sun at last comes out, people crowd onto the beach, and Elijah persuades two boys and their shy young mother to have a drink of lemonade in the shade that his umbrella provides. When the people under the umbrella next to Elijah's mistake this woman for his wife, she seems content when Elijah fails to correct their misimpression. Elijah is elated. As the conversation proceeds, however, his nervous laughter grows awkward until his new friends perceive that Mrs. Green is not his wife, but probably is his girlfriend. There is some embarrassment over this confusion, but again the young mother does not correct the false impression. More bathers settle nearby, and soon Elijah is manic with delight at the boisterous party that he feels he has assembled. Life seems wonderfully different than it was just one week earlier. Elijah frolics in the water, flirting with the young single women and holding the young mother up as he teaches her how to float on her back.

As the sun lowers, Elijah's anxiety returns, and he tries to enlist friends for next Saturday's party. When the beach empties, loneliness sweeps over him; for the first time since morning he remembers his own family at home. He feels that he has done an awful thing for just one day of fun, and now he must face the problem of how to repay the money that he has borrowed. After sitting by himself for a long time, he decides that he must sell his umbrella, even if he retrieves only the fifteen dollars that he owes to his son. As he approaches prospective buyers, however, he soon learns that their needs do not match his, or that his offer to sell cheap makes people suspect that he is a thief who is trying to sell something that he stole. Humiliated, and chased off the beach by a self-righteous lifeguard, Elijah sits in his car, shaken, scared, and disillusioned. In this confused state, he feels that he truly has stolen both the umbrella and the joy of the day. Now everyone has gone home, there are no umbrellas in sight, and by next Saturday he will be too tired to enjoy the beach after pouring hot ore all week at the mill.

Themes and Meanings

This story presents a personal crisis of a kind that is common in the lives of working and middle-class men and women: the dilemma of choosing between satisfying their own personal needs and meeting the needs of their dependents. The immediate circumstances of their lives prevent them from having both. For example, for Elijah to meet the needs of the family to which he is committed by marriage and parenthood, he must sacrifice a personally satisfying worklife and the object that he sees as the means of fulfilling his dream of emotional satisfaction. If he chooses to serve himself, he will betray and neglect his family.

One approach to resolving dilemmas of this kind is to identify one's personal values and rank them, then choose what is the most valuable, even at the cost of losing what is less valuable. Clarification often involves a realistic look at one's life, in order to see if a valued aspect might actually be an illusion. Cyrus Colter's story dramatizes that process in the life of an ordinary person. In Elijah's case, everything that is at stake is strongly charged with emotion and seems to be very valuable; therefore the process of clarification, ranking, decision-making, and right action, is difficult and painful.

Colter does not promise that his character's life will henceforth be entirely happy. The story leaves it to the reader to decide whether Elijah makes the wise choice.

Style and Technique

The style in which this story is told, featuring ordinary language and sentence structure, highlighted by vivid imagery, combines with its point of view and symbolism to allow the reader to see Elijah's life as he sees it. At the same time, it maintains distance as a thoughtful outside observer of what is actually going on. Although the narrative point of view is third-person omniscient, it focuses on Elijah's viewpoint, presenting almost everything as it is seen and understood by him. Even details that are especially important from the reader's outside point of view, such as the clownish shape of Elijah's legs and the near-hysteria of his laughter, with its chilling effect on the other bathers' perception of him, also are vaguely perceived by Elijah himself and contribute to his eventual realization that his dream of romance is an illusion.

Elijah's consciousness, like the story's setting, is divided between the beach and his home, but the powerful unifying force is his consciousness of family. He tries to deny the claims of his family at home, only to pursue his fantasy of romance, ironically, through a misunderstanding and falsification involving a quasi-family at the beach. The father of the boys at the beach is absent, just as Elijah himself is absent from his children.

The device that focuses the conflicting forces in Elijah's dilemma is the symbol that is presented in the story's title. The beach umbrella functions like another and more common symbol, a flag. Normally it carries only practical meaning and power, for persons sharing the culture of a time and place. It offers a kind of protection but may, at the same time, be merely a decoration. In a crisis, however, the visual thing may take on associations that charge it with emotional dimensions of meaning, so that it no longer merely stands for a thought about life, it now participates so fully in meaningful action that it becomes the thought itself. For other bathers, the umbrella remains a practical thing; however, they see Elijah differently when he owns one—as he knew they would. For both Elijah and the reader, however, the umbrella carries Elijah's full thought of escape into the colorful vitality of feeling free and desired. And like all effective symbols, its fullness as a thought includes the inescapable dark side of what gives it meaning. If Elijah continues to be thoughtful, thinking symbolically by means of the thing which, in his crisis, has drawn him to it, inevitably the umbrella will bring him to realize the necessity of surrender and the possibility of defeat. Perhaps he will also find an unexpected kind of victory.

Tom Koontz

BECAUSE WE ARE SO POOR

Author: Juan Rulfo (1918-1986)
Type of plot: Social realism
Time of plot: Early twentieth century
Locale: Jalisco, Mexico
First published: "Es que somos muy pobres," 1953 (English translation, 1962)

> *Principal characters:*
> THE NARRATOR
> TACHA, his sister
> THEIR FATHER
> LA SERPENTINA, Tacha's cow

The Story

Swollen from torrential rain, the river near the narrator's village has been rising for three days. Everything is going from bad to worse. The rain has ruined the harvest and the narrator's aunt has died. Moreover, La Serpentina, the cow belonging to his twelve-year-old sister, has been swept away by the river and drowned.

The noise of the river awakens the narrator. It is so loud that he thinks the roof of his house is collapsing. As he gets up, the noise grows louder and closer. The river has a rotted odor, and there is no sign that the rain will let up. When the narrator looks toward the village, he finds that the river has jumped its banks and is slowly rising along the main street. The water rushes into the house of a neighbor woman named Tambora. On the far banks of the river, a large tree in the dead aunt's yard—the only tamarind tree in the village—has been uprooted and swept away, dramatically proving that this flood is the largest in many years.

In the afternoon the narrator and his sister Tacha climb a ravine above the river, which they watch in fascination for hours. The river's roaring is so loud that it drowns out the voices of people near it.

From other people discussing the river's damage, they learn of La Serpentina's demise. A man has seen her washed away, although just why the cow drowned cannot be determined. Perhaps she tried to cross the river; more probably the water reached her while she slept, and the frightened animal cramped up in the water. She must have bellowed for help, but help had not come. She had a calf, but the narrator cannot tell if it survived. Tacha's father intended the cow to play a key role in his daughter's life; it was to be her dowry. While she was growing up, she could rely on the cow to attract a good husband who would always love her. Without a cow, finding a good man will be difficult.

Tacha's father is upset because the cow was intended to save her from the fate of her two older sisters. The sisters were reared to be God-fearing, obedient, and respectful, but they went astray. Their mother, who cries and prays for them, has racked her memory in vain trying to understand what misled them. Their father thinks they went bad because they were wild by nature and were poor. While adolescents, they started meeting men at the river at all hours of the night—and day. The men taught them bad things. The narrator saw his sisters rolling naked on the ground, each with a man on top of her. When their father could no longer tolerate his daughters' behavior, he ran them off, and they went to a nearby town to be prostitutes.

Now it appears that the same fate awaits Tacha, unless the calf is found. Any day now her pubescent breasts will attract a man. She stands on the ravine in her pink dress beside the narrator and cries. The water streaming from her eyes is dirty, as if the river has gotten inside her. The noise from her mouth sounds like the river. The rising river splashes its stinking water on her face. As she cries, her little breasts ceaselessly bounce up and down, as if they are suddenly beginning to swell, and she has started on the road to ruin. Whether the calf, now her only hope, will be found is unknown.

Themes and Meanings

"Because We Are So Poor" was first published in 1953 as part of Juan Rulfo's collection *El llano en llamas*. On one interpretation, the central focus of the story is the river and the damage it does to the impoverished lives of the narrator's Mexican village. It has ruined the harvest, carried off a large village tree, and rushed into a woman's house and threatened to drown her chickens, which must be of great importance to her.

The plain on which these people scratch out a living is arid. Through the Mexican Revolution's land distribution plan, the characters have received title to land on this plain, but it requires a pickax to plant even a seed. Ironically in this desert world, when rain does come, it comes as an unwelcome destructive force, engorging the river to flood levels.

In Rulfo's world, nature is never benign. It presents an overwhelming force against which puny human powers struggle and lose. The inevitability of this defeat constitutes the fatalism that threads its way through Rulfo's fiction, particularly in this story, in which nature's power literally engulfs humanity. For example, Rulfo describes Tambora's flooded house as "already part of the river." More ominously, the river has figuratively entered Tacha, whose crying resembles its roar. Her tears are the waters of the river already drowning the hope of her young life, as it drowned the cow that was to save her.

From another perspective, the story's focus is the fate of Tacha. Although her future remains uncertain, all signs point to her entering prostitution. The small chance of the calf's survival provides the slimmest hope that she will escape the degraded life of her sisters. Human nature conspires with external natural forces to place the girl a single step from the path trod so ruinously by her sisters.

The narrator remarks how Tacha is "shooting up like a rod," her breasts beginning to fill out. They are high and pointed, the kind that bounce around "promising to be like her sisters'." Such breasts will catch the attention of everyone, including bad men. Her father has seen Tacha's future in the pasts of his other daughters, and with the cow gone and her sexuality bursting, can find no barriers to her following in her sisters' path—"she'll end up going bad; mark my words, she'll end up going bad."

The theme of helpless humanity before the forces of nature within them as well as outside them pervades the story. For Rulfo, something seems dark, even rotten about physical as well as human nature. The river stinks, and tears are dirty water like the river. Human nature fares no better; lust lurks nearby, ready to destroy the family.

Perhaps nature is less threatening to the rich, who can build their lives on higher ground. Their homes do not become swamps; their daughters need not sell their bodies. If a crop fails, there are reserves. The fatalism of those who inhabit the Jalisco plain, on the other hand, is predicated on their poverty. Thus, Tacha's father believes there are two reasons for his elder daughters' fall. One is their wild nature, which the parents did everything to counter. The other is that "we were poor in my house." Poverty makes inevitable the triumph of hostile nature.

Rulfo intimates all this without moralizing or sentimentality. Yet, it is difficult to imagine one's not feeling sympathy for his characters. Such sympathy does not always arise in his stories, in which murder, vengeance, and the like abound. But here, decent people who are "very" poor strive for the good but are assaulted by uncontrollable forces that undo their painfully contrived attempts to improve their lives. The darkling plain gives no light and shows no compensation for those whose lives Rulfo paints so starkly.

Style and Technique

"Because We Are So Poor" (which has also been published as "We're Very Poor") takes the form of an interior monologue of the nameless brother of Tacha, whose fate dominates the story. The reader discovers at the end that the action takes place at virtually a single moment, as the narrator stands with his sister above the rising river, contemplating her situation and the river below. As in other Rulfo stories, time is frozen. The narrator speaks directly to the reader about the circumstances before him now. The title itself is the present tense, and the story artfully weaves past and present together.

The prose in all Rulfo's short stories is taut and spare, as if to mirror the grim reality he describes. In "Because We Are So Poor," he relates his story in little more than fifteen hundred words but manages to evoke the world of his characters and portray vividly their poverty and forlorn lives.

Augmenting the realism of life on the plain unrelieved by either joys or some final, comic victory of its people, is a sense that the narrator's thought process is woven into the narrative. He thinks out loud as he alters his account of the cow's drowning from one line to the next; he speaks of climbing the ravine with his sister in the past tense, but eventually one discovers that this past is actually the present.

Rulfo uses a fine sense of dramatic pacing. He shocks the reader and builds to a climax, although time is telescoped into a single moment. He introduces the loss of the cow at the beginning, but the impending fate of Tacha is evident only at the end, indeed, in the last line.

Charles F. Bahmueller

THE BEGGAR MAID

Author: Alice Munro (1931-   )
Type of plot: Domestic realism
Time of plot: The early 1950's
Locale: Ontario, Canada
First published: 1977

Principal characters:
ROSE, a university freshman
FLO, her stepmother
DR. HENSHAWE, her landlady
PATRICK BLATCHFORD, a graduate student who is
  heir to a department store fortune

The Story

After growing up in the little town of Hanratty, Ontario, Rose wins a scholarship to a prestigious Canadian university. During her first semester there, she finds a comfortable place to live, a part-time job, and a male admirer. She meets Patrick at the campus library when she is working a weekend shift, reshelving books, and he is one of the few people studying there. When she asks him if he has seen a man who has just grabbed her in the almost deserted building, he rushes to her defense. Rose can tell at once that he is both high-minded and high-strung—a nervous man who wants to become a history professor. She also soon sees that he is infatuated with her. She does not know, however, that he is the heir to a family business. She dates Patrick partly to spite her landlady, a spinster former English professor who encourages her "scholars" to stay away from "boys." To Rose's surprise, the landlady likes Patrick and tells her that he is one of the most eligible bachelors on campus.

During the Christmas holidays, Patrick takes Rose to visit his family's luxurious home in British Columbia. Rose feels completely out of place among Patrick's parents and sisters, but so does Patrick. After returning to the university, they become engaged, and Rose takes Patrick to meet her family in Hanratty, where Patrick is taken aback by the working-class culture and the country accents. Rose increasingly wonders what Patrick sees in her or wants from her. Nevertheless, she finds herself saying all the right things to people who ask to see her engagement ring and ask about her wedding plans. As year-end exams approach, she breaks off her relationship with Patrick, but relents when she meets him to return his ring.

They marry and have children, but continue their pattern of separation and reconciliation, with subtle variations, for a decade. Eventually, they divorce. Another decade later, when Rose is a successful television interviewer and Patrick is a successful professor, they see each other in an airport. Rose smiles, realizing that she could throw herself at Patrick again, but knowing better. He makes an ugly face. What remains of their relationship is this story, which she tells to many friends and lovers in the new age of honesty.

Themes and Meanings

The story's title is a cultural allusion of the sort that Patrick likes to drop on people, looking shocked if they do not understand it. He tells Rose that "The Beggar Maid" is the title of a famous work of art, a painting of a poor but beautiful young woman who wins the love of a king and marries him. Rose assumes that that is how he sees himself—as a gentleman rescuing a waif. It is not, however, how she sees herself. She feels no need to be rescued and often must reassure Patrick that he is not a weakling.

Rose only remembers one book from Patrick's shelves, but his fascination with that book says a good deal about his attitude toward her and her own difficulty with his attitude. The book is Robert Graves's *The White Goddess: A Grammar of Poetic Myth* (1948). It represents a genuine tribute to the goddess and the muse, but also a dilemma for women interested in the arts, as it sees their job as being to inspire poets, rather than to be poets themselves. When Patrick insists on calling plump and dark Rose his "White Goddess," she calls him her "White God" and throws snow in his face to make her point. The snow jolts him into doing something manly for once, but when they climb out of the snowbank he returns at once to coddling apologies.

The dramatic question of this story is not whether Rose will win Patrick's love (she does so at once) or even whether she will win his family over (which she can only do when grandchildren are in the offing). The question is whether she will keep him. Even before Rose throws snow at Patrick, and especially after he apologizes for retaliating, she senses something wrong with their relationship. Their physical relationship is good, once she can stop pretending and start enjoying herself. Patrick's intentions are entirely noble, but he sees himself and Rose as being from "two different worlds." He says so, and she cannot forget. He thinks his own world is better, but Rose regards her own as equally valid and much more comfortable. Rose is uncomfortable in Hanratty only when she brings Patrick there and feels obliged to try to speak as he does.

Style and Technique

"The Beggar Maid" is the fifth in a series of ten stories about Flo and Rose. It appears in a collection with their names as a subtitle, and is the title story in the American edition (1979) and the British edition (1980). The original Canadian edition (1978) takes its equally suggestive title from the last story, "Who Do You Think You Are?" Alice Munro uses this technique of interconnected stories in other volumes, moving more than one reviewer to wonder whether she is writing novels rather than story collections. Each of her stories stands perfectly well on its own, but all belong to the larger fictional world of Hanratty, Ontario—much as William Faulkner's stories are about the people in a fictional Mississippi county. "The Beggar Maid" first appeared on its own in *The New Yorker*, but it has definite connections to the stories that come before and after it in Munro's collection. In "White Swans," Rose makes her first trip to Toronto after winning an essay competition, with Flo's warnings about white slavers ringing in her ears and the new surroundings being defined in contrast to the old. In "Mischief," Rose falls in love with a married man while she is still married to Patrick.

The whole cycle of stories, as one might call it, extends from Hanratty into the world at large and back again in Rose's memories. The first story gets its title from Flo's curiously poetic threats to Rose: "Royal Beatings." The last gets its title from Flo's nagging question: "Who Do You Think You Are?" Rose narrates all these stories, but she has learned the art of storytelling from Flo and, in telling stories to her friends and lovers, she comes to realize how much her life has been shaped by her small town origins. Munro is a provincial writer in the best sense. She finds God in the details of everyday life. The details are North American, to be sure, and Canadian even more so, but they come from the place where Munro grew up. Hanratty is a "ratty" little town of Munro's own creation, but it bears much in common with Wingham, Ontario, where she was born and raised. Her fictional university town is not named, but it is just as clearly modeled on London, Ontario, where she attended Western University for three terms before marrying a Vancouver man in 1951. Rose's story is not straight autobiography. Unlike Rose, Munro was not orphaned, and her marriage lasted a decade longer than Rose's. The parallels between Rose's life and her own, however, are unmistakable.

Fascination with details often pushes writers into longer works of fiction. Such fascination makes Margaret Atwood, a Canadian writer of Munro's generation, want to know what kind of appliances her characters have in their kitchens, and the answers make her best known fiction run to some length. Munro has found a way to give details associated with special moments in a life, and to remind the reader of those details in other stories. When Rose thinks about taking Patrick to Hanratty, readers know what she is up against if they have already read about her vivacious stepmother and the local butcher; Rose need only think of their names. When Flo returns Patrick's passion for history with a grotesque local story, the reader recognizes the stepmother who carries on in earlier stories. The reader also hears Flo as never before, through the mildly scandalized ears of her future son-in-law and the nervously horrified ears of her stepdaughter.

Alice Munro writes in the language of the people. Some characters may be world travelers, such as Dr. Henshawe; others have not strayed far from Hanratty. Readers learn about Rose's development through the development of her language, and occasionally they hear the voice of experience, reflecting on her own story after many years. "The Beggar Maid" is very much a story of Rose.

Thomas Willard

THE BENCH

Author: Richard Rive (1931-1989)
Type of plot: Social realism
Time of plot: Mid-twentieth century
Locale: Cape Town, South Africa
First published: 1963

Principal character:
KARLIE, a young man

The Story

After Karlie has lived all of his life in a remote rural part of South Africa, this is his first visit to Cape Town, a bustling metropolis in which all sorts of people rub shoulders. More obviously than in his more segregated home town, Cape Town shows the tensions that result from the rigid system of separation of races known as apartheid. Karlie sees people of all colors—some black, some white, and others mixed.

As the story opens, Karlie is standing in a large crowd that is listening to a black speaker who is proclaiming the rights of black majority, the working class to whom he refers as the proletariat. Karlie is impressed by what the speaker is saying, since it seems to be the first time that he has even considered the possibility that blacks do, in fact, have any rights at all. He notices that two white detectives are taking notes on everything that is being said at the meeting.

As Karlie listens, he recalls the advice he received from elders in his own community. Ou Klaas, for example, taught him that God created blacks and whites separately, and therefore they should continue to live separately.

On the platform with the speaker is a white woman in a blue dress and Nxeli, whom Karlie recognizes as a famous trade-union organizer. As he watches, the white woman gets up and begins speaking. She encourages the black crowd to refuse to play by the rules imposed by the whites: Blacks, she says, should sit wherever they please, and go wherever they want.

As he leaves the meeting, Karlie is both confused by the new ideas and exhilarated. He doubts whether anything of this sort could ever be put into action in his own little town, but he is beginning to think it might be a possibility. At the train station that will send him home he notices, in a new way, a bench labeled "Europeans only." Inspired by all that he has heard and the sense of individual responsibility that the speakers have aroused in him, he decides to sit on the forbidden bench.

At first, no one seems to notice him. Time passes, and he thinks that his protest may go unheeded. After a while he eases into his new situation, and sits simply because he is tired. At that moment a young white man shouts at him to get up off the bench. Karlie neither speaks nor moves. As the white man continues shouting, a crowd gathers. Different people express different reactions. Some are outraged that Karlie will not sit on the benches reserved for blacks. Others declare that he should be allowed to sit wherever he wishes.

A policeman arrives and tells Karlie to move. Again, Karlie remains silent and stays where he is. As the policeman begins shouting, the white woman who gave the speech Karlie heard approaches and defends Karlie's rights. Nevertheless, the policeman begins beating Karlie; he puts handcuffs on him and drags him away. At first Karlie struggles and tries to hold on to the bench; when he sees that this is hopeless, he stands up and goes with the policeman, smiling and asserting the arrogance that he now feels.

Themes and Meanings

This is the story of a young man's coming to consciousness of his rights and responsibilities. Richard Rive is focusing on a defining moment in Karlie's life, and the reader knows that the protagonist's life will never again be what it was before this fateful day. Whether he is treated badly in jail or not, he can never go back to his little village as the naïve fellow he was that morning. He has become a man.

The disturbing words that Karlie hears on his first visit to the city are described by Rive as if the young man had wandered into a church and had overheard a foreign revelation that was completely unexpected and totally liberating from his passing understanding of himself and of his possibilities. The notion that he might have all the rights of a white man seems, at first, far too good to be true, as if the political message was the good news that the word "gospel" actually means. Rive describes the young man as a young convert who is filled with the enthusiasm that follows from entrance into any new belief system. His somewhat precipitous action that soon follows the speech seems perfectly natural if viewed in this religious context: Karlie wishes to put into practice the invigorating message that has changed his interior life.

It is as though Karlie has been given a new set of eyes, and he views the world around him in much different terms. Those who had once seemed bigger than life—his elders in the village and, especially, the whites in the far-off city—now seem his equals. In some important sense, they also seem to be his inferiors, since Karlie now recognizes that those who had advised him to cower timidly in the face of the unfair laws are, in fact, less-than-noble examples. They are frightened, small men who have grown accustomed to a limited domain for their lives. Unlike them, Karlie has taken the next step and asked the all-important question that leads to change in any society: Why are things this way? Karlie may be technically defeated in his act of civil disobedience, but he now finds himself identifying with a different group of role models: He now sees himself as one of those who proudly hold their heads high and smile as they are dragged off to jail.

Richard Rive, whose father was an African American and whose mother was a mixed-race South African, is alert to the influence that the racial struggle in the United States has had in African politics. He dedicates the story to Langston Hughes, the African American short-story writer and poet. In this story, Karlie, although not from a cosmopolitan part of the country, nevertheless is aware of the Black Power move-ment and of the challenge that it presented to white authority everywhere. In some ways, Rive's story is an African version of the factual Rosa Parks story, in which a Southern black woman in the United States refused to give up her seat in a bus to a white man as the discriminatory laws demanded.

Style and Technique

Part of the success of this story is its utter simplicity. The language is completely straightforward and the techniques are in no way complex. It is as though Rive looks directly into his character's uncomplicated system of logic and constructs his story as a perfect mirror of Karlie's mental processes. If the narrative were more subtle, or the vocabulary less accessible, the story would not have its powerful impact. Readers are shown Karlie's step-by-step movement from innocence to commitment, and nowhere along the path are they made conscious of the roadway itself. Rive thereby convinces them that Karlie, who might represent so many other young men like himself, can, in fact, take this uncharacteristic action and go against the timid advice of his elders.

Rive uses the bench as a symbol for arbitrary territorial borders that are used to maintain an unjust social structure. That an act as meaningless in itself as sitting on a bench could prompt such virulence in many of the whites points out that they see much more meaning in the bench than it deserves. For them, it is a symbol of their control of the rules of the game: They are the ones who have the power to define, quite arbitrarily, what this simple bench is. If a native African feels free to violate this definition, who knows how many others they might also choose to redefine, and some with far greater consequences. Rive's character, for all his simplicity, recognizes the power of symbols.

Rive constructs the story as an implied conversation between the speakers on the platform and the village elders who had counseled Karlie to know his place and to play along with the white overseers. As Karlie is won over to the words of rebellion, he begins to see Ou Klaas and the other accommodators in a less favorable light. He recognizes that they have been treated all their lives like pack animals, and he answers their implicit advice with a firm "No."

John C. Hawley

BEYOND THE PALE

Author: William Trevor (William Trevor Cox, 1928-   )
Type of plot: Domestic realism
Time of plot: 1979
Locale: County Antrim, Northern Ireland
First published: 1981

> *Principal characters:*
> DOROTHY MILSON (MILLY), the narrator and protagonist
> MAJOR R. B. STRAFE, her lover
> CYNTHIA STRAFE, the major's wife
> DEKKO DEACON, an old friend
> MR. and MRS. MALSEED, proprietors of Glencorn Lodge
> KITTY, the waitress
> UNNAMED YOUNG MAN

The Story

This tale of four English bridge players who habitually go on a summer holiday excursion to the same lodge in County Antrim, on the coast of Northern Ireland, examines what happens when something disrupts the "casual comedy" to reveal hidden unpleasant undercurrents in their lives. The story's narrator, Milly, insists on the perfection of the ritualized patterns of the foursome. For many years they have spent the first two weeks of June at Glencorn Lodge, hosted by Mr. and Mrs. Malseed. She notes approvingly that this year things are just the same as always at the lodge, and that all is well. Milly sees little outside the narrow field of her vision. The behavior of the foursome is equally unchanging. They go on drives and walks to the same locations; there is a day when Strafe and Dekko go fishing; they play bridge after dinner; and, most importantly, they maintain a tacit agreement never to talk about each other. Their reserve allows Milly and Major Strafe to carry on their love affair in the evenings after the major's wife Cynthia retires; the Strafes have separate bedrooms and the lovers assume that Cynthia does not notice them.

On the first night, an unwelcome stranger disrupts this comfortable routine. He is an unhappy young man whom the four friends and the Malseeds feel is out of place. When Milly and the men go walking the next day, Cynthia talks with the young man, who then commits suicide, leaving her terribly upset. The others immediately assume that the young man has made a pass at Cynthia, whom Milly mentally criticizes for her lack of assertiveness in "allowing" an improper advance. Indeed, the young man has approached Cynthia, but not sexually. Rather, he has revealed to her that he has just murdered an old girlfriend to stop her from making bombs for the Irish Republican Army (IRA). He returned to Glencorn to kill himself because he and his girlfriend had frolicked there as children. As Cynthia recounts the man's story, the two later parted, with the girl growing up to make IRA bombs and the young man eventually killing her to stop the violence. He has committed suicide (by walking into the sea) to expiate his guilt. (The man's suicide resembles a famous Irish death—that of the legendary hero Cuchulain, who drowned himself after discovering he had killed his own son in combat.)

Cynthia strings together a narrative that links Irish history, the intimate history of the two young unfortunates, and British (and by extension, their own) culpability. Embarrassed and disturbed, the other three vacationers try to deny the validity of her tale, putting it down to shock, or to bad form on her part. Meanwhile, the Malseeds, parodies of hotel propriety, anxiously try to hustle Cynthia away from the scene. Before she is shunted away, Cynthia plays her trump card. Summoning Kitty, the dining room waitress, she announces that she knows all about the affair between Strafe and Milly, that Dekko and Strafe have never passed beyond the adolescent level of development, and that from the safety of their domesticity in Surrey or their idylls at Glencorn, they blindly ignore the horrors of murder and armed occupation in Ulster. She then departs, but the damage is done, and the illusory perfection of Glencorn Lodge is destroyed. Even then, however, Milly cannot bring herself to admit the justice of what Cynthia has said. Instead, she wishes that it had been Cynthia who had died in the sea. She dismisses Cynthia's narrative as "awful rigamarole" and sees the two children as having "grown up into murdering riff-raff."

Themes and Meanings

"Beyond the Pale" incorporates many of William Trevor's favorite themes: the loss of innocence (both real and false), the barriers and false fronts that people erect to hide from unpleasant truths, the intersection of the political and historical with the personal, the misery visited on people devoid of love, and the ways in which violence destroys both victim and perpetrator.

Although the children of Cynthia's Irish narrative grow up in a fallen world, it is more particularly the fall from a false and illusory Eden that fills the story's center. The Malseeds have created a garden setting in which the four English people can indulge their fantasy that life is perfect, that violence and unpleasantness exist elsewhere and that they all get along splendidly. The Malseeds themselves, however, are a transplanted English couple who affect a phony Irish manner; their very "tastefulness"—the studied effort to preserve the Georgian style of the building, the perfection of the garden, the resident pet Dalmations, the rooms not numbered but named after flowers—suggests rather questionable taste. Yet even in the biblical Garden there was a serpent, and the Malseeds' garden, built as it is on falsehoods, cannot return them to a prelapsarian (before the fall) state. Even the Malseeds' name (*mal* is from the Latin for "bad"), reveals that evil has entered this world already.

The world of Glencorn Lodge, like the implied social contract among the four friends, who never criticize each other or speak of anything more serious than old school hijinks, is a barrier, a "pale" erected around what they regard as their civilized existence—just as the English erected a pale around Dublin in 1395. Only Cynthia, with her interest in Irish history, understands that what lies beyond the pale is real life, that what is inside—no matter how desirable—is a tissue of deceit. The notion of actions that lie outside boundaries runs throughout the story, from the discussion of "unsuitable" guests being excluded from the lodge, the violence of the two former lovers, Cynthia's tirade, and, most notably, the violence of a decade of civil strife and military oppression in Northern Ireland and the spread of violence to London.

Yet as Trevor shows repeatedly in his fiction, especially in the fiction set in Ireland, the personal cannot exist independent of the historical. Individuals who try to live by a private code of decency and compassion find themselves drawn into the quagmire of violence and revenge. Their own stories are taken over by stories much older and much bigger than themselves. So too in this story. Cynthia cannot fathom, nor can we, what caused the young girl of her story to become the bomb-making woman who drove her childhood sweetheart to kill her, nor what moved him to commit that desperate act. "Evil," as Cynthia says, "breeds evil in mysterious ways." The origins of the violence in Northern Ireland, as Trevor reminds us, go back hundreds of years. The "Pale" dates back nearly six centuries, while the Battle of Boyne, which secured British rule over the island, took place in 1690, and the Act of Union binding Ireland to England was passed in 1800. Yet the young couple dies scarcely even aware that they are fighting battles not of their own choosing.

The heartlessness of the actions of characters in the story is a by-product of an inability to love. Milly is driven by selfishness rather than passion, as is Strafe, while Dekko has never been able to commit himself to anyone on a mature level. The trajectories of the lives of the two young people demonstrate the ruin that comes about once love falls from their lives. More generally, Trevor implies, the horror and evil that Cynthia delineates stems from a more generalized inability to love one's neighbor.

Style and Technique

Trevor is a modern master of the realistic story whose narrative style is so smooth and understated that it rarely calls attention to itself. Yet here, as in his other stories, that understatement is tied to an unreliable first-person narrator, and readers do not notice until late in the story just how much she has been hiding. The other notable feature is Cynthia's framed narrative, which veers away from quiet realism toward the mythic and the incantatory as she invokes Irish history and legend to indict herself and her friends for their lack of sympathy and understanding. Her nightmarish poetic style brings out the hostility in the more earthbound Milly, who attempts to see the embedded narrative as the ravings of a madwoman, and as a usurpation of her rightful place as the one who controls the story. Yet Milly is fighting a losing battle: Her realism has masked a fantasy, just as Cynthia's fantastic narrative has unveiled a clearer version of reality. An act of imagination is required to arrive at truth, just as an awareness of violence is required to attain any hope of peace.

Thomas C. Foster

BIG BAD LOVE

Author: Larry Brown (1951-)
Type of plot: Domestic realism
Time of plot: Late twentieth century
Locale: A small town in Mississippi
First published: 1990

> *Principal characters:*
> LEROY, the narrator and protagonist, a lonely man
> MILDRED, his wife

The Story

After the narrator (whose name is not revealed until the end of the story) states that his dog is dead, the rest of his narrative unfolds in its shadow, as its inert body lies in the front yard waiting to be buried. Other animals also play roles in the story. A cat belonging to the narrator's wife, Mildred, catches and slowly kills a young rabbit, while training its kittens to hunt. The narrator considers killing the cats because of their cruelty to the rabbit. He recalls a time when he raised rabbits for food, but gave it up because having to kill them became too painful.

Mildred is sexually frustrated "because of her over-large organ." The narrator drives around in his truck and finds an old friend who gives him a beer. Then he goes home to shower and shave. Knowing that Mildred will return shortly, he drives off again to continue his drinking. In a crosstown bar, he drinks and plays pool with several women whom he would like to pick up. After failing in this endeavor, he drives home, following a circuitous route in order to avoid the police and to get home as late as possible so that he will not have to perform for his sexually insatiable wife.

Unashamed of himself, the narrator does not think of himself as inadequate; his wife simply needs more than he as an average man can provide. At the bar he recalls how he met Mildred: He was in Destin, Florida, recovering from his separation from his first wife. When he saw Mildred, he was sexually attracted immediately, so he divorced his first wife and married her. On their wedding night, he discovered that something was badly amiss. The next morning Mildred explained that she truly was virtuous and that it was not overuse that had made her organ so large. The narrator realized his predicament: Once again in an impossible relationship, as he knew that he would never be able to fulfill Mildred's desires. Throughout his narrative, he thinks about how sad he is, trying to make the impossible happen.

When he finally arrives home, he finds the house is dark and empty. Mildred has left a note saying that she has met another man and is going away with him: "He has the equipment to take care of my problem and we have already 'roadtested' it."

Leroy does not bury the dog. His sorrow and despair grow deeper as he realizes again that he could never satisfy his wife. He resolves to bury his dog in the morning and start looking for a new wife after that.

Themes and Meanings

Larry Brown's central theme in this story is that all creatures—humans, cats, rabbits, and dogs included—want to give and experience love. Giving and experiencing love is such a difficult thing, however, that no one and nothing can do it completely satisfactorily.

The dog dies in the first line of the story. It is therefore unable to provide any sympathy or help with the human character's attempts at love and affection. The mother cat loves her kittens but shows her love by fetching a baby rabbit, which she teaches her kittens to stalk and kill. At first, the kittens do nearly nothing and the rabbit runs away. This happens several times before the kittens finally begin to attack it fiercely. In an act of compassion, a movement of brave existentialism, the narrator kills the rabbit.

The cats belong to Mildred, and the narrator once raised rabbits. Just as the cats slowly beat down the rabbit, Mildred is beating down Leroy. And just as the rabbit can do nothing about his situation but try to escape, only to be caught repeatedly and faced with an ever-worse situation, Leroy cannot escape his own predicament.

The underlying question that this story poses is not how to love, but whether love is possible at all in a world that is so cruelly unjust that people act without meaning or ability to gain spiritual or even physical gratification. Bad things happen to good people because bad things happen to everyone and everything. It is often not the fault of the individual who is only a very small force in an unpredictable and often unkind natural world.

Leroy married Mildred because of her sex appeal, but soon learned that he could never reciprocate the sexual pleasure that he had hoped to gain for himself. Although Mildred does not blame him for being inadequate, she still wants him to improve and give her more. Leroy is the rabbit that runs away only to be caught and hurt slightly more each time.

This fatalistic, even hopefully fatalistic type of existentialism, appears frequently in the writings of Larry Brown. When Mildred is found to be with another man, Leroy is not jealous. He is only saddened that he could not give her the sexual pleasure that is apparently the only means available for achieving a state of love or having a meaningful relationship. He wishes that he could give his own life meaning and that he could help others to do the same, but obviously, he cannot.

Style and Technique

Brown presents his protagonist here as a hopeful fatalist. Leroy's inability to change his condition in life is marked and poignant in that the character often declares hopeful wishes. He considers events that would help him to find a happier existence and these thoughts are very funny—in the same way that jokes are funny because they hurt. The protagonist is symbolized by traits of the rabbits that he mentions. He is running from his bad love relationship, just as the rabbit is running from the cats that will eventually kill it. In the bar, Leroy plays pool with three women, but leaves when bigger and more burly men enter the bar. Then he drives his truck on backroads to avoid run-ins with the police, running and hiding again from those who would do him harm. Leroy is not cowardly, though, any more than a rabbit running from cats is cowardly. It is his position in life to be weak and timid. Leroy is living as well as he can, accepting his fate and drinking to relieve the pain inherent to the human condition.

Brown's ear for authentic dialogue is an asset to this story. His use of language is in the tradition of the deep South, genuine and honest, though no intensely obscure dialect or vernacular appears. Instead, the story is short and the style is quick and handy, easily readable and understood, and the turns of phrase and situations presented are mostly clear and funny. This is not written in an exceedingly wordy or old-world literary style; it is written as ordinary people speak and perhaps as they think.

Beaird Glover

BIG BOY LEAVES HOME

Author: Richard Wright (1908-1960)
Type of plot: Social realism
Time of plot: Early twentieth century
Locale: The American South
First published: 1936

> *Principal characters:*
> BIG BOY, an adolescent who becomes a man
> BOBO, his friend, who is tarred, feathered, and burned by a white mob
> LESTER and
> BUCK, two black boys who are shot
> BERTHA HARVEY, a white woman who happens upon the four boys when they are naked
> JIM HARVEY, her husband
> LIZA MORRISON, Big Boy's mother
> SAUL MORRISON, his father
> LUCY MORRISON, his sister
> WILL SANDERS, a truck driver

The Story

The story is divided into five distinct sections. The first opens on a hot day, as four adolescent African American boys laugh and play in the woods, singing and joking about sexually related matters, and tussling and rolling around in the grass like young pups. In the second section, they arrive at a swimming hole, where they are determined to swim despite its no-trespassing sign, which clearly tells them that "Ol man Harvey don erllow no niggers t swim in this hole." After playfully frolicking in the water, the boys dry themselves in the sun—black and naked. Their innocence is accentuated by the black winged butterfly hovering near the water, the droning of a bee, and the twittering of sparrows. As the sun dries their skins and warms their blood, they laugh nervously about the risk they are taking, when a white woman suddenly appears.

This woman's sudden intrusion destroys the boys' innocent frolic, forcing them to scramble about, hiding their nakedness and trying to get at their clothes behind where the woman is standing. The woman screams, calling for her husband. As Big Boy dashes for the clothes, he is as frightened as the woman is and stops three feet from her. Just then, her husband, Jim, arrives; he is wearing an army officer's uniform and is carrying a rifle. He immediately shoots Lester and Buck; the boys appear to be headed for his wife, but they are actually running toward Bobo, who is holding their clothes. When Jim points his rifle at Bobo, Big Boy lunges and grabs its barrel. As Big Boy fights with Jim, he accidently shoots him. When the man falls, Big Boy and Bobo turn to look at the woman, who screams and falls at the foot of the tree. Big Boy drags the crying Bobo through the woods.

In the third section, the boys head for home, leaving childhood behind them forever. Knowing that they will be lynched, Bobo can think of nothing else. Big Boy clings to the thought that he must get home to his parents. As he stammers out his story, his father, Saul, castigates him for not going to school and makes sure that the boys did not touch the white woman. Other black men arrive as Big Boy's mother presses his head to her bosom and comforts him. Elder Peters confirms everyone's fears by urging that they get Big Boy away immediately, because there will be a lynching. Everyone understands that Big Boy is defenseless. When Brother Sanders says that his son Will is driving a truck to Chicago the next morning, Big Boy proposes to hide overnight in a brickyard kiln. His mother sends him away with hot cornpone, and he asks her to tell Bobo to join him where he is hiding.

In the fourth section, Big Boy runs toward the sunset clutching his hot cornpone. He goes over the crest of a hill and selects the largest of the kilns that he and his friends had dug the week before. Before he climbs into the kiln, he kills a big snake and stomps its head into the dirt. While imagining more snakes inside, he enters the enclosure and waits for Bobo, thinking over the events that have occurred. He regrets each and wishes that he had brought his father's gun—a thought that leads him to fantasize about killing several white men before he is lynched. He imagines newspaper headlines such as "Nigger Kills Dozen of Mob Befoo Lynched!" He smiles as he imagines stomping a white man as he has the snake. He knows, however, that any opportunity to display real courage and rebellion is only a fantasy.

When Big Boy hears a mob of white men and women looking for him, he overhears someone saying that they have already burned down his parents' home. He watches in helpless horror as barking dogs chase Bobo, whom the mob tars, feathers, and burns, after taking his finger and his ear as souvenirs. Someone in the mob says, "Ef they git erway notta woman in this town would be safe." Afterward the mob disperses, leaving Big Boy alone in his hole. As the mob passes his hole, a dog smells him and barks into the hole. Fearing that the dog will reveal his presence, Big Boy kills it and falls asleep holding its body in his arms.

The fifth section opens at daybreak, with Big Boy on his knees in a puddle of rainwater, staring at the dog's stiff body. He feels that he is waking from a dream, when he hears a truck approach. The driver, Will Sanders, opens a trapdoor behind his seat and pushes Big Boy into the truck, letting the trapdoor fall. As Big Boy rides off, he hears the lumber mill's six o'clock whistle. Later Will stops and gets him a drink of water in his hat. The story ends as the truck speeds Big Boy northward, jolting him, as he turns on his side to sleep. Initiated into violence, he is now a man.

Themes and Meanings

"Big Boy Leaves Home" is the first story in Richard Wright's 1938 volume *Uncle Tom's Children*. In his autobiography he says that this story poses a question: "What quality of will must a Negro possess to live and die in a country that denied his humanity?" His story's sympathetic, omniscient narrator focuses on the imagined threat of black manhood to white people, the irrational violence with which white people confront their fears, and the trap into which a black man matures. From the beginning of the story, the boys know that they will be lynched if they are discovered on the white man's property: Buck says that the no-trespassing sign means that there "ain no dogs n niggers erllowed." The dog parallel continues as Big Boy pulls off his clothes and calls out, "Las one ins a ol dead dog!" The white man kills Big Boy's friends just as Big Boy later kills the barking dog.

The boys' joking about the impotence of old man Harvey, the landowner, indicates that they also instinctively know that their threat to the white man is related to white perceptions of black virility. The white woman who inadvertently happens upon them does not stop to think that she is standing between them and their clothes; she is so much a product of her own social conditioning that she cannot control her own ignorant and unfounded fear. Even though her husband, Jim Harvey, stands behind the authority of his army officer uniform and holds a rifle in his hand, he is so helpless when Big Boy and Bobo confront him that he loses every pretence of rationality and reverts to fear and violence.

The only characters who take the time to think things through are Big Boy, his loving, prayerful family, and their supportive brethren. However, they all know that his situation is hopeless and that his only alternatives are flight, emasculation, or death.

Style and Technique

When Richard Wright lived in Chicago, he observed the callous brutality of a huge white mob that cut the heart out of a lynched man and dismembered his body. The fact that his story falls into five distinct sections that correspond to the five-part structure of a classical tragedy is a significant part of the tragedy of the circumstances.

The narrator skillfully associates images from nature with the boys' innocence, the lonesome train whistle that reoccurs with the unknown north, the battered snake with the fantasies of retaliation, the "bluesy" songs and spirituals with the slavery that still exists, and the truck with the freedom train of the underground. Wright's consummate artistry is reminiscent of the fourteen poems that he published in the two years just before he wrote this initiation story; its success encouraged him to continue to write fiction.

Constance M. Fulmer

BIG FISH, LITTLE FISH

Author: Italo Calvino (1923-1985)
Type of plot: Fable
Time of plot: The 1940's
Locale: Italian Riviera
First published: "Pesci grossi, pesci piccoli," 1950 (English translation, 1984)

> *Principal characters:*
> ZEFFERINO, a boy who is a skillful fisherman
> HIS FATHER, a man with a passion for limpets
> SIGNORINA DE MAGISTRIS, a woman saddened by love

The Story

The boy Zefferino is completely at home in the ocean, moving effortlessly through it and relishing the beautiful denizens that he hunts and destroys. Speargun in hand, he trails a bream underwater and discovers an enclosed pond. Here he finds not only beautiful fish, but also Signorina de Magistris, a fat woman wearing a bathing suit, who sits weeping on a rock. Zefferino's reactions are a mixture of sympathy and confusion: The sight of a woman crying saddens him, but he is unable to understand how the beautiful location, crammed with such a variety of beautiful fish, can fail to please her. Although she tells Zefferino that she weeps because she is unlucky in love, she knows Zefferino is too young to understand.

Zefferino first attempts to soothe his melancholy companion by inviting the woman to sample the pleasure of swimming underwater with his mask; when she proves incapable of enjoying this because of her tears, Zefferino switches tactics, hoping that the beautiful fish he catches will amuse her. He first catches a large silver and black bass and places it in a small, natural basin; but Signorina de Magistris is not pleased. Unhappy herself, she sees only the numerous tiny holes in its silver body made by sea lice.

With each new fish Zefferino hauls out of the sea, Signorina de Magistris detects the same indications of suffering and misery. What the inexperienced boy accepts as an inlet of unimaginable wonders, the heartbroken woman perceives as a "marine lazaretto, an arena of desperate duels."

After having caught or killed a gilthead, a bogue, and several other fish, Zefferino captures a big octopus. Reluctant to abandon his treasure in the small basin they find for it, Zefferino nevertheless swims off in the hope of catching the whole octopus family, while Signorina de Magistris stays and quietly observes the living octopus. While she absentmindedly caresses its coils, the octopus winds around her arm, seizing her, and she begins to scream.

Having ranged too far from Signorina de Magistris to come to her aid, Zefferino can only turn and observe that the octopus seems to be stretching out another tentacle to strangle her. Zefferino's father, who has wandered over in search of his son, easily dispatches the octopus with his knife as Signorina de Magistris faints. Zefferino's father has already cut the octopus into pieces when the woman awakens. Although Zefferino studies her features to determine whether she will begin to cry again, she appears able to suppress the overflow of her grief as Zefferino's father carefully explains to her the secret of a good octopus fry.

Themes and Meanings

"Big Fish, Little Fish" is a fable about illusion and reality, conveyed in contrasting perceptions. Zefferino perceives the world as an exciting novelty. "This was a place rich in fish, like an enclosed pond; and wherever Zefferino looked he saw a flicker of sharp fins, the glint of scales; his joy and wonder were so great, he forgot to shoot even once." A child, his perceptions are spirited and naïve.

By contrast, Signorina de Magistris' perceptions are darkened by her grief. When Zefferino first asks her if she appreciates how full of fish the pond is, she responds that she cannot see anything because she cannot stop crying. When Zefferino yearns to have her share his contentment with the size and beauty of the fish around them, Signorina de Magistris can only notice the evidence of suffering upon their bodies. Afflicted with an agonized sense of herself as victim, she sympathetically regards the alcove as a refuge for animals sentenced to agony, while Zefferino, secure in his innocence, knows only the excitement of the hunt and the dazzle of the moment.

Innocence and experience offer conflicting points of view, but neither adequately comprehends reality: Both are solipsistic and illusory, based upon expectations, falsified by projections of the self. Should the flicker of sharp fins arouse a throb of fear in Zefferino that perhaps a shark is near? It does not. Signorina de Magistris' perceptions are more knowing, informed by experience, but she indulges herself in a romantic fantasy about the sensitivity of fish, and thus strays into danger. Relieved because the octopus appears to be unblemished, she entertains thoughts of health and life, and thus carelessly becomes its intended prey. Ironically, her sense of herself as a victim seems to facilitate her becoming a victim. In the water, the fat woman resembles the big fish and Zefferino the little fish, but their points of view contradict their physical size. Zefferino views the world through the eyes of a hunter—a big fish—while Signorina de Magistris looks through the eyes of a victim—a little fish.

While Zefferino and Signorina de Magistris are one pair of opposites, together they present an additional contrast to Zefferino's father. The father, who is unnamed, never wore a proper bathing suit, and never strayed from the rocky shore; he appears as a human cipher, empty except for his passion for limpets. Having little identity, neither big fish nor little fish, neither hunter nor victim, Zefferino's father is comparable to a limpet, dryly tenacious in his hold upon his life: a survivor. Accordingly, he is incapable of fantasizing that the octopus is a melodramatic villain or a delightful spectacle. He perceives the octopus simply and objectively, and his behavior, in contrast to Signorina de Magistris' paralyzing hysteria and Zefferino's wildness, is precise and efficient.

The perceptions of Zefferino's father, realistic though they might be, seem somewhat alien and comical. Presenting Signorina de Magistris with the octopus to eat, a highly pragmatic act, appears strangely inappropriate because of its cold irrelevance to her temperament and her emotions. Italo Calvino makes the humorous point that the concerns of Zefferino's father seem insensitive and unrelated to human experience, and therefore somewhat unintelligible. In composing a fable about perception, Calvino concludes with an enigmatic moral: Since human beings perceive relativistically, within relational frameworks comparable to oppositions, such as big fish-little fish, they mistake reality for their own interpretations; however, reality beyond the compass of their interpretations, our own human, undetachable identities, would be foreign, meaningless, and empty.

Style and Technique

"Big Fish, Little Fish" unfolds in a series of visual images, almost like a film montage. The reader learns about characters primarily by seeing the world through their eyes or by looking at them, often through one another's eyes. Zefferino's father is introduced in "rolled-up shorts and an undershirt, a white duck cap on his head." Signorina de Magistris is first described as "a white hand swaying" in the water, then, as a fat woman in a bathing suit. Zefferino, himself, is all eyes: "From every cranny of the rocks, or among the tremulous beards swaying in the current, a big fish might suddenly appear; from behind the glass of the mask Zefferino cast his eyes around, eagerly, intently." It is, of course, a chance to gaze through his mask that Zefferino hopes will ease the ache in Signorina de Magistris' heart. Later he wonders, if the sight of a bass or umbra will not make her stop crying, what will? The pronounced importance of seeing for Zefferino reflects its centrality to the story.

Contrasting visual images provides for characterization. Looking at the captured bass, Zefferino is thrilled by its iridescence, but Signorina de Magistris grieves instead to see evidence of parasites. Zefferino joyfully proclaims his bream to be a champion fish, and the narrator remarks that it was impossible for the boy to imagine seeing a bigger, more beautiful fish; but Signorina de Magistris sadly observes "the throat that had just swallowed the little greenish fish, only to be ripped by the teeth of the spear."

Even Zefferino's father's only perception of Signorina de Magistris as "the woman," contrasts tellingly with Zefferino's fixed perception of her as "the fat woman." By having the boy consistently describe Signorina de Magistris as "the fat woman," Calvino playfully reminds us that this is a story about subjectivity and points of view. Among the many possible interpretations of Calvino's title, "Big Fish, Little Fish," one may refer to Signorina de Magistris alone, as she is first perceived by Zefferino and later by his father.

Michael Scott Joseph

BIJOU

Author: Stuart Dybek (1942-   )
Type of plot: Antistory
Time of plot: Present
Locale: A film festival at an unspecified location
First published: 1985

Principal character:
AN UNNAMED NARRATOR, apparently a film critic

The Story

The narrator announces the screening of a foreign art film at a festival. The film challenges the audience in several ways; it is shot in black and white, with unpredictable light values, so that it often appears as a negative. Shades of gray are rarely used, and the narrator speculates that in the tropical country where the film was made, everything is vibrantly colored so that "even vanilla ice cream is robin's-egg blue." Black, white, and especially gray are colors that the narrator apparently associates with the West, industrialized Europe and the United States.

The film's "only acknowledged influence" is an obscure poem by Victor Guzman, "the late surrealist dentist of Chilpancingo" in Mexico. Guzman's poem "Laughing Gas" has given the director his inspiration for its one source of color, that of tongues. Eventually, the narrator says, the screen becomes "nearly technicolor with tongues."

Although the narrator describes the violent film—which tells of a failed guerrilla revolt against an oppressive military regime aided by the CIA—in some detail, it apparently has no plot. The most lurid moment of violence concerns the tearing out of the prisoners' tongues when they refuse to talk. The tongues, which bleed in various colors, are kept in a coffee can on the brutal colonel's desk. A young private vomits as he buries the can the next morning, and then the sound diminishes until it is reduced to the noise of the projector. Then fragmented subtitles race past, followed by freeze-frames of photos of the poor and of tourists, then shots of churches and universities with occasionally legible subtitles flashing political messages, such as "Where there is no freedom words fill the mouth with blood." Following what seems to be blurred documentary footage of violent scenes, during which the metallic background noise increases to a screech, the film apparently ends with another subtitle: "Even the hanged have no tongues to protrude!"

As the lights then go on, the stunned audience reacts in various ways, many applauding as if they have seen live theater. The narrator then predicts the critical reaction to the film, which is generally favorable, but clichéd: "Uncompromisingly powerful, it demands to be seen. . . ." (from *The Village Voice*). The audience leaves as a final image appears on the screen behind them, "of an indigo tongue working at a husk of popcorn stuck in a gold-capped molar." In effect, the audience is presented with an "inside" image of a member of the audience doing something banal, despite the horror he or she has just witnessed. The film's credits list the actors, writers, director, and others, expanding to include the soldiers, students, and peasants actually involved in the world of the oppressive regime, the audience, and even "the myriad names of the dead."

Themes and Meanings

On the simplest level one might say that the readers and the audience of "Bijou" both get an obvious message about repression and violence, about the brutalization of peasants and "our" involvement in the cruelty because of the CIA's role in overthrowing the rebels. The thematic thrust of the film also concerns freedom of speech, so it might be argued that the film is an allegory on that theme. The narrator speculates that although the audience may gasp and stare in silence, they have been conditioned to accept, even to expect, such violence on screen. Of course the same might be said for the readers, who also accept the violence of this story.

While the film audience within the story reflects on the significance of the terrifying film they have been watching, readers reflect on both the content of the film and the narrator's description of the audience's reactions. In effect, the story is about being an audience. We are told that members of the audience think they are at the festival not to "censor but to discern." That is, they see their role as essentially passive, simply to respond to what they see, not to think about it or to take action. They seem most concerned with issues that appear abstract and "academic." Is the film's violence a "statement," or "merely further exploitation"? "Is this perhaps the Cinema of Cruelty?"

The fact that the audience is so stunned and confused at the end (are they angry at the "oppressors" or at the film?) and that one critic even claims that the "ultimate praise" for a film is that it causes us "to confuse celluloid images with flesh and blood," suggests how powerful art, whether a film or a story, can be. It implicitly warns us against complacency or neutrality (the comfortable objectivity of the audience and critic). The image of the indigo tongue working on a husk of popcorn mocks the audience, which at the end is reminded that they, too, are actually part of the human drama they have witnessed. The readers might add their own names to the credits as well.

Style and Technique

In *The Coast of Chicago* (1986), the collection in which "Bijou" appears, Stuart Dybek, a Chicago native, mixes realistic narratives about urban life, usually involving young male protagonists, with a few unconventional stories like "Bijou." Bijou is a rather old-fashioned name for a movie theater, and that is ironic, given the avant-garde nature of the film being described. Bijou is also French for "jewel," and the word can be applied to anything, including this story, that is exquisitely wrought or well made.

Dybek gives his unnamed narrator the distance, if not the "aloofness," of the critic and commentator in the first sentence of his story, having him use the French phrase, *dernier cri* (the latest fashion). There is something pretentious about the narrator throughout. Note, for example, his overly elaborate description of the "modern hospital" in the wretched country where the film was made: "In the modern hospital, set like a glass mural against the sea, ceiling fans oscillate like impaled wings of flamingos above the crisp rhythm of nurses." The second simile in particular is the product of someone who is being precious about language, as in the use of "siren" as a verb in the following sentence: "As ambulances siren, they flash through color changes with the rapidity of chameleons."

Although the narrator has keen powers of perception, he shows no emotion in his account of the horrors. "Scene follows scene documenting torture in the modern military state," he says flatly. Throughout his narrative he exhibits his knowledge of film history, from Charlie Chaplin and Orson Welles to Sam Peckinpah, and at the end of the story he can anticipate the phrasing in various kinds of critical reviews. That is, the narrator, who is arguably the main "character," if not the only one, in this story, is presented as not only disinterested or objective but also as uncommitted and uncompassionate.

Dybek's story exhibits most of the characteristics associated with postmodernist fiction: a prevailing sense of irony; rejection of a clear specific setting, conventional plot, or character development; employment of the present tense in preference to the traditional narrative past; avoidance of a moral or ethical stance; and the use of absurd premises.

Literary theoreticians have observed that any story is in effect a "re-presentation" of reality. The levels of re-presentation in "Bijou," however, are multiplied. We "read" the story of the film at second hand, while the audience actually experiences it. Yet the film itself, as viewed by the audience, is a re-presentation of reality, so the audience is getting it secondhand, which means we readers are getting it thirdhand, and of course we are well aware that the entire story is itself a re-presentation by Stuart Dybek. Part of what "Bijou" is all about is the distance that exists in art between the audience and actuality.

Ron McFarland

BLACK IS MY FAVORITE COLOR

Author: Bernard Malamud (1914-1986)
Type of plot: Psychological realism
Time of plot: The late 1950's
Locale: New York City
First published: 1963

> *Principal characters:*
> NATHAN LIME, the narrator and protagonist, a forty-four-year-old Jewish liquor merchant in Harlem
> ORNITA HARRIS, his estranged girlfriend, an African American widow
> CHARITY QUIETNESS, his black cleaning woman
> BUSTER WILSON, an African American neighbor boy during Nat's childhood

The Story

Nat Lime, a Jewish liquor dealer in Harlem, is searching for understanding, trying to explain his attraction to African Americans. He begins his monologue by describing his cleaning woman, the kind but puzzling Charity Quietness. He addresses an imaginary audience from his Brooklyn three-room apartment, where he has lived alone since his mother died. On his day off from his liquor store, he eats lunch in his kitchen while his black maid eats in the bathroom.

Although Nat jokes about this absurdity, he is hurt by Charity's refusal to join him and says that the rejection is her choice. He has offered to let her eat in the kitchen alone, but she prefers lunching in the bathroom. On an earlier occasion she accepted his offer but could not finish her meal. For nearly two years now she has eaten alone in the bathroom. Anticipating his audience's objections to this point, Nat says, "If there's a ghetto, I'm the one that's in it." As a Jew he has a historical right to define the ghetto, even though his joke implies a more contemporary definition of the word: the urban areas containing large concentrations of minorities.

With Charity, as with the other black people, Nat's attempt to develop an individual relationship fails, leading him to consider contemporary racial issues. His characteristic response to anything is to analyze it, and he tries to place his personal experiences within a larger context. In his defense, he offers two illustrations of his "fate with colored people." The first is the memory of his attempt to befriend Buster, a twelve-year-old black boy whose neighborhood bordered Nat's in prewar Brooklyn. Both were poor. Nat's father, a garment worker, died when Nat was only thirteen, and his mother sold paper bags on the street until she was stricken with cancer. At ten Nat was obsessed with the differences between his and Buster's neighborhoods, and he fantasized about them.

His clumsy attempts at closeness led only to one visit to the black family's home. This was Nat's introduction to a worse poverty than his, and he found it repellant.

Buster rejected Nat's friendship, leaving Nat puzzled and feeling guilty about having stolen money from his mother in order to buy movie tickets for Buster and himself. After receiving many gifts, Buster ended their encounters by surprising Nat with a punch in the mouth. Buster's accompanying personal and racial slurs bewildered Nat, who had felt a kinship with him. Asking what made him deserve such treatment, Nat received no answer. Even at forty-four, Nat does not accept the idea that gifts might be considered bribes instead of tokens of friendship. He tries to make a joke about his own ignorance of Buster's evident dislike of movies.

Aside from his late mother, Ornita Harris, a black woman, is the only love of Nat's life. At first, Ornita ignores him when he picks up her glove on the street. Later, when she buys liquor at his store, he recognizes her and gives her a discount. She is cautious about his overtures, being skeptical of "white men trying to do me favors." After Ornita becomes a regular customer who receives discounts, she eventually goes out with Nat.

As Nat describes their romance, obstacles to interracial relationships and his complex attitude toward black people dominate his story. This Jewish merchant who operates a liquor store in Harlem with "colored clerks" wants to see himself merely as a man trying to romance a woman. Ornita, however, is constantly aware of society's barriers as she falls in love. After their dates, she insists on taking taxis home, but when a taxi strike forces them to ride the subway and then to walk home, they are assaulted and robbed by three black youths as a kind of punishment. Nat's attempted explanation of his respect for black people only makes matters worse.

Eventually Nat's interest in Ornita moves from curiosity to genuine love. His marriage proposal, however, forces her to leave without saying good-bye. When her brother reveals her departure without plans to return, Nat is struck nearly senseless. As he painfully makes his way home, he tries to help a blind black man cross the street and is overpowered by a neighborhood woman who misunderstands his motives. Once again Nat opens himself to physical and psychological pain.

Themes and Meanings

A product of its time, Bernard Malamud's story poses a universal question. He published it between the time of the Montgomery, Alabama, bus boycott of 1955 and the passing of the federal Civil Rights Act in 1964. It thus appeared during America's transition from Jim Crow laws to the legal assault on racial discrimination. Although New York was then considered racially free, or at least indifferent, prejudice was evident in daily behavior throughout the nation and reflected traditional attitudes. By allowing Nat to tell his story, Malamud forces readers to confront the ambiguities and complexities influencing personal relationships in modern American life. Racial stereotypes still exist in these characters' minds. Even Nat, who sincerely believes he is not prejudiced, reveals ingrained attitudes through his language and his unintended condescension toward African Americans.

In order to highlight the lack of understanding in racial matters, Malamud holds a mirror up to urban society so that it can face a harsh reality. Stereotypes and fears remain operative although individuals seek to eradicate them. Nat, for example, is unaware that as a Jewish liquor dealer located in Harlem he represents the kind of exploitation that blacks feel powerless to combat. In their automatic response to Nat, the black youths damage their community and reinforce stereotypes. Only Ornita is willing to risk a personal relationship, and even she is eventually defeated.

The title "Black Is My Favorite Color" becomes especially poignant by the end of the story. The protagonist's fixation on blackness illustrates a much-discussed Jewish identification with African Americans and their shared experience of persecution. Although Nat does not seem interested in Jewish observances, he is reminded of his ethnicity in brutal ways. Can he move beyond this condition in order to search for the good? The story ends with such a display of Nat's naïveté that the reader sees that his self-image is still intact. Readers are left with the question of whether Nat will conform to suit society or society will adapt to the reality of his search for human unity.

Thus, Malamud leaves the reader with an enduring human question: Is there a place in society for a man who continues optimistically to search for truth? Or is society correct in judging such a man as stubborn and unwilling to face facts?

Style and Technique

The story is the monologue of a first-person narrator, related in a conversational style with some humor. Nat intentionally tells the reader everything he knows in a tone that varies from self-deprecating and joking to defensive, passionate, or matter of fact. He is unaware, however, of how much he unintentionally reveals about himself and of how certain of his weaknesses dominate, placing his good intentions in the background.

As a convincing and largely credible narrator, Nat describes in realistic detail the New York that visitors expect and fear—a city in which youths rob liquor stores, innocent people are mugged, landlords squeeze money out of their ghetto tenants, and altruism is suspect. The focus is on the black ghetto, seen by an outsider, a Jew who is himself similarly stereotyped by the larger society.

The naïve, even unrealistic suggestion of color in the title becomes a metaphor for racial identification which dominates the story's images. Just as blackness in a literal sense hinders vision and therefore calls for contrast, contrast between black people and white people becomes Malamud's technique for connecting plot with theme. Most of the story's episodes build around contrasting views generated by racial differences; in one way or another, each episode represents a larger societal issue. Images of blood parallel those of blackness and are equally powerful in conveying the philosophical issue undergirding the story: Nat's growing awareness of "one human color . . . the color of blood."

With these techniques, an apparently rambling personal reminiscence is transformed into a skillfully controlled journey toward a universal human truth.

Emma Coburn Norris

THE BLACK MADONNA

Author: Muriel Spark (1918-   )
Type of plot: Social realism
Time of plot: The 1960's
Locale: Whitney Clay, a fictitious English town
First published: 1967

> *Principal characters:*
> LOU PARKER, a housewife with no children
> RAYMOND PARKER, her husband
> ELIZABETH, her widowed sister
> TINA, her friend
> OXFORD ST. JOHN and
> HENRY PIERCE, two black Jamaicans who befriend the Parkers

The Story

A Madonna figure carved from bog oak is placed in the Church of the Sacred Heart. Its black composition and angular lines make it an object of attention as well as worship in the growing English town of Whitney Clay.

Lou Parker and her husband Raymond are an apparently happily married—though childless—couple who live comfortably in their Whitney Clay apartment. They have cultivated their tastes in an aristocratic manner which they feel sets them apart from their middle-class acquaintances. As Roman Catholics, they are troubled about their lack of offspring, but they are active church members and participate in several guilds and confraternities with fellow members and friends.

Lou prides herself on cultivating aristocratic sensibilities, but the narrator regards her not as snobbish, but only "sensible." When Raymond's automobile factory hires some Jamaican workers, the couple befriend two of them, Oxford St. John and Henry Pierce. The Parkers delight in their "equal" friendship with the black men and even take Henry with them on a family vacation to London, where they visit Lou's impoverished widowed sister. Lou, Raymond, and Henry are appalled at the conditions in which Lou's sister and her eight children live. Yet, when Henry attempts to compare the "slum mentality" of Lou's sister Elizabeth with folks in Jamaica, Lou is offended and insists that no comparisons can be made. After all, Lou thinks to herself, Elizabeth is white. Moreover, Elizabeth is not completely destitute since Lou faithfully sends her sister a pound each week.

Lou's enthusiasm for her friendship with the two Jamaicans soon wanes. Oxford seems too common and Henry too coarse. Meanwhile, the reputation of the Black Madonna in the local church increases. The Parkers learn that penitents who approach the unusual icon have their prayers answered and are granted requests. In particular, childless couples have in some cases been blessed with children. Eventually the Parkers experience the power of the Madonna. After Lou prays to be rid of Oxford, the Jamaican announces his plans to move to Manchester. Lou's prayers for Henry's welfare are also granted. Buoyed by the apparent efficacy of petitions to the Black Madonna, Lou asks Raymond to join her in prayer for a child. After fifteen years of marriage, however, Raymond is no longer anxious for parenthood and suspects that Lou is more interested in testing the Madonna than in gaining a family. Lou wins him over by arguing that God will not give them a child if they are not "meant to have one."

Lou's eventual pregnancy attests the effectiveness of the couple's prayers to the Madonna—until their daughter is born. The baby is black, so they reject it. Perhaps, the narrator suggests, it is risky for one to get what she prays for.

Themes and Meanings

Muriel Spark delights in exposing the foibles of human nature. In "The Black Madonna" she employs elements of her own Roman Catholic faith to reveal the hypocrisy of Lou Parker and her husband. While Raymond and Lou view themselves as "progressive" and open-minded in accepting Oxford and Henry as their equals, Spark uncovers their prejudices. The Parkers lack true Christian charity at all levels. Lou, it appears, merely practices acts of benevolence and prayer for selfish ends, such as using her friendship with the Jamaicans to prove to others how accepting she is of those who are "different." She uses the weekly pound that she sends to her poor sister to make herself feel charitable. Finally, she attempts to use her prayers to the Black Madonna to provide what she thinks she wants. In each case Spark unmasks the self-centered motive behind Lou's outwardly unselfish behavior.

The rejection of the infant at the close of the story gives weight to Spark's theme. The reader understands the embarrassment the Parkers must feel. Their friendship with the black men creates suspicion in everyone's mind, including Raymond's. Did Oxford or Henry father the child? Lou's insistent denials of impropriety offer no remedy for her shock and embarrassment. Consequently, the couple's shame is magnified when Lou's sister Elizabeth confirms that their cousins also had dark skins—a fact suggesting there is black blood in Lou's ancestry. The child symbolizes the Parkers' humiliation; it is impossible for them to see it as God's answer to their prayers. Their rejection of the baby amplifies the shallowness of their religious faith.

The linkages between "The Black Madonna" and Spark's own Christian world view are evident. Lou's priest tells her that as a Christian she must accept suffering, but Lou replies that she cannot be expected to "go against [her] nature." Therefore she resists personal sacrifice and renounces the child instead. Unlike the Virgin Mary, Lou is unwilling to rear a child whose origins are suspect or whose life may bring suffering and humiliation as did Christ's. In contrast to the Madonna, Lou is an unholy mother; unwilling to suffer, refusing to sacrifice, she rejects the gift for which she prayed.

Style and Technique

Neither cluttered nor verbose, Spark's prose emphasizes dialogue and action. Spark often employs a detached tone in her fiction that creates a distance between the reader and her characters. Such distance makes it possible for the reader to evaluate the words and deeds of the protagonists without feeling sympathy for them. In "The Black Madonna," the narrator adopts a satiric tone, for example, insisting that Lou is not a "snob"; however, Lou's behavior clearly reveals otherwise. Similarly Raymond's disowning of the child is revealed through his actions. He smashes the cot he has made for the infant and insists that blood tests be performed to rule out the possibility that another man is the baby's father.

Spark assembles her short story plots carefully; accordingly she employs a series of parallels in the structure of "The Black Madonna." First she emphasizes the contrast of the exterior and the interior, reinforcing the discrepancy between the characters' religious practices and their deeds. The Black Madonna is a "new" statue carved from "old" bog oak. In the same way Whitney Clay is expanding from its old village limits to a sprawling new industrial town. From these exteriors, Spark moves to a description of the Parkers' apartment in the new part of town. The couple's exterior seems attractive as well. Yet the life the Parkers have carved for themselves contains nothing new. Their Roman Catholic beliefs have not given them new natures. On the contrary, they harbor old prejudices and ignorance. Even Lou's "common" friend Tina insists that if the child were hers, she would "never part with her." Tina's genuine response contrasts with Lou's self-deception and moral imbalance.

The story is framed with parallel references to the Madonna and the child. It begins by describing the statue and closes with the rejection of the Parkers' child. After the child is born, the Madonna is no longer mentioned. Both figures are the objects of attention. Penitents and admirers come to view the statue, and in the same way, nurses in the hospital gather continually around the black child while ignoring the cries of the white infants. The baby is described as "perfect," "lovely," and "beautiful."

In addition, Spark's use of names adds to the ironic humor of her tale. Lou selects Thomas and Mary as possible names for her unborn child. After the baby's birth, Elizabeth tells her that their mutual cousins Tommy and Mary were dark skinned with "nigro" hair. Thus, Lou inadvertently chooses the same names for her child as those used by throwbacks to her black ancestry. When Lou decides that Mary is too common for a first name and selects "Dawn," Raymond complains that Dawn is not a Christian name but lets Lou have her way. Ironically the child Dawn Mary lives up to her name by shedding light on the Parkers' inability to love.

Spark's short fiction combines elements of humor and drama in plots that reflect moral truth. "The Black Madonna" demonstrates the danger of self-deception and Spark's distaste for hypocrisy. The Madonna's power to answer prayers can be viewed as an opportunity to extend either revenge or redemption to the Parkers. Spark's characters thus reside in realms that are simultaneously natural and supernatural, and both forces are at work in the plot to bring knowledge or enlightenment to characters and readers alike.

Paula M. Miller

THE BLACK QUEEN

Author: Barry Callaghan (1937-   )
Type of plot: Psychological realism
Time of plot: The 1970's
Locale: Toronto, Canada
First published: 1981

> *Principal characters:*
> HUGHES, a costume designer
> McCRAE, his lover of ten years

The Story

McCrae and Hughes are a male couple who have been living together for ten years. They are fastidious men and proud of their life together in their old colonial house surrounded by a pale blue picket fence. Although their neighborhood has undergone radical change over the decade, becoming a transient area with a multicultural population, McCrae and Hughes are acutely conscious of the significance of their elegant old house and lifestyle: "It gave them an embattled sense of holding on to something important, a tattered remnant of good taste in an area of waste overrun by rootless olive-skinned children." While their Eden has fallen into a wasteland condition, they see themselves as custodians of a bygone era of culture and beauty.

The ten-year relationship has lost much of the early eroticism of their younger years. Their lives have become highly structured by the roles each has consciously and unconsciously adopted. Hughes is a successful costume designer, and McCrae spends much of his time attending to household duties and functioning as a "wife" and homemaker. One of the characteristics that initially had attracted Hughes to McCrae was the Cuban heels McCrae wore and his lacquered nails. Hughes saw his role in their relationship as a husband and protector for the more domestic McCrae.

This formerly happy couple is not getting along these days, principally because they are becoming dissatisfied with how quickly they are aging and the toll that this process is taking on both of them, although they avoid any overt reference to their dilemma. They are alarmed over their loosening thighs, bony feet, and yellowing toe nails. They silently yearn for tenderness from each other over their melancholy entrance into rueful middle age. They feel lost and depressed in their separate bedrooms; they become embarrassed when they accidentally touch each other while having their bedtime cup of tea in the kitchen, as they had done for years, using their lovely green and white Limoges cups. They cannot bear their thinning wrists and sagging chins. They joke with each other about the possibility of bringing home a beautiful young man, but are keenly aware that such behavior would constitute a serious betrayal of everything they believe has differentiated them from the "vulgar" crowd. Change, more than anything else, increasingly troubles and confuses them because they are becoming aware that they have no control over it.

The one area in their life that remains invulnerable to the ravages of time is their expensive stamp collection. It has become a symbol of their ability to transcend time and to regenerate and preserve their own unique Eden, in which things do not have to change, do not fall to decline and decay. They have refused to acquire many of the new stamps because they are crude and lack the refined and delicate qualities of their older stamps. Hughes would sometimes hold a stamp up to the light with his tweezers and say, "None of this rough trade for us."

One day, as they are browsing in a stamp store in a downtown area, they each experience a major epiphany when they come across an expensive stamp of Queen Victoria in her widows' weeds. McCrae expresses a great desire to have "that little black sweetheart." When the owner of the shop smirks, Hughes suddenly insults McCrae by snorting: "You old queen, I mean why don't you just quit wearing those goddamn Cuban heels, eh? I mean why not?" He then storms out of the shop. When the owner asks McCrae what has just taken place, McCrae snarls at him and struts out.

Throughout the following week, they are deferential to each other, not wanting to ruin the Mother's Day dinner party they have each year with three other gay couples. Their dinner party has become a celebratory event that always leaves them feeling good about their committed and faithful relationship. As McCrae prepares the traditional meal of stuffed pork loin, however, he listens as the couples enter the house, hears a particularly stupid old joke coming from the dining room, and becomes deeply aware that their lives have become almost unbearably routine.

As McCrae stares at his reflection in the window over the sink, he undergoes a second threshold experience. He takes a plastic slipcase out of a drawer and removes the precious dead-letter stamp—the Black Queen—and brazenly licks it and pastes it on his forehead. McCrae then marches into the living room to serve hors d'oeuvres. Hughes is stunned as McCrae announces, "My dears, time for the crudités." As McCrae passes the tray among the guests, he winks at the unbelieving Hughes.

Themes and Meanings

The theme of this brilliantly rendered short-short story is not immediately obvious, but after a few readings it becomes clear. Time as destructive duration—J. Alfred Prufrock's old enemy—is making itself felt in the lives of these two aging homosexual men. The crisis of aging and their need to preserve the best of the past have become almost daily preoccupations for both of them, as they see themselves and their world swamped by decline and decay. Their valuable stamp collection becomes more than a mere hobby; it becomes a vivid symbol of their need to preserve the values of their youth unsullied by the degenerating effects of a mindlessly changing materialistic world. Their growing dissatisfaction with each other and an alien world seems to find temporary relief in their discovery of a rare and expensive dead-letter stamp of Queen Victoria in her widows' weeds—the Black Queen of the title.

The figure of Queen Victoria in mourning becomes an apt metaphor for their waning relationship, which has been based on their mutual attempts to preserve their youth, their almost-Victorian lifestyle, and their value system. As the Victorian era was swept away and replaced by a prevailing philistinism, so too has time and their seedy neighborhood deepened their sense of redundancy. As McCrae stares into the kitchen window, stuffing the same old roast pork and preparing the raw vegetables and homemade dip, he decides that things must change, the old musty values must somehow be replaced or renewed. By pasting the Black Queen, which he secretly bought as a gift for Hughes, in the center of his forehead, he symbolically removes it from the sacred and timeless sanctuary of their stamp album and brings it, almost sacrilegiously, into the rough-and-ready world of the present. McCrae has, symbolically, become the Black Queen by humanizing that figure and releasing it from the obligation of symbolizing the bittersweet loss of a bygone era. When he passes around the raw vegetables and announces, "My dears, time for the crudités!" he is also declaring that he and Hughes must learn to live in the here and now. The word "crudité" refers to raw vegetables, but also means coarse language or offensive passages in a text. McCrae becomes the agent who rawly announces that they must face the harsh realities of the times and live in the fallen world. Humor, exemplified by satirizing the sacred icon of Queen Victoria, can redeem them from their Victorian values and lifestyles. McCrae's coquettish wink at Hughes may become the first step in the eventual acceptance of themselves as the aging "queens" they always dreaded they would become.

Style and Technique

The most impressive and effective technique that Barry Callaghan uses throughout this compact parable about growing older is the way he transforms the recurrent images of McCrae's Cuban heels, the couple's Victorian house, and Queen Victoria in her widows' weeds into deeply resonating metaphors for what the story is actually about. Their carefully tended old house becomes a symbol of their successful efforts in preserving the past in the midst of change. Callaghan's use of the stamp of the Black Queen becomes the controlling metaphor of the entire story because it symbolizes the couple's unconscious mourning for a genteel past that has disappeared; that is, a Victorian sense of refinement and manners that belonged to another time. The concluding image of McCrae "crowning" himself with the Black Queen pulls together all the images of the story into one, remarkable symbol. McCrae publicly identifies himself as the Black Queen and simultaneously brings that icon into the sullied world of the present, an act that becomes a crucial reminder to his lover and the rest of the aging homosexual couples that time is unrelenting and they may as well enjoy themselves as much as they can and quit hankering after their lost youth. The raw vegetables he serves to the guests become a kind of sacramental last supper commemorating a bittersweet but belated confrontation with the raw facts of reality.

Patrick Meanor

BLACK VENUS

Author: Angela Carter (1940-1992)
Type of plot: Fantasy
Time of plot: Mid-nineteenth century
Locale: Paris
First published: 1980

> *Principal characters:*
> DADDY (CHARLES BAUDELAIRE), a French poet
> JEANNE DUVAL, his black mistress

The Story

On an autumn afternoon, a tall, young black woman named Jeanne entertains her lover, Daddy. They are in a Parisian apartment furnished with Persian carpets and rare books. She is sad. Daddy tries to cheer her up with his fantasy about life on the tropical island where he will take her one day; however, she does not want to think about the West Indies and the old slave trade. She lights a small cigar with a discarded page of Daddy's writing and drinks rum. When he asks her to dance a slow dance that he has created for her, she strikes poses calculated to show her otherness. After they make love, they go out into the city, transformed.

Themes and Meanings

Halfway through this story, the narrator identifies Daddy as Charles Baudelaire, the author of *The Flowers of Evil* (1857), and the woman as Jeanne Duval, whom Baudelaire met in 1842 and "kept" as a mistress. After warning the reader that biographers know almost nothing of this woman, the narrator constructs an imaginary life for her. According to this story, Jeanne was born on Martinique. Her grandmother was a slave who was born on a ship from Africa and orphaned at birth. After legal slavery ended on the island, Jeanne's mother went off with white sailors, leaving Jeanne with her grandmother. When Jeanne reached womanhood, her grandmother sold her to a sailor, thereby perpetuating the slave trade. She was brought to France, where she contracted syphilis and entertained in a cheap cabaret. After attracting the attention of Baudelaire's friends with her raw sexuality, she became his mistress. After Baudelaire died of syphilis, his papers and books brought enough money to let Jeanne return to Martinique, buy a fine house, and live to a ripe old age. She also eventually died of syphilis.

In a note to this story, Angela Carter explains that several of Baudelaire's poems that are thought to be about Jeanne Duval are known as the "Black Venus" poems. Carter has absorbed these poems into the story, especially "The Jewels," which tells about the dance. Carter's "Black Venus" is thus a network of literary allusions. Nevertheless, Baudelaire fades into the background; all the story's attention goes to Jeanne. Baudelaire is referred to by name only three times in the story, and only to situate the poet in relation to his muse. When Jeanne is said to die of the "Baude-lairean" syphilis, there is the irony that she may have given him the disease, though he gave it a voice and made it a symbol of the "decadent" imagination.

Baudelaire and Jeanne are a study in contrasts. He is weak and fastidious, never going out without gloves, always afraid of mussing his clothes. Tall and strong, she enjoys her body and her sexuality. As lovers, he is slow to rouse, and she is uniquely able to arouse him. Different as they are, though, they suit each other well because both are exiles. He is out of sorts with the Age of Progress, as the nineteenth century was sometimes called; while she is far away from her sunny Caribbean childhood home and still farther from her African heritage. But when he watches her bejeweled body, and she feels him watching, they are transported to the earthly imagination of the poets; specifically, they are transported to Cythera, the mythical island sacred to Venus, the goddess of love. When their bodies are joined in the act of love, they undergo an alchemic transformation.

Carter insists on the economics of their relationship. Jeanne thinks she is just as much a prostitute as the women who dance for any man with money. She knows that "Daddy" likes to strike a patriarchal pose, and that he fantasizes about her as a slave. He likes to reject the morality of bourgeois society by publicly flaunting his black mistress, even in the company of his white former mistresses. Perhaps he is also fulfilling the dreams of imperial France by equating what is female with what is foreign and making both the object of his pleasure. Outwardly he is exceptionally eloquent, while she is almost mute. Nevertheless they are representative of modern love. Carter suggests that "woman" as we know her is less a product of biology than of man's fantasies. She does not force the point, however; she is writing a story, not a speech.

There is a traditional irony in the story. Baudelaire, the poet, finds his themes when he looks at a silent woman. His *The Flowers of Evil* is a product of Jeanne's fantasies. Carter takes the irony further by letting the reader hear Jeanne's unspoken reflections, and thus revealing to readers of Baudelaire's poems who their real author was. The final irony is that, although the poet uses his mistress as a commodity, paying her keep and demanding his due, she ultimately has a claim on his estate. His manuscripts become her ticket back to the West Indies, where she enjoys the paradisiacal surround-ings that he only could imagine.

Style and Technique

Carter draws many images from Baudelaire's poetry that capture the world-weariness that Baudelaire called ennui. The albatross of Jeanne's fantasy is the same as the bird in Baudelaire's poem "The Albatross." The ship of her dreams is from his poem "The Beautiful Ship." Even the real things in his world—the cat, the hashish pipe, the autumn afternoon, the rising moon—are taken from poems. It seems that one might reconstruct his *The Flowers of Evil* from the thoughts of this one afternoon, if only one knew a little more. Carter's style is close to prose poetry when she describes the afternoon. When Daddy tells his fantasy about the tropical island, he sounds like a doting lover and a hashish smoker. When he says that she dances like a snake, she laughs because she knows how snakes look when they move; they twist and jerk their bodies because they have no feet. Baudelaire's poem "The Dancing Snake" will never be quite the same to anyone who has read this remark.

The joke may be on Baudelaire, but the eroticism is undeniable. It cannot be called pornography because it unites two willing companions; it climaxes in genuine lyricism, not in four-letter words. Readers are expected to see what arouses both lovers, and what bores them, too. They are expected to enjoy Daddy's decadence—to know his "forbidden fruit" from inside out. Then, when the style shifts to straightforward narration, readers are expected to reflect on the economic aspect of Daddy and Jeanne's relationship—economic in the literal sense of housekeeping. Readers can see what each character gives the other and receives in return. If there is anything obscene about the relationship, Carter seems to suggest, it is the society that has made them exiles, a society that treats women as "only" women, and that regards most women as slaves.

Most of these parallels emerge only from reading "Black Venus" and *The Flowers of Evil* together. The pleasure derived from reading "Black Venus" the first time comes from finding that one is reading about a famous pair of lovers. The pleasure derived from later readings is that of finding how deeply Jeanne influenced the poet, and perhaps from learning how much Carter has influenced one's understanding of Baudelaire.

There are deliberate anachronisms in the story. For example, Carter quotes from a bird book first published in 1961, to help develop the albatross lore. She compares Jeanne Duval to Josephine Baker (1906-1975), the African American woman who became the rage of Paris nightclubs between the two world wars. Baker is as important to the story as Baudelaire's mother, who gets only the briefest mention as the person legally entitled to whatever the dying poet left. A fictional man who whisks Jeanne off to Martinique gains more credibility in the story than the real person who described Jeanne as a hopeless paralytic after Baudelaire's death. Literary characters, notably Eve and the Serpent in the Bible and Helen and Mephistopheles in Johann Wolfgang von Goethe's poetical drama *Faust* (1808-1832), become more important than any of the minor characters in Jeanne's story, for they are the literary archetypes that she and the poet embody. The truth that counts, for Carter and for Carter's Baudelaire, is the truth of the imagination.

Thomas Willard

BLIGHT

Author: Stuart Dybek (1942-   )
Type of plot: Social and psychological realism
Time of plot: The mid-1950's through the late 1960's
Locale: Chicago
First published: 1985

> *Principal characters:*
> DAVE, the narrator
> ZIGGY ZILINSKY,
> STANLEY "PEPPER" ROSADO and
> JOEY "DEEJO" DECAMPO, his friends

The Story

This is a story of four teenage friends who come of age on the streets of southside Chicago. In a neighborhood whose streets have no names, they search for something with which to ally themselves, a place to claim as their own.

Blight is everywhere; they appropriate the word into their vocabulary so that it—the word "blight" itself—becomes the definitive influence on their world. When their neighborhood is proclaimed an Official Blight Area, they change the name of their band from the No Names to the Blighters. Baptized in the good name of blight, the Blighters know firsthand the beauty buried underneath the buildings boarded up and blackened by arson, with bulldozers waiting in the wake. Blight is a state of mind, a level of consciousness and perception, and the Blighters—Ziggy, Pepper, Deejo, and Dave—have heard "the music of viaducts"; they have been to "churches where saints winked."

A series of anecdotal digressions weaves an interrelated mosaic of visual impressions that all rise out of a shared sense of place: a Chicago that owes more to invention and the imagination than it does to the restrictions of a realistically detailed map. The narrative focus shifts from character to character, offering glimpses that range from the magically fantastic to gritty urban realism. Between two mid-century wars— Korea and Vietnam—the Blighters begin to see the world in a new light: a movement from innocence to experience. Early in the narrative, the Blighters consider the men returning from fighting in Korea as "our heroes." Eventually, the Blighters go their separate ways. Ziggy decides to become a Trappist monk and hitchhikes to the monastery down in Gethsemane, Kentucky. Pepper joins the Marines after his pregnant girlfriend, Linda Molina, moves to Texas to live with relatives. Deejo grows his beard and hair long and enjoys some local musical notoriety by recording a record that he persuades several southside bartenders to put in their jukeboxes. Dave, the narrator, eludes the military draft by hiding out in college, where he is thrust back into the past when a professor reads Percy Bysshe Shelley's "Ode to a Skylark" (1820)—a poem that begins "Hail to thee, blithe spirit"—in a way that makes "blithe spirit" sound like "blight spirit." During the spring, Dave takes the El train back to the old neighborhood, "back to blight." He finds that the neighborhood is "mostly Mexican," but the bars still have their old names. In a world in which everything is at once familiar and strange, Dave has a moment of ecstasy, "as if I'd wandered into an Official Blithe Area," as if the blight of his childhood has been mythically transformed, by memory and forgetting, into a city of bliss.

Themes and Meanings

In "Blight," Stuart Dybek explores the relationship between identity and perception. His characters see themselves in relation to how they see their world—how others tell them how to view their world. Ever "since blight had been declared we were trying . . . to determine if anything had been changed, or at least appeared different." But in truth nothing has changed. It is the same old place, the same impersonally numbered streets of southside Chicago. The only significant difference is that the world has been given a name, a name that "sounded serious." What has defined them—though they do not yet know it—are all those "familiar things we didn't have names for": the bars and churches, drunks and junkmen who push wobbly carts up and down the streets and alleyways collecting rags and scraps of metal. Dybek beautifully transmutes the ugliness that is generally associated with urban blight into a lush, magical cityscape, in which rows of tulips "sprouted tall, more like corn than flowers." He grants his narrator the lyrical power to recall by name those images that inhabited and shaped his sense of self. He and his narrator succeed in locating a new language, a new way of naming things. They peel back the layers of blight so that rarely seen aspects of Chicago's ethnically mixed southside—a neighborhood put on the map by such gritty American realists as Nelson Algren and James T. Farrell—are revealed to readers in a new and wholly regenerative light.

Dybek's fascination with how the world is perceived is evident in the opening paragraphs of "Blight." Variations of the verb "to see" appear in thirteen of the story's first twenty-one sentences. Dybek's landlocked "coast of Chicago" is the kind of place in which reality is not always what it seems. What some might consider to be a blight zone is also a place where "people had managed to wedge in their everyday lives." In his fiction, Dybek straddles the border between appearance and reality. He brings a world that is oftentimes seen through conflicting pairs of eyes into focus. He urges his readers not only to look, but to see.

Style and Technique

Blight, Deejo's never-to-be-finished Beat novel, opens with the line, "The dawn rises like sick old men playing on the rooftops in their underwear." His second sentence, which runs twenty loose-leaf pages scribbled in ballpoint, shifts the focus away from the sick old men by describing "an epic battle between a spider and a caterpillar." As Dybek's narrator of "Blight" points out, "It seemed as though Deejo had launched into a digression before the novel had even begun." He also wants it known that it is not Deejo's "digressing that bothered us. That was how we all told stories," including Dybek himself.

Dybek's digressions are intentional—a stylistic device that serves to widen the scope of the story much as the characters themselves undergo an expansive growth of their perceptive powers as they migrate out of childhood, backward and forward through adolescence, and into the world of adults. Just as "Blight" stretches and challenges its own boundaries as a story through digression, its characters begin to step further outside—they too begin to challenge, to see a way to step out through—the confines of their world: outside the neighborhood of childhood. The anecdotal nature of this story spools the narrative line outward and sideways at the same time, as if each digression, like each character, is threatening to break out, branching off into its own territory, its own story. Dybek brings it all back together, however, with the recurring refrain: "Back to blight."

In stories, digressions are often perceived as distractions, a failure on the part of the writer to tell a story straightforwardly, from beginning to end, without breaking the reader out of what one critic calls "the fictional dream." In "Blight," Dybek employs a digressive, kaleidoscopic method of storytelling that gives the world and the story's narrative structure a jazzy, rhythmic, point-counterpoint quality that is more often found in music. "Blight" thus reads much like a song: a rarely heard B-side from a time when "rock and roll was being perfected."

Peter Markus

THE BLIND MAN

Author: D. H. Lawrence (1885-1930)
Type of plot: Psychological realism
Time of plot: Shortly after World War I
Locale: The English Midlands
First published: 1922

> *Principal characters:*
> MAURICE PERVIN, a farmer blinded at Flanders
> ISABEL PERVIN, his wife
> BERTRAM ("BERTIE") REID, Isabel's friend from childhood

The Story

Maurice Pervin, a world war veteran, has settled on a farm in the English Midlands after being blinded in combat during his second tour of army duty in Flanders. He and his wife, Isabel, have employed a tenant couple to manage the farm. Maurice discusses details of production with his manager and assists him with such tasks as attending to the domestic animals, while Isabel continues to review books for a Scottish newspaper. She is pregnant and the Pervins are both anxious about the child because their first-born died in infancy during Maurice's initial posting in France. During the year that the Pervins have been living on the farm, a wonderful intimacy has developed between them as Isabel has devoted herself to her husband's needs, and their "connubial absorption" has effectively shut out the world beyond the farm. Isabel has joined Maurice in a private realm of solitude approximating the darkness of his existence, and she shares to some extent his "dark, palpable joy," but the absence of any contact with society has also produced a void within her, inducing a feeling of exhaustion and emptiness. When Maurice is periodically struck with devastating depressions that cause him to question his value as a man following his loss of vision, Isabel finds it impossible to be with him in spite of her professed commitment.

At this crucial juncture in the Pervins' lives, one of Isabel's old acquaintances, Bertie Reid, a Scottish barrister, arrives for a visit. He and Isabel have shared a cerebral friendship—an instinctive understanding—since childhood, and Isabel is eager to renew their sprightly conversation and become involved with someone who is actively participating in a social flow. Reid is almost a polar opposite of Maurice, witty, quick, and ironical in contrast to Maurice's more direct, methodical manner. He is also small, thin, and wispy, whereas Maurice exudes strength and has a prepossessing physical presence. Although the two men have never gotten along, they are willing to try to establish some kind of friendship for Isabel's sake. She has a feeling that they should get on together, but many impediments prevent this from happening.

When Reid arrives, he and Isabel immediately resume an easy familiarity that tends to exclude Maurice. Reid is both fascinated and repulsed by Maurice and his wound, and Isabel is torn between her pleasure in Reid's company and a realization that her fortress of solitude with Maurice has been invaded. Her attitude toward Reid has always been a mixture of delight at his polished, cosmopolitan style and contempt for his lack of sexuality. She knows that Reid thought of himself as neuter at the center of his being. She appreciates Reid's attempt to understand Maurice's loss, but knows that he cannot understand Maurice's compensatory sensual deepening, a quality that Isabel finds inexplicably thrilling. During most of the evening, Maurice remains quiet, eventually excusing himself to attend to farm matters, but he actually seeks the relief of his own special place, the barn where he knows every turn and corner and where the animal life is exhilarating, the elements of the weather refreshing.

As the night winds on and Isabel begins to find Reid's chatter tiresome, she asks Reid to bring Maurice back from the stable. The moment that Reid steps outside, it is clear that he has left the protective sanctuary of his indoor world and entered an alien environment, the natural world of elemental forces in which Maurice thrives. Repelled by the farm animals, Reid tries to overcome his uneasiness in Maurice's presence and real conversation begins. Both men are tentative, but Maurice clearly has not had an opportunity to air his fears about being a dead weight, and correctly deduces that Reid understands Isabel well enough to assess his concerns. Encouraged by Reid's reassurance, Maurice makes a request that is essentially an attempt to extend the aura of intimacy that he shares with Isabel to include Reid. First, he asks Reid if his scar is shocking. Reid's candid reply is taken as a willingness to continue, and Maurice then asks if he may touch the barrister, the farmer's way of seeing and knowing. For Maurice, this is a gesture of love; to Reid, it is a threat of psychic annihilation. Nevertheless, "out of very philanthropy" indicating some generosity of spirit, Reid permits Maurice to grasp his head and then complies with a request to place his own hand on Maurice's disfigured eye-sockets. This is a moment of dramatic intensity that penetrates to the inner core of both men's primal selves.

When they return to the house, Maurice tells Isabel that they have become friends because he has made the kind of physical contact that is his means of expressing hot, poignant love. Isabel is pleased but befuddled, because she can see that Reid has undergone a devastating experience that has destroyed his composure and left him with "one desire—to escape from this intimacy." The last sentence of the story describes Reid as "a mollusc whose shell is broken."

Themes and Meanings

Although D. H. Lawrence was an intelligent man with a solid grasp of European cultural history, he admired the instinctual wisdom of unlettered men who lived unreflective and untroubled lives in close contact with the natural world. "The Blind Man" is an exploration of two forms of male behavior, which represented for Lawrence the extreme tendencies of masculine identity. The essential difference between the men is in their response to the woman they both cherish. Without directly supporting either man's position completely, it is obvious that Lawrence is much more sympathetic to Maurice, but that he does not consider Maurice a complete or fully formed individual, or condemn Reid as one without any estimable qualities.

Maurice is the embodiment of Lawrence's lifelong love for the features of the

English countryside, of his belief in the possibilities of illumination through sexual intimacy, and of his fascination with a special kind of brotherhood among men. Maurice's strong contact with the earth gives him an elemental strength anchored in something fundamental, and his intelligence and over-sensitive demeanor are part of his blood prescience, a form of insight not readily appreciated by conventional society. His loss of vision, however, is indicative of Lawrence's concern about a total reliance on "blood contact with the substantial world" and the devastating term "cancelled" shows both Lawrence's fear that such a man has no place in the modern world and his knowledge of the importance of his own intellectual aspirations.

Bertie Reid—whose first name echoes Lawrence's middle name, "Herbert," as a clue to Lawrence's intentions—is conceived as an attempt to confront some of the things about which Lawrence was ambivalent, just as Isabel both admires and despises him. Reid's cleverness, his facility with the etiquette of polite society, his status as a "*littérateur* of high repute," and his financial success are attributes that Lawrence envied, even as he disliked many of those who had them. Reid's almost literal obliteration at Maurice's hand and his designation as a neuter illustrate Lawrence's dismissal of a cultivation that is divorced from corporeal reality, and his reed-thin airiness is much less appealing than Maurice's earth-bound mental slowness.

Isabel is appropriately feminine in the context of her era, "rich with approaching maternity" and is responsive to Maurice's earthy passion, but her artistic inclination is her most interesting facet. The men are too rigidly compartmentalized for any real merging of interests, and Isabel cannot reconcile the extremities that they represent. She is the symbolic union of their realms, responsive to Reid's cultured sensibility, slightly fearful but still excited in "the animal grossness" of Maurice's dark lair, and able to draw Maurice happily into her delicate parlor. For Lawrence, she is the theoretical fusion of mind and skin that he envisioned as the result of the application of an artistic consciousness to the natural world. His portrait of her is sympathetic, since he endorses her creative aspirations and his version of her femininity. She is an early conception of the fully integrated personality that he tried to imagine in his later work.

Style and Technique

That a story written in the first quarter of the twentieth century could endure until the century's end is a testament to the psychological insight and mastery of craft that D. H. Lawrence possessed. Writing at a time when the short story was still a relatively new form for serious writers, Lawrence introduced many of the motifs that are now considered essential characteristics of traditional short fiction. His ability to invest archetypal patterns of behavior with singular humanity, to evoke a world of sensual resonance through poetic language, and to shape a mood of psychological authenticity through dialogue and detailed description of settings are among the reasons his classically constructed stories retain their freshness and narrative excitement.

Leon Lewis

THE BLOODY CHAMBER

Author: Angela Carter (1940-1992)
Type of plot: Fantasy
Time of plot: The twentieth century
Locale: Paris and Brittany
First published: 1979

> *Principal characters:*
> THE NARRATOR, the protagonist, a gifted young pianist
> THE MARQUIS, her wealthy sophisticated husband, whose
> first three wives have died
> HER WIDOWED MOTHER, a brave and strong woman
> JEAN-YVES, a blind piano tuner

The Story

An anonymous narrator remembers her wedding night and the events that ensued. On that night she lies in her train berth too excited to sleep, as she goes from her mother's small Paris apartment to the Breton castle of the man she has just married. Her husband sleeps in an adjoining berth; they have agreed to delay consummating the marriage until they arrive at the castle.

The narrator scarcely knows her husband, except for the facts that he is older, richer, and more experienced than she. She is only seventeen, and quite innocent, whereas the Marquis has already been married three times. She does not love him, she tells her mother; but she does want to marry him. She remembers when he took her to the opera the night before the wedding. He insisted that she wear one particular item from the trousseau he had bought—a thin white muslin shift, tied under the breast—as well as his wedding gift, a choker of rubies that resembles "an exquisitely precious slit throat." When he stared lasciviously at her, she averted her eyes until she caught sight of herself in a mirror, suddenly seeing her own body through his eyes and sensing in herself, for the first time, "a potentiality for corruption."

At dawn they arrive at his castle, which the tide cuts off from the mainland half of each day. Her husband introduces her to the sinister housekeeper, displays his other wedding presents—a piano and a portrait of St. Cecila—and leads her to a bedroom filled with mirrors, funereal lilies, and an enormous bed. There he undresses her, examines her, and fondles her until she begins to respond. Suddenly, he leaves her to explore the house on her own while he attends to some business. In the music room, she discovers that her new piano is out of tune. In the library she discovers a collection of pornography. When her husband finds her there, aghast, he leads her back to the bedroom, makes her don the choker of rubies, and deflowers her.

After their lovemaking, the telephone rings: Urgent business calls her husband to New York for six weeks. After he breaks this news to her, he gives her a huge set of keys, one for each lock in the castle, so that she may take care of things in his absence.

One key, however, she must not use. He tells her that it is the key to his heart, or rather to his hell—the "dull little room" where he might sometimes go to imagine that he is not married.

After her husband leaves, the new bride tries to distract herself. She meets Jean-Yves, a blind young man hired to tune the piano. She then calls her mother and finally begins to search the castle "for evidence of [her] husband's true nature." Eventually, inevitably, she seeks out the forbidden chamber, unlocks it, and enters. There she finds the bodies of her husband's first three wives, each apparently murdered in a different way: one strangled, one hanged, and one pierced to death in the Iron Maiden. Startled, the narrator drops the key into the pool of the last wife's blood. Then she picks it up, slams the door, and flees the room. She cannot leave the castle, however, until morning, when the tide goes out and the castle is again connected with the mainland. To calm herself, she plays her piano; when the tuner creeps in to listen to the music, she finds herself telling him what has happened. Jean-Yves determines, by the sound of the sea, when it is beginning to recede. But when she looks out the window, she sees her husband's car heading toward the castle.

She tries to wash the blood from the key, but to no avail. Her husband demands the keys and finds the bloodstained one, his face displaying "a terrible, guilty joy." He presses the key to her forehead, transferring the stain there. Then he tells her to put on her white muslin shift and ruby choker and prepare for decapitation. All the servants have left, except Jean-Yves, who can provide little help. As the narrator glances desperately at the window, she sees a magnificent horsewoman riding furiously toward the castle; it is her mother. At the moment that the Marquis' sword is about to fall, her mother shoots him dead with a single bullet.

Now, the narrator tells us, she lives quietly and happily in Paris with her mother and the piano tuner. She has given away most of the Marquis' wealth, and his castle houses a school for the blind.

Themes and Meanings

A feminist revision of the folktale of Bluebeard, "The Bloody Chamber" emphasizes a woman's new awareness of female power, her own sexuality, and her responsibility for her own fate. One of the most significant changes that Angela Carter makes in the story is its ending. In most versions, Bluebeard's last bride is rescued by her brothers. The narrator of "The Bloody Chamber" is rescued, at the last possible moment, by her strong mother. The narrator apparently arouses her mother's concern when they speak on the telephone. In another sense, however, she grows more like her mother as the story progresses. When she finds herself in the bloody chamber, she remarks, "Until that moment, this spoiled child did not know she had inherited nerves and a will from [her] mother."

If the narrator discovers a new sense of women's power, she also discovers her own sexuality. From the beginning, her relationship to her husband is shaped by his sadistic voyeuristic desires and her arousal in response to them. (The imagery of the bloody key and secret chamber symbolically emphasizes the theme of sexual discovery.)

Gradually, however, she learns to distinguish between her husband's desire and her own. Indeed, instead of seeing her body—as manifested in mirrors, images, and paintings—through her husband's eyes, she inaugurates a romance with the gentle piano tuner who cannot see her at all.

The ending of Carter's story makes it clear that the narrator should accept some responsibility for her situation. The Marquis may be an ogre, but she is partly complicit in their relationship because of her avarice, vanity, and own masochistic desires. The story's disturbing last lines reveal the narrator's sense of guilt: "No paint nor powder, no matter how thick or white, can mask that red mark on my forehead; I am glad he cannot see it—not for fear of his revulsion, since I know he sees me clearly with his heart—but, because it spares my shame." The lines also suggest, ironically, that she still identifies with her physical appearance, that she still tries to change it, and that she still evaluates it in terms of how a man might see her.

Style and Technique

This story about desire and sexuality is a pleasure to read. Carter's style is sensuous, evocative, and filled with sensory descriptions, from the Marquis' skin, with its "toad-like, clammy hint of moisture," to the key to the forbidden chamber, which slides into the lock "as easily as a hot knife into butter." Such richly observed descriptions also serve to foreshadow the heroine's fate. For example, when she browses through the sumptuous leather-bound books in her husband's library, the titles stamped in gold upon their spines foreshadow her own story: "The Initiation," "The Key of Mysteries," and "The Secret of Pandora's Box." She idly turns the pages of another book, a book of pornography whose sadistic and misogynistic images also prefigure her plight; one is called "Reproof of Curiosity," another "Immolation of the Wives of the Sultan." These pornographic images are especially significant because the narrator becomes acutely aware of herself as her husband sees her. The emphasis on the narrator as a visual object—comparable to an illustration out of one of her husband's books—is underscored by descriptions of her clothes, arranged on heads, hangers, and shoe trees in her dressing room, and of her body, reflected in multiple mirrors in her bedroom. Moreover, the narrator thinks of her husband's first three wives—whose bodies she later finds in the bloody chamber—as portraits in a "gallery of beautiful women." Indeed, she describes them in terms of their appearance on the stage, in an artist's engraving, and in a fashion magazine. Her husband identifies her, apparently, with the portrait of the martyred third century Saint Cecilia that he has given her, and threatens that she will experience a similar martyrdom.

By alluding to other narratives, other illustrations, and other images that repeat the experiences of the young bride, Carter reminds us that the narrator's story is in some way a repetition of the stories of the three wives who have preceded her. At the same time, her literary allusions, in particular, acknowledge that "The Bloody Chamber" is itself a witty, erotic, and subversive feminist revision of "Bluebeard."

Susan Elizabeth Sweeney

THE BLUE CROSS

Author: G. K. Chesterton (1874-1936)
Type of plot: Detective and mystery
Time of plot: Early twentieth century
Locale: London
First published: 1911

> *Principal characters:*
> FATHER BROWN, a Roman Catholic priest and amateur sleuth
> ARISTIDE VALENTIN, chief of the Paris police
> FLAMBEAU, a notorious French thief

The Story

Aristide Valentin, the head of the Paris police, arrives from Holland by boat at the English port of Harwich. He is pursuing an infamous thief and con man named Flambeau, to whom Parisian reporters attribute numerous mysterious and unsolved crimes committed in the French capital. Flambeau has become somewhat of a sympathetic rogue in the eyes of certain Frenchmen, and Valentin definitely wants to arrest this troublemaker, who has managed to avoid arrest by the French, Belgian, and Dutch police. Valentin's chances of catching Flambeau seem slim, however, because all he knows about the man is that he is six feet four inches tall. Valentin certainly cannot arrest every tall man whom he encounters in England, but he is a tireless investigator. During his train journey to London, Valentin sees many short people, including a rotund Roman Catholic priest who tells him that he is carrying a valuable silver cross with blue sapphires to a eucharistic congress in London. A skeptic with no love of priests, Valentin regards this priest with contempt for revealing such information to a stranger.

After a quick visit to Scotland Yard, where he speaks with his English colleagues, Valentin formulates a plan for finding Flambeau. He decides to look for Flambeau in out-of-the-way places, believing that an escaped criminal such as Flambeau will avoid public places such as banks and railroad stations. As he eats breakfast in an Italian restaurant, he notices an odd, short clergyman who is attracting attention by putting salt in a sugar bowl and throwing soup against a wall as he leaves. The waiter who has served the priest complains about the mess. Soon after Valentin leaves the restaurant, he comes upon a vegetable and fruit shop where a short priest has just switched the signs for oranges and nuts and knocked the apples from a table. The upset greengrocer tells Valentin in what direction short and tall priests have gone. When Valentin learns from a policeman that the priests have boarded a bus for Hampstead, he commandeers a police car to follow it. He believes that the tall priest is probably Flambeau and that the short one might well be the priest whom he had met on the train.

Valentin looks for anything that will tell him where Flambeau may be in Hampstead. Soon he spots a restaurant with a broken window. The restaurant's proprietor tells him that a short priest has just added ten shillings to his bill to pay for the window that he was about to smash with his umbrella. Thinking that this priest must be an escaped lunatic, the distressed proprietor tells Valentin that the two priests are headed for Hampstead Heath, where Valentin and his English colleagues soon find them.

Just before the police arrive, the two priests have a short theological discussion in which the tall priest denounces reason, while the other explains that Christianity enables us to reconcile faith and reason. The short priest, who turns out to be Father Brown, realizes that the other man's attack on reason constitutes such "bad theology" that the man cannot be a true priest. When the tall man threatens Father Brown with physical violence unless he turns over his blue cross, Brown points to the policemen hiding behind a nearby tree who then arrest Flambeau.

The story ends with Valentin admitting that Father Brown is a master detective who has behaved strangely deliberately in order to make the police follow two priests who would otherwise be inconspicuous.

Themes and Meanings

Since his death in 1936, G. K. Chesterton has remained justly famous for the five volumes of his stories in which Father Brown is an amateur sleuth. The first Father Brown story to appear in print, "The Blue Cross" illustrates Father Brown's ability to combine theological insights with intuition in order to solve puzzling crimes. At first glance, little distinguishes him from hundreds of other English parish priests. His drab exterior, however, hides his profound intellect from both Valentin and Flambeau, who mistake appearance for reality. Ironically, Flambeau shares with Valentin the belief that Father Brown is incapable of defending himself. Neither Valentin nor Flambeau realizes that Brown thinks intuitively and accurately and is a wise and objective judge of human behavior.

"The Blue Cross" illustrates Father Brown's ingenious ability both to save his own life and to solve a puzzling crime. Father Brown realizes that the police cannot protect citizens from criminals at all times. He must take an active role in dealing with the crime that Flambeau intends to commit. His religious superiors have entrusted Father Brown with a valuable cross that a thief should not be allowed to steal. Father Brown senses intuitively that the tall priest cannot truly be a priest, because Flambeau relied on "bad theology" in affirming that Christianity was incompatible with reason. He concludes that any man who pretends to be a priest can only be up to no good. Although he does not understand at the beginning of this story exactly which crime Flambeau plans to commit, Father Brown realizes that it is not in his interest to be left alone for long with this potentially violent criminal.

Father Brown also senses intuitively that Valentin is not a totally objective detective who would go out of his way to protect Catholic priests. As Valentin and Father Brown travel together from Harwich to London, Valentin laughs at Father Brown, believing that the eucharistic congress which Father Brown will attend "had doubtless sucked out of their local stagnation many such creatures, blind and helpless, like moles disinterred." The virulence of his hatred for Catholics helps Father Brown to realize that Valentin does not care if a crucifix is stolen. Father Brown must therefore appeal to Valentin's desire to solve another crime in order to prevent physical harm to himself and the theft of the blue cross that he is carrying.

"The Blue Cross" nicely illustrates the complex motivations for human behavior. When he learns that a priest has apparently committed acts of vandalism, Valentin is delighted because he believes that sending a priest to prison will decrease public admiration for the Catholic church, which he hates. Father Brown understands clearly that he needs police protection, but he must act in such a way that policemen will follow him without his revealing his intentions to Flambeau, whom he properly fears. It is ironic that the skeptic Valentin unintentionally serves the cause of religion. For Father Brown the arrest of Flambeau is important above all because it permits a valuable religious object to be displayed at a congress of English Catholic priests. The arrest of Flambeau does, however, also possess broader religious significance. In later Chesterton stories, Father Brown frequently visits him in prison, and Flambeau eventually converts to Catholicism. After his release from prison, Flambeau becomes a law-abiding private detective who assists Father Brown in numerous cases. There are many different levels of irony in "The Blue Cross" and in many other detective stories written by Chesterton.

Style and Technique

Reading a G. K. Chesterton detective story is an intellectually challenging experience for readers who try to solve the crimes themselves; it requires pulling together seemingly unconnected clues. Many elements in "The Blue Cross" reveal Chesterton's masterful command of paradox. At first glance, Father Brown's behavior is incomprehensible, both to the other characters and to readers. The restaurant owner whose window Father Brown smashes with an umbrella believes him to be an "escaped lunatic," and the greengrocer whose apple stand he knocks over believes him to be a "fool." However, if Chesterton's readers feel that there is a method to Father Brown's apparent madness, they must try to discover the connections among all these paradoxical actions. Gradually, readers come to realize that Father Brown's actions are essential for his own protection and to prevent the valuable blue cross from being stolen by Flambeau. It is difficult not to react intellectually to many Father Brown stories because Chesterton constantly challenges readers to discover the true explanation for many seemingly unconnected and strange clues.

"The Blue Cross" was the first of fifty Father Brown stories that Chesterton published between 1911 and 1935. Chesterton wrote in an extremely refined and witty style which still pleases and challenges readers today. His extraordinary skill in combining intuition with theological insights into human behavior remains unique in the history of detective fiction.

Edmund J. Campion

THE BOUND MAN

Author: Ilse Aichinger (1921-   )
Type of plot: Fable
Time of plot: Summer
Locale: Unspecified
First published: "Der Gefesselte," 1953 (English translation, 1955)

Principal characters:
THE BOUND MAN
THE CIRCUS OWNER, who promotes the bound man
THE CIRCUS OWNER'S WIFE, who cuts the cords

The Story

A man awakened by strong spring sunlight discovers that he is bound, but in a loose way that makes him smile. He can move his legs a little, and his arms are bound to themselves, not to his body. Wanting to cut the cord, he finds that his knife, money, coat, and shoes are missing. There is also blood on his head.

After several attempts, he manages to stand up. Unable to walk, he hops away like a bird, and hears stifled laughter. Realizing that he might not be in a position to defend himself frightens him.

He heads for the nearest village. As evening falls, he learns how to walk in his bonds. He feels that he is in the power of the earth, which sometimes comes up toward him like a swift current. Before midnight, he lies down and sleeps.

The next morning, he goes through the intricate maneuver of picking up an empty wine bottle, intending to smash it and cut his bonds with a sharp edge. He is seen, however, by the owner of a circus, and becomes its chief attraction. The owner is delighted by the charm of his movements, which "seemed like the voluntary limitation of a high speed."

Everyone who goes to the circus goes to see the bound man. He is different from the other performers because he does not remove the cord between performances, although he can free himself if he wants to. To bathe, he jumps fully clothed into the river each morning. Since he never reveals anything of his past, and keeps to the same simple story of how he found himself bound, the villagers begin to think that perhaps the man has bound himself, or that he is in league with the circus owner.

As autumn approaches, the circus owner speaks of moving south. Then one of the circus wolves escapes and causes trouble in the village. No one can catch it. As the bound man returns through the woods from watching the sunset, he is attacked by the wolf. In one movement, he hurls himself on the animal and brings it down. As though intoxicated, he feels that he has lost the superiority of free limbs that causes humans to be subjugated.

At the next performance, the hostile crowd insists that the bound man kill another wolf. The circus owner's wife, fearing for the bound man's safety, cuts his cords at a crucial moment. Feeling his blood flowing downwards, he grabs a gun from the wall of the cage and shoots the animal between the eyes.

Eluding his pursuers, he comes to the river at dawn. It seems as if snow has fallen, removing all memory.

Themes and Meanings

The main interpretive question raised by Ilse Aichinger's story concerns the nature of bonds. Written in the aftermath of World War II, the story seems to be a criticism of the direction that humankind was taking. People were distancing themselves from nature, and society was becoming preoccupied with the invention of high-powered weapons. In taking this direction, humankind was neglecting and denying the positive aspects of its basic animal nature. Something essential was missing in modern society. The bound man reverses this trend by voluntarily going back to the basics, dispensing with things commonly considered indispensable: his knife, money, coat, and shoes. He is, as it were, reborn. He has no past because his experiment is an alternative unfolding of human evolution from the very birth of man. What if one could go back in time and do things differently? Would it not be preferable to remain in one's natural state, in touch with the earth and the animals, one's body in perfect shape, responding to one's instincts?

The bound man felt himself in the power of the earth. He was exhilarated by the rediscovery of his physical potential and felt "that he had reached a speed at which no motorcycle could have overtaken him." Human beings were not made to ride around on machines that give a false sense of speed and power. Aichinger suggests that the ultimate experience of strength or speed stems from self-discipline and practice, from accepting human limitations and pushing against their boundaries, rather than reaching for easy and uninspired solutions. The most rewarding sensations result from developing one's potential, from the pride of self-reliance, and from accepting and adjusting to one's natural limitations. One line in the story stands out both typographically and thematically. When the bound man swoops down on the wolf like a bird, and he knows "with certainty that flying is possible only within a certain kind of bondage."

Aichinger implies that people have lost touch with nature through an overly cerebral approach to all situations. They have money, motorcycles, and guns, all artificial solutions. With her subtle sense of humor, Aichinger shows that humans are incurably intellectual. The spectators at the circus ask "about the ratio of the cord lengths to the length of his limbs." She also states that the bound man himself poses the greatest danger to his bonds, for his head and neck are too free. On dark mornings, he forgets the cords, moves against them, and might be tempted to cut them.

The greatest problem, however, is that a human is a social animal, reliant on others, and always subject to peer pressure. It is next to impossible for an individual in the late twentieth century to revert back to nature. The bound man needs the care and protection of the circus owner, who in turn must satisfy the spectators. Only children try, unsuccessfully, to emulate him. Among adults, the opinion is that he should be relieved of his bonds and be allowed to join them. The story is thus an exploration of an idyllic retreat, coupled with the recognition that it cannot be realized.

Style and Technique

Aichinger's use of landscape parallels the evolution of human beings and suggests the passage of time. When the bound man awakens at the beginning of the story, he is outside under a flowering elder bush. He feels compelled to head for the nearest village. Later, as a member of the circus, he moves from village to village, and these are located along a river. He is thus symbolically following the course of civilization.

The scene in which he is completely at one with nature, in which he kills the wolf as one animal kills another, is set in the woods. He feels "tenderness for an equal, for the erect one in the crouching one," and nature personified approves of his action: "He could feel the softness of the withered leaves stroking the back of his hand."

Once the bonds are cut he does not return to the woods, but to the river. Time flows on. There is no going back.

Aichinger's sadness at this realization is reflected in her use of the seasons. At the beginning of the story it is spring. The sun is getting stronger and making life outdoors possible. All summer long, the circus draws record crowds. Then autumn comes. Not only has summer run its course, so too has the popularity of the bound man. Preparing for winter, the spectators are no longer attracted by natural man. After he shoots the second wolf for them, it is winter, with ice floes on the water and snow, "which removes all memory." Humankind has entered an unhappy age of sophisticated weaponry, and seems to have forgotten what it means to be truly alive.

With the contrast in the killing of the two wolves, Aichinger draws a stark comparison between the way people once lived and twentieth century life. When the bound man kills the wolf in the woods in self-defense, there is an exhilarating feeling of fair competition between equals. When the unbound man shoots the wolf in the cage, however, there is only a feeling of disgust that such a beautiful creature should be wasted in this manner.

"The Bound Man" illustrates the paradoxical position of modern humankind. In thinking that people have thrown off all bondage, they are now less free than ever before. They are experiencing the "deadly superiority of free limbs which causes man's subjection." Their civilization is a circus. They are their own worst enemies. With all their so-called technological advances, they have lost touch with the earth.

Jean M. Snook

BOY IN THE SUMMER SUN

Author: Mark Schorer (1908-1977)
Type of plot: Psychological realism
Time of plot: The 1930's
Locale: A farm in the rural United States
First published: 1937

Principal characters:
WILL, the boy of the title, a college dropout and lover
RACHEL HARLEY, a college student and the object of Will's attention
MAX GAREY, a college professor and the second suitor of Rachel
MRS. HARLEY, Rachel's mother

The Story

After dropping out of college during his third year, Will has taken a job in an accounting office in the city. He visits longtime sweetheart Rachel, who is still a student. Rachel is now vaguely enamored with Professor Max Garey, one of her English teachers, who happens to visit her at the farm while Will is there. The three lie in the sun near a farm lake. When Max reads poetry to Rachel, Will grows angry and takes a walk. The couple break up as an immediate consequence.

Themes and Meanings

The story contains several tensions and conflicts, including the expected competition between Max and Will for Rachel's love. This rivalry, though important, is secondary to the tensions experienced by Max and Rachel in their relationship as lovers. Also evident are conflicts relating to being in school and not being in school, having a future and not having one, differences between the country and the city, between biological love and spiritual fulfillment, and between youth and age. For both Rachel and Will, the breakup occurs with the utmost passivity. They accept their differences and move on, each parting in the interests of the other and denial of self, for the matter of peace and inevitability, given the differing directions their lives have taken.

The tale here is not so much one of a broken love relation caused by a "triangle" or by lives that have taken opposite courses; rather, the story is about the manner and necessity of disintegration of a relationship in which the two characters do love each other in both deed and fact. The story's primary revelation is that their parting is necessary because they love each other. They do not agree to separate because of the obstacles worked upon them by circumstances, nor is the second suitor, Max, a serious contender for Rachel's love.

The story has no surprises; the inevitability of the couple's separation is made clear by the tone and atmosphere from its opening paragraph. There is an overwhelming recognition that parting is the only way each of them can survive, that their love can survive only if they are not together. Just as it is understood that their love will not grow, it is clear that it will not be destroyed.

Mark Schorer makes explicit his most important theme in the final section of the story. Will realizes that "Maybe living is really a lot of little dyings." Accordingly, the dissolution of the relationship is not only made complete but is poignantly put into perspective in the overall scheme of human behavior and value. The characters must get on with life—which means they must stoically accept a permanent separation. They also realize that such events will happen to them again—that life itself is a series of partings that must be accepted.

This realization is accomplished after Will acknowledges that "We were both in love with much more than each other." In the manner of youth, each defined love as something far more important than the feelings (as deep and real and emotional as these are) for the other. All meaning in life for them became bound in the experience of the relationship such that their love has taken a life of its own. This third entity is what they mutually agree to kill off in themselves. The author reveals this as an act of maturity and heroism on their behalf, a decision that may leave them with something better, more lasting, and more meaningful than a youthful idealism doomed to failure. Rather, they now can retain respect for one another and for themselves; they are hurt but at peace.

With this realization, other items must also be voided from their collective life as they reassume their individual identities. Rachel will remain in the country on the farm, while Will must return to the city. Similarly, Rachel will remain in school under the influence of professors such as Max Garey, and Will will not return to them or to their way of thinking. Schorer also emphasizes a difference in their spiritual ages; until the end of the story, Rachel appears to be older than Will; these descriptions are reversed when Will comes to understand that living is a matter of "a lot of little dyings."

Will learns another lesson from his experience with Rachel. She acknowledges that she truly loves him, but at the same time she is honest enough to admit that she loves Max Garey more. For the moment this is true, but it is clearly only a matter of time—and probably sooner rather than later—until her relationship with Max ends as well.

In the meantime, each character is left only with human activity. They leave the lake, go back up the slope to the Harley home—to the lights and sounds of voices. They return to movement and understanding, and they help each other do so, even though their farewells have already been said and they have functionally dismissed one another from their immediate and future lives. Will, as the "boy" in the summer sun, has learned that mature people must accept having others walking in and out of their lives. That he is now left alone is not as important as the fact that he is prepared to be left alone in the future, time after time—to live through a series of "little dyings" until he finally reaches physical death.

Style and Technique

Mark Schorer tells this story entirely in a straightforward manner. There are few surprises, no startling character revelations, no unexpected twists of the plot, and no deep symbols upon which the meaning rests. The action moves slowly through the summer afternoon, carried forward primarily by dialogue, description, and details. Every aspect of the story is deceptively simple, since nothing much seems to be happening. In fact, little is happening, except to Will, who is learning a great lesson of how to get on in life, as well as what love is all about. What he learns is that it is all a matter of coming to an end and that one must be prepared to live through life by experiencing and accepting a series of returns to what he calls "aloneness." His effort in life is to get through these relationships—to exit from them—"somewhat less empty, less deadly calm."

Schorer's message is directly connected to his style of writing. The repetition of short, simple sentences (most of the story is dialogue between Will and Rachel) reveals and accents the thoughts and feelings of the two main characters. Their simple thoughts about love are expressed in simple sentences using only basic vocabulary. To reinforce this technique, the author's third-person omniscient voice replicates it. That is, the characters both speak and are spoken of in the same manner and toward the same effect. The emptiness and calmness of Will's existence at the end of the story are described in language that not merely reflects but enhances the emptiness and calmness of life.

Another effect of this simplicity in syntax and vocabulary is that the two lovers are depicted not as children—but as childlike. They foolishly believe that their feelings are complex, that they know things about each other and about love that others have not known or experienced before. Their conversation, however, proves them to be not unique but mundane. The tone of their talk and of the story itself exhibits the banality and blandness of real life in the modern world, a place where love is not and cannot be accomplished—but can only be lived through until arrival at its newest, most recent, advent of death.

Carl Singleton

THE BOY WHO DREW CATS

Author: Lafcadio Hearn (1850-1904)
Type of plot: Fable
Time of plot: An unspecified time long ago
Locale: Rural Japan
First published: 1898

> *Principal characters:*
> THE BOY, a young temple acolyte
> THE OLD PRIEST, his teacher and master

The Story

The protagonist, the youngest son of poor, hardworking farmers, lives in a country village of old Japan. Because he is small, weak, and bright, his parents send him to the village priest to be trained for the priesthood. The boy learns well and pleases his master in almost all ways, but he persists in one act of disobedience—drawing cats whenever he can. Although warned to stop, he continues, as if possessed by a spirit, to draw cats in every color, pose, and mood.

The boy's disobedience causes the old priest to send him away with the advice to stop trying to become a priest but instead become an artist. The priest cautions the boy to avoid large places at night and keep to the small. Puzzled by the strange warning, the boy reluctantly leaves his temple home and walks to the next village, where there is a large temple at which he hopes to continue his religious training.

He arrives at the temple at night, only to find it deserted and covered with thick layers of dust and cobwebs. He does not know the temple has been abandoned because a bloodthirsty goblin now lives there. Earlier, soldiers entered the temple at night to kill the goblin but did not survive the attempt. The unsuspecting boy sits quietly and waits for temple priests to appear. He notices large, white screens, wonderful surfaces for drawing cats, and soon has drawing ink and brushes ready. He unhesitatingly draws cats, not stopping until he is too tired to continue. Sleepily he remembers the old priest's warning as he lies down, so he crawls into a small cabinet and pulls the door closed before he sleeps.

Hours later, the boy wakes to sounds of horrible screaming and fighting. He cowers silently while the fight rages, and only ventures out after daylight streams into the room. He finds a floor wet with blood and, lying dead, a monster goblin-rat the size of a cow. Scanning the temple, he notices the wet, blood-red mouths of the cats he has drawn on the screens. Suddenly he understands the priest's advice, and realizes that his cats have destroyed the goblin in the vicious fight he has overheard. The boy later becomes a famous artist, whose pictures of cats can still be seen in Japan.

Themes and Meanings

In this fable, the fate of the boy illustrates the mysterious power of nature to save or destroy human life. This young artist has devoted himself to cats, and in drawing them, he wholeheartedly worships the genius, or spirit, of cats within himself. This natural genius guides him on his path to becoming a famous artist. First it sends him from his obscure temple home in the unknown village, and later it saves his life when a ravenous spirit, the enormous rat-goblin, seeks to attack and destroy him. The soldiers who earlier entered the temple at night to slay the goblin and did not survive the attempt illustrate the danger of facing life's difficulties without a powerful natural ally, such as the cat genius of the young boy, to protect and fight for oneself.

This traditional Japanese fable expresses themes central to the ancient Shinto religion of Japan. "The Way of the Gods," Shinto is a nature-based system of beliefs, according to which the world is guided by nature gods, composed of the powers of nature, and the enduring spirits of dead ancestors, who acquire supernatural powers after death. These ghosts continue to exist with supernatural power in the world, influencing the lives of their descendants and other nearby humans. Together, these spiritual forces influence natural events, such as rain, tides, harvest, birth, and death, for evil or good.

The Shinto gods and spirits protect and care for those humans who pay homage to their ancestors and the ancient powers of nature through prayers and offerings of food, music, dance, and other gifts. In Hearn's story, the cat spirits protect and save the life of their devoted boy artist, just as other satisfied benign gods and spirits look after their faithful worshipers. In contrast, those neglected gods and spirits who receive no prayers and offerings become vengeful. Like the murderous rat-goblin, these forgotten ones attack and devour those who failed to remember them.

The old priest, wise in spiritual matters, recognizes the boy's real devotion to drawing cats as his way of pleasing the gods. So he advises the boy to give up the study of religion and follow his true path. His warning to avoid large places and keep to small suggests that he knows about the crisis the boy will face on his way to becoming a great artist.

Another element of the story, the cats drawn on the white temple screens, suggests the way Shinto gods interface with the human world. The boy's drawings, executed with skill and devotion, become a medium of spiritual power: In the dark night, they come alive to attack and kill the goblin. Later these cat drawings show evidence of their magical power in the marks of wet blood remaining on their mouths. In this vivid image of sketched black-and-white cats with mouths dripping in red blood, we perceive Shinto's mystical interplay between nature's supernatural powers and human action.

Style and Technique

Lafcadio Hearn has described his style as simplicity and worked to touch readers with simple words. He hoped that his writing style would reveal meaning as a glass transmits light. His subjects were often the favorite folk tales and legends of common people, which he told in a brief and direct way to capture their mood and meaning without adding extra elements. The story reveals this direct style in a passage describing the boy: "He was very clever, cleverer than all his brothers and sisters; but he was quite weak and small, and people said he could never grow very big." Such description reminds readers of a childhood time when they heard folk tales remembered and told by elders during quiet evenings, or read and reread in favorite childhood books. A childlike mood of honesty and directness is echoed in the simple, direct writing style.

Another childlike element captured in Hearn's writing style is fantastic, vivid imagery. Consider the scene of death the boy finds in the morning: "The first thing he saw was that all the floor of the temple was covered with blood. And then he saw, lying dead in the middle of it, an enormous, monstrous rat—a goblin-rat—bigger than a cow!" This impossibly large rat surrounded by a huge pool of blood on the temple floor invites us to suspend our knowledge of actual rats and enter a lurid world of horrible possibilities. The scene vividly portrays the dangerous situation the boy unwittingly entered.

The same fantastic kind of imagery ends the story. "Suddenly the boy observed that the mouths of all the cats he had drawn the night before, were red and wet with blood." The realm of the two-dimensional cats and the magical world of goblins have intersected in conflict, leaving evidence of victory as well as defeat. Invisible goblins bleed, and paper-and-ink cats bite with weapon-sharp teeth.

While the naïve simplicity of style and vividness of fantastic imagery lead readers to see the story events in a childlike way, Hearn includes narrative details that give the story a realistic tone. An example is the fact that after priests prudently abandoned the haunted temple, the goblin made a light shine in the temple to tempt weary travelers to rest there. A light shining at the window is a signal quickly recognized and understood by weary travelers everywhere. In another instance of realism, the story ends with a comment that the boy's cat drawings can still be seen by travelers in Japan, adding a note of seeming historical evidence to the fantastic tale. These realistic details offer a comforting flavor of the familiar, everyday world to the eerie story.

Hearn's storytelling style evokes a mood in which the reader sees and understands the world as children do. It also evokes a feeling for a more ancient mythical time, when humans lived in an exciting primitive world populated by giants, dragons, and warrior heroes.

Patricia H. Fulbright

BOYS AND GIRLS

Author: Alice Munro (1931-   )
Type of plot: Domestic realism
Time of plot: World War II
Locale: Southwestern Ontario, Canada
First published: 1968

Principal characters:

THE NARRATOR, an unnamed eleven-year-old girl
LAIRD, her younger brother
MOTHER, a homemaker
FATHER, a fox breeder
HENRY, the family's hired man

The Story

An eleven-year-old girl living on a fox-breeding farm with her parents and younger brother, the narrator details the work of the farm: the killing, skinning, and preparation of the silver foxes; their feeding and watering; and the killing of horses to get meat to feed the foxes. All this work is a normal and everyday part of life to the narrator, who takes great pride in helping her father with the outdoors chores. She blushes with pleasure when her father introduces her as his "hired man," but dreads the dreary and monotonous work inside the house. She is apprehensive about her mother's plans for her when she grows older and must take on more traditional female roles. Though she loves her mother, she also sees her as an "enemy" who is plotting to take her away from more important pursuits. The girl also tries hard to avoid her grandmother, who constantly nags her to behave in more ladylike ways.

During the winter the family keeps two horses until they must be killed for meat for the foxes. Mack is an old and indifferent horse; Flora is a high-stepping and nervous mare. The girl has never seen a horse killed before, and curiosity compels her and her brother to watch their father shoot Mack. Though she tries to shrug off Mack's death as inevitable, she worries about its effect on Laird. She also feels ashamed, wary, and restrained around her father for the first time.

Other things are changing. Laird is now big and strong enough to match his sister in a fight. The narrator starts wondering if she will be pretty when she grows up; she tries to fix up her side of the room that she shares with Laird to make it more adult; she feels increasingly distant from both Laird and her father, but is still not entirely allied with her mother. In the past she fantasized about being a hero or a rescuer; now she daydreams about being rescued.

The story climaxes when the narrator realizes that Flora will be shot the next day. She is playing with Laird in the field when Flora breaks away from her father and Henry, and tries to escape toward the lane. After her father shouts to her to run and shut the gate, she reaches the gate in time to prevent Flora from getting away. When Flora runs toward her, however, she opens the gate as wide as she can. As Laird and the men go out in a truck to catch Flora, the girl puzzles over why she has disobeyed her father and sees that she is no longer "on his side."

When the men return after shooting and skinning Flora, Laird announces that his sister is responsible for the horse's escape. When told that his daughter is crying, the father says that "she's only a girl." The words both forgive the girl and push her aside.

Themes and Meanings

Alice Munro has often written about the seemingly unbridgeable gap that separates men and women. In "Boys and Girls," this gap is examined in the small world of a farm. Because the narrator is female, she is expected to behave in a subdued and frivolous way, to be devoted to domestic chores, and to ally with her mother against "male" pursuits such as farming, shooting, and heroism. The girl rebels against these stereotypes. Initially she identifies more readily with her father than with her mother, noting that her father's work seems important and interesting while her mother's is depressing. Her mother says that she feels she does not have a daughter at all, and looks forward to the day that Laird can be a "real help" to her husband. When that day arrives, her daughter will be expected to work indoors.

Several of Munro's stories examine the pain and necessity of children "choosing sides." Here the daughter is proud that her father appreciates her hard work, but she is ambivalent about the violence and callousness that is necessary to please him. At first, it seems that Munro intends the girl's guilty reaction and feelings of horror at Flora's death to be stereotypical "feminine" responses, just as her brother's casual acceptance is a "masculine" reaction. Munro suggests, however, that these expectations are arbitrary and hurtful to both genders. At first Laird is shocked by Mack's shooting; later he comes to regard the killings as a sort of male bonding, and he deliberately distances himself from the situation. His sister sees that her rebellion (opening the gate) is useless and only causes her to lose her father's trust, but it is impossible for her to ignore her conscience.

A girl, the narrator realizes, is something that she must become; her gender forces a whole complex of behaviors on her. She resists by working with her father, by slamming doors, by asking questions, and by staging elaborate daydreams in which she is the hero. Munro suggests that this resistance is eroded partly through social expectations and partly through the girl's reluctant complicity: She is torn between wanting her father's respect and trust and her growing awareness of the subtle cruelty in his job. She also grows apart from Laird; their final separation occurs when Laird tells their father she has allowed Flora to escape. Laird's betrayal makes her realize that she is no longer a part of the "outside" world of the farm, chores and violence; however, she is not yet comfortable with her mother's world. At the end of the story she acknowledges that maybe she is "only a girl," but she is unsure whether this label is liberating or enslaving.

Style and Technique

Munro writes stories about everyday people and ordinary events that trigger flashes of insight. Here the narrator is unnamed, possibly because her identity is determined so fully by her gender. Interestingly, her brother's name, Laird (a Scottish word for "lord"), also reveals his status in a sexist society. Other small details reveal Munro's vision of the splits between men and women, nature and civilization, and wealth and poverty. The "heroic" calendars on the wall depict noble savages exploited by whites; Henry sings a racist song; wealthy women who are far away will wear the furs that are bought with the deaths of the foxes and horses.

Munro's tone is ironic and deliberately deflationary. At first her narrator has grand dreams of action, heroism, and acclaim, but later the daydreams show her as a passive beneficiary of someone else's heroism. These differing fantasy roles show the strict split between the genders. Similarly, the repetition of the phrase "only a girl" shows how society puts an imaginative and energetic girl firmly in her place. The story's coming of age theme uses several traditional symbols. The horses, representing the freedom and independence with which the girl identifies, are callously killed; the "inside" domestic world is stifling, while the "outside" world of nature is harsh.

The girl tells her own story, but leaves many events to the interpretation of the reader. She begins by telling about her hatred of housework and her happiness in helping her father, but interrupts this with an aside: "I have forgotten to say what the horses were fed." This technique shows the girl's ambivalence about her father's work; omitting this important detail allows her to relate the story about the killing of Mack. The point of view is that of an adult looking back on her youth, attempting now to understand events whose meaning eluded her at the time. She attempts to analyze the reasons for her behavior, but admits that she cannot understand why, for example, she disobeyed her father—only that it seemed her only real choice at that time.

As with many Canadian writers, Munro's use of setting is crucial. The world of the farm mirrors the exploitative world outside. Like Flora, the foxes are beautiful, wild, and ultimately helpless against their fate. Like the girl, the animals rebel against their "use" by the civilized world, but it is impossible to escape. The father's change in attitude to his daughter from "my new hired man" to "only a girl" signals his acceptance of her secondary status in his world. Like his daughter, the father has also chosen sides.

Michelle Jones

BRAINS

Author: Gottfried Benn (1886-1956)
Type of plot: Psychological realism
Time of plot: 1914
Locale: Germany
First published: "Gehirne," 1915 (English translation, 1972)

Principal character:
RÖNNE, a young physician who loses touch with reality

The Story

A young doctor named Rönne is riding a train in southern Germany, on his way north to stand in for a clinic doctor who is going away on holiday. For the past two years, Rönne has worked in pathology. After having two thousand bodies pass through his hands, he feels strangely exhausted.

As he rides the train, he notes such sights as scarlet fields that seem to be on fire with poppies and houses that appear to be propped up by roses. He thinks to himself that he should buy a notebook and pencil with which to record things before they pass out of sight. He cannot remember when things stopped sticking in mind.

At the hospital precinct, Rönne sees only hospital employees and patients. His mood is solemn as he discusses professional matters with nurses, to whom he leaves such matters as fixing lamps and starting motors. As he works with patients, Rönne becomes both preoccupied with his hands and somehow detached from them. He deals with patients' lungs, or fingers, but never with whole persons. As Rönne becomes preoccupied with his thoughts, he finds it increasingly difficult to separate the relevant from the irrelevant. All around him, space seems to surge off into infinity. Often he twists his hands and looks at them.

Once a nurse sees Rönne smelling his hands and manipulating them oddly, as though squeezing open a large, soft fruit. One day a large animal is slaughtered in the hospital as Rönne happens to come along. As its head is split open, Rönne takes its brain in his hands and forces it apart. The nurse recognizes his gesture as identical to that which she earlier saw him perform.

Gradually, Rönne becomes irregular in his duties. When he is asked to contribute his opinion on a topic, he goes to pieces. In search of mental rest, Rönne walks in the gardens. There he feels the upsurge of life in the earth; however, it stops short of entering him. He retreats to his room, where he locks the door and lies stiffly on his back, allowing the earth to bear him gently and smoothly through the ether and past the stars.

Eventually the doctor in charge of the clinic is recalled. He is kind to Rönne, who tries to explain his obsession with his hands. After having held thousands of "them in these hands of mine . . . some soft, some hard, all ready to dissolve," he is now holding his "own" in his hands and cannot stop probing into the limits of its possibilities. What are brains all about, he asks. Weary, he seeks release. He wishes to be borne aloft by wings into the midday sun.

Themes and Meanings

"Brains" is the first of Gottfried Benn's five stories about Rönne. Together these stories portray the disintegration of the character's ego, whose foundations were built on fragile intellectual constructs, and his gradual return to health as he permits himself to experience emotional and intuitive interactions with the world he inhabits. This story has strong autobiographical roots in Benn's own disastrous personal experience in psychiatry—which was his first career choice. After losing the ability to concentrate on individual cases, he—like Rönne—was dismissed.

The central theme of "Brains" is the eternal dichotomy of human intellect and emotion: in biblical terms, the fallen state of man. Benn was not alone in the early twentieth century in stressing the inherent antinomy in human nature. Following a long trend in German philosophy, the novelist Thomas Mann dealt extensively with the conflict between the Dionysian impulse in human beings, which is characterized by the acquisition of creative, imaginative power, and the critical, rational power embodied by the Apollonian impulse. The very terminology makes clear the roots of this idea in mythology.

Another way of representing this dichotomy in mythology and religion is through the use of the right hand and the left hand, with the right hand representing the intellect and science, and the left hand representing intuition, emotion, the arts, and deep spiritual insight. It was not until the late 1960's that modern science validated this duality with the "split brain" theory. Intuitively, Benn has availed himself of this symbolism in "Brains." In the most dramatic gesture, which occurs almost exactly in the middle of the story, Rönne splits open an animal brain, which seconds earlier was alive. This is the repeated motion of his hands witnessed by a nurse, a motion that symbolizes his ongoing preoccupation with the nature and possibilities of the brain. After having seen brains in all sizes and conditions, he knows that they consist of twelve chemical substances, but substances which "combined without awaiting his command and which would separate again without consulting him." Science is inadequate to probe the essence of human nature. Disregarding a nurse who loves him, and who could be thought of as embodying one road through and beyond his mental breakdown, Rönne in this first story feels primarily intellectual frustration.

Benn's use of hand symbolism is extraordinarily subtle and accurate. Near the beginning of the story, Rönne looks at his right hand and muses that the "power of Life is so great . . . this hand will never be able to undermine it." The right hand represents science and the intellect. Rönne is taking the wrong approach to the fundamental questions of life. He repeats his mistake later in the story, when he taps a finger of his right hand against one on his left hand "and there was a lung underneath." The right hand is pushing down the left, science is pushing down intuition, and the result is singularly prosaic.

Rönne's urge to rationalize, indeed the weight given to intellectual fragmentation of the world into reducible discrete components by the mechanistic world-view of the late nineteenth century, is at the heart of his malaise, and the intellectual malaise of the first decades of the twentieth century. Rönne has fragmented his world to the point that he can make only the most infantile observations. "He lay on his back in a reclining chair, the chair was in a square room, the room was in a house and the house was on a hill."

Yet his situation, even in this first story, is not entirely hopeless. There is no recognized schizophrenia which does not resemble states that other cultures regard as holy or curative. In addition to showing that Rönne is on the wrong track, Benn points the way back to health. Not only do right and left represent the intellectual and emotional respectively, so do north and south, an ancient metaphysical construct brilliantly employed by Thomas Mann in his story, "Tonio Kröger" (1903), with which Benn was undoubtedly familiar. It is suggestive that "Brains" begins with Rönne "on his way north" while still attempting to apprehend his world entirely through the intellect. At the end of "Brains" Rönne longs to fall into ruins "of the south." The word "south" alone introduces the concept so important for Benn that means not only gardens, summer, and the "upsurge of life in the earth," but also South Sea islands, the simplicity of a previous, more primitive existence, indeed, the Garden of Eden before the fall. Yet one knows from Genesis that reentry is barred by two angels with flaming swords. The price of reentry is the dissolution of the personality. Rönne, at the end of "Brains," seems prepared to make that sacrifice.

Style and Technique

"Brains" is an exemplary piece of expressionist prose. As in expressionist painting, in which connections to reality may be tenuous and colors subjective, the emphasis in expressionist literature is not on the external world, but on inner reality. Few authors are better able to conduct readers convincingly through the enigmas of the human mind than Gottfried Benn. He not only studied psychiatry, but personally experienced the terrifying dissolution of the self portrayed in "Brains." His story is a case history that apprehends the experience as well as the symptoms. It focuses on experience and its manifestations; its more poetic passages have the ring of immediate experience about them. "Brains" is a masterful and rare exploration of the spontaneous collapse of the ego and a regression to the first questions of life: Who and what am I? There are also mystical concerns.

To illustrate the tenuousness of Rönne's grasp on his present time and place, Benn uses the stylistic technique he calls montage: The last few lines consist of fragmentary and disjointed associative remarks. Paradoxically, while reflecting Rönne's loss of more ordered thought patterns, this stylistic technique enables him, by dispensing with complete syntax, vastly to expand the range of his imagery, to transcend and trivialize his own immediate time and surroundings as he concentrates in an ecstatic rush of association on a wealth of feelings and sensations, on exactly what is needed to counterbalance his overly cerebral and narrow approach to existence. "Brains" may, in fact, be seen as a microcosm of Benn's work, of his cosmic overview and transcendent, at times humorous response to daily events, which are indeed dated. He deals with fundamental truths.

Jean M. Snook

THE BRIDGE

Author: Pamela Painter (1941-   )
Type of plot: Psychological realism
Time of plot: The 1980's
Locale: Cambridge, Massachusetts
First published: 1985

Principal characters:
    AN UNNAMED WOMAN, with a bag of groceries
    AN UNNAMED WOMAN, with a baby or a bunch of flowers

The Story

As a woman on her way home with a bag of groceries crosses a bridge, she sees a younger woman ahead of her cradling a bundle. The bundle might contain flowers or a baby; the first woman cannot tell which. She thinks that if she catches up with the woman and finds that it is a baby that she is carrying, she might smile at the baby, admire its hair or nose, and ask how old it is. Or she might say, "What lovely flowers," although she believes that this remark will not lead to much conversation.

As the first woman thinks about all this, the young woman stops and leans over the edge of the bridge as if something in the water has caught her eye. The protagonist stops also, sets down her groceries, and peers down to learn what it is the young woman sees in the water below. Just as she looks back up, "in a graceful curve as of a ballet gesture," the young woman throws the bundle over the side of the bridge. The protagonist tries to guess the weight of the package—does it contain a spray of flowers or a helpless infant? She cannot tell which. She tries to scream, but cannot, realizing immediately that whether it is a baby or flowers will make no difference, as she will not tear off her jacket and scarf and leap into the river. As she looks down, she still cannot tell if what she sees is a flower or a baby's bonnet, or if it is paper from around flowers or a baby's blanket.

Finally, the protagonist runs up to the young woman and asks what she has thrown off the bridge; however, the young woman acts as if she does not know what she is talking about, or as if her act is insignificant. She merely says, "I think it is going to rain again. It's ruined everything I planned." After the young woman walks away, the protagonist sets down her own grocery bag, "as if it contains bottles, quarts of heavy rich milk." She then takes a cantaloupe out of her bag, palms it as if it were a basketball and heaves it into the river. As the story ends, "she tries to remember the soft plop of entry, and failing that, listens for a cry."

Themes and Meanings

The protagonist's witnessing of the other woman's throwing of an object off the bridge is the single event in this story. It hardly seems enough to justify a complete story, even one as short as this. Yet, it is not the event that supplies the story's central interest, as bizarre as that event may be; rather, it is the protagonist's reaction to what she sees, or thinks that she sees. Her reaction seems more than just that of the horrified response of a bystander witnessing a possible tragedy. Her feeling that a baby may have been thrown into the river seems somehow personal; when she confronts the young woman, she feels a "new emptiness" and half believes that something has died for her. This is thus a story in which the motivation of the protagonist who observes the action is more important than that of the young woman who is at the center of the action. The real mystery of the story is thus not what is in the bundle that the young woman throws, but why the protagonist reacts as she does.

What makes "The Bridge" challenging is that in spite of the dramatic event at its center, it does not, at first glance appear to be a story that communicates any strong thematic significance. Like the woman in the story, readers are inclined to ask what happened. Moreover, as readers expect a story to have some thematic meaning, they ask what it all means. Finally, as human beings interested in other human beings, they ask what can we know about these characters. The reader's central interest is with the protagonist; the young woman who throws the bundle off the bridge is simply a catalyst whose behavior helps to reveal something about the protagonist, for it is her stake in the action that seems most important in this story.

"The Bridge" begins with a common human inclination to watch a stranger and idly invent a story about that person. When people do this, the stories that they make up are usually reflections of their own need. What can we know about the protagonist's needs in this story? One knows little about her beyond the fact that she has a husband, as she wonders what she will tell him about the young woman on the bridge. Moreover, the fact that her groceries contain only two lamb chops suggests that she and her husband live alone. The fact that she wonders how much a baby weighs suggests that she has never had children of her own. Although she thinks that the bundle contains flowers, she is more inclined to suspect that it contains a baby.

Drawing on these details and their implications, the reader might assume that the protagonist suspects that the young woman has thrown a baby off the bridge because that action is an objectification of her own childlessness. When she runs up to the woman, she experiences a feeling of emptiness objectified by the fact that she sets down the grocery bag because it feels heavy, as if it contains quarts of heavy rich milk—an image suggesting the fullness of the maternal characteristics that she herself lacks. Finally, her act of heaving the cantaloupe off the bridge as she mimics the woman's throwing off the imagined baby is an image of her own loneliness. It objectifies her own lack of what she thinks would fulfill her.

Style and Technique

As has been typical of most short fiction since Anton Chekhov first developed modern techniques, "The Bridge" communicates its meaning by simple description and implication rather than by exposition, by allegorizing, or by overt metaphor. The method of communicating meaning in the story is covert rather than overt, and readers must make their best guesses about its significance, drawing on the few details that the writer provides. What communicates meaning in "The Bridge" is not the time-bound cause-and-effect sequence of its events, but rather the implications the reader can derive from the details clustered about the protagonist. The image of the flowers floating on the water, for example, suggests the death of something, even as the image of the floating object resembling a baby's cap suggests the bleakness of the woman's emptiness.

Although subtle and covert, many details in the story imply that the protagonist longs for a child, does not have one, and sees the action on the bridge as an objectification of her own loss. The details of the story do not lead the reader to identify with or condemn the young woman, but rather to feel the protagonist's emptiness and lack of identity. For example, when she runs up to the young woman, she looks back down the bridge to determine just how far away she was, but she cannot find a point to identify her place along the railing of the bridge.

The protagonist's relation to the central action of the story is not a simple one. Although the protagonist identifies with the young woman when she first sees her, making a comparison between the way they are dressed, this does not mean that the protagonist may have killed her own baby, or that she identifies with anyone who kills a baby; rather, it suggests that the action that she witnesses is a dramatic objectification of her longing and loss. Her projection of her own assumptions on to the young woman and her invention of a story about a baby being thrown off a bridge create a hallucinatory, dreamlike effect. The reader does not feel that the story takes place in the real world so much as in a metaphor of the protagonist's situation. The final scene, when she picks up the cantaloupe and, like a catapult, heaves it into the river, is a poignant image of the human effort to cope with an event by projecting it outside the self and acting it out. It is an attempt to gain some control over the despair of loss and helplessness by acting out a metaphoric objectification of that loss. As the protagonist tries to remember the soft plop of entry, she listens for a cry that she will never hear.

Charles E. May

BRIDGING

Author: Max Apple (1941-   )
Type of plot: Domestic realism
Time of plot: 1973
Locale: Houston, Texas
First published: 1984

> *Principal characters:*
> DADDY, the narrator
> JESSICA, his nine-year-old daughter
> KAY RANDALL, a thirty-three-year-old Girl Scout leader
> SHARON, Jessica's psychiatrist
> MRS. CLARK, the narrator's den mother when he was a Cub Scout
> JOHN CLARK, her son

The Story

Today is the first whole day that the narrator has left his daughter, Jessica, alone since his wife died from a complicated neurologic disease eight months earlier. His housekeeper, Juana, is taking care of Jessica while he attends a Girl Scout meeting. Jessica is an avid baseball fan and she and her father have season tickets to the Houston Astros. Her conversations with her father are often about famous players, their batting averages, and their relative greatness. Tonight Jessica must watch the Astros game on television, a fact that upsets the family routine greatly.

The narrator has volunteered to assist the Girl Scout leader, Kay Randall, because he wants to encourage Jessica to reach out to others her age. So far, however, she has resisted joining the scouts. To demonstrate to her the importance of sticking to one's commitments, the narrator is leaving her home tonight as he takes twenty-two young girls on a field trip to east Texas to collect wildflowers.

During this trip his mind wanders and he recalls various events—from earlier today, from a week or so earlier, and from his own childhood. He remembers his conversations with Jessica over the past two months; he encouraged her to give scouting a try, but her response was that Kay Randall and the scouts can never replace her lost mother. He recalls, as well, his own Cub Scout experience, when he was Jessica's age. His den mother, Mrs. Clark, was so large that she could not sit in normal chairs—she had to use couches. When she walked upstairs she filled them completely. Her son, John, was stocky. Although ten-year-olds generally find such people humorous, the scouts looked upon Mrs. Clark and her son with a certain respect because they carried themselves with a certain dignity. Also, they had a difficult life since Mr. Clark had been killed in the Korean War.

The narrator also thinks about his recent conversations with Jessica's psychiatrist, whom she sees twice weekly. The doctor diagnoses the girl as suffering from separation anxiety and congratulates the father for being able to express his anger. But she hopes that both Jessica and her father will be able to trust the world again, despite their recent loss. The father recalls an interview with his daughter's school principal a few weeks earlier, when Jessica was reprimanded for listening to a baseball game in class instead of participating in the lesson.

During the scout field trip, the narrator is surprised to realize that he is actually enjoying himself. He learns from Kay Randall that she has separated from her husband because he only had time for his work; she adds that although she is lonely, her life is all right. When he returns home from the field trip, his daughter tearfully greets him. He hugs her, but in his heart recognizes that this is only the first of many times that he will have to leave her on her own.

Themes and Meanings

The title of Max Apple's story suggests its theme, which is played out on a number of levels. The reader first sees it in the motion that Kay Randall makes to explain how Brownies become Girl Scouts: She holds her hands out from her chest with her fingertips on each other. It takes a full year for little girls to go through this "bridging" process of moving to the more mature level of scouting. It is, therefore, not something that one can rush. Significantly, as the Brownies imitate Miss Randall's motion, so too does the narrator—thereby suggesting that he also must do a certain amount of bridging as the story progresses.

Jessica's difficulty in moving beyond the trauma of her mother's death is, however, the most obvious bridging on which the narrator focuses. How, he wonders, can he get his daughter to break out of her shell and socialize with others her own age? He understands that she prefers to stay home and watch television because she is afraid of losing anyone else, or of being hurt herself, but he knows that life demands that people find ways to move past tragedies and dependence upon their parents, and that they assert their independence and self-confidence.

Jessica still seems unprepared to bridge with her peers. She instead lives vicariously through baseball. One wonders if Jessica used the language of baseball equally obsessively when her mother was alive, and if it is now her surest way to maintain a close relationship with her father. If so, this, too, is a sort of bridge. This may explain why Jessica turns her attention to another sport, basketball, at the close of the story: Because baseball no longer keeps her father with her, she must find another bridge.

Her father, of course, has his own difficulties following the loss of his wife. He notes that life is throwing curves and fastballs at him and his daughter and that they feel like they are standing blindfolded at home plate. He seems to be trying to fill the role of both parents. On the one hand, he finds himself the only male in the female world of Girl Scouting; on the other hand, he tries awkwardly to get to know other women. He recognizes a kindred spirit in Kay Randall, but ultimately decides that he cannot bridge in any meaningful way with her because all they really have in common is sadness and the Girl Scouts.

Most pointedly, the narrator suffers through the trial of finding a way both to protect his daughter and to prepare her adequately for a world in which people die. He recalls

John Clark, the Cub Scout who had to mature without having a father around, and wonders if Jessica's schoolmates feel the same way about her that he once felt about John, namely, that John had a certain seriousness about life that they all admired. He knows, however, that the death of John's father could at least be portrayed as heroic, and therefore meaningful. By contrast, the death of Jessica's mother was incomprehensible—a sudden attack from nowhere. He ultimately draws the heartbreaking conclusion to which all parents must come: that he can be a scout for his daughter, but he cannot make the actual journey for her.

Style and Technique

Max Apple typically incorporates famous people into his stories, and often uses games as metaphors for American society. In this story he manages to do both by employing baseball and some of its most famous players. The story takes place on the day that Houston Astro star Nolan Ryan became the all-time major league strikeout king. This coincidence also implicitly reminds Jessica and her father that in order for someone to become a strikeout king, many other people must strike out. Life is like that, and we must roll with the punches. The narrator is also setting an important example for his daughter, reminding her that while watching games is fine, being a player is even better—even if more dangerous.

Jessica's language is worth noting, as well. She uses baseball jargon in a way that is traditionally associated with boys. Meanwhile, her father is echoing the language of the Girl Scout leader. There is a kind of role reversal implied in the game that Apple plays here, and that serves his theme well. The narrator, after all, mentions several times that he thinks his daughter understands life better than he does. In the face of the real dangers out there, her fear is quite legitimate.

But this is also Apple's way of parodying cultural clichés, reminding the reader in a gentle way that the games that define social roles in the United States do not ultimately get us through serious crises, which are anything but games. No one is keeping score, he seems to imply, and it is difficult to figure out what the rules are. As with most of Apple's fiction, the story has both a bittersweet tone that recognizes life's inscrutable challenges, and a quietly optimistic sense that whatever answers there are can be found in the ordinary lives of ordinary people.

John C. Hawley

BRIGHT AND MORNING STAR

Author: Richard Wright (1908-1960)
Type of plot: Social realism
Time of plot: The 1930's
Locale: Near Memphis, Tennessee
First published: 1938

> *Principal characters:*
> JOHNNY-BOY, a communist activist
> SUE, his mother
> SUG, his brother
> REVA, a woman in love with Johnny-Boy
> BOOKER, a man who joins the Communist Party
>   in order to betray it

The Story

In the first of the story's six sections, Sue, an elderly and dignified black woman, recalls her burdensome life and efforts to survive the death of her husband and the births of her sons, Sug and Johnny-Boy. Both sons believe in the promise of the Communist Party to end strife between the races and economic classes. Sug, however, is imprisoned for his Party activities, and Johnny-Boy, like many Richard Wright characters, is fleeing from white people who seek to identify Communist Party members in order to destroy both them and the party. Sue and Reva, a white woman in love with Johnny-Boy, share a well-founded concern for Johnny-Boy's safety.

In the next section, Johnny-Boy explains to his mother that he is committed to communism for economic, not racial reasons, noting that black people cannot fight rich bosses alone and that only by working with white Party members can they attain economic equality. Sue believes that Johnny-Boy is blinded by his idealism, but her maternal love does not allow her to prevent his attending a Party meeting, even though Reva has warned her that the sheriff and other white men plan to raid the meeting.

In the third section the sheriff arrives to determine the whereabouts of Johnny-Boy and the meeting. He brutally beats Sue, but she will not tell him anything. Angered by her defiance, the sheriff knocks her unconscious. Sue's pride, her ability to maintain her secret, and her pronouncement that she has the strength to remain silent, is her nearly fatal undoing.

In the fourth section, Sue, her son, and the black race are betrayed when a white man named Booker arrives, ostensibly to warn those planning to attend the Communist Party meeting of the sheriff's intention. And in his manipulation of Sue in her weakened state, Richard Wright's Booker does indeed reveal his Judas-like qualities. When he leaves, Sue fears she has revealed her secret to the wrong person.

Sue's fears are confirmed in the next section, in which Reva reappears and warns Sue not to trust Booker. The warning comes too late, so Sue decides to take action.

She arms herself with a gun and her conviction that she will go to the spot where she believes the sheriff is waiting for her son and the other Communist Party members.

In the final section of the story, the battle lines are drawn clearly: black versus white, the powerless versus the powerful, Sue and her son versus the sheriff and his conspirators. After Sue sees the sheriff break her son's kneecaps and his ear drums because he will not reveal the names of his comrades, she sees Booker, the man for whom she is really waiting. She shoots Booker, thereby killing the man whose betrayal has destroyed her son, his dreams, and her own. Sue, in turn, is killed by the white posse, her blood adding to the drama of the final battlefield scene.

Themes and Meanings

"Bright and Morning Star" is the fifth and last story in Richard Wright's collection *Uncle Tom's Children* (1940), whose title is an obvious allusion to Harriet Beecher Stowe's antislavery novel *Uncle Tom's Cabin* (1851-1852). If, as President Abraham Lincoln suggested, Stowe's novel started the Civil War, then Wright's story continues the saga of war, specifically the war between blacks and whites. Divided into six sections, the story uses communism as the racial battleground.

If Sue's murder were the end of the story, "Bright and Morning Star" might be viewed as a tragic tale of the powerful destroying the powerless. This, however, is not the final note in this last story in *Uncle Tom's Children*. On the contrary, Sue dies victorious, finally realizing that what she had viewed as the "white mountain" of the race that had persecuted her was now toppled through her action. She lies on the ground, in her last moments of life, without struggling; she is at peace, experiencing an intensity of life in her last moments. She realizes that the white men may think that they have killed her, but in reality, she has actually relinquished her life before they could take it from her, thus controlling her own destiny. When her lips move soundlessly, mouthing the words "yuh didnt git yuh didnt yuh didnt," Sue becomes one with her bright and morning star.

The theme of betrayal is at the heart of "Bright and Morning Star," a story whose title suggests hopes and dreams and aspirations—all of which are destroyed by both human and ideological means. In the first case—that of human betrayal—the obvious culprit in this story is Booker, the white turncoat who joins the Communist Party to identify its members, thereby ingratiating himself with the sheriff and elevating himself in the Southern community in which he resides. Booker's name is clearly an allusion to Booker T. Washington, whom Wright and others have viewed as a black man whose accommodation to white precepts betrayed his own race. Wright's Judas-like Booker accomplishes his plan of betrayal, only to be shot by the woman who most symbolizes the values and humanity that he denies.

Perhaps more subtle than this human betrayal, however, is the ideological betrayal of the Communist Party. Johnny-Boy explains to his mother that the Party will connect blacks and whites, destroying economic distinctions so that blacks can obtain equality and justice by working alongside more privileged whites. Just as Richard Wright demonstrates the naïveté of that dream in *Native Son*, his autobiographical novel published the same year as *Uncle Tom's Children*, and in his autobiography *Black Boy* (1945), so he suggests in "Bright and Morning Star" the destructive idealism inherent in the Communist Party. Betrayed by that idealism, both Johnny-Boy and his mother are victims of a Judas that is not merely one person—Booker—but actually a deceptive vision that blacks and whites can be united by the ideological tenets of communism.

Style and Technique

Consistent with a major theme of the story—Booker's Judas-like betrayal of Sue and her son—a major technique to communicate this theme is Wright's use of religious imagery. This imagery is obviously demonstrated in the title of the story, which is a reference to a spiritual that Sue remembers from her childhood: "Hes the Lily of the Valley, the Bright n Mawnin Star/ Hes the Fairest of Ten Thousan t ma soul. . . ." This musical context is reinforced by frequent references to traditional black Christianity. Repeated throughout the story, these references speak to the role of religion in Sue's life as a stable, reassuring belief that the toil and struggle and burdens of life on this earth—a painful life for Sue, to be sure—will be replaced by a Resurrection such as was experienced by the Jesus in whom she deeply believes. This is her vision.

Sue's vision, however, is replaced by another vision, one that she views as "a new and terrible vision." The vision of Christianity is replaced by the vision of communism, and Wright's imagery dramatically underscores that replacement: "The wrongs and sufferings of black men had taken the place of Him nailed to the Cross; the meager beginnings of the party had become another Resurrection." This new and terrible vision might have been a source for a new and terrible world order, one in which justice and equality and humanity rule. Instead it is betrayed by Booker and the sheriff and those others who, like the biblical Judas, are more concerned with their security than others' survival. In this battle, the bright and morning star shines over a battlefield in which both the betrayer and the betrayed are destroyed.

Marjorie Smelstor

THE BROTHER

Author: Robert Coover (1932-   )
Type of plot: Parody
Time of plot: The time of the biblical Flood
Locale: Probably the Middle East
First published: 1969

Principal characters:
THE NARRATOR, an unnamed man who appears to be Noah's brother
HIS WIFE
HIS OLDER BROTHER, also unnamed, but probably the biblical Noah
HIS BROTHER'S WIFE

The Story
The narrator contemplates the most recent of his elder brother's "buggy ideas": building a boat—a rather large boat, in a field far from any water. Although he is skeptical, as are his and his brother's wives, he does what he always has done for his simple-minded sibling. He helps and humors him, though he also wonders how his brother has managed to learn so much about boat-building. Devoting more and more time to helping his brother, the narrator guiltily neglects both his own farm and his pregnant wife. She, however, manages to sow enough seed to ensure their survival during the coming year if it rains sufficiently. After the boat is completed, the brother takes up residence on board, much to his wife's disgust and the narrator and his wife's amusement. Then rain begins to fall. Initially the rain gives the young couple a reason to stay indoors together, but as it floods their fields and ruins their crops, the narrator's wife wonders despairingly whether they should have wasted their time building a boat themselves. When the downpour turns into deluge, the narrator goes to his brother to seek temporary refuge for himself, his wife, and his unborn child, but he is silently rebuffed. Fighting the rising waters, he reaches the relative safety of a nearby hill, from which he sees the boat sailing into the distance and his own house nearly covered.

As the story ends, the narrator—after a futile attempt to save his wife—is back on the hill again. He calculates that he may have a day left if the rain continues. Unable to see his brother's boat, he wonders how his brother knew the rain was coming. He concludes that "it's not hard to see who's crazy here I can't see my house no more just left my wife inside where I found her I couldn't hardly stand to look at her the way she was."

Themes and Meanings
"The Brother" appears among the "Seven Exemplary Fictions" section of Robert Coover's first collection, *Pricksongs & Descants* (1969). Dedicated to Miguel de Cervantes, the author of *Don Quixote* (1605, 1615), Coover's gathering of early works

resembles in effect—although not necessarily in original intention—Cervantes' own *Novelas ejemplares* (1613). Written as exercises in various narrative styles, the latter's "exemplary fictions" do more than entertain the reader and enable the writer to become adept in various narrative forms and styles. As Coover explains in his own "Prologue," they "struggle against the unconscious mythic residue in human life" in order to expose "adolescent thought modes and exhausted art forms." Just as Cervantes struggled against outmoded medieval ways of thinking and writing, Coover, no less comically and self-consciously, struggles against the "mythic residue" of that more modern age that Cervantes himself helped usher in. More specifically, Coover "struggles against" two of the most powerful modern "myths." One involves the primacy of rational thinking, the other the primacy of the individual artist and the prizing of his or her originality (the modern equivalent of the divine inspiration that sanctions Noah's building his ark).

The struggle is evident in the terms that Coover uses to describe his work. "The Brother" is not so much a short story as a "pricksong," or a "descant" (terms for what is essentially the same musical form), and a "fiction—something man-made and therefore every bit as artificial as a musical composition. Coover's comically combative stance is even more noticeable in his choice of the Noah legend from Genesis as his base text. Coover's ironic retelling of the familiar Judeo-Christian myth of Noah and the Flood undermines the authority of the original in several ways. Most obviously, it presents the Noah figure as considerably less than the "just man and perfect" commended in Genesis. No less important, it gives eloquent if somewhat idiosyncratic voice to a character whom the biblical account prefers to silence: one of Noah's numerous and nameless, but here entirely sympathetic and memorable, siblings. This is the narrator, the younger brother, whose entreaties fail to move Noah. In questioning and thus undermining the biblical justification both for the Flood and for Noah's deliverance, Coover also subverts the larger dominant Judeo-Christian mythology. Yet even as he does so, he manages to persuade the reader of the power and pleasure of myth as myth, as fiction. Unlike realistic fiction, which offers a window through which the reader can view the world, "The Brother" offers an art of self-consciously wrought artifice. In it, the medium (fiction, language) is more real than the "world" that medium seems to represent. Thus, Coover's story struggles not only against the power of established myths, such as that of Noah and the Ark, but against the power of established literary forms such as literary realism as well. Literary realism—the dominant literary mode of the past few centuries—assumes that art imitates life. "The Brother" suggests something quite different: that art imitates art.

Style and Technique

The first of *Pricksongs & Descants*' two epigraphs provides a useful introduction to the narrative technique of Coover's collection in general and to "The Brother" in particular. It is, "He thrusts, she heaves," from John Cleland's semipornographic novel, *Fanny Hill* (1748-1749). This epigraph calls the reader's attention to the story's sexual dimension, one that Coover highlights by translating the perfunctory "begats" of his biblical source into an emotional and sexual bond connecting the narrator and his pregnant wife. Less obviously but no less importantly, the epigraph underscores two other stylistic relationships found in "The Brother." These are the ones between old-fashioned narrative drive and new-fangled narrative experimentation on the one hand and between the original story of Noah and the Flood and Coover's variation on this mythic theme on the other. Indeed, it is Coover's ability to combine entertaining narrative and narrative theory that unifies his collection's twenty fictions despite obvious and rather considerable differences in their subject matter and style.

Coover takes considerable pains to make the lives of his story's protagonist and his wife both sympathetic and "real." Not only does he endow them with a depth of feeling; he provides them with the very existence that the biblical story denies them. Against the "thrust" of this realistic, or mock-realistic surface, however, Coover posits the "heave" of narrative technique. One of the most important and noticeable ways in which he focuses the reader's attention on manner over matter (or manner as matter) is by rendering the entire 2,900-word story in the form of a single uninterrupted and largely unpunctuated sentence. There are no periods, semicolons, or even commas, only quotation and question marks and a sprinkling of hyphens and dashes. The technique is certainly unusual but not at all original. In much the same way that Coover borrows the story's ostensible subject matter from the Old Testament, he borrows his "sentence structure" from Molly Bloom's famous soliloquy at the end of James Joyce's *Ulysses* (1922).

Other narrative techniques serve Coover's thematic purposes equally well. He develops his story cumulatively rather than causally (thus the frequent use of the connective "and"). He narrates the entire story in the present tense (a technique that ultimately adds a blackly humorous touch in light of the narrator's final predicament). Coover also chooses not to name his characters (in effect reducing them to their narrative functions—such as brother, husband, wife, or child—while parodying the parabolic quality of so many Bible stories). Coover also literalizes clichés, such as "would I help him for God's sake," and introduces other forms of dramatic irony for equally comic effect (as in the narrator and his wife's wishing for rain and getting a deluge). Finally, Coover's retelling the Noah story in a contemporary and decidedly colloquial idiom, and from a Huck Finn-like vernacular perspective, adds yet another comically jarring note and thus further undermines the seriousness as well as the explanatory power of the biblical version.

Robert A. Morace

THE BUCK STOPS HERE

Author: Stuart M. Kaminsky (1934-   )
Type of plot: Mystery
Time of plot: 1957
Locale: Independence, Missouri
First published: 1989

> *Principal characters:*
> HARRY S TRUMAN, the former president of the United States
> LIEUTENANT PEVSNER, an Army Intelligence officer
> CARL GADES, a professional assassin
> KOSTER and FRANKLIN, Secret Service agents assigned to
> protect Truman

The Story

Lieutenant Pevsner of Army Intelligence rushes overnight from Washington, D.C., to the Truman Library in Independence, Missouri, because word has been received that Carl Gades plans to kill former president Harry Truman the next day. Truman had refused to pardon the man's only brother, Arthur, who recently died in prison after serving ten years for trying to blow up a plane.

Pevsner is assigned to this case because he is considered a "hawk," one whose photographic memory allows him to see and then recall every detail of a scene. While on another Army assignment, Pevsner saw Gades three years earlier and he remembers many details about the man—including the unusual shape of his left ear, his blue eyes, and even the freckles on his wrist. Nevertheless, Pevsner doubts if he can recognize Gades, who is known as a master of disguise. No one in the Secret Service, however, has ever seen Gades.

Pevsner is exhausted when he arrives in Missouri, but he has no time to spare, since it is expected that the attempt on Truman's life will occur at 3:00 P.M. that same day—one month, to the minute, after Gades's brother died. Pevsner studies the layout of the library and the people who are working there. It is being used by Truman, though the final stages of construction are still taking place. Characteristically, Pevsner notes small details about each of the clerical staff, painters, and people who make deliveries—even Koster and Franklin, the two armed Secret Service men assigned to guard Truman. He especially notices how similar these agents are in height, facial appearance—including their brown eyes—and the gray suits that they wear.

Pevsner questions the former president, who is surprisingly unconcerned and refuses to alter his schedule. After showing Pevsner around his office, a replica of the Oval Office of the White House, Truman invites Pevsner to lunch. Afterward, Pevsner is so tired that he takes a brief nap under a tree. Suddenly, however, he is startled awake. His powers of observation have forced themselves into his subconscious, and he realizes how Gades has disguised himself. The last time that Pevsner saw Franklin, he noticed that the man's eyes were blue, not brown. He rushes to Truman's office, where he finds the door is locked. Through a window, he sees that Gades is holding Truman prisoner, apparently waiting for the exact minute of his brother's death to kill him.

From Koster, Pevsner verifies that "Franklin" has been assigned only recently to Independence. It is now obvious that Gades somehow disposed of the real Franklin and substituted himself. He has probably removed the contact lenses that made his eyes appear brown because of an eye irritation. When Pevsner and Koster break down the office door, Gades points his gun at them before they can act. Meanwhile, Truman sits, calmly facing death, even taunting his would-be murderer. Suddenly, with the cane that he carried on his famous walks, Truman strikes his assailant's gun hand, breaking his wrist. The would-be assassin is then quickly disarmed and captured. When Pevsner compliments Truman on his quick action, the former president merely smiles and points to the famous sign on his desk: THE BUCK STOPS HERE.

Themes and Meanings

A little-recognized fact about most of Stuart Kaminsky's mystery novels is that they are also historical fiction. "The Buck Stops Here" is deliberately set in the past. Also, it must be recognized that the story is primarily escape literature. Although some crime fiction deals with larger issues of morality and character, Kaminsky has not done this in depth here.

Although Pevsner is the narrator of this story and its ostensible protagonist, it is Truman who is the hero. The contrast between the two is made clear, even though Kaminsky leaves readers to draw the proper conclusions. Pevsner is the intellectual and the observer of life. Indeed, the only talent that he possesses, so far as we are informed, is his unusual ability to retain what he has seen. Although a young man, he is so fatigued by his travel that he literally sleeps on the job, a situation that confines him to a relatively passive role until the conclusion.

On the other hand, this story can be read as Kaminsky's paean to Truman, as it emphasizes the former president's considerable strengths, including his intelligence and belief in the dignity of his former office. It is Truman who emerges as the decisive man of action and resolves the stalemate. As Pevsner and Koster, an armed Secret Service man, are immobilized by the gun trained on them, Truman risks his own life and disarms a dangerous professional killer.

Style and Technique

Kaminsky employs few stylistic flourishes, rarely using metaphors or other forms of word imagery, instead devoting the story's limited space to straightforward narration in order to build suspense. As in Frederick Forsyth's novel *The Day of the Jackal* (1971), about a real plot to assassinate French president Charles de Gaulle, Kaminsky's potential victim is a real person, so there can be no doubt about whether the targeted victim will be killed. Nevertheless, there is considerable uncertainty about how the potential assassination will be thwarted and whether the would-be assassin will escape.

Although Pevsner is essentially faceless, and even partly nameless, Kaminsky allows the reader to identify with him as a first-person narrator with an urgent assignment. He places Pevsner firmly in a tradition which has become especially important in detective fiction since the 1970's: His protagonist is an essentially ordinary man, possessing neither the enormous intellect nor the eccentricity of a Sherlock Holmes.

Unlike some historical fiction, "The Buck Stops Here" is remarkably free of anachronisms. Only a reference to "a Marcello Mastroianni hat" fails to ring true, as it predates the Italian film actor's general recognition in the United States. On the other hand, Kaminsky does not attempt to superimpose 1980's political attitudes on 1957. There are references to the CIA and FBI, but no criticism, as both organizations were generally held in high public regard during the 1950's. Moreover, it was clearly not the author's intent to reevaluate Truman's controversial political decisions. Instead, Truman appears in a fictional, "private" matter.

Although it is not clear until the story nears its end who Gades is in disguise, Kaminsky does not use all the elements of the classic detective story. He provides few clues, and alibis are not a factor. He assembles a relatively large cast of potential suspects, but says little about each of them. However, the one legitimate clue to the identity of Gades is subtly but openly placed in the story: Before Pevsner takes his nap, he mentions that Franklin's eyes are blue, even though he does not consciously realize it until later. Kaminsky thus adopts one of the devices of the traditional puzzle by playing fair with his readers, allowing them, if they are sufficiently alert, to spot this clue before Pevsner does. Ultimately, however, his story is a thriller, requiring physical activity for its resolution following a brief period of considerable suspense. Thus, Kaminsky has effectively combined two subgenres of crime fiction.

Marvin Lachman

THE BURNING HOUSE

Author: Ann Beattie (1947-   )
Type of plot: Psychological realism
Time of plot: The 1970's
Locale: Fairfield County, Connecticut
First published: 1979

> *Principal characters:*
> AMY WAYNE, the mother of a young son
> FRANK WAYNE, her husband, an accountant
> JOHNNY, her lover
> J. D., Frank's former college professor
> TUCKER, the owner of a New York City art gallery
> FREDDY FOX, Frank's gay halfbrother

The Story

Amy hosts a group of her husband's friends who are visiting for the weekend. She is the only woman in the house, but Frank's homosexual halfbrother, Freddy Fox, is her confidante and likes to help her in the kitchen. Freddy is already high on marijuana, however, and begins to flick ashes into the sauce that Amy is making. In the next room, her husband Frank, who does the books for Tucker's art gallery in Soho, listens to jazz and rock music and to Tucker's gossipy stories about artists and performers. Tucker seems to have picked up most of his stories in gay bars in Greenwich Village; Freddy suggests to Amy that there is a homosexual motive in Tucker's choice of artists to show in his gallery. Much to his annoyance, Freddy himself becomes a topic of conversation; he has failed to finish college and now drifts from one anonymous sexual relationship to another. After dinner, Amy catches Freddy up on a secret that they share, namely that she knows that Frank is having an affair with a woman named Natalie. When Amy's young son Mark, who is on an overnight visit with a neighboring child, wants to come home, Amy senses that her child's anxiety is a reaction to Frank's affair, which has made him cold and unavailable.

While Amy washes the dinner dishes, J. D., who was once Frank's college adviser, appears at the kitchen window wearing a goat mask, frightening Amy into dropping a glass and cutting herself. J. D., who has lost his way, found the mask in a Goodwill bin. His late arrival for dinner adds to the offbeat and disorderly atmosphere. Having abandoned teaching in despair after his wife and son were killed in an automobile accident, J. D. is constantly on the move; he plans to fly to Paris the next day. While J. D. helps Amy treat her badly cut finger, Amy's lover, Johnny, telephones. J. D.—who introduced them—is aware of the affair, but Amy is worried that her husband will overhear, so she pretends that Johnny is someone else. Johnny, who is also cheating on his spouse, pretends to be calling to check the weather in Key West. The brief conversation with Johnny causes Amy's sense of disorientation to grow. She begins to feel she is out of touch with the true identities of the people around her. Beneath the surface charm and insouciance of her husband's friends, she begins to see them as vulnerable, lost boys. Although J. D. appears to be off on a jaunt to Paris, Amy knows that his life is really on hold; she sees that Freddy's use of marijuana is less recreational than desperate; and she knows that Tucker is a needy and lonely man. In spite of these insights, Amy does not feel close to these men—she feels as if they are merely photographs of people, rather than people themselves; her life feels unreal to her.

Before they retire for the night, Frank says something about storms in Key West that leaves Amy unclear as to how much he knows about her relationship with Johnny. Unable to sleep, she asks Frank to make some kind of decision about their future together. Is he staying or going? Frank tells Amy that she should not blame herself for what has gone wrong, and that although she is surrounded by men, she does not really understand them. Men, he says, are like little boys who think that they are going to the stars. Like the cartoon characters Spider Man, Buck Rogers, or Superman, men, he says, are always psychologically up in the sky, looking down on earth. In a very real sense, he tells her, "I'm already gone." He is telling her that he will never take his place in her household as an adult male; even worse, he has abandoned her emotionally.

Themes and Meanings

The main theme of this story is conveyed by its title. There is not a literal burning house anywhere in the narrative; the image of the burning house is a metaphor for Amy's marriage. It is J. D. who, late in the story, alludes to the story's title when he jokingly refers to that "wicked fairy tale crap," which decrees that if you do something you know to be wrong, "your heart will break, your house will burn." In this context, Amy's house is burning. While she and her husband seem to be enjoying an amusing weekend with their arty friends, in reality their marriage is falling apart. Beneath the conviviality is a sense of hellish despair. Their guests are on the road to perdition as well. They represent the "peace and freedom" generation of the 1960's that has lost its way, drifting aimlessly and lovelessly through unstructured, empty lives. The characterization of men as a series of make-believe or cartoon characters, combined with their use of drugs and alcohol, indicates not only a delayed maturity but a loss of common humanity. The image of the goat mask, which suggests dionysian celebration, also indicates a tragic metamorphosis in the character of the men around Amy.

The title also suggests the heavy use of marijuana cigarettes in the story. The golden age of the 1960's, an era of youthful romanticism that first empowered the postwar baby-boomers, has in this story ended in a circle of drug-dazed lost souls who seem to float through a field of unstable and provisional relationships. They have neither meaningful work nor happy personal lives, and their dreams of love and liberation have ended in neurosis and even nihilism.

Although Amy's house is burning metaphorically, she maintains an overly calm and unaffected persona. Like Alice in Wonderland, Amy seems at first to be a remote and dispassionate observer of the madness around her, but the reader comes to understand that although she has erected an invisible wall, or a mask of glass between herself and the others, she is in fact deeply hurt. Her cut finger becomes an image of a deeper, emotional wound. At the end of the story, when Frank gives her a list of nice things to think about in order to help her sleep (such as flowers or a shooting star), his last rather malicious suggestion is that she imagine she has been given a chance to do her life over again—an image revealing that Amy knows she has lost. In contrast to the antic behavior of the men around her, prancing in goat masks, telling funny stories, getting high, Amy seems to be sunk in a depression. She seems emotionally paralyzed and unable to decide whether to leave her husband, although she desperately wants to do so. Instead, she is overwhelmed with feelings of regret and failure. The underlying sense of emptiness and isolation, even of existential nothingness, has left her in a helpless, drifting condition. It is as if nothing that she does will make any difference or even speak to the abandonment and despair that she feels she must endure.

Style and Technique

Ann Beattie writes in a minimalist style, but in contrast to other minimalists, her characters are more economically and culturally privileged. She uses various telling details, such as references to the college campus, Paris vacations, the art of Mark Rothko, or the music of John Coltrane or Lou Reed, to indicate that her characters belong to an upscale bohemian cultural world. Although her characters inhabit an elite cultural and economic circle, her way of describing them is low-key, even flat. Her first-person point of view is drained of color and feeling through the use of an uninflected voice reminiscent of Ernest Hemingway's "hard-boiled" style. This colorless, cool, detached voice sometimes becomes a vehicle for deadpan humor, but more often it suggests a numbed or despairing sensibility.

Like other minimalists, Beattie deploys plot sparingly. "The Burning House" links together a series of almost pointless episodes that do not build to a conventional turning point or conclusion. One senses that at the end of this weekend, nothing has happened. This lack of consequence is communicated by a deliberately plotless structure and a deliberately monotonous, banal tone of voice.

Margaret Boe Birns

BUTCHER BIRD

Author: Wallace Stegner (1909-1993)
Type of plot: Social realism
Time of plot: World War II era
Locale: Saskatchewan, Canada
First published: 1941

> *Principal characters:*
> THE BOY, less than twelve years of age
> HIS FATHER
> HIS MOTHER
> MR. GARFIELD, an elderly English neighbor

The Story

The events of "Butcher Bird" take place during a single afternoon. A family sets out to visit their new neighbors, Mr. and Mrs. Garfield. Mr. Garfield is an Englishman, whose talk of scientific farming methods and making the desert bloom has reached the family. The father clearly has no desire to visit them, but the mother wants to be neighborly, so they go.

The mother's and boy's experiences during this visit are vastly different from the father's. For the mother and her son, the Garfields' home is a place of wonder, beauty, and discovery. There is a rug in the house, there is music, and outside, in this barren country, are trees that Mr. Garfield has been trying to grow from cuttings taken down at Old-Man-on-His-Back, a nearby spot where a creek comes out of the hills. To the father, however, the Garfield home represents everything that he is not, so he is scarcely able to behave pleasantly.

The visit gets off to a bad start because the father is determined not to like Mr. Garfield. When Mrs. Garfield serves lemonade without ice, the father's face reveals his contempt and disdain; he has just spent two weeks digging an icehouse in order to have ice-cold water and beer during the hot season.

Mr. Garfield then shows the boy his gramophone. As the delighted boy inspects this curious machine, his father sharply commands him to keep his hands off; Mr. Garfield, kindly insisting that the boy cannot harm the gramophone, undermines the father's authority. Soon the father is moodily looking out the window, and tension grows in the room. Realizing this, Mr. Garfield gropes somewhat helplessly for something to say, some way of reconnecting with his guests. He turns to the boy, asking him questions about his life on his family farm and what he does with his days. When the talk turns to hunting, Mr. Garfield leaves the room for a moment and returns with a .22-caliber gun, which he offers to the excited boy. Mr. Garfield looks to the boy's mother for permission; the boy looks to his father, who nods his approval. The gift is given conditionally, however: Mr. Garfield makes the boy promise to shoot only at predators, not at birds or prairie dogs. What about butcher birds, the boy asks. The boy's mother explains to her host that butcher birds, also called shrikes, kill all sorts of things just for the fun of it and then hang their victims on the post or barbed wire of a fence. Mr. Garfield's response is significant: "Shoot all the shrikes you see. A thing that kills for the fun of it. . . . " Leaving the sentence unfinished, he shakes his head, and his voice gets solemn.

As soon as the family drives away from the Garfields' farm, the father roars his laughter at Garfield's pacifism, his trees, and his gentleness, as he scorns and ridicules the man. His scorn turns to incredulity when he realizes that his wife likes this neighbor, and then to rage when he senses that his wife's attitude toward Garfield is a judgment against him. They argue, their anger escalating, each determined to have the last word. The boy is on the porch with both his parents, the father helping him clean the gun, which has been neglected. A final, calculated comment from the mother fuels the dying argument and the father's dwindling anger. Enraged, he takes aim at a sparrow scratching for bugs in the yard. His wife warns him not to shoot the helpless bird; the boy yells, "No." Still the father, quietly mimicking Mr. Garfield, pulls the trigger. Drawn to the dead bird, the boy picks it up, getting blood on his fingers, and asks his mother what he should do with it. Likening the father to the butcher birds, the mother tells the boy to leave the sparrow there, that his father will want to hang it on the fence.

Themes and Meanings

Wallace Stegner's story takes its meaning from two themes that unfold simultaneously. One is a delineation of the character of the father and the effects that an ungenerous, hard land has had on his spirit and personality. The other is the story of a young boy's rite of passage into a more complex world in which his father loses stature and authority in his eyes. The gift of the gun is a pivotal moment in this story. Although the father is the one in the story who represents killing, it is Mr. Garfield who gives the gun—the implement of death—to the son. Now that taking life is no longer the exclusive domain of the father, it gains a new dimension: It must be done thoughtfully. When Mr. Garfield gives the gun conditionally, making the boy promise to kill only cruel and bloodthirsty animals, the boy's sense of responsibility changes dramatically. He now has two mentors; his father is no longer the absolute authority, so he must weigh ethical questions within a more complex system of thought and feeling.

These two interdependent themes take on greater significance in the historical context of the story's creation. Originally published in January, 1941, "Butcher Bird" speaks directly to the contemporary debate over the war in Europe and the question of whether the United States should become involved. The story speaks to painful, difficult decisions about whether to kill, whom to kill, and—if they exist—the justifications for killing. The boy, as well as the reader, is caught between the values represented by the father and Mr. Garfield. By the end of the story, the father has revealed himself to be hotheaded, to kill out of anger and a need for control, and to do so indiscriminately. Mr. Garfield introduces a more pacifist position; his conditional gift of the gun forces these questions to the surface.

Style and Technique

Wallace Stegner was an exceptionally economical writer, communicating much with few, telling details. For example, the information that the father has spent two weeks digging an icehouse so that he can have cold beer and ice water during the summer suggests that he is a hard worker who focuses on satisfying his desires. When this detail is contrasted with his adamant refusal to spend even a small part of his afternoon to drive his wife to Old-Man-on-His-Back so that she can cut willow slips, the icehouse takes on new meaning, exposing the father's selfishness, his domination and control of his family, and his ability to thwart his wife's desires.

Stegner's use of perspective in this story also contributes beautifully to his creation of the father's "butcher bird" personality. The story is told by an unidentified third-person narrator, whose perspective and sympathy lie with the boy. The first few paragraphs demonstrate that the weather strongly influences—almost determines—the mood of the father, a wheat farmer, and the father's mood dictates the actions of the boy and his mother—whether they will have to walk and talk quietly through the house so as not to aggravate the father's already foul temper. The experience of living on the farm, with this particular father, is related as the boy's experience. We see all excursions as adventures for the boy. The detail of the soft gingersnaps is a boy's, not an adult's, weather barometer. As the argument between the parents intensifies, Stegner offers a series of details by which the boy marks the progress of a familiar pattern. He marks his father's snorts and taunting, his mother's persistence, trying to concentrate on his gun and close out the sound of his parents' battle. As children so often are, the boy is desperate to do or say something to intervene and make the situation better.

Stegner artfully places the boy between the characters of the father on the one hand and his mother and Mr. Garfield on the other; the boy is also caught between the positions that these two opposing parties represent. By making the boy the point of perspective, Stegner maximizes the emotional impact on the reader. Sympathizing with the boy, the reader also is placed in the uncomfortable position between the father and the mother, between killing and nurturing, between hard-earned survival in an inhospitable land and the luxuries of music and flowers.

Julie Thompson

BY THE WATERS OF BABYLON

Author: Stephen Vincent Benét (1898-1943)
Type of plot: Science fiction
Time of plot: The future
Locale: New York area
First published: 1937

> *Principal characters:*
> THE NARRATOR, the son of a priest
> HIS FATHER, a priest who encourages his son's search
> for knowledge but values traditional taboos

The Story

The Forest People compete with the Hill People, who have slightly more advanced skills in spinning wool, hunting, and using metals. The priests of the Hill People have not forgotten the old writings and have some knowledge of healing—such as how to stop bleeding. Bound by superstition and taboos based on experience, tribe members are forbidden to go east, cross the great river, enter the Dead Places, or touch metal not purified by priests. These strictures have been in force throughout tribal memory. In addition, the people fear spirits and demons and have an ancestral memory of a "Great Burning."

A young member of the Hill People, the narrator has studied for the priesthood under his father. He has learned chants, spells, and medical secrets, and has made dangerous journeys searching for metal in spirit houses. Now he has come of age and has reached the time of initiation and spirit journey. He undergoes purification rites, answers questions about his dreams, and tells his father about the vision that he sees in the smoke of the fire. His vision is of a gigantic Dead Place in its time of glory; although his father fears that his son's strong dream will eat him up, he sends his son on the journey of discovery required as the final initiation into the priesthood. After fasting, the young man awaits a sign. After he sees an eagle flying east and kills a panther by shooting a single arrow through its eye while it attacks a white fawn, he is convinced that he is right to break tribal taboos and journey to the Dead Place.

He travels east for eight days, following a "god-road" that time and the forests have reduced to great blocks of stone. He is driven by his thirst for knowledge and his desire to regain the secrets of a lost civilization whose forest-encroached ruins hold clues to the past and signs for the future. As he travels he observes that the causes of the taboos ("burning" ground, strange fogs) have disappeared, so he bravely crosses the forbidden river and enters "the Place of the Gods."

Wild cats and packs of wild dogs roam the ancient city, and pigeons fly overhead. There are subterranean tunnels and huge temples, food in enchanted boxes and jars, strong bottled drinks, bronze doors without handles, high-rise dwellings with inexplicable machinery, lovely paintings, and books. The young would-be priest gazes over the ruins—with their broken bridges and tumbling towers—and envisions the city at the moment that it died: huge, restless, destroyed by fire from the skies from weapons of unimagined horror, followed by a poisonous mist that left the ground burning for aeons. When he sees a "dead god" sitting by a window looking out on the ruined city, he realizes that the "god" is only a man and that despite its wonders, this city, New York, was once a city of men like himself. He longs for the knowledge they possessed and is sure of his ability to use that knowledge more wisely than they. As a new priest he will help his people make a new beginning, recapturing lost knowledge from the broken city in order to build again.

Themes and Meanings

Originally titled "The Place of the Gods," this Stephen Vincent Benét story initially seems to be set in an unspecified, early period of American Indian history. It is, however, actually a prophetic warning of dread future possibilities. Although modern people's almost magical powers have allowed them to harness electricity and nuclear power, build subways and elevators, drive cars, fly planes, and create washers and driers, electric stoves, and refrigerators, Benét warns that people must still learn to control the savages in themselves that lead to war and annihilation.

The forbidden river of the story, with its "bitter waters," is the Hudson River ("Oudis-sun"); the "god-roads" are complex highway systems; the door with no handles is an elevator entrance; "UBTREAS" is the "Subtreasury"; the statue of "ASHING" is of George Washington, and the other great men are Abraham Lincoln, Moses, and, ironically, Biltmore (reflecting the grandeur of the Biltmore Hotel); the "chariots" of the vision are cars and trucks; the magic torches are electric lights; the falling fire that causes the "Great Burning" and the poisonous mist is from a super bomb, and the resultant fallout causes radiation poisoning. This past civilization is thus present-day civilization; present-day people are the dead whose secrets the Hill People seek.

Writing two years before World War II began, with a sure sense of the destructiveness of World War I and a fear of the new technological might that would be unleashed in a second world war, Benét envisions the possibility of people bombing themselves back to the Stone Age. Before the fire-bombing of Dresden or the nuclear bombing of Hiroshima and Nagasaki, Benét looked into the human heart and read there the strange mixture of positive and negative that could compel human destruction: a thirst for knowledge, experimentation, advancement, and control of natural forces coupled by ignorance, internecine conflict, and a willingness to use power before its disastrous potential is fully understood. His young narrator is proud of his own tribe's superiority to the Forest People; he enjoys outwitting them and makes fun of their food ("grubs") and their inability to detect his stealthy movements; he is a capable hunter with an instinct for the kill. In other words, the seeds of competition and of conflict, of racism and of blood sports are present, ready to grow alongside the narrator's growing technical knowledge.

The title heightens the poignant ironies: "By the Waters of Babylon" takes the reader back to the origins of Western civilization, to the Tigris and Euphrates and a magnificent ancient culture savagely destroyed, then later rebuilt. The title suggests that this pattern of two steps forward, three steps back, is an ancient one, endlessly repeated. The narrator's references to "chariots" reinforces that connection with Babylon. The title also recalls the haranguing warnings of Old Testament prophets. The human race, as personified in the enthusiastic neophyte priest, is forever a sorcerer's apprentice—who knows just enough for self-injury, while failing to learn from history. History is cyclical. Great nations rise and fall. Just as mighty Babylon fell, forever losing its secrets and greatness, so, too, might New York fall. And in each beginning are the seeds that will produce an ending. This story is prophetic about nuclear and human destructiveness, and seems more possible today than it did when first published, eight years before the first nuclear bomb was exploded.

Style and Technique

A major part of what makes Benét's story compelling, its language captures the dignity, simplicity, and repetition of oral tradition. For the Hill People, the ancient writings are sacred, and religion is bound up with translation and interpretation. The narrator, a "Noble Savage," speaks in simple sentences. His repetition echoes oral chants or storytelling: "It is forbidden to go east. It is forbidden . . . It is forbidden . . . this is most strictly forbidden." His simple imagery derives from nature: "like the buzzing of bees," "cold as a frog," "knees like water," knowledge that is "a squirrel's heap of winter nuts." "Fire" and "burning" images equate the narrator's desire for knowledge with both the Promethean gift of fire and knowledge and the destroyed city. At the beginning of his journey the narrator feels as "naked as a new-hatched bird" and his father warns him that "Truth is a hard deer to hunt." By its end he looks forward to when he will become chief priest and vows that then "we shall go beyond the great river" for "we must build again." That final phrase contains the ultimate irony: the human race's eternal desire to progress contains within it the arrogance, pride, and ambition that guarantee future disaster.

Gina Macdonald

THE CARDINAL'S FIRST TALE

Author: Isak Dinesen (Baroness Karen Blixen-Finecke, 1885-1962)
Type of plot: Fable
Time of plot: Eighteenth century
Locale: Italy
First published: "Kardinalens tredie Historie," 1957 (English translation, 1957)

> *Principal characters:*
> CARDINAL SALVIATI, the frame narrator
> THE LADY IN BLACK, a woman whom he counsels
> PRINCESS BENEDETTA, the cardinal's mother
> PRINCE POMPILIO, his father
> ERCOLE, their one-eyed first son
> ATANASIO, their older twin son, named by his father and
> destined for the church
> DIONYSIO, their younger twin son, named by his mother and
> destined for the worldly arts

The Story

When a lady in black asks Cardinal Salviati, "Who are you?," he replies not with a straight answer but with a story.

The cardinal's mother, Benedetta, was married at fifteen to Prince Pompilio, a nobleman of forty-five. She bore him a son, as expected, but the boy was weak and physically deformed. Pompilio then took his young wife to the country, following the advice that she would benefit from being away from the temptations of city life.

In their country villa Princess Benedetta matured and experienced a discovery of self. She transformed from a traditionally submissive wife to a woman of self-awareness. Her change grew out of her love for singing, which surpassed even her prior love for literature. In singing she found a language all her own.

The climax of her self-transformation occurred during a trip to Venice to see Pietro Trapassi Metastasio's opera *Achilles in Scyros* (1736), whose music awakened her entire sense of identity. Within a few hours, every particle of her nature underwent a change, and she triumphantly became her whole self. Her awakening was realized in her spiritual communion with the *castrato* Marelli when their momentary gaze into each other's eyes united them, bestowing manhood on him and imparting passion to her—a mentally virginal woman. Afterward, Benedetta was impregnated by her husband, but she knew the spiritual father of her child to be the *castrato*.

Benedetta and her husband then disagreed about how to rear their unborn child. The prince was determined that if the child were a boy, he should be a pillar of the church, and that he should be named Atanasio, after the church leader Athanasius. Benedetta was determined that any son she bore should become an artist of the world and be named Dionysio, after the "God of inspired ecstacy."

Benedetta eventually bore identical twins, resolving the conflict. Only six weeks later, however, a tragic fire took the life of one of them. The sole means of differentiating the twins was a blue ribbon that Dionysio wore round his neck; it was burned away, so the prince declared the surviving baby to be Atanasio. Benedetta did not contest his decision, but secretly called the child Pyrrha—the name given to Achilles by his mother in *Achilles in Scyros*, believing him to be Dionysio.

Atanasio excelled at both ecclesiastical classics and secular skills and eventually was ordained into the priesthood. The first son, Ercole, died soon afterward, leaving Atanasio his parents' sole heir. Following the deaths of Pompilio and Benedetta—which complete the story—Atanasio became both an earthly and a heavenly prince.

Returning to the frame story, the cardinal and the lady in black discuss the nature of character and the value of the story. The cardinal explains the distinction between story and the newly popular—at the time—form of narrative, the novel. He argues that the novel is a valuable but human-contrived form focusing on character, while the story is a divine art in which all elements, including character, unite to form a whole.

Themes and Meanings

The world that Isak Dinesen describes through God's voice in "The Cardinal's First Tale"—diverse elements uniting into a divine whole—explains both her understanding of identity and her argument for the value of the story itself. The question of identity, which the lady in black poses to the cardinal, rightly begins the story, for it introduces the narrative impulse and establishes the foundation for Dinesen's defense of her own art form. "Who are you?" is answered with a story of the cardinal's parents, his own conception, and his childhood. The birth of identity is introduced early on, even prior to the internal story, when the lady in black distinguishes between the cardinal's having "created" her and his having shown her the self that already existed, the self created by God. This distinction is important because it emphasizes the self as part of divine creation, not as formed by man. Here she also describes her self as a uniting of "fragments . . . into a whole." Her life is not simplified—in fact, she sees it as a *furioso*—but its elements are "in harmony."

The lady's metaphorical reference to music heightens the connection to Benedetta's "birth" of selfhood at the opera; the princess merges with the music and "triumphantly [becomes] her whole self." Most important, this birth, "the pangs of which [are] sweet beyond words," not only "needed" but also "made use of, every particle of her being." All facets of an individual, even those which might seem contradictory, are not only necessary but will work in concordance to establish one's whole identity.

The symbolic force of this idea is developed in the child Atanasio. Atanasio and Dionysio are opposites—constructed by their parents as such, one destined for the church, the other for artistic ecstasy. When one child dies, the surviving son is forced to adopt both his father's and his mother's vision of his identity. This is literally true because his father believes him to be Atanasio and his mother secretly believes him to be Dionysio. However, merging the seemingly conflicting personalities of the priest and the artist is not difficult: The child Atanasio excels at both ecclesiastical and secular studies and skills, and the adult Atanasio, the cardinal, declares vehemently that, though these two halves of him exist, they are not incompatible, not even always distinguishable. As a servant of God, the cardinal accepts that God has created a world "with all things necessary to the purpose in it" and that his childhood history and present personality are but one example of this.

Under this concept of "all things necessary," story, the genre, becomes glorified. Characters who are sympathetic, knowable, and appealing are what the writers of novels attempt, but in focusing on character novelists sacrifice the story; novels, according to the cardinal and Dinesen herself, are a consciously constructed "human art" wherein events occur merely to facilitate character development. The defense of the story delivered through the voice of the cardinal is founded in Dinesen's belief that character is only one element of the story—all elements of which must be present and work together to create the whole. The cardinal charges that "*sans* story the human race would perish," and, indeed, the story as a genre matches perfectly the description of the world as described by God: "a sublime world, with all things necessary to the purpose in it, and none left out."

Style and Technique

Reflecting the sublime world presented within her story, Dinesen creates through her style a world of grandeur elevated from the mundane. "The Cardinal's First Tale" is delivered with a controlled formality of language that separates the reader from the authorial presence, emphasizing the distance between the imagination of her story and daily life. Similarly, though Dinesen's characters may be intriguingly individualized through detailed traits—for example, the development of the princess through her unique passion and convergence with music—their speech is indistinct, revealing them to be extensions of the authorial voice. These techniques punctuate the artificiality of the story, validating it as story instead of an attempt to portray reality.

The structure, like the style, is not merely complementary to the intended meaning but a vital element in the formation of that meaning: Form as part of content asserts the concept that the unity of all parts will effect the whole. Narrative framing is a device that further develops her story's central idea. The external and internal stories are so tightly interwoven that neither can be seen as a facilitator of the other; for example, the large theme of self-realization through the unifying of seemingly disparate parts is initially presented by the lady in black in the frame, intensifies in the story of Benedetta's individual growth, is dramatically symbolized by the twins who become one, continues in the discussion of the dualistic yet harmonious personalities of priest and artist, and culminates in the comparison of God's creation of the world to the nature of the genre story. The interconnections establish a fluidity that demands a reading which is holistic rather than fragmented, which melds the frame and internal story. Finally, then, the very process through which the reader experiences Isak Dinesen's narrative is integral to the revelation of this story's message and, indeed, the nature of all stories.

Tiffany Elizabeth Thraves

THE CARIBOO CAFE

Author: Helena María Viramontes (1954-   )
Type of plot: Social realism
Time of plot: The 1980's
Locales: An American city and El Salvador
First published: 1985

> *Principal characters:*
> SONYA, the young daughter of a Latino immigrant to the
>   United States
> MACKY, her brother
> THE COOK, the owner of the Cariboo Cafe
> JOJO, his dead son
> NELL, the cook's former wife
> PAULIE, a café patron
> A WASHERWOMAN, from El Salvador
> GERALDO, her young son

The Story

In the first of the story's three parts, a young girl named Sonya has lost the key to her father's apartment that she usually keeps on a string around her neck. Her father works by day while she goes to school, and her brother Macky is tended by Mrs. Avila. Today Sonya has brought Macky home from Mrs. Avila's house; she arrives at the apartment before she realizes that her key is missing. Street smart, but young, she tries to guide her brother back through the ghetto area where they live to Mrs. Avila's house, but quickly becomes disoriented.

As they walk, Sonya observes various human examples of homelessness, poverty, and vice. She sees a man and innocently thinks he might be the father of a classmate at her school (because both schoolmate and man are African American). She considers approaching the man for help, when he is suddenly stopped, searched, and taken away by the police. Her father has taught her to fear the police—who work in league with immigration officials—so witnessing this incident confirms to Sonya that what he says about the authorities is accurate. She seizes her brother by the hand and they run into the unfamiliar warehouse district of the city. Tired and frightened as darkness falls, they head toward the lights of a café that Sonya spots in the distance.

The second part of the story is narrated by the owner of the Cariboo Cafe, who is in the process of rationalizing some of his recent actions and ruminating about his life. Something has recently happened in his café that makes patrons avoid it and which makes the man scrub stains off its floor. He tries to be fair to the odd assortment of people who enter his place, including the disabled and those down on their luck. He is especially kind to a man named Paulie, who has a drug or mental problem (which may stem from his experience in the Vietnam War), because something about him reminds the man of his own son, JoJo, who was killed in Vietnam. The café owner's level-headed wife, Nell, has left him, and he misses her. One day, he recalls, a disheveled Latina woman ordered food for two children sitting with her in a booth. The younger child (whom he thinks of as Short Order) reminded him of JoJo as a little boy. The boy's sister appeared distrustful. After they left, the owner saw a television news bulletin about two missing children and recognized the boy as the one in his café.

The next day immigration agents raid a nearby factory and some workers run into the café to hide. Although the owner recognizes them as regular customers, he gestures toward their hiding place when the agents enter, and they are taken away in handcuffs. Shaken by this incident, he is further distressed to see the woman from the day before return with the two children.

The final section of the story is the first-person narrative of an unnamed El Salvadoran woman whose five-and-a-half-year-old son, Geraldo, was taken off the streets by army officials and never seen again. Along with other women whose children disappeared, she went to the authorities at the "detainers" (where bodies of people accused of helping the Contras were collected) trying to find her son. Crippled by her grief and the sadism that she encountered while seeking information about her son, she finally gave up hope of regaining her life in El Salvador. With the help of her nephew Tavo, she crossed the border into the United States from Juarez, Mexico.

While working as a housecleaner, the woman one day sees a boy in the street whom she believes to be Geraldo; he is with a girl. The woman takes both children to eat at a café, where the cook is kind to the boy, and then takes them home, where she bathes the boy lovingly and sings to him, tucking him into the bed. She dreams of taking him home and having their old lives of harmony restored. The next day she returns to the café with the children.

At this point the stories of the bereft mother and café owner converge. When the owner sees the children, he calls the police. After they arrive, the point of view shifts from the owner to the woman, who desperately tries to stop the police from taking the boy—whom she believes to be her own Geraldo—away from her. As the owner cowers behind the counter, the woman clings to the boy and fights a policeman holding a gun with all her might; in him she sees personified the officials with whom she dealt at home, and she vows to herself not to allow these uniformed men to take her beloved son from her again.

Themes and Meanings

"The Cariboo Cafe" is a story of the terrible psychic wounds wrought by political repression and displacement. Two of its primary themes are the randomness of terror at the hands of powerful authorities and the banality of evil. Readers see the latter in the young guard with whom the mother pleads in El Salvador and in the hazy thoughts that lie behind the café owner's actions. For Helena María Viramontes' Latino characters, the world is a dangerous place. Racism is insidious: The café owner sees himself as a relatively good and generous man, but he feels no loyalty or connection to the Spanish-speaking workers who frequent his café. He can thus turn them in to the police without thinking and does not clearly understand the discomfort he feels as they are taken away.

In using two different settings for her story, Viramontes draws parallels between the kinds of repression experienced in the United States and in El Salvador. In Central America her characters are subjected to a reign of terror instigated by a totalitarian and corrupt military regime. In the United States undocumented Spanish-speaking residents live in poverty and in fear of relocation or reprisal from police acting in conjunction with immigration officials. Viramontes explores the terrible emotional consequences of such forms of repression and the intensity of the urban environment of poverty. The horror, loss, and bewilderment that her characters experience sharply contrast with their simple desire to live a decent life unencumbered by fear.

Style and Technique

In its sensitive treatment of the themes of social marginality and alienation, "The Cariboo Cafe" recalls the work of Carson McCullers. Viramontes uses narrative and characterization techniques similar to those of McCullers' novel *The Heart Is a Lonely Hunter* (1940). These include revolving points of view, the presentation of overlapping personal realities, and the use of projection as a device. In "The Cariboo Cafe" both the woman and the café owner project an identity onto the figure of the inarticulate little boy that is based on their own deprivations and inner needs—much as McCullers' characters do with the deaf mute at the center of her novel.

Using a nonlinear structure to great effect, Viramontes creates a kind of kaleidoscope of human pain and longing in which many details go unmentioned and from which the reader must sort out meaning. She tells events out of sequence and from multiple standpoints, ending the story in the midst of conflict, without revealing exactly what happens to the children and the woman. The story first jumps between the different characters' consciousness, revealing their inner motivations, choices, and perceptions, and then brings them together in a tragic web of misunderstanding that apparently leads to the El Salvadoran woman's being shot by the police. Although Viramontes never makes it explicit, one suspects when the story ends that what the café owner had to scrub off the floor was the distraught mother's blood.

In the Cariboo Cafe's neon sign all the lights are burnt out except those forming what the characters read as the double "zeroes." The place that gives the story its title is thus the site of negation. It is a point of encounter for people whose lives are deemed worthless by others—lives which seem to add up to nothing when measured by fate.

In bringing her protagonists together at the café, Viramontes makes essential use of irony. Privy to the inner thoughts of the characters, the reader knows that there are commonalities between the café owner who has lost his son and wife and the mother who has lost her child, but each character's true reality remains unknown to the other. Instead, they face each other as if over an abyss, and the harm, trauma, and loss that has brought each of them there adds up to fatal consequences.

Barbara J. Bair

CATHEDRAL

Author: Raymond Carver (1938-1988)
Type of plot: Domestic realism
Time of plot: c. 1980
Locale: New England
First published: 1981

> *Principal characters:*
> THE NARRATOR, a shy and awkward but sensitive blue-collar worker
> HIS WIFE, who once worked for Robert as a reader and secretary
> ROBERT, their overnight guest, a blind man in his late forties

The Story

The narrator describes a small incident in the lives of ordinary people. A blind man named Robert is coming to have dinner and stay overnight. The narrator's wife worked for him for one summer about ten years earlier. They became friends and have continued to correspond by using cassette tapes.

The narrator, who lacks social graces, is apprehensive about having to entertain Robert. He does not know what he should do or say. Jealous of the former relationship between his wife and Robert, he is suspicious. He knows that his wife has told Robert about him and has probably complained about his faults. This makes him feel guilty, insecure, and somewhat hostile toward both his wife and Robert.

The blind man proves to be such an outgoing, amiable person that one can understand why he made such a strong impression on the narrator's wife that she has corresponded with him for years. Despite the narrator's conversational blunders, the two men get along well; they drink together and smoke marijuana together after dinner. Under the influence of the marijuana and alcohol, the narrator lets down his guard with Robert.

Robert's handicap has compensations: It has made him compassionate, tolerant, and open-minded. Being dependent on others has made him trusting, and this trust leads him to reveal intimacies that he might otherwise not share. As the evening progresses and the narrator's wife falls asleep on the sofa, he and his guest grow closer. Finally he finds himself describing a documentary about cathedrals being shown on the television screen. Robert admits that he has no idea what a cathedral looks like, although he knows they required hundreds of people and decades to build. He persuades his host to sketch a cathedral while he holds the hand moving the pen. Through this spiritual contact with the blind man, the narrator discovers artistic gifts that he has never suspected that he owns.

The narrator sheds his inhibitions and sketches an elaborate cathedral with spires, buttresses, massive doorways, gargoyles, and a throng of worshippers. It is a unique and memorable experience which forms the story's climax. The narrator not only shares his vision with the blind Robert, but he simultaneously shares Robert's inner vision. At the same time, both share the spiritual vision of men who lived centuries earlier and collaborated to build the beautiful, mystery-laden gothic cathedrals of Europe.

Themes and Meanings

Raymond Carver wrote mostly about the joys and sorrows of politically powerless and socially insignificant working-class people. In this respect he resembled John Steinbeck, whose best-known work is the Depression-era novel, *The Grapes of Wrath* (1939). Carver differed from Steinbeck, however, in having no political agenda. Steinbeck was a socialist for most of his life, believing that the lives of the masses could be improved by government intervention and by substituting faith in socialism for faith in God. Carver was remarkably apolitical in his writings; he seems to have had a healthy lower-class distrust of politicians and anyone else who did not work with their hands.

Like many contemporary minimalist writers of his era, Carver displays a nihilistic view of life. His favorite theme in his stories and poetry is alienation or anomie. The latter is the feeling that many people have of being only half alive, of being on a treadmill or in a rat race, of being trapped in meaningless jobs, of not being able to love and not being able to relate to others—perhaps especially of not being able to see any higher meaning to life.

After shedding his inhibitions through liquor and marijuana, and feeling somewhat invisible in the presence of his sightless house guest, the narrator confesses that he does not believe in religion or anything else. "Sometimes it's hard," he says, "You know what I'm saying?" Robert replies: "Sure, I do." Although the narrator knows that cathedrals are products of a great religious faith that existed during the Middle Ages, he confesses that "cathedrals don't mean anything special to me. . . . They're something to look at on late-night TV."

The cathedral that the narrator and Robert draw on the side of a shopping bag might be seen as symbolizing the vestiges of religious faith in the Western world. It is significant that the men copy a cathedral seen through the modern medium of television, because science and technology have been particularly responsible in undermining traditional religious faith since the Middle Ages.

The joint artistic creation of these late twentieth century men represents their pathetic wish for a spiritual life which is an unavoidable part of their humanity. These hapless strangers—one a man who hates his job, drinks too much, has no friends, and seems on the verge of divorce, the other a blind widower, a former Amway distributor with a bleak future—come together momentarily because of their common yearning for a more fulfilling and spiritually more meaningful life. The epiphany described in this story is of the smallest possible kind—a sort of "mini-epiphany" appropriate to a minimalistic story. The narrator concludes with the ambiguous understatement of an inarticulate man: "It's really something."

Style and Technique

Raymond Carver is generally considered the leading writer of the school of fiction called minimalism, which—as its name implies—eliminates all but the most important details. Minimalists are noted for using simple language and focusing on factual statements, implying rather than attempting to explain precisely what is going on inside their characters. The reader of a minimalist story is forced to make inferences from what the characters do and say. For example, it can be inferred that the narrator of "Cathedral" and his wife are not getting along well and might be on the verge of divorce. Indeed, the most striking thing about "Cathedral" is its simplicity of language. This type of narration from the viewpoint of a simple, uneducated man creates an impression of truthfulness, as the narrator seems too naïve to be dishonest or evasive.

Characteristically, Carver neither names nor describes the two principal characters and does not even reveal where the story takes place. Like other minimalist fiction writers, such as Ann Beattie, Carver deletes every word that he possibly can and even deletes punctuation marks whenever possible. The effect of minimalism is to engage one's imagination, forcing the reader to make guesses and assumptions and thereby participate in the creative process.

In "Cathedral," as in many of his other stories, Carver uses a narrator who is a faux naïf, like the narrators of Mark Twain's *Adventures of Huckleberry Finn* (1884) and J. D. Salinger's *The Catcher in the Rye* (1951). Such "naïve" narrators supposedly do not understand the full import of what they are telling. This narrative device enhances verisimilitude, characterizes and creates sympathy for the narrator, and provides a basis for humor. The typical point of stories involving faux naïf narrator-protagonists is that they experience events that teach them something about life or about themselves, thereby making them less naïve. In identifying with the narrator, the reader vicariously experiences the learning event and feels changed by the story.

Minimalist short-story writers often write about seemingly trivial domestic incidents and tend to avoid what James Joyce called "epiphanies"—sudden intuitive perceptions of a higher spiritual meaning to life. Minimalists have been attacked as having nothing to say because they do not offer solutions to the existential problems they dramatize in their stories. In a typical Carver story, little changes; his endings might be called "mini-epiphanies." This is characteristic of minimalists, who usually display a nihilistic outlook and do not believe there are answers to life's larger questions, such as Who am I? What am I doing here? Where am I going? Carver's "downbeat" endings tend to leave the reader depressed or perplexed—and this is the intention. Carver tried to capture the feelings of alienation and frustration that are so much a part of modern life.

Raymond Carver has been credited with single-handedly reviving interest in the short story, a genre which had been perfected by American authors beginning with Nathaniel Hawthorne and Edgar Allan Poe but had been rapidly declining in popularity and social influence with the advent of television after World War II. Some readers dislike Carver's stories because they seem depressing or pointless. Others appreciate them because they are so truthful. He writes about working-class folk who lead lives of quiet desperation, are chronically in debt, and often drown their sorrows in drink.

He tells bitter truths but has an indestructible sense of humor that always shines through. It is impossible to appreciate "Cathedral" without being aware of its offbeat humor, such as in the narrator's offer to take the blind man bowling and his wife's reaction to that bizarre suggestion. The subtle humor spicing this poignant story is typically Carveresque.

Bill Delaney

THE CHASER

Author: John Collier (1901-1980)
Type of plot: Horror
Time of plot: c. 1940
Locale: New York City
First published: 1951

> *Principal characters:*
> ALAN AUSTEN, a young man who is very much in love
> AN OLD MAN, a dealer in magical potions

The Story

Alan Austen, a young man who is passionately in love with a young woman who is indifferent to him, comes to the establishment of a mysterious old man who deals in magic potions. Austen has been told that he can buy a potion that will make the object of his affections fall madly in love with him. The old man shows little interest in the financial profit to be gained from selling Alan a love potion. Instead, he devotes most of his sales talk to recommending a potion that he calls a spot remover or a life cleaner, a powerful poison that is undetectable in an autopsy. Without ever saying so directly, the old man is suggesting that the time will inevitably come when Alan will want to murder the woman whom he now loves so desperately.

The potent poison costs five thousand dollars for a single teaspoonful, while the love potion costs just one dollar. Alan cannot believe his good fortune. He seeks the old man's assurance that the love potion will be effective. The old man ruefully assures him that it will make the woman fall so completely in love that she will cling to Alan and make him her sole interest in life.

After their marriage, the young woman will want to know everything that Alan is thinking, everything that he has done when he was away from her, and everything that he intends to do when he leaves again. She will demand all his attention. She will be insanely jealous. The reader gradually gets the picture of a suffocating relationship that would drive anyone to distraction, even to thoughts of murder. This is not the picture that Alan visualizes, however, because he is held so tightly in the grip of passion that he can think of no greater happiness than to be in the company of his loved one perpetually.

Alan finally purchases the vial of love potion for one dollar. The old man assures him that he only deals in such potions to establish customer relations. People who want love potions are invariably young and have little money. Later in life, when they are more affluent, they will come back to him to buy his real moneymaker, the tasteless, undetectable poison that will rid them of the hateful, clinging, sexually unappealing, aging spouse.

Alan seizes the vial, thanks the old man enthusiastically, and says, "Good-bye." The old man replies, *"Au revoir,"* a French phrase that might be translated into English as, "I'll be seeing you."

Themes and Meanings

Collier's message in "The Chaser" is clear, although he never states it in words: Love is only a temporary illusion. People fall in love and believe it will last forever. While they are in the grip of this illusion, they will do anything to obtain possession of the loved one. Once the illusion has dissipated and grim reality has intruded, the former ardent lover realizes that he or she has tied himself or herself for life to a stranger who may be totally incompatible, and who does not fulfill all the wonderful expectations the illusion of love initially created. At that point the lover has two choices: either to remain in a loveless relationship and live a life of pretense, or else to find some means of obtaining freedom.

In "The Chaser," the old man emphasizes the fact that the young man's loved one will cling to him so tenaciously that he may have to use drastic means to free himself from her clutches. She will make herself disagreeable by demanding all his time and attention. Since the price of the love potion is so cheap and the price of the chaser, the vial of undetectable poison, so exorbitant, Collier implies that it is easy to fall in love and to get married, but very difficult to extricate oneself from such a legally, socially, and morally binding relationship after discovering that marriage is often monotonous, expensive, overly demanding, and sexually unsatisfying.

Collier was cynical about human beings in general and wrote several stories in which a husband kills his wife. A good example is his "De Mortuis" (1951), in which an unworldly middle-aged man, who finds out that the beautiful young woman he married is notorious as the town slut, decides to murder her and bury her body in the basement. Many of Collier's short stories deal with human wickedness. He exposes both his male and female characters as being greedy, selfish, dishonest, immoral, and sadistic. In fact, it might be said that Collier's dominant theme was human depravity. His misanthropy and pessimism would have prevented him from becoming a popular writer if he had not had the wisdom to leaven his stories with humor.

Collier resembles Ambrose Bierce whose *The Devil's Dictionary* (1906) cynically defines marriage as "The state or condition of a community consisting of a master, a mistress and two slaves, making in all, two," and love as "A temporary insanity curable by marriage or the removal of the patient from the influences under which he incurred the disorder." Collier would certainly have agreed with these definitions, as well as with most of the other definitions in Bierce's bitterly cynical book. Like Bierce, Collier made his grim philosophy palatable to the average reader by sprinkling his stories with humor, a humor that was often based on the contrast between fact and fantasy, between expectation and outcome, between illusion and reality. Like most humorists, he had a great deal of melancholy in his temperament. His humor is laughter in the dark.

Style and Technique

In this exceptionally short work, Collier uses a strictly objective technique. He briefly describes the two characters and the setting in the opening paragraphs, then lets his characters tell the story almost entirely through their dialogue. This technique is perfect for the author's purposes, because he wants his message to dawn on the reader without his having to spell it out. It is interesting to observe how Collier displays his technical virtuosity by suggesting the debilitating effects of long years of married life while respecting the classic Aristotelian unities of time, place, and action.

The entire story unfolds in only a few minutes and is confined to a simple setting. It contains only two characters, and these two are sharply contrasted so that it is easy to visualize both and to imagine how their voices sound. One is young, the other old. One is idealistic, the other realistic. The young man is governed by his passions; the old man has been disillusioned by long years of living and is governed by the cold light of reason. The young man is interested in love; the old man is only interested in money. The young man has his whole life ahead of him but acts as if he is pressed for time; the old man obviously is at the end of his life but acts as if he has all the time in the world.

Collier often wrote unrealistic stories with realistic settings. He was noted for putting his genii, jinns, sibyls, demons, and ghosts in contemporary Manhattan and London apartments. The old man in "The Chaser" is a mystical character who belongs in a medieval folktale. What is he doing in twentieth century New York? Characteristically, Collier does not bother to explain how this sorcerer ended up here. Collier did not expect most of his stories to be taken seriously. This paradoxical element contributed to the quixotic humor to be found in most of his fiction.

Collier's style is light, witty, whimsical, playful. He plays with literary conventions, and his fiction is full of literary allusions, hints of connoisseurship, sophisticated dialogue, and French words and phrases. He invariably sounds cultured, worldly, and well educated. He was born in England and had the tastes and values of an English country gentleman. He often has been compared to writers such as Noël Coward, P. G. Wodehouse, and Somerset Maugham, all of whom wrote about upper-class people who were far more interested in manners and money than morals. The world they wrote about was at its zenith in the first quarter of the twentieth century. The Great Depression and World War II had a sobering effect on the tastes of American and European readers, and Collier, along with many other sophisticated writers, experienced a sharp decline in popularity as a result.

Bill Delaney

CHECK!

Author: Sławomir Mrożek (1930-   )
Type of plot: Fable
Time of plot: An unspecified modern time
Locale: Courtyard of an old palace, presumably in Poland
First published: "Szach," 1962 (English translation, 1968)

> *Principal characters:*
> THE NARRATOR, an unemployed man who substitutes for a piece in a game of living chess
> HIS ILL FRIEND, the regular white Bishop
> THE WHITE KNIGHT, a chess piece who gives advice
> THE BLACK ROOK, the jingoist who wants to win

The Story

Two friends who have in the past worked together at trivial jobs meet on a day when a storm threatens. Complaining about his various physical ailments which will worsen if he is caught in a storm, the man who has been working regularly as a piece in living chess games asks the narrator to substitute for him. He describes the life-sized chess game as a public spectacle in which people dressed as pieces move about on a great outdoor board controlled by players sitting on elevated platforms. He regards it as a relatively easy way to make money—so long as the weather cooperates, which it rarely does. The people serving as chess pieces are not volunteer chess aficionados— who tend to quit when they dislike how the game is going—but disinterested people who are paid for doing a job. The narrator's friend has worked his way up to playing the white Bishop, for which he gets more money and does more work than the pawns. The narrator agrees to fill in for his friend when the latter assures him that the chess match is just the private sport of two old men and that the white Knight will give him practical advice.

When the narrator arrives at the courtyard, he is put off by its ominous and gloomy atmosphere, the pathetic tattered shoes that the chess pieces are wearing beneath their monstrous papier-mâché cardboard costumes, and by the threats of a black Rook. Nevertheless, he locates the white Knight, who shows him how to dress, how to smoke and eat surreptitiously, and how to exploit the stratified system.

It does not take the new Bishop long to realize that the two old chess players controlling the game are incompetent. The Knight confirms his fears that the game has neither rhyme nor reason, telling him that the two senile players sometimes even leave the pieces out overnight. After the Bishop has been moved about randomly for some time, it begins to rain and gradually intensifies. During the long intervals between moves, the Knight warns the Bishop about the cruel, heavily booted black Rook, who will do anything to win.

Eventually the white Bishop can endure the tedious game no longer. Not caring whether white wins or loses, but keeping out of the black Rook's way, he decides to cheat so that a King can be checkmated. Although he captures the drunk black Bishop and two pawns, he discovers that the balance of the game has not changed. Someone on the other side must be cheating as well: It is the black Rook, who is now openly kicking white pieces. The Knight anxiously observes what is happening, but cannot help the Bishop for fear of jeopardizing his own job, and he leaves after being brutally captured by the Rook.

When only the two Kings, the black Rook and the white Bishop are left, cheating is no longer possible. The Bishop tries to reason with the Rook that since the game is obviously a draw, they should all go home, but the Rook refuses to listen. Fearing that the Rook will injure the white King, the Bishop stealthily steers the sleepy old man off the board, with angry cries of "Check!" rising over the storm. When they near the gate, the Rook closes in on them, but inspired by fear, the Bishop takes off their cardboard costumes, throws them as far as possible, and hides. As the Rook repeatedly stabs the sodden costumes, the Bishop and the King walk out of the courtyard.

Themes and Meanings

None of the characters in Sławomir Mrożek's allegory have real names, yet their positions on the giant chessboard provide clues to what their lives may mean. The narrator, who substitutes as the white Bishop, is a basically decent man, trying to eke out a living at a series of insignificant jobs. Like his hypochondriac friend, he is only a human who must live, so he hopes for as pleasant a job as possible even though he is at the mercy of changing circumstances. Human chess pieces who care about the game do not last long; only the regulars who work for pay survive long. Their workplace, like chess, is not an egalitarian structure. With time and effort, some can rise in status, even if their lack of intrinsic value is betrayed by the vulgarity of their papier-mâché costumes and the shabbiness of their footwear. Even more important, might makes right in this society. The black Rook is reincarnated in all levels of society, from schoolyard bullies to totalitarian rulers. Nameless individuals can survive in such settings but rarely with their dignity intact, as seen by the demeaning tricks they must perform just to eat and smoke. Even the dignity that might come from helping fellow humans is corrupted by a system that encourages its playing pieces merely to go along. The Knight sympathizes with the Bishop's plans but does not want to jeopardize his job. In the end, the Bishop outwits the evil Rook; spurred by fear and cunning, he escapes from the game. He earns his dignity by initiative alone.

On the cosmic rather than the political scale, the chess game takes place in a closed universe under the control of a God who is worse than absent; he is incompetent. The senile chess players cannot even see the logical plays, much less the beneficial ones. They might be seen as representing a dualism of equally balanced good and evil, but that seems unlikely in a chess game in which there is no inherent rightness to one side or the other. Rather, together the players symbolize a world in which any deity that may exist is neither good nor powerful. Because God is evil and weak, humans must figure out how to survive on their own, at odds with Him as well as the world. Neither rationality nor altruism is an effective guide to living in this gloomy courtyard of a universe in which "clever architecture had joined space to enclosure." With physical and moral freedom only an illusion, humanity is trapped by an absurd cosmic chaos. Decent people cannot count on the "happy accident" of chance. In this world in which the absence of good creates a vacuum, cruel rooks can rush in to take control. The reader must even question the ultimate fate of the escapees. Perhaps on a political level, fear and cleverness can create an escape route, but cosmically, what lies outside the chess game? The weather and the jobs are just as bad out there; prior to joining the game, the substitute had been demeaned by showing the theater spectators his boil. There is no place that protects human freedom and dignity.

Style and Technique

Sławomir Mrożek is primarily known as a playwright in Poland's post-World War II avant-garde tradition, but throughout his literary career he has produced numerous short stories and cartoon collections. "Check!" is a prime example of his typically allegorical approach to literature in which, as his biographer remarked, his "characters are symbolic representation while situations illustrate theses."

On a strictly literal level, "Check!" makes sense. The narrative has a clear beginning, middle, and end. Mrożek's plain verbal style reinforces the simplicity of his plot. The words themselves make inherent sense at the surface level. The reader knows what is happening—because the words reveal it in reportorial fashion—when the Bishop is recruited, when he dresses, receives instructions, tries to cheat and outwit the Rook, and when he and the King make their escape.

Though simple, Mrożek's language is also vivid and visual. For example, in describing the chess pieces the narrator says: "Only their feet, protruding from under the fantastic dress, remained normal, shod in a variety of old shoes. Above them necks and heads of horses, their teeth bared, each tooth the size of a tile, the severe-looking, geometric and crenelated Rooks, and saucer-like ruffs of the bishops." It is this juxtaposition of "reality" and grotesque images that, as Martin Esslin, writing about the theater of the absurd, claims, allowed East European playwrights to produce something of significance without being censored. Additionally, the characters in "Check!", as in Mrożek's other short stories collected for *The Ugupu Bird* (1968), are anonymous. Each chess piece is an Everyman trapped in a dangerous closed society, and by extension, Everyman trapped in the modern world.

The absurdity arises, therefore, from the situations that Mrożek describes so visually. The event reported is not the puzzle. "What does this mean?" is instead the puzzle. The ordinariness of the language highlights the seriousness of the fable's "moral." The elements of the logical plot, anonymous characters, and matter-of-fact tone combine to produce both a biting satire and tragic fable about the human condition in a world where people would have been better off if God had been dead because He is doing such a dreadful job of running the universe. If only life—not just in totalitarian Poland, but everywhere—were just a chess game!

Barbara J. Hampton

THE CHILD OF QUEEN VICTORIA

Author: William Plomer (1903-1973)
Type of plot: Social realism
Time of plot: Early twentieth century
Locale: Lembuland, Africa
First published: 1933

> *Principal characters:*
> FRANT, the protagonist, a young Englishman
> COLONEL MACGAVIN, his sponsor in Africa, a Scottish trader
> MRS. MACGAVIN
> SERAPHINA, a Lembu woman
> UMLILWANA, Seraphina's fiancé
> AN ELDERLY PROPHET

The Story

A young Englishman named Frant arrives in Africa to work as a volunteer in a trading post owned by Scottish-born Colonel MacGavin, who drives him to his store. Each man strains to maintain a hearty persona while imagining that the other resents him for representing values of another generation.

Frant stays in a room in the MacGavin's tiny house while serving in the trading post. The MacGavins treat him as a social inferior; however, as a white man, Frant is considered to be superior to his African customers, with whom he becomes friendly. In common with local Africans, Frant dislikes the MacGavins, who in turn dislike almost everybody. Frant's relatively jovial attitude increases sales, a fact for which the MacGavins are grudgingly grateful.

One day an attractive, young African woman named Seraphina enters the store and speaks with Frant. After she leaves, he fantasizes about sleeping with her and perhaps even marrying her. Because white people do not do such things with Africans, Frant worries about his desires and about the possible consequences of such a liaison. When MacGavin accuses him of being attracted to an African, Frant spews forth a diatribe against blacks so vitriolic that it frightens even himself.

After a long absence Seraphina returns with a huge snakeskin that she gives to Frant, explaining that she killed the snake herself. After Frant thanks her, he and Seraphina admit to liking each another, then Seraphina leaves. Frant hangs the snakeskin in his bedroom.

As Christmas approaches, the MacGavins invite Frant to accompany them as they visit other British residents in the region. Frant shocks them, however, by proposing to remain home alone. On Christmas Day he wanders about aimlessly before deciding to walk to Seraphina's village. Along his way he meets a young man named Umlilwana, who claims to be Seraphina's brother. Umlilwana tells him that he knows he and Seraphina like each other, adding in a friendly tone that such an attraction is not good because the races do not belong together. Frant is initially suspicious of Umlilwana's motives, but the young man's amiable manner persuades Frant to believe him when he says that Seraphina is away for two weeks visiting relatives.

After the holidays, heavy rains arrive and continue for weeks. In the middle of January Frant defies an impending storm by hiking to Seraphina's village. As he approaches her valley, he meets an elderly man who trades at MacGavin's store and who calls him "Child"—a diminution of "Child of Queen Victoria." Distraught, the man says that the storm has flooded the valley, drowning all its inhabitants. When Frant asks about Seraphina, who he believes to have been away visiting relatives, the man says that she never left the village and that Umlilwana was actually her fiancé. Frant considers plunging into the heavy waters to drown himself in the same torrent that swallowed Seraphina. Instead, he utters a single sob and heads home.

Themes and Meanings

William Plomer's "The Child of Queen Victoria" vividly illustrates race and class prejudices that dominated the historical period in which he sets his story. The tale's ironic theme suggests that human nature remains the sole constant in issues concerning social justice; despite the individual's desire to eradicate inequality, individual pride in righteousness will cause one to feel superior and therefore unequal to those whom one wishes to befriend. In addition, Plomer suggests that human nature, with all its flaws, resists redemption or transformation by man or woman alone. He further suggests that people are—by their very natures—destined to conquer one another, and implies that although such a truth is terrible, people can rise from their state of pathos and approach tragic nobility only when they fight what must be a losing battle against their natural, evil impulses.

At the beginning of the story, MacGavin and his wife appear pompous, prejudiced, and insensitive. Motivated by greed and insecurity, they must isolate themselves in their imagined superiority. Their notion that Africans are subhuman may be attributed to common white racial prejudices; however, their belittling of Frant—a fellow white man who gives them valuable free labor—proves that they have developed their prejudices even beyond those in vogue at the time.

Frant initially appears to be superior to the MacGavins in questioning the racial ideas with which he was reared. He is able to communicate honestly with Africans, who recognize his sincerity. One elderly African man, for example, pays Frant mock homage by calling him "Child of Queen Victoria." MacGavin cannot believe Frant allows an African to call him that, but Frant replies, "Why, he's old enough to be my grandfather!" His reply demonstrates his respect for both his elders and for people of another race—a deference that MacGavin lacks. Frant's sincerity diminishes, however, as he begins congratulating himself for his own open-mindedness. By catering to his own hubris, his selfless motives turn selfish and self-conscious, and he comes to regard himself as superior to those people he claims to respect.

Frant first sees Seraphina as a sylph-like woman surrounded by light, a vision of an angel. Their conversation is brief and mysterious, so that the image that stays with

Frant is ethereal. While MacGavin is used to having his way with African women who patronize his store, Frant is neither so boorish nor so indiscriminate. His attraction is to Seraphina alone, a woman named by a Christian missionary who said that God chose her identity. It is no coincidence that Seraphina means snakelike, for she is to Frant as the serpent is to Adam and Eve in the Garden of Eden.

Frant dares contemplating escape from the mold in which his Victorian era has cast him by turning his back on traditional attitudes and following his inherent instincts for freedom, fun, and adventure. In his diatribe to MacGavin condemning all blacks, he protests too much; it is not Frant, but his training speaking. His anger is toward the Victorian beliefs that still trap him, not toward blacks, as he pretends. Seraphina lures Frant with a real snakeskin, symbolic of the snake that taunts Eve in the Garden of Eden. Frant's Christmas Day romp in the MacGavin's garden parallels his state of mind: He determines to renounce the societal prejudices that daunt him and to pursue his happiness—Seraphina—into a paradisiacal new era. His naïveté causes him to trust Umlilwana, just as Adam trusted Eve, and Frant returns home to brood while building tropical storms foreshadow his fate.

What Frant learns too late is that Umlilwana has lied to him, and Umlilwana's lie has shaped his sorrowful, if wiser, future. The fact that Umlilwana, an African, lies is important, as it underscores Plomer's point that all peoples are equal in their self-serving human natures. Frant wants to throw himself into the waters that drowned Seraphina. Against his will, his Victorian upbringing dominates his romantic nature, and as a dutiful representative of Everyman of his era, he turns back toward a life in which he is doomed to live as a true child of Queen Victoria.

Style and Technique

Plomer's choice of an omniscient narrator who reports primarily in the third person, but occasionally speaks with the first-person "we" and the second-person "you," reinforces the story's theme by emphasizing that events happening to others are like those that occur in the lives of all human beings. The author avoids using the first-person "I," which would cause the reader to disassociate from experiences that would thereby seem personal instead of universal.

The tale's ironic tone mimics its ironic message. For example, Plomer writes, "We hear a great deal about sex nowadays; it is possible to overestimate its importance, because there are always people who pay it little attention or who apparently manage, like Sir Isaac Newton, to get along, without giving it a thought. Frant came of a susceptible family." The author's subtle-yet-constant humor acts as an essential lubricant to the story's somber theme.

Plomer's frequent allusions couched in figurative language define and enhance his style. While his similes and metaphors foreshadow forthcoming events, they also personify emotions and conditions so the intangible becomes tangible and so the reader can see, touch, taste, hear, and smell what the people of Plomer's world feel. When Frant initially contemplates his African landscape, at first sight it seems, "like so many African landscapes, a happy mixture of the pastoral and the magnificent, but those who lived under its influence came to feel gradually a mingled sense of uneasiness and sorrow, so that what at first seemed grand became indifferent or menacing." Those sunny hills seem to "be possessed by a spirit that nursed a grievance." Similarly, when Frant congratulates himself for being better than the white people around him, Plomer writes that this attitude "shut him up in a cell of his own (as it were) closely barred with high principles."

L. Elisabeth Beattie

CHILDREN OF STRIKERS

Author: Fred Chappell (1936-   )
Type of plot: Social realism
Time of plot: Late twentieth century
Locale: A mill village in the South
First published: 1980

Principal characters:
A TWELVE-YEAR-OLD GIRL
A YOUNGER BOY, her companion

The Story

On a gray day, two poor children trudge along a riverbank path that leads away from their homes in Fiberville, a cluster of bungalows named for the paper mill where the adults work. The girl occasionally picks up pieces of trash from the ground and examines them. When the boy sees her put something in her pocket, he insists on seeing it. She refuses, however, and when he dashes at her, she slaps him. They walk on.

Eventually, the girl gives her companion a hint. She has found a baby's foot, she says. Excited, the boy begins to speculate about how the foot was cut off of the baby. Perhaps, he thinks, some girl was forced by a boyfriend to kill her baby and cut it up. Now that the girl has the boy's interest aroused, she tries to strike a bargain with him and asks what he will give her if she shows him her find. The boy admits that he does not have anything to offer. He suggests that she does not either and that she is making up her story about the baby's foot.

To prove the boy wrong, the girl shows him the foot. When the boy realizes that the foot belonged to a doll, not a real baby, he angrily knocks it out of her hand. After the girl picks it up again, the children examine it together, trying to guess why someone would mutilate a doll in this way. The cut is so clean that the boy insists that the act was carefully planned—not the result of an impulse—so that it must have been performed by an adult. With evident delight, he tries to imagine what tool was used—a knife or a meat cleaver—and he again insists that an adult was involved. Finally, the girl agrees with him.

Turning back toward the settlement, the children consider other mysteries in their lives, particularly their parents' unhappiness and the presence of angry outsiders in the neighborhood. Although they do not understand exactly what is happening in Fiberville, the children sense that the same kind of anger that would cause a man to cut off a doll's foot has now taken control of their families and their community.

Themes and Meanings

At first glance, Fred Chappell's "Children of Strikers" may seem to be simply a story about violence. The central incident in the plot is the discovery of an amputated foot; although the foot belonged to a doll, not a person, the children see it as evidence of an unknown adult's fury. Moreover, the final paragraph describes the tension among labor strikers and leaves the impression that some violent action is inevitable. Such an interpretation, however, is too limited. This work is actually intended to demonstrate what modern industrial society does to nature and to human nature.

Chappell begins his story by showing how the paper mill has affected the local environment. The river has a noxious stench, the result of chemicals it collects when it flows through the mill. Its banks are black and covered with debris. How this pollution may have affected the health of the workers who live below the mill can only be guessed. Clearly this rape of the environment is not a new development, as the children do not even notice the foul odor. Ironically, to them the ruined river is a source of pleasure; the trash that it flings upon the banks is their treasure trove.

Just as the mill owners are indifferent to nature, it is hardly surprising that they have no interest in the welfare of their workers. They have callously placed the workers' houses downriver from the polluting mill, and have obviously forgotten about them. The workers' cottages are not only small, they are also shabby and ill kept. Although the workers' misery has been intensified by their strike, it seems probable that they were driven to strike out of desperation. One can see evidence of the degree to which the workers were exploited in the pitiable condition of their children. The girl's sweater is so thin that it does not begin to keep her warm. Furthermore, both children look unhealthy, the boy pale and pasty, the girl sallow. The fact that they do not run, as one would expect children to do, but merely shuffle along the path, is further proof that they are malnourished.

Even more devastating than the physical results of grinding poverty is its emotional legacy. Young as she is, the girl has already surrendered to despair. When she looks ahead, the author reports, she sees only day after day of the same kind of misery. She has no dreams; her future holds no possibility of joy.

It is, of course, ironic that the macabre discovery of a baby's foot should bring the children brief pleasure. The primary significance of this central incident, however, can be seen in the way they react to their find. The girl's first impulse is to keep it from the boy, out of pure meanness; his response is to try to seize it. When she slaps him, he is not surprised. There are other telling details. When his imagination cuts loose, the boy speculates about a young mother forced to kill her unwanted baby. After he learns that the foot belonged to a doll, he invents another scenario for murder. Obviously, violence is part of the context of their lives.

When the author has the children think about the atmosphere in their homes in the last paragraph, he suggests an explanation for the violent impulses that he has recorded. To assume, however, that the strike is what brings about violence would be to miss the point of the story. If violence comes, it will be as a direct result not of the workers' protest, but of the factory owners' systematic abuse of their employees and their contempt for the natural environment. There is nothing perfunctory about Chappell's choice of a title for his story. The plight of the two children does not only explain the reason for the strike; it also constitutes an indictment of twentieth century industrial society, which cares for nothing but production and profit.

Style and Technique

In writing, "Children of Strikers," Fred Chappell keeps a considerable distance between himself and his subject. As an objective observer, he describes the landscape and the appearance of the children, and he continues to play this part as he reports their actions and their conversations. Even when he reveals their thoughts, as in the poignant passage when the girl looks into her dismal future, Chappell refrains from making the kind of comment that one might expect from an omniscient narrator. By thus restraining himself, he avoids the possibility of becoming sentimental or of showing his own feelings about such injustice. By simply outlining the situation and permitting readers to draw their own conclusions, he makes the story far more effective.

Although self-effacing, the author does not absent himself from his story. It is his voice that provides all the descriptions of the river, Fibertown with the factory towering over it, and of the children themselves. Without such details—which the children could scarcely be expected to provide—readers would have an incomplete picture. Moreover, the very difference between the perceptions of the adult observer and those of the inexperienced children emphasizes the latters' vulnerability. For example, the author reveals that the polluted river has a terrible odor. This in itself is bad enough, but when he goes on to say that the children are hardly aware of the smell, it is evident that they have lived with it so long that they simply take it for granted. They are too innocent to realize that they are being victimized.

Chappell's skill in juggling voices is also evident in his conclusion. Here he uses his own heightened lyrical style to reveal feelings that the children cannot express. Not until the final sentence, however, does Chappell finally make what might be considered an authorial comment, but even then the poetic quality of his prose leaves the words open to interpretation. Like the children themselves, Chappell's readers are left in a world which seems to be ruled by darkness.

Rosemary M. Canfield Reisman

CHILDYBAWN

Author: Seán O'Faoláin (John Whelan, 1900-1991)
Type of plot: Domestic realism
Time of plot: Unspecified, apparently twentieth century
Locale: Ireland
First published: 1957

> *Principal characters:*
> BENJY SPILLANE, a forty-one-year-old bachelor who lives with his mother
> MRS. SPILLANE, his apparently widowed mother
> ANGELA, his girlfriend, a fellow bank employee

The Story

Mrs. Spillane has received an anonymous letter alerting her to the fact that her middle-aged bachelor son has been romantically involved for years with a young woman at the bank where he works. Horrified, she broods for a few weeks before questioning Benjy indirectly, by suggesting that a gossipy friend has implied that he is planning to marry someone. When he scoffs at her suggestion, she is placated and relieved. After Benjy's spring vacation in France, however, his mother receives another anonymous letter, informing her that the young lady at the bank, Angela, went to France with him. Unwilling to confront Benjy directly, she begins steaming open his letters until she finally finds one from Angela that confirms her worst fears.

Mrs. Spillane turns to a priest for guidance, but is miffed when he only suggests that she pray for Benjy's early marriage. Certain that that idea would appeal no more to Benjy than it does to her, she takes another tack, attempting to involve Benjy in her devotion to Saint Monica, mother of the profligate-turned-saint, Augustine. Benjy, however, is more interested in the sinful chapters of Augustine's *Confessions* than its redemptive sections. After an argument with his mother, he takes his dog for a walk, which quickly ends at the neighborhood pub. With Benjy out of the house, the sanctimonious Mrs. Spillane enjoys the interests that she hides so as not to trouble him: brandy and betting on the ponies.

Still unwilling to confront Benjy about Angela, Mrs. Spillane resorts to deep sighs, sad smiles, and thoughtfully heating his pants in the mornings and removing his galoshes when he gets home. After three months of enduring his mother's unexplained martyred air, Benjy is more than ready for his summer holiday. Convinced that Angela will accompany Benjy, Mrs. Spillane decides to report her son's indiscretions to the bank manager. The manager gives her no comfort, however. After telling her that his employees' personal lives are not his to control, he informs her that Benjy's future advancement at the bank is more likely to be impeded if he remains unmarried. Furious, Mrs. Spillane snarls that she would rather "see him in his pools of blood at my feet than see him married to that Jezebel!" The day after Benjy returns from his holiday, he collapses at his mother's feet in a puddle of blood from a burst ulcer and is rushed to the hospital.

Benjy barely survives physically; emotionally, he is a changed man. Now his evenings are spent quietly at home with his mother or doing charitable works for the church. Liquor and betting are exorcised from his life. His mother, however, continues to indulge in her bad habits, but now they are driven further underground. One night Benjy discovers evidence of his mother's other side: empty brandy bottles, old betting slips, grocery bills, and the anonymous letters. Convinced that his own dour behavior has driven her into secretly drinking and gambling, he begins encouraging her to have tiny drinks at night, and he insists on placing small bets for her. Later he is shocked to discover that her grocery and butcher bills are far in arrears and concludes that his vacations with Angela have prevented his mother from keeping up with the bills— until, that is, he learns that she also owes the betting office more than £125. After he returns to his office that afternoon to find Angela flirting with a teller, he can barely get through the rest of the day.

After dinner, he announces to his mother that he is considering marrying a woman from the bank. To his astonishment, she says that she wishes he had married a long time ago because his new piety is making her miserable. After pondering his situation, Benjy breaks the tension with a laughing riposte at his mother, and they begin planning his wedding over stiff shots of brandy. All that remains is for Benjy to convince Angela to take him back—which she agrees to after several hours of unspecified activities in her landlady's parlor.

Benjy and Angela finally marry five years later—after Mrs. Spillane's death.

Themes and Meanings

The two main characters in "Childybawn" live a life that is uncommon in modern Western urban society, but one which was not terribly unusual in rural Ireland even in the twentieth century. Although the synergistic relationship between the middle-aged bachelor and his lonely mother appears exaggerated, it illustrates several themes: the interdependence underlying even dysfunctional relationships, the secret vices of apparently upstanding citizens, the consequences of lack of communication in relationships, and the ways in which a change in one person in a relationship forces a change in the other until balance is restored.

Although Mrs. Spillane is appalled by Benjy's secret relationship with Angela, she is equally dishonest with her son, waiting for him to leave the house in the evenings before she has her shot of brandy, "or if the poor heart was weak, or overexcited, maybe two." Both Benjy and his mother manage to maintain a comfortable domestic situation, while preserving a secret wild side. Mrs. Spillane's approach to confrontation with her son is no more direct than the communications of the anonymous letter writer who sets the plot in motion; rather than question him directly about his relationship with Angela, she resorts to sighing, then putting pictures of Saint Monica and Saint Augustine in his room, and finally going behind his back to the bank manager demanding that the young woman in question be fired. When Benjy finds the evidence of his mother's secret drinking and betting, he is convinced that his own behavior has driven her to such pursuits. Rather than discuss it with her directly, he unexpectedly begins to encourage her habits. She accedes but feigns reluctance, while continuing with her indulgences on an even larger scale when Benjy is out.

Style and Technique

"Childybawn," is filled with Irish expressions and spellings that firmly root the story in rural Ireland: "Wisha, I dunno now where did I get that?" "Amn't I his mother?" "You bloody ould rip of hell you!" Its title means "fair-haired child ("bawn" is an Irish word meaning "fair-haired"). Rural Ireland has changed so little over the years that the story could have been set as easily in the nineteenth century as in the twentieth; the few definitive clues to the fact that it takes place in the twentieth century include references to Angela's wearing seamed nylon stockings and slacks, and the fact that Benjy and his mother go to the movies.

"Childybawn" appeared in the 1950's, after Seán O'Faoláin had been publishing stories for approximately thirty years. O'Faoláin has said that his stories of that time were his first attempts to look at his countrymen with a more satirical eye. Although this story succeeds in highlighting its characters' foibles, it relies on several strained coincidences to advance the plot. In the apparently small town in which the Spillanes reside, for example, it is hard to believe that Benjy and Angela could be romantically involved for years, much less travel regularly together to the Continent, without either the bank manager or Mrs. Spillane being aware of it. The bleeding ulcer that brings on Benjy's near-deathbed conversion, coming shortly after his mother's curse that she would rather see him in a pool of his own blood than married to Angela, is another example of forced contrivance used to advance the plot.

It is appropriate that the two main characters are vividly and equally drawn, to the exclusion of the minor characters, because they exist and function as a couple, as Benjy points out, with no apparent self-consciousness, early in the story. By contrast, Angela's motives for staying in the lengthy relationship are never explained; in fact, she has no dialogue other than the brazen words in the letter Mrs. Spillane finds. Again, this fits the story: Angela understands that she will never replace Mrs. Spillane in Benjy's priorities; early in the story, the narrator recalls her saying it made Angela sick to see Benjy and his mother together; at the end, when Benjy asks her to marry him, she first suggests he marry his mother, since he is so fond of her. Her perceptions are, of course, borne out by the fact that the engagement drags on for five years, until Mrs. Spillane dies.

Irene Struthers

CHINA BROWNE

Author: Gerald Vizenor (1934-   )
Type of plot: Social realism
Time of plot: Around the 1960's or 1970's
Locale: Beijing and Tianjin, China
First published: 1988

Principal characters:
CHINA BROWNE, a Native American woman visiting China
AN OLD CHINESE WOMAN
CINCH, an American teacher
ANGEL, Cinch's wife, also a teacher

The Story

China Browne is sitting in a railroad station lounge, reading and absorbing the sights, sounds, and smells of her surroundings. English-language travel posters on the wall behind the ticket counter reveal that she is in China. She has been in the country only three days, but the harried American couple who soon join her in the Beijing lounge are beginning their second year as teachers in China. When the heavily burdened teachers learn that China Browne—carrying only an overnight pack—is going their way, they impose upon her to carry their heaviest piece of baggage.

As the three Americans head down the crowded stairs of the Beijing terminal for the departure platform to Tianjin, China finds herself behind an old Chinese woman. The woman, wearing peasant clothing and a visored cap with a red star, has traditionally bound feet; she is carefully descending the steps, not realizing that China is helping her by slowing the surging crowd behind them. A moment later China smiles at her, but the woman, who recognizes her as a foreigner, reacts with suspicion.

China continues her friendly overtures toward the old woman, introducing herself in Chinese and offering assistance, but is sorely repaid for her efforts: The old woman calls her a "foreign devil" and shouts irrational accusations at her. China feigns imperturbability and is admonished by the seasoned American couple not to befriend the Chinese. Inwardly, however, she wonders how to promote harmony in these unfamiliar circumstances. Her instincts ordinarily allow her to "overturn mistrust and suspicion"; but "with no natural cues to the humor" around her, she has to work harder than usual.

Upon arriving in Tianjin, China lags behind the two American teachers so that she may see the old woman again. She watches the woman cross the street and head down the rough concrete steps leading to the cool riverside. At the bottom level, the woman trips and falls into the river. Chinese passersby seem indifferent: As the woman struggles vainly to pull herself out onto the concrete walkway, no one moves to help her. China pulls the woman out herself, and this time is rewarded with a smile. She lovingly unbinds the woman's feet, massages her toes, and dries them with her bandanna, "the same cloth she [often] drew between her own toes in meditation." Both women rest briefly by the river. For the moment, time stands still, even moves backward. In this interlude, China finds harmony and relief from the crush of time. The two women part friends, and the old woman gives China two gifts: her cap with the red star and a small round metal herb box. Finally, China is rudely returned to the fast-paced time of the Americans' "measured world" when the two teachers find her and scold her for the delay and anxiety that she has caused them.

Themes and Meanings

The introduction of the two American teachers soon after China scans the grammatically tangled travel slogans draws attention to the slightly warped forms of English around her. Cinch's nonstandard spoken grammar (for example, "Angel and me are teachers here") would be insignificant were it not for the unstated assumption that American teachers overseas are hired, at least partly, to serve as models of standard American English as well as to promote good will. All of Cinch's initial dialogue (printed in run-on form, with comma splices), together with the couple's actions and frequently expressed lack of good will, reinforces two apparent aims of the author: to show that the couple's ideas are often wrong and to make China Browne shine by comparison. Angel, for example, is anything but an angel: In addition to unloading her heaviest piece of baggage on China, she crassly belittles China's Native American ancestry. The woman's "mock blonde" hair color intensifies the contrast between her and the millions of dark-haired Chinese around her. Finally, when they are not complaining, Angel and Cinch display the smugly superior condescending attitudes of the stereotypically ugly American cultural imperialist abroad. Unlike them, China speaks softly, looks more like the Chinese, and works at fitting in—even though she also is distinctively American, for both the abrasive American couple and the old Chinese woman immediately see that she is not Chinese.

The old Chinese woman's character, less fully defined than those of the others, befits her role as a symbolic link between past and present, a link suggested also within a subtitle that is sometimes used with the story: "Red Stars and Bound Lilies," both of whose nouns allude to the old woman. The red star on her Maoist army hat, symbolizing the revolutionary turmoil of twentieth century China, may explain her initial paranoia, for China's Cultural Revolution of the 1960's and 1970's caused great unrest and fear among the people. On the other hand, the woman's bound lilies—a common Chinese metaphor for bound feet—symbolize ancient tradition. Vizenor's sole fully contextualized use of the metaphor may not convey its dual meanings adequately to English-speaking readers, yet it is clear that the old woman's "golden lilies" (upon which she "wobbled" unsteadily), the "bound lilies" on the cover of the herb box, and the "bound lilies" of the subtitle all signify the same thing—bound feet.

Feet, as well as people, are by tradition bound. In passing along the small herb box and its contents, the old woman symbolically connects China Browne to an old Chinese tradition—which the modern American teachers quickly disparage as worthless and possibly dangerous. The teachers obviously prefer their large burdensome box and the expensive modern device within, which will inevitably break down, become worthless, and be thrown away. Their box represents a value system based on new material possessions. The teachers, whose examples in this case should not be followed, exist in jarring contrast to China, her values, and her world.

China Browne's less materialistic ideals, like the small round herb box, take but small space and yet may be held, treasured, and passed on for generations. Similarly, her desire to make meaningful contact with those around her represents a universally esteemed human trait. In her encounter with the old woman, she demonstrates the life-sustaining and life-affirming rewards shared when two people meet and understand each other, despite linguistic and cultural traditions that are literally a world apart.

Style and Technique

Although Gerald Vizenor's understated humor in this story typifies his style, his language and plot here are more straightforward than usual. Vizenor's characters ordinarily act more strangely, his plots contain more bizarre twists, and his creative use of language leans far more toward the punningly incomprehensible. Some puns here are almost subtle enough to be dismissed as mere details: For example, the mangled English travel ads in the Beijing station (especially "Make Wind on a Phoenix Bicycle") may serve simply to identify the setting as non-English.

Vizenor's best extended pun, of the elusive sort that he often uses, may be his repeated reference to the capital-punishment article on the newspaper in which the teachers have wrapped a package. The joke is that the unending care for and carrying of their material possessions constitutes a form of punishment which the materialistic capitalists Cinch and Angel joylessly endure. Only the incident of China shouting into a "panic hole" eludes easy explanation; however, multiple references to the hot weather may suggest that the topsoil has dried and cracked under the stress of the summer heat. Despite this story's uncharacteristic clarity (relatively speaking), Vizenor's trademark word-play and tricks with names abound.

The characters are realistically drawn, with little overt mingling of fact and fiction. Only China's claim that her grandfather was "the Baron of Patronia" exemplifies the way in which Vizenor often blurs distinctions between the real and the imaginary. In another story in *The Trickster of Liberty* (1988), in which "China Browne" originally appeared, China reveals that her family lives on the White Earth Reservation—a real reservation in west-central Minnesota, where Vizenor spent much of his own childhood. As in many of Vizenor's stories, such distinctions underscore the oddly realistic and humorous ways in which reality and fantasy often blend indistinguishably.

William Matta

CHRISTMAS EVERY DAY

Author: Heinrich Böll (1917-1985)
Type of plot: Fable
Time of plot: 1947-1948
Locale: Probably Cologne, Germany
First published: "Nicht nur zur Weihnachtszeit," 1952 (English translation, 1986)

> *Principal characters:*
> THE UNNAMED NARRATOR
> UNCLE FRANZ, a businessman
> AUNT MILLA, his wife, who loves Christmas
> FRANZ, their son

The Story

After World War II, apparently in Cologne, Uncle Franz Lenz's wholesale grocery business is bouncing back from a slight wartime interruption. The Lenz family—Uncle Franz, Aunt Milla, Johannes, Lucie, young Cousin Franz, and assorted grandchildren—have come through the conflict almost intact. Only Aunt Milla has been deeply unsettled by the recent bloodbath—because her Christmas celebrations were curtailed.

Cousin Franz is something of a conscience for the family, a young man of notable piety who scandalizes them by becoming a boxer. The first to notice how badly askew things are, he has little sympathy with his father, identified by the narrator as the kindest of men—who provided his wife a private bomb shelter and a car to take her to the country whenever air raids threatened—nor with his mother, who is still grieving that ornaments on her Christmas tree were damaged by nearby bomb explosions and that Christmas festivities were cancelled in 1940.

Now that those unpleasant times are over—the narrator can scarcely bring himself to mention the war by name—Aunt Milla is insisting that Christmas be restored right down to the angel at the tip of the tree, who actually whispers "peace." Uncle Franz is prosperous enough by 1946 to gratify his wife's wishes. He spares no expense to obtain the decorations, food, candies, and candles that Aunt Milla had enjoyed in the old days. When it comes time to take down the Christmas tree at Candlemas (February 2), the usually charming old lady begins to scream. Neurologists, priests, and psychiatrists are summoned to the house, but the shrieking goes on unabated for almost a week. Cousin Franz, who will not participate in indulging his mother, suggests a visit by an exorcist, but Uncle Franz comes up with a different solution: a new tree to replace the old, and Christmas all over again.

Because it is nearly carnival time, Christmas decorations are not to be found in the city's shops, nor are trees for sale. Uncle Franz's connections allow extraordinary measures: An import license from Czechoslovakia is obtained; phone calls are made to toy companies; and grandchildren are dispatched to the forest with an ax. Soon arrangements are complete. When Aunt Milla is at last summoned to the Christmas room, everything appears normal, and she is able to call in the family to light the tree and sing carols.

To avoid upsetting Aunt Milla, Christmas Eve will become a permanent event. As other people sing "Come, Lovely May," "Silent Night" will resound from the Lenz house. In June, the parish priest refuses to continue taking part in the nightly ritual, but a replacement for him is easily found, and a firm contracted to replace old trees with fresh ones.

The enforced Christmases gradually begin to take their toll, and family members ask to be excused from attendance. Lucie, the first to succumb, suffers a nervous malady touched off by the sight of Christmas cookies.

Now Cousin Franz's earlier prognostications and the narrator's reluctant admission that symptoms of disintegration are appearing in his family come back to haunt the reader: Johannes has quit his choral society, sick to death of German songs; Uncle Franz has hired an actor to impersonate him at the nightly sessions around the Christmas tree, has taken a mistress, and is indulging in unethical business practices. He is even ready to pay professional actors to play the roles of family members in order to fool Aunt Milla.

As the two-year anniversary of this charade approaches, the narrator admits that Cousin Franz has been right. He sees that nightly singing and a diet of marzipan are having a bad effect on the smaller children and arranges to have the children replaced by wax dummies. He notes that his cousins have all suffered psychological disturbances. Johannes has joined the Communist Party. Lucie, a confirmed bar-hopper, is planning to leave Germany with her husband. The artificial Christmases continue, but the participants are drinking more than they should and indulging in petty thievery. Only Aunt Milla and the priest seem unaffected. When the narrator learns that the angel who whispers "peace" is activated by a phonograph in the next room, his disillusionment is complete. He visits his cousin Franz, now in a monastery, who tells him that life is punishment. Moral responsibility, Böll seems to say, must be assumed; denial is poisonous.

Themes and Meanings

"Christmas Every Day" can be seen as an allegory of Germany's failure to accept responsibility for its past and a cautionary tale admonishing Germany—and, by extension, all humankind—to mind its moral house. Böll accuses his country of closing its eyes to the recent horrors of Adolf Hitler's Nazi repression. The new German Federal Republic, he says, is a bogus state, morally and ethically bankrupt, which attempts to present Germany to the world as a land of decent people with solid middle-class values, lovely music, and endearing traditions. Where, he asks in effect, is the penitent confession that this is a country in which millions of people still living supported the brutal invasion of their neighbors? Why are Christmas carols being sung by those who built death camps to destroy other human beings or, at the very best, by those who chose not to see what was going on?

In "Christmas Every Day," things stand for other things, but it is not always possible to identify them exactly. For example, it is hard to say with certainty what Böll means about one priest's taking another's place at the Christmas Eve festivities. Perhaps he is thinking of those clergymen, both Protestant and Roman Catholic, who resisted Nazi rule and the others who quietly acquiesced to it. In short, not even those well versed in modern German history and in literature will agree entirely on the meaning of the story, although its gist is startlingly clear.

Style and Technique

As a satire highly critical of postwar German society, "Christmas Every Day" juxtaposes realistic details, such as accurate descriptions of everyday life, with strange, unlikely incidents and details. For example, while the Lenz family sings real songs and eats real Christmas cookies and candies around a real Christmas tree, such devices as individuals being replaced by actors or even wax figures alert one to the fact that there is more here than meets the eye.

This sort of juxtaposition suggests that there is something wrong and dangerous about refusing to recognize what a society has done. The Lenz family, gently bullied by a tyrannical wife and mother, indulges in preposterous make-believe verging on hypocrisy—just as Germany was doing, Böll implies, in the years of the Economic Miracle (the period of unparalleled prosperity that began only a few years after Germany's surrender to the Allies, and continued through the next two decades and beyond).

Böll likewise employs motifs that have become icons in much of his fiction to drive his point home. The pleasant qualities of middle-class German life serve Böll like a two-edged sword. In much of his fiction, loving families, little gifts, decorated birthday tables, and fresh flowers represent the civilizing elements of society that, fragile as they are, stand like mighty fortresses against totalitarianism and its armies of flunkies. Often a shared drink in a Hungarian tavern is more meaningful in his humanistic view than a troop movement. At other times, these same gestures, festive customs, and bourgeois ceremonies, take on a threatening aspect. Such is certainly the case in "Christmas Every Day," in which German Christmas practices, which much of the Western world has embraced, become symbols of a sort of mass denial as an entire culture attempts to ignore its horrific past. If such a perspective seems confusing—two different ways of regarding the same thing—it is only because Böll himself has never quite resolved the contradiction. He has never decided if fallible humanity is capable of triumphing over the forces of selfishness, intolerance, and hate that constantly assault it. Even though he considers his country guilty of terrible crimes against humankind, he refuses to judge his people as collectively guilty. To do that would be to engage in a Nazi-like racism, to declare that Germans are racially moral inferiors, ethical "subhumans"—a notion that he positively rejects.

James E. Devlin

A CHRISTMAS MEMORY

Author: Truman Capote (Truman Strekfus Persons, 1924-1984)
Type of plot: Domestic realism
Time of plot: The 1930's
Locale: Unspecified, but probably Monroeville, Alabama
First published: 1956

> *Principal characters:*
> BUDDY, the narrator, who recalls a Christmas when he was seven
> HIS COUSIN, a woman in her sixties with the spirit of a child

The Story

The adult narrator of this story nostalgically remembers the last Christmas that he enjoyed as a seven-year-old boy with his "sixty-something" cousin, who called him Buddy in memory of a boy who had once been her best friend. Buddy lives with this cousin and other relatives in a spreading old house in a country town (which probably represents Monroeville, Alabama, where Truman Capote lived with his four unmarried adult cousins until he was about ten).

As they have done each year, Buddy and his favorite cousin inaugurate this Christmas season with a late November fruitcake baking, which entails gathering windfallen pecans and a visit to the dilapidated shack of Mr. Haha Jones to buy whiskey. They finance this operation with money that they have accumulated through the year in their Fruitcake Fund. After four days of baking, their fruitcakes are ready for delivery to friends—"persons we've met maybe once, perhaps not at all," who include President Roosevelt and the bus driver Abner Packer.

At this particular Christmas, the delivery of the fruitcakes is followed by a celebratory sharing of the last two inches of whiskey in the bottle used for the fruitcakes. Buddy, his cousin, and her dog Queenie all get slightly tipsy, moving two other relatives to scold Buddy's cousin for corrupting a child. The next morning's adventure heals all, however, as Buddy and his cousin search deep into the woods for their Christmas decorations. They gather wreaths, chop down a tree, laboriously drag everything home, and dress the tree with homemade decorations. They then wrap gifts, secretly making one another kites. On Christmas morning they wake early and make enough noise to rouse the others. After the presents are opened, Buddy and his cousin go to the pasture below the house to fly their new kites.

This is the last Christmas they spend together. The next year, Buddy is sent to a military school and then to a new home. Years later he receives news that his cousin has died—an event that he feels intuitively before the news arrives. As he grows older and feels winter coming on, he often thinks of "a lost pair of kites hurrying toward heaven."

Themes and Meanings

There is an obvious sadness and sense of loss at the passing of the cousin in this story, but most important, "A Christmas Memory" reveals a preoccupation with the theme of children suffering from the dominance of unfeeling adults. As a seven-year-old, Buddy was an innocent young boy who would not realize the full impact of insensitive, adult domination until later in life. The real hero of his memoir is his cousin, who remains a child at heart even into her sixties. The villains of the story are their relatives, a shadowy group of adults who do not display the sensitivity and the joy for life that Buddy and his cousin share.

The story's villains are initially curtly described simply as the "other people [who] inhabit the house, relatives; and though they have power over us, and frequently make us cry, we are not, on the whole, too much aware of them." The point of the story, however, is that these adults cannot be ignored forever. The wonderful times that Buddy and his cousin enjoy are inevitably interrupted by reminders of the presence and domination of these unfeeling adults. Buddy and his cousin lack ready money for their annual fruitcakes because they only receive "skinflint sums [that] persons in the house occasionally provide (a dime is considered big money)." Two angry relatives burst into the whiskey-drinking scene, "potent with eyes that scold, tongues that scold," and their annoyance on rising so early on Christmas morning is followed by an artificially leisurely breakfast that delays the two "children" from opening their presents. The unimaginative and practical Christmas gifts that Buddy receives indicate the gulf between him and the other adults. Naturally, he is disappointed with socks, a Sunday-school shirt, handkerchiefs, a hand-me-down sweater and a subscription to *The Little Shepherd*. "It makes me boil," he recalls. Finally, these all-powerful adults, "Those who Know Best," send Buddy away to military school and a new home, separating him forever from his dear cousin.

Other adults in the story reinforce the theme—for example, the lazy wife of the rich mill owner who is offended because Buddy and his cousin will not sell their Christmas tree. Initially, Mr. Haha Jones, "a giant with razor scars across his cheeks," appears to be another unfeeling adult. He is called Haha because he never laughs; however, he ultimately shows a more playful side. He smiles at their request for whiskey and instead of charging them two dollars, asks only for a sample fruitcake in return. He is finally declared to be different, "a lovely man." Some of Buddy and his cousin's "friends" are adults, but they also are different from the adults of their immediate family circle. They are mostly strangers who display sensitivity and friendliness—such as the Roosevelts, who send thank you notes for the fruitcakes, and the Wistons, a young California couple who once spent a pleasant hour chatting with the family on the porch after their car broke down.

Style and Technique

The most important stylistic feature of "A Christmas Memory" is the sense of immediacy that Capote creates by writing in the present tense. Although he writes as an adult remembering a childhood experience at least twenty years earlier, he avoids the feeling of distance that narrating a memoir in the past tense would create or the impersonal objectivity that a third-person narrator might lend. Anxious to create a strong emotional context, he favors the immediacy of the present tense, almost as if he would prefer the memoir to be a play. Indeed, in 1966 the story was adapted for television, with Capote reading the story as a voice-over narrator.

The story begins by asking readers to become an audience, almost as if they were sitting in a theater: "Imagine a morning in late November. A coming of winter morning more than twenty years ago." Before the first paragraph ends, the story slips into the present tense, thereby creating a dramatic quality: "Just today the fireplace commenced its seasonal roar. A woman with shorn white hair is standing at the kitchen window."

This immediate dramatic quality is maintained throughout the story. At times it describes past events that are important to the moment—"Once we won seventy-ninth prize, five dollars, in a national football contest"—but it is always quick to return the reader's attention to the dramatic present—"at the moment our hopes are centered on the fifty-thousand-dollar Grand Prize being offered to name a new brand of coffee." At times, Capote even includes what might be seen as stage directions—"Enter: two relatives. Very angry. Potent with eyes that scold, tongues that scold. Listen to what they have to say." At other times, he writes what sounds like directions in a film script: "Morning. Frozen rime lusters the grass" or "Home: Queenie slumps by the fire and sleeps till tomorrow, snoring loud as a human."

The story ends with "This is our last Christmas together. Life separates us," using "is" instead of "was." Even as Capote recalls the passage of time that eventually led to the death of his cousin, he holds on to the present tense as long as he can—"a morning arrives in November, a leafless, birdless coming of winter morning, when she cannot rouse herself to exclaim: 'Oh, my, it's fruitcake weather!'" In the last words of the story, Buddy is an adult again, but he still remembers in the present tense: "That is why, walking across a school campus on this particular December morning, I keep searching the sky. As if I expected to see, rather like hearts, a lost pair of kites hurrying toward heaven."

Terry Nienhuis

CHROMA

Author: Frederick Barthelme (1943-   )
Type of plot: Neorealism
Time of plot: The 1980's
Locale: American suburbia
First published: 1987

> *Principal characters:*
> THE NARRATOR
> ALICIA, his wife
> JULIET and
> HEATHER, their neighbors

The Story

The unnamed narrator explains that his wife, Alicia, is not home this weekend; she is with her boyfriend, George. As part of their "new deal," Alicia spends every other weekend with him. The narrator is therefore spending Saturday with his attractive neighbor, Juliet, a fitness and health buff in her twenties. Juliet lives next door with her girlfriend, Heather, who is thirty-five. At a restaurant, Juliet tries to get the narrator to say what is bothering him, but he is unwilling to discuss it. She abruptly announces, "When we go back to the house I want to make love to you."

When they return to Juliet's house, she sits the narrator down on the sofa. Looking out the sliding doors, he notices that Heather and Juliet do not have a real Weber barbecue. Juliet tries to seduce him, but the narrator feels uncomfortable with the idea. They hug and kiss but do not have sex.

Later in the afternoon the narrator is out driving and comes upon Heather, who has been shopping and is riding the bus. He gives her a ride home. As they talk, Heather urges the narrator to take a stand against Alicia's relationship with George. She also expresses concern about the narrator's and Juliet's interest in each other. Upon arriving home, they find Alicia working with some potted plants. Alicia invites Heather and Juliet to join them later for dinner. After Heather leaves, Alicia suggests that they go inside for a nap.

Juliet and Heather arrive at eight. There is a phone call from George in the middle of dinner, and Alicia goes into the other room to talk privately. Heather and Juliet become uncomfortable; Juliet gives the narrator a "sweet look out of the tops of her eyes." After Heather and Juliet leave, he tells Alicia about his earlier dalliance with Juliet. Unhappy, Alicia points out that their "deal" was that she would be free to go out while he stayed home and remained faithful to her. Pointing out that he looks unhappy, she asks if he will be okay if she goes out, clearly hinting that he should ask her to stay home. He does not pick up his cue. "Maybe I ought to stay?" she asks; he replies, "I'm O.K." Soon George arrives, honking his horn to summon Alicia.

The narrator watches television alone, fantasizes about Juliet, and eventually falls asleep. He is wakened by the doorbell. It is Heather, upset because Juliet has told her that she kissed him and offered to make love to him. The narrator tries to placate her, telling her that it was a sweet gesture, but one that nobody took seriously. Heather blurts out, "I don't want us in your mess." He admits that he feels "lousy" about the whole situation.

Alicia returns before midnight. She asks the narrator to talk to her while she takes a bath. He tells her that he did not sleep with Juliet but that they had a "terrific time." He stares at his wife, thinking that she is beautiful. They finally talk seriously, wondering aloud if they are "in trouble," as Heather had said, and wondering why he is becoming interested in Juliet, which was not part of the plan. Alicia guesses that they can save their marriage if they want to. Then she holds up her hands in a way that the narrator interprets to mean that she wants to straighten out something very important. Instead, she says that she is hungry for—"*dying for*"—cheese ball and has been thinking about it all night long. She will even make it herself. The story ends with the narrator trying to sort out his feelings as his wife has thrown him yet another curve. "She's so beautiful," he thinks.

Themes and Meanings

Among Frederick Barthelme's concerns in "Chroma" are the disconnectedness of modern American life, the inadequacy and unreliability of conversation and language, and the roles of the sexes. As in much of his fiction, the characters are given no histories beyond a few sketchy details. The reader never learns the protagonist's name or occupation or how long he has been married to Alicia. The locale is never identified, except that it is an American suburb. In neither the protagonist's thoughts nor his conversations does one get any sense of where he is from or where he wants to go. The story exists very much in its present moment (the narrator speaks in the present tense), in frequently trivial actions and conversations. Its suburbanites are disconnected both from their own histories and from one another. In Barthelme's modern America, people are more connected to the objects and surfaces of everyday life—a barbecue seen through a window, shirts and a plastic fish bought on a shopping trip, the cover of an *Artforum* magazine that the narrator likes "pretty much"—than to anything else.

Conversations in "Chroma" frequently confuse the characters and the reader alike. When Heather asks the narrator if he and his wife are "still playing Donkey Kong," he has no idea what she means; she does not either, it turns out—"I just said it." Twice other characters speak to the narrator using words or phrases so confusing that he simply echoes them. When his wife comments on his sad expression, for example, calling him "melancholy in the mug," he replies, "Mug?" Heather explicitly comments on the struggle to make oneself understood. Mimicking karate chops in the air, she says, "I don't even know what I'm talking about. . . . I'm having my ongoing struggle with the language."

More problematic than these language difficulties is Barthelme's distrust of people's very thoughts. Believing that people's views of the world are transitory and unreliable, he generally has his characters say very little about their perspectives on life. As the story begins, for example, the narrator avoids telling Juliet what is bothering him for fear that he will say "a lot of junk now that won't be true this afternoon." Later, the narrator thinks about "how fast things fly through your head when you're thinking, about how you see only key parts of stuff." This is a tantalizing idea, but Barthelme seldom gives readers a good look at those "things." Therefore— and this is the case with much neorealist or minimalist work—the reader never learns enough about the characters to decide how to feel about them. To a great extent, they remain ciphers, as disconnected from their own thoughts as they are from one another.

In Barthelme's stories it is often the women characters who make things happen and who display the outward manifestations of strength and aggression. Whenever Alicia appears in the story, she calls the tune. It was her decision to have an affair (although that word is never used); her husband simply goes along with the idea. At one point, Alicia playfully pushes him a couple of times. Similarly, Juliet announces that she wants to make love to him, and he obligingly lets her "march" him to her house. He describes Juliet as having neck muscles that ripple prettily. Heather offers to have Juliet break George's nose, and Heather likes to spout her own version of tough-guy talk. Compared with these women, the narrator—and, one might guess, the unseen George, with his "discreet" beeps of the horn—is remarkably passive. Beyond this tweaking of stereotypes, there is another noteworthy aspect of sexuality. As in a number of Barthelme's stories, sex is alluded to regularly and even offered, but it is not actually engaged in—yet another example of the connections between people that are never made.

Style and Technique

Barthelme is frequently called a minimalist (an identification that he does not relish); his writing has also been classified as neorealism or pop realism. Rather than attempting to depict reality, he creates a fictive world that is at once an oblique reflection and a reinterpretation of reality. Essential to the creation of this world is extreme specificity regarding visual details (gestures and objects) and, usually, extreme vagueness regarding a larger sense of place and time. In the dialogue of "Chroma," Barthelme creates skewed phrases and expressions that do not quite belong to the world outside the story. Heather, with her hilariously offbeat slang, threatens the narrator by saying, "You touch the doughnut girl, I'll do your teeth in piano wire." Alicia refers to herself doing "the rope-a-dope all over the place."

One element of Barthelme's style that has attracted considerable comment is his tendency to describe scenes and actions through an accretion of brand names and proper nouns. Another is his detailed, almost hyper-real, descriptions of everyday objects. In "Chroma," the brand names are relatively unobtrusive; on the other hand, the reader learns that Heather and Juliet do not have a "Weber barbecue" but never learn the narrator's name. A beautifully described scene that is almost a still life encapsulates Barthelme's ability to combine brand names and description to create a unique and somehow mysterious world. The narrator is home alone. In silence, he looks at a shadow cast on the wall by the "mercury vapor street lamp" shining through the Levolors; it is "broken by a gladiola on the pedestal where we always put outgoing mail." He is captivated; he sits there, watching the shadow ("it's gorgeous") and feeling like someone in an Obsession ad. Clearly Barthelme (who studied both art and architecture), as well as his characters, appreciates such sudden moments of beauty. Indeed, they are perhaps to be preferred to the uneasy, even vaguely threatening, human interactions that he describes. Barthelme criticizes but can also take delight in modern life, as when flowers, window blinds, and streetlights can produce a momentary respite from its uncertainties.

McCrea Adams

CIMARRON

Author: Francine Prose (1947-   )
Type of plot: Domestic realism
Time of plot: 1983-1984
Locale: Cimarron Acres trailer park, near Oneonta, New York
First published: 1989

> *Principal characters:*
> CORAL, a young expectant mother whose husband has been killed
> MARGO, her mother-in-law
> GENE, her father-in-law
> LEE, a talkative neighbor
> TRACY, Lee's "clairvoyant" daughter
> PAUL, Coral's brother-in-law

The Story

Shortly after resigning herself to the fact that her husband, Kenny, will be absent from the birth of their first child, Coral sees a television news broadcast reporting that Kenny has been killed in Beirut, Lebanon. He is a victim of a terrorist car bomb attack on his military barracks. Over the ensuing weeks, Coral takes poor care of herself. Still numbed by Kenny's death, she exists only mechanically. She is thus relieved when her in-laws, Gene and Margo, take charge of her life by moving her to their somewhat unkempt rural trailer court at Cimarron Acres.

As more time passes Coral and Margo become closer. Coral also gets to know Lee, a single mother who lives in a neighboring trailer. Lee's conversations center on the perils of being a single mother and her conceited ten-year-old daughter, Tracy—who Lee believes is gifted with "second sight."

As Coral spends her free time taking walks, she notices the details of Cimarron Acres. At first she is uneasy with the ugly environment, especially a landfill behind the trailer. As she studies the mildly unpleasant children and mothers who inhabit the park, she worries about how her own child will turn out. Meanwhile, she also becomes acquainted with Kenny's brother Paul, who occasionally has dinner with his parents.

As the weather grows warmer, Coral gets bigger and her routine continues with little change. At times, Coral, Margo, and Gene laugh together at Coral's accurate impersonations of little Tracy and Margo's impersonations of Lee. One day Lee bursts in to announce that she has won five hundred dollars in a lottery with numbers that Tracy picked. Lee uses the money to prepare a special birthday party for Tracy.

Feeling relaxed on the day of Tracy's party, Coral is finally comfortable among her new neighbors and they are now used to her. As she and Paul sit together in Lee's yard, watching the festivities, Coral suddenly realizes that she has forgotten to buy Tracy a gift. Although she is not particularly fond of Tracy, she feels awful because she knows that each childhood birthday comes only once. Meanwhile, Tracy and Lee make a big production out of gathering presents from the guests. When Tracy sees that Coral has no gift for her, she calmly tells her of a "vision" she has had of Coral's baby in heaven, lying happily next to the Doberman who killed it. At first Coral is overcome by the fact that anyone—even a child like Tracy—can be so cruel to a pregnant mother. Then she realizes that her baby will be healthy, as Tracy is only being vindictive.

The story concludes with Paul's distant voice coming to Coral as she hugs her well-rounded stomach and thinks about her baby.

Themes and Meanings

"Cimarron" first appeared in a collection of short stories by twenty-two writers that was designed to benefit Share Our Strengths, a campaign against hunger, homelessness, and illiteracy. In some ways the tragic circumstances experienced by Francine Prose's character Coral might suggest a basis for the problems addressed by the campaign. After abruptly losing the emotional and physical support of her husband, and pregnant with her first child, Coral becomes little more than an automaton. In deep shock she gazes repeatedly at pictures of Beirut in *Newsweek*, doing little more to care for herself than making mechanical trips to buy frozen dinners—one meal at a time. Though she realizes that this life is "unhealthy, and probably bad for the baby," she cannot break her cycle of despondency.

Though issues of poverty and homelessness are not central to this story, one senses that the root causes for these conditions—such as loss through death, isolation, or alienation—are being suggested. In that respect, it is not so much that Margo and Gene offer Coral a place to live, but that they present her with safe haven, a place where she can reassess her life and heal. As the story progresses, it conveys a slow movement toward Coral's restoration of her strength and wits. Just as it is clear that Coral is a survivor, it is apparent that her willingness to live with Gene and Margo comes from her core of strength and knowledge of self. She is not presented as either self-destructive or foolish. At first Coral is disturbed by Cimarron Acres, with its "one frozen-solid brown road, rutted and covered with dog turds" and its "junk machinery everywhere," but gradually she understands that she needs the "solid presence" of Margo's shoulder on which to cry.

The characters of Lee and her daughter Tracy allow Prose to explore the further theme of coping in a sometimes hostile world. As Coral begins to become herself again, she thinks that she might be able to relate to the apparently independent Lee, only to realize that Lee is not quite the role model that she first appeared to be. For example, Lee's campaign to have a school-bus stop moved to the other side of the road reveals a selfish interest rather than one aimed at general betterment. When Lee is not boasting about Tracy, her conversations are limited to forceful declarations about the hard lives endured by single mothers, laced with horrific anecdotes. Yet Lee's self-absorption (or her self-destructive chain smoking), may not necessarily be indictments. Lee may simply represent another kind of survivor—one whose circumstances force her in a different direction. The difference between Coral and Lee is that Coral has the support of people who care. Yet Prose also leaves it clear—as ten-year-old

Tracy chillingly predicts to Coral her baby's mutilation—that we remain prepared for the almost unlimited evil exhibited by those "just waiting . . . so they can drive into you and blow you up."

Style and Technique

Prose presents a realistic portrait of Coral's struggle to get on with her life. It succeeds because it first allows the reader to believe in what Coral has to endure. Coral's reactions immediately after hearing the news of her husband's death are not unlike those experienced by anyone who has abruptly lost a loved one. Coral's initial responses are almost surreal as the rituals of the funeral and visitors offering consolation take on the cartoon-like qualities of a wacky animated feature for her. Afterward, as she settles into a bare existence, Prose again hits the mark, achieving for the reader a feeling of sluggish inertia as Coral stares at her *Newsweek* magazines, heats frozen dinners, or lies awake nights worrying about her baby.

The next stage of Prose's story takes Coral from her nearly catatonic existence to one of renewed strength and hope. Though real change will take more time, the progression is discernible in gradual degrees. After relocating to Margo and Gene's trailer, Coral meekly submits to Margo's suggestions and commands. All the time she is conscious of her unborn baby, and it is evident by her concern about the landfill, for instance, that even before she begins to recover, her baby is foremost in her mind.

As Coral gradually reawakens to the world around her, the characters of Lee and Tracy are introduced. Because they are both odd figures, they initially provide a source of fun as Margo and Coral take turns mimicking them. Later, Lee becomes a yardstick by which Coral seems to measure her own fitness for motherhood. What this demonstrates is Coral's own gradually reawakening desire to be a mother. It is another step in her transition from shock to a state approaching normality.

Paul is little developed in the story; however, his function does not necessitate fully rounded characterization. Through his character the reader can further estimate the degree of Coral's own healing. At first, Paul's habits (such as throwing the dinner napkin into the trash after the meal), only remind Coral of Kenny, but gradually she begins once again to focus on her own physical and emotional needs concerning men. The character of Paul allows the reader to perceive Coral's slow movement away from withdrawal and toward integration. As if to focus attention on Coral's recovery, Prose allows only a minimal suggestion of romantic interest between Coral and Paul at the story's end. What is important is the fact that Coral is now finding her own strengths again.

George T. Novotny

CLARISA

Author: Isabel Allende (1942-   )
Type of plot: Fantasy
Time of plot: Unspecified; possibly the 1980's
Locale: A city somewhere in South America
First published: 1989 (English translation, 1991)

> *Principal characters:*
> CLARISA, a poor, saintly woman known for her charity
> EVA LUNA, her friend, the narrator
> THE JUDGE, her aged, reclusive husband
> DON DIEGO CIENFUEGOS, a congressman, national hero, and long-
> time friend of Clarisa's

The Story

Eva Luna tells the life story of her old friend Clarisa, who died of amazement when the pope arrived for a visit and was met in the street by homosexuals dressed as nuns. (The reference is likely to one of John Paul II's visits to South America in the early 1980's.) The bizarre old woman, who is well into her eighties, is widely considered to be a saint but from performing humble and improbable miracles such as curing hangovers and minor illnesses.

Eva traces the story of Clarisa's life from her unhappy marriage to a greedy and vulgar provincial judge who is still alive and would be about a hundred years old. Traces of Clarisa's aristocratic upbringing show in her talent as a classical pianist, but after the birth of their two retarded children, her husband closed himself up in a malodorous room, where he has lived in silence for more than forty years. Clarisa was forced to sell their possessions and take up the sewing of rag dolls and baking—of wedding cakes, ironically—to keep the family together. Although her ancestral home is dilapidated, she manages to hold onto it.

Clarisa deals admirably with her children's abnormality, considering them pure souls immune to evil and treating them with great affection. She believes that God operates by a doctrine of compensation, and her faith is rewarded when she gives birth to two healthy sons who are kind and good and who help with their retarded brother and sister until they die in an accident involving a gas leak.

Throughout her life, Clarisa practices charitable acts despite her poverty. In one episode, she talks an armed robber into accepting her money as a gift so that he will not commit a sin, and then insists that he join her for tea. Her special talent, however, is in getting funds from the wealthy by working at cross purposes. For example, she convinces the influential politician Don Diego Cienfuegos to donate a refrigerator to the Teresian Sisters even though he is a socialist, arguing that the sisters provide free meals for communists and other children of the working poor who make up the congressman's constituency. She and Cienfuegos subsequently become lifelong friends.

After the homosexuals disguised as nuns disrupt the papal visit to protest the pope's stands on divorce, abortion, and other issues, Clarisa tells Eva that she has seen too much, and she predicts her imminent death. Eva notes that her old friend has developed two bumps on her shoulders, "as if her pair of great angel wings were about to erupt." As her last days approach, Clarisa eats only flowers and honey. To her deathbed come all the people to whom she has shown charity throughout the years, including the robber (now a professional thief who steals from the rich, and is not, as the reader might anticipate, reformed), a madame named "La Señora," and Don Diego Cienfuegos.

The dying Clarisa attempts to make amends with her repulsive husband to no avail and tells Eva that she feels she has sinned in some way. When Eva recognizes the similarity between Clarisa's two healthy sons and Don Diego—now a national hero—she assumes that that is her friend's grave sin. Clarisa insists that it was not a sin, "just a little boost to help God balance the scales of destiny." Clarisa dies without suffering, not from cancer, as the doctors diagnose, and not of saintliness, as the people believe, but, Eva says, of astonishment that goes back to the pope's visit.

Themes and Meanings

Isabel Allende presents in her stories, and in three of her four novels, a world in which the corrupt and powerful—who are generally male, macho, and brutal—are defeated by the innocent and powerless—who are generally female, maternal, and virtuous. It could be argued that through her fiction Allende, the niece of Chilean Marxist president Salvador Allende, who was assassinated in 1973, seeks to correct the abuses traditionally associated with life and politics in Latin American society. Whereas justice often seems to occur only randomly in real life, it is almost always the outcome in Allende's fiction.

Despite her own misfortunes, Clarisa remains compassionate and loving. She is affectionate with her difficult retarded children, and her kindness is transmitted to her normal sons. Her acts of charity bring her deserved popularity and renown, and she dies peacefully. Her wretched husband, however, who becomes a recluse because he cannot bear the disillusionment of having sired two retarded children, is doomed to a life of self-imposed, monkish isolation, although Clarisa does continue to feed and care for him. We are not invited to sympathize with his plight, because he is introduced as a man whom she marries simply because he was the first person to ask her and because he is associated with avarice and vulgarity. In short, the good are rewarded and the evil are punished. Clarisa's simple and sensible view of justice is also implicit in her theory of compensation, that God balances advantages and disadvantages in life.

In "Clarisa," as elsewhere in Allende's fiction, the oppressed classes are superior to the ruling class, both in their humanity and in their spirituality. Clarisa is saintlike in her simple and active piety. What distinguishes her charitable acts is her boundless understanding of human weaknesses. This understanding, ironically, is the source of her power.

Style and Technique

Isabel Allende has been influenced by the magic realists, whose work has dominated Latin American writing since Jorge Luis Borges began to make his mark in the 1950's. These writers are concerned with the representation of the miraculous within the real, so their work usually is realistic, but with some elements of fantasy. With writers such as Luisa Valenzuela and Gabriel García Márquez, fantasy tends to dominate, but Allende maintains a light touch. For instance, Eva Luna notes that her friendship with Clarisa has lasted to this day and that her old friend's death has only put a slight crimp in their communication. She also mentions that Clarisa has bumps on her shoulders that seem to be the beginnings of angel's wings. Allende does not emphasize such fantasy elements, however, and most of the story is grounded in credible reality.

On the other hand, the reader's credibility is almost always strained. In "Clarisa," the reader is asked to accept the crazed husband living forty years in isolation and the protagonist living in a rundown house where the walls "sweat a greenish mist." Such details are sufficient to keep the reader alert to whatever comes next; the reader is also encouraged to be open-minded. Allende also promotes an atmosphere of unreality by neglecting to situate her stories in any particular city or country, although it is usually apparent that the setting is somewhere in South America. The reader may suppose any given story is set in Peru, where Allende was born, or in Chile, where she grew up, or in Venezuela, where she lived for a number of years until moving to northern California, or elsewhere on the South American continent.

An epigraph at the front of *The Stories of Eva Luna* (1991), the book in which "Clarisa" appears, concerns Scheherazade and the famous *One Thousand and One Nights*. These exotic tales of adventure and romance, known sometimes simply as *The Arabian Nights*, were translated into French early in the eighteenth century and into English in the early 1840's. In her novel *Eva Luna* (1988), and in these stories, Allende presents Eva as a sort of natural storyteller with a magical gift of sorts, a modern-day Scheherazade whose stories reestablish justice in the world, often by employing ironic reversals. The implication would seem to be that in a corrupt or violent world, one must work counter to expectation if one hopes to succeed. For example, in "Clarisa" the judge turns out to be unjust in the way he treats his children, and Don Diego succeeds in politics despite, not because of, being incorruptible.

Ron McFarland

THE CLIFF

Author: Charles Baxter (1947-   )
Type of plot: Fable
Time of plot: The 1970's
Locale: The California coast
First published: 1984

> *Principal characters:*
> THE OLD MAN, the teacher of the spells
> THE BOY, his fifteen-year-old protégé

The Story

A young boy is being driven to a cliff at an unspecified location on the California coastline. The driver, a cantankerous old man, interrogates the boy en route, suspicious of his experience with women, how well he has memorized the old man's instructions, his moral, spiritual, and emotional purity, and his impatience to get started with the initiation into what the old man calls "the spells." Noting the old man's incessant coughing and smoking, his occasional hits from the wine bottle stashed under his seat, and his irritability in general, the boy wonders aloud about the old man's purity, whether or not he still believes in the spells. Outraged by the boy's temerity, the old man reminds him that his body has been pure. More important, he tells the boy that he, the old man, is the spells. Besides, he adds, "nobody is ever pure twice."

When they arrive at the cliff, the old man orders the boy to remove his shoes and sweatshirt, and to make a circle in the dirt with his feet. The boy reminds the old man that there is no dirt, but the old man insists he follow his orders. So the boy traces an invisible circle around his body and then speaks to the horizon, using the words the old man has given him. The old man hands him one end of a rope, takes another swig of wine, and then lets out the slack as the boy jumps down the slope of the cliff.

At this point the boy takes it into his mind to "swoop toward the cliffs." The ambiguity of the phrase—is he imagining flight while rapelling down a cliff or he is actually flying?—is maintained as he soars and dips above the old man. Even as he does so, he begins to realize that this kind of flying is not for him. He wants to "fly low, near the ground, in the cities, speeding in smooth arcs between the buildings, late at night." The boy grins down at the old man, who has "forgotten the dirty purposes of flight."

Themes and Meanings

Charles Baxter's story is yet another rendition of the age-old conflict between the generations. It concerns the meaning of tradition, what gets passed on to the next generation. This story suggests that tradition is never received in the pure form of its transmission. Those who constitute the next generation will always alter or transform the tradition in some way, reworking in order to make it their own, to satisfy their own needs and desires.

From the beginning of the story until the moment the boy takes off, the old man is a grouch, suspicious of the young boy's worthiness. He wheezes, coughs, smokes, and swigs wine even as he preaches the virtues of faith, hope, charity, and love and insists on moral and physical chastity for the initiate. Baxter provides a clue to the source of this wanton self-destructiveness when, responding to the boy's query if he still believes in the spells, the old man insists, "I am the spells." Despite the sop to ritual and the sacred—summarized in the boy's drawing an invisible circle around himself, removing his shoes as though he is on holy ground, removing his sweatshirt to expose his unsullied heart—the old man knows that the only spells are those that he himself wills. Perhaps when he was young some older man taught him to believe in something outside himself, something just beyond the horizon of human knowledge. Now an older man, no longer innocent, no longer pure, he knows that the only spells are those he himself imagines.

The bitterness of this knowledge also inflates the old man. Having the secret of the spells that the young boy desires gives him power over the boy. Yet he knows this knowledge of the spells, once revealed, will release the boy from his power. Hence the old man's sour demeanor, his ejaculations of platitudes—faith, hope, love, and charity—that he regards as a sham. At the same time, the old man understands that the knowledge of the spells must be passed on if it is not to be lost forever with his death. In the character of the old man, Baxter paints a picture of paternal resentment. This resentment is directed at the boy, but its source is the mortality of the old man. The old man knows and resents the fact that his mortality demands the passing on of knowledge.

Yet something happens when the man sees the boy soar above him; he begins laughing and, for once, is no longer coughing. It is as though the boy's flight momentarily revitalizes the old man, taking him back to his innocence and ignorance when all was possibility, when the future beyond the horizon could still be imagined, before all knowledge. The boy knows this, knows that his flight has pleased the old man, has made him pure again, if only momentarily, if only under the hallucinogenic power of the imagination. This flight does not, however, satisfy the young boy. He wants something else, wants to be somewhere else: to soar, not to fly low; to enjoy not the salty exuberance of the ocean, but the stagnant air of the city. In this moment of joy and communion between the old and young, the young boy and the old man are already going their separate ways.

Style and Technique

This story has all the requisite features of the fable or parable. It is very short, even by short-story standards, a mere three-and-a-half pages. The subsequent compressed plot—an old man and boy drive to a cliff from which the boy leaps into the sky and begins flying—lends to the story an aphoristic universality. This universality is reinforced by the general treatment of the setting and characters. Readers never learn the name of the cliff or the names of the characters. As a story about a cliff, an old man, and a boy, it takes on mystical, even transcendental depth, precisely because nothing is named or tied to a specific place or time. Finally, the magical climax of the story places it beyond the realm of the ordinary and everyday. This is a story that has something transcendental to say, like all fables.

One literary device that Baxter employs here is allusion. "The Cliff" rewrites the Daedalus and Icarus myth, this time in Icarus' favor. Rather than viewing flight merely from the point of view of tradition—flight as a sign of liberation—Baxter also portrays flight here as the youthful dream of an old man who, because he is no longer young, wants a young boy to follow in his wake so that he, the old man, might live vicariously through the young boy. Seeing the boy flying above him, the old man is suddenly young again. He loses his cough and again finds joy in the simple things of nature: "'The sun!' the old man shouted. 'The ocean! The land! That's how to do it!' And he laughed suddenly, his cough all gone. 'The sky!' he said at last." All the traditional images of freedom—the sea, the cliff (from which one must leap into transcendence), nature in general—are the jealously guarded terrain of an embittered old man. For the young boy, however, it is the city, the girls in their apartments, the musty air of urban squalor, that coaxes. When one reads that the young boy wants to "fly low . . . speeding in smooth arcs between the buildings," one can imagine that what this boy really wants to do is precisely what the old man cannot imagine doing: Drive a car fast through the streets. The car is here the symbol for the new generation, the post-Romantic world of urban life. For the old man, the car is a motor vehicle that has one purpose: to take him out of the city and into the country. For the boy, in a car, one can fly low, girlwatch. This is what it means to fly in this modern-day fable.

Tyrone Williams

COACH

Author: Mary Robison (1949-)
Type of plot: Domestic realism
Time of plot: The 1970's
Locale: Pennsylvania
First published: 1981

> *Principal characters:*
> HARRY NOONAN, the Coach
> SHERRY, his wife
> DAPHNE, their daughter
> TOBY, a college news reporter

The Story

Harry Noonan dries breakfast dishes as he waits for a college reporter to arrive for an interview. He has been hired to coach the freshman football team. His wife, Sherry, asks him to rent a studio for her, where she can do her painting. Their daughter, Daphne, is looking in the refrigerator for something to eat. She wants to stay for the interview, but Coach says no. He remembers a fall night seven years earlier when he set Daphne on a football field during the half-time ceremonies; she was dressed in a football uniform with the number "$1/2$" on her back. Now, Daphne asks him for help with her algebra. He declines, so she asks her mother, who says forget it.

After the reporter, Toby, arrives, he asks only a few questions and takes no notes. He then engages Daphne in conversation. Afterward, Daphne remarks that Toby was nice and Coach tells her that she would be wasting her time on him—like "trying to light a fire with a wet match." When the newspaper interview appears the next day in the *Rooter*, it is full of inaccurate information, making Coach furious. Trying to console him, Sherry says that Daphne liked it.

Coach takes Daphne out for ice cream in order to explain why he is renting an apartment for Sherry. He denies Daphne's suspicion they are separating and tells her about Sherry's five-year plan for self-development. Coach is distracted from the conversation when one of his new players drives up with his parents. Upset that he cannot remember the boy's name—Bobby Stark—Coach mockingly chastises him for eating ice cream, aware that Bobby's parents and other people are grinning.

When Coach begins his football practices, he learns from Bobby that he has a good chance of coaching the varsity team next year. When he goes home, excited with this news, he is disappointed to find no one there. Sherry has left a note saying she is at "her place" and Daphne is with "Toby K. someplace, fooling around." Coach grabs a beer. While he showers, Daphne comes home. Hearing sounds, Coach goes to the bedroom, expecting to find Sherry, but is surprised to find Daphne dancing and posing in front of the mirror. When he mocks her, doing "the Daphne," she is embarrassed. Coach begins telling her his good news, but she only says "let me out, please."

Back in the kitchen, Coach drinks more beer and begins constructing a "dream team" roster of former players. Daphne comes downstairs, wearing a team shirt with *Go* on the front, *Griffins* on the back. Pretending to be Daphne, Coach apologizes to himself for her being rude to him upstairs. Conciliating him, she asks Coach about the prospects of his team this year. He offers her a beer. Sherry comes in with a few groceries. Daphne grabs the Oreo cookies. Sherry asks for a beer and says that she cannot paint. Coach reassures her, but she adds: "An artist? The wife of a coach?"

Themes and Meanings

"No one at home"—so begins the next-to-final scene of "Coach." The phrase expresses Mary Robison's concern about the disintegration of the American family. There is no true intimacy between Coach and his wife. Just as he is obsessed with his coaching career, she wants only her "room apart." Neglected by both, Daphne must look out for herself. Significantly, she is searching for food in the refrigerator when she appears in the story. This signifies her need for emotional and intellectual nourishment as well. Her parents are unconcerned about her schoolwork, although she is taking make-up courses, and both refuse to help with her algebra.

A fifteen-year-old adolescent, Daphne is becoming interested in boys. When Toby mildly flirts with her, she rolls her chin seductively on her shoulder. Oblivious to her need for parental guidance, Coach and Sherry are glad when she is off with Toby, out of their way. Coach's insensitivity to Daphne's feelings are revealed at the Dairy Frost, where he is more upset that he cannot remember Bobby's name than he is concerned about Daphne's apprehension that her parents are separating. His insensitivity is also demonstrated when he makes fun of her dancing before the mirror.

Rather than encourage the development of Daphne's individual identity, Coach, with the complicity of Sherry, uses Daphne to support his own ego. He probably wanted a son instead of a daughter, a boy such as Bobby Stark. Failing this, he turns Daphne into his personal cheerleader. The charm bracelet that her parents put together for her has a miniature football and a megaphone on it. Daphne, however, is starting to imitate her parents by looking out for number one. She has stopped wearing the charm bracelet and serving food at Sunday dinners honoring Coach's best players.

Robison sees far-reaching implications in the ways that parents such as Coach and Sherry treat their children. Coach's attempts to dominate Daphne and his and Sherry's failure to provide for her needs parallel the development of industrialism at the expense of nature. This is suggested by the fact that Coach teaches history courses at the college on European Industrial Development and the Atlantic World. In high school he taught World History and Problems of Democracy. Coach takes his teaching job no more seriously than he does his role as Daphne's father. When Coach describes one of his courses as a refresher course "in nature," Toby corrects him: "or out of nature."

In finding a parallel between Daphne and nature Robison expresses her own concern for the future of civilization. The greatest problem of democracy, she implies, is the disintegration of the family. Her story asks what America—what the world—will be like in the future without healthy, well-adjusted, well-informed citizens.

Style and Technique

"Coach" is written in a realistic style, with an emphasis on dialogue, which is ironic, as the characters communicate with each other only superficially. The point of view is third-person, limited omniscient, as Robison enters only the mind of Coach. This is also ironic, because there is very little in Coach's head. Most important, however, is Robison's use of Greek myth and patterns of imagery. She alludes to the myth of Daphne and Apollo in the name Daphne. In mythology, Apollo, the sun god, is charmed by Daphne's beauty and pursues her. About to be overtaken, she prays for help and metamorphoses into a laurel tree, which becomes the favorite of Apollo. Robison links Coach to Apollo by using words and images that associate him with the sun. His last name, Noonan, contains the word noon, implying the sun. References are made to the sun porch of Coach's house; the colors of his new team are maroon and gold; he tells Daphne to "be on the beam"; and his influence on her is implied when she takes "sun on her back, adding to her tan." Something akin to emotional sunburn is suggested when Coach embarrasses Daphne in the mirror scene: "You are beet red," he says. Robison puns on beet, pronounced like beat, which means both punished and defeated.

Like Apollo, Coach causes Daphne to metamorphose into a tree. A travesty of this event occurs in Coach's memory of the eight-year-old Daphne on the football field wearing a player's jersey and helmet. "Lost in the getup," she is transformed into "a small pile of equipment." Toward the end of the story, Coach succeeds in transforming Daphne into a tree, but not as he would wish. She escapes from him, as Daphne did from Apollo, and becomes dead to his demands for unconditional adoration. He yells at her: "Hey! Why am I yelling at wood, here?" The tree is dead.

Robison extends the significance of Daphne's transformation into a tree with a series of nature images: "green water . . . sliced by a power boat," "frog in a blender," "lime-eaten grass." In each case, nature is violated by machines and other products of modern civilization. Robison uses further nature images to relate her meaning to evolution. References are made to "warm salt-water," the origin of life; an insect, "a plastic ladybug"; an amphibian, the frog; a reptile, "a green family with scales"; and a mammal, "it's monkey time."

Robison also alludes to the evolution of civilized man. The Daphne and Apollo myth invokes ancient Greece and the beginning of Western civilization, and the subject matter of Coach's courses includes both European and American history. Robison questions the direction of evolution. By using animal images to describe Bobby, referring to his "rump and haunches," as well as Coach, who "trotted for the sidelines," Robison suggests that human beings are regressing on the evolutionary ladder. Sherry jokingly refers to their family as "having scales." In their survival-of-the-fittest lifestyle, they are becoming reptilian.

James Green

THE COAL SHOVELLER

Author: Keith Fort
Type of plot: Antistory
Time of plot: The 1960's
Locale: Washington, D.C.
First published: 1969

> *Principal characters:*
> THE NARRATOR, an author and professor
> MICHAEL, his alter ego
> MARGARET, Michael's wife
> AMELIA, Michael's small daughter
> REGINALD COWPERSMITH, another alter ego
> AN AFRICAN AMERICAN COAL SHOVELLER

The Story

A writer tries to create a short story while looking through his window at an African American man shoveling coal into a basement across the street. He experiments with various stylistic approaches and characters, but repeatedly gives up. After his first abortive attempt, he writes: "To ask words to make fiction into photographic realism is to demand a performance which they are totally incapable of giving."

He begins a personal story. His six-year-old daughter enters his study and breaks his concentration, so he takes her outside into the snow. He is only imagining this scenario, however, as he is actually still writing. Once again he stops. He now is beginning to sound like James Joyce in "The Dead" (1914)—a story that ends with a typical Joycean epiphany. He writes: "I am inclined to agree with those who say that literature (no matter how negative the theme) which reinforces the habit of extracting ideas from reality panders to the self-interest of the middle class."

Still determined to persevere, the narrator next begins a story involving an old woman telling her grandson about Washington, D.C., of the past. Now his sentences sound like the convoluted, hypnotic prose of William Faulkner. He does not like to imitate, but candidly admits: "I wish I could honestly see the fall of the Old South as tragic in the way that Faulkner did."

Increasingly frustrated, he indulges in self-recrimination, blaming himself for being emotionally bankrupt, nihilistic, arrogant, and narrow-minded. He now decides to try writing a visceral, action-packed story and invents a young white coal shoveller named Reginald Cowpersmith, who uses his status as a building employee to get into a young woman's apartment in order to rape her. After getting well into a convincing yarn, he breaks off and exclaims: "God, but I hate bastards who write stories like that."

Finally, he tries to write a satirical vignette in which an anonymous writer befriends the black coal shoveller in a bar frequented by middle-class whites vaguely associated with the arts. He wants to expose the hypocrisy of white liberal intellectuals by introducing a real lower-class black into their midst. His imaginary coal shoveller gets along well with his imaginary white liberals, but fails to understand his creator's complaints, such as his complaint that "art has been dehumanized so that no man can honestly write on anything but the problem of writing." The mystified but compassionate coal shoveller quite reasonably asks his creator why he keeps trying to write if he finds it so frustrating. The writer replies, "in my business it's publish or . . . ," stopping before saying "perish." Instead, he releases a smokescreen of hyper-intellectual verbiage. He obviously covets his privileged position as an intellectual and professor even though he questions the value of any literature that people like himself produce.

Like its predecessors, his new story fizzles out and the narrator finds himself back at his window, watching the man shoveling coal. He states that he does not want to turn on the light because it will prevent him from seeing out the window, but that he cannot continue writing because it is now too dark.

Themes and Meanings

"The Coal Shoveller" is an important work in which Keith Fort has found the ideal form for expressing the problems of many aspiring writers. Although dissatisfied with the old styles—especially realism and naturalism—they cannot find new styles that will liberate them to express themselves. The main theme throughout this story concerns the difficulty of being honest. Its narrator admires many great writers of the past and appreciates that they were great because they wrote what they passionately believed. He wishes to emulate them, but without imitating them. As a modern man, however, he finds it difficult to know in what he should believe. Traditional religion has been undermined by science, and socialism has been discredited by its practitioners in Russia, China, and elsewhere.

The narrator's abortive attempts to concoct a story based on a man shoveling coal are efforts to discover what he himself truly believes. His mind is full of ideas, but he does not know whether he really believes any of them. His indictment of certain anti-intellectual writers suggests that he would agree with William Butler Yeats's assessment of the modern condition in "The Second Coming" (1921): "The best lack all conviction while the worst are full of passionate intensity."

It might be argued that the theme of "The Coal Shoveller" is the difficulty of finding a theme, because a theme represents what a writer believes. It is appropriate to such an experimental story that its theme and meaning should be the search for theme and meaning. One thing in which the author does believe is the truth. He cannot force himself to regard the coal shoveller as either a victim or a hero. Such attitudes can lead into stylistic dead ends and ideological traps. He rejects one style after another because he feels that although they might have been appropriate for authors such as Alain Robbe-Grillet, James Joyce, Henry James, William Faulkner, Jack Kerouac, J. P. Donleavy, and Henry Miller, they are false for him. He does not mention Ernest Hemingway, who was one of the most influential writers of the twentieth century, but he would certainly subscribe to Hemingway's dictum that a good writer's most essential gift is a built-in, shockproof bunk detector, the "writer's radar" that all great writers have. The author does not know what he believes in, but he knows what he does not believe in, and that knowledge serves as his radar.

It may be more difficult to be creative in modern times because people have become too educated, too intellectual, and too sophisticated. The problem that many aspiring writers have in creating fiction is related to problems that others have in trying to read fiction. Many readers, because of the glut of media information that they absorb, have become too intellectual and too jaded to believe in fiction. People are increasingly asking why they should be concerned about the problems of people who do not even exist.

It is understandable that short story writers should wonder whether they have anything meaningful to communicate when their labor is largely a labor of love. Short fiction might become obsolete without the patronage of literary journals subsidized by academic institutions. It is not unusual for writers—like the narrator of "The Coal Shoveller"—to be professors, and for them to wonder whether they are writers who teach, or teachers who write. If writers persist despite guilt, frustration, and self-doubt—as the author and his alter egos do in "The Coal Shoveller"—they may create new forms of fiction more suited to alienated, agnostic modern times. Writers such as Fort are creating forms that often seem like bizarre amalgamations of fact and fantasy. The problem of the writer—like many other problems—may prove to be an opportunity in disguise.

Style and Technique

Although an experimental work classified as an antistory, "The Coal Shoveller" has important elements in common with conventional stories. In order to interest the reader, any story must be dramatic. Drama is provided by conflicting motives, which have been categorized as "man against man," "man against nature," and "man against himself." "The Coal Shoveller" falls into the last category. Its narrator is strongly motivated to write a story but finds, after a number of false starts, that he cannot do so. His strong motivation to persevere is what keeps the reader wanting to learn whether he ever succeeds.

William Shakespeare's *Hamlet* (1600-1601) is a classic example of "man against himself." Fort's protagonist resembles Prince Hamlet in being intelligent: He has too much education, he has read too many books, he has too much imagination, and he thinks too much. He is his own worst enemy. If dramatic conflict usually involves a protagonist pitted against an antagonist, then the narrator of "The Coal Shoveller" can be seen as both protagonist and antagonist.

"The Coal Shoveller" is a combination story, essay, and journal entry. The reader forms the impression that the narrator is in the habit of writing in this manner. He writes about his thoughts, observations, and problems, including problems in trying to find something worth writing about. Occasionally he comes across the germ of an idea that he can develop into a full-fledged story.

On the occasion that is chronicled in "The Coal Shoveller," the narrator is not necessarily defeated in his attempt to write a short story. What he is going through is his own personal method of working, his way of jump-starting his creativity. He may not be able to expect a successful outcome every time that he uses this technique, but he is better off writing about writing—or writing about writing about writing—than he would be simply staring at a blank sheet of paper. It would be a mistake to regard him as a failure because he has not succeeded in writing a story about a man shoveling coal. He has produced germs of several stories that might one day blossom into finished works.

Bill Delaney

COME OUT THE WILDERNESS

Author: James Baldwin (1924-1987)
Type of plot: Psychological realism
Time of plot: c. 1960
Locale: New York City
First published: 1958

> *Principal characters:*
> RUTH BOWMAN, a twenty-six-year-old African American secretary for an insurance company
> PAUL, her white lover, an aspiring painter
> MR. DAVIS, an African American executive at her insurance company

The Story

Ruth Bowman, a young African American woman, begins her day by talking with and making love to her white lover, Paul. She feels desperately dependent upon his affection, but also senses that he is slipping away. After she gets to her job as a secretary for an insurance company, she tries not to worry about Paul but fails. Her grim day is relieved when Mr. Davis, an African American executive who is about to be promoted, offers to make her his personal secretary. At noon a chance encounter leads to Ruth's lunching with Davis. It is the beginning of a friendship that Ruth wants to welcome, but which she resists out of distrust and feelings of unworthiness. Her despair returns when Paul fails to return home that night as he has promised, and she is left alone, worrying.

Ruth wants to marry and raise children, but Paul seems to assume they will never marry. Ruth loves him, and he treats her kindly and seems to be concerned for her welfare; however, she also hates him, especially when she detects his unconscious condescension toward her gender and race. As she grows more sure that she is losing him, her reflections become more bitter. While she wants to believe that love will release her from guilt and terror, loving Paul imprisons her in guilt. She also feels imprisoned in silence; she cannot tell Paul what she really thinks, thus calling him to account for his failures, because then he certainly will leave her sooner, as no marriage promise holds him.

Ruth's deepest and most pervasive source of suffering is undeserved guilt. Although she knows that her feelings are unfair, she cannot escape the conviction that she deserves to suffer and is unworthy of love and happiness. She ran away from home after her older brother caught her with a boyfriend in the barn. Although she had not yet done anything worthy of blame, everyone assumed that she had and that what she wanted must be evil. Her brother called her "black and dirty," linking her sexual desires with evil, family betrayal, and skin color. She has since spent her life trying to escape these labels and undo these connections. So far, however, she has failed and all of her relations with men seem to be poisoned.

The story ends as she walks briskly through the crowded New York streets, trying to hide from herself and others the fact that she does not know where she is going.

Themes and Meanings

The old Negro spiritual from which this story takes its title celebrates the joy and release felt by one who accepts belief in Jesus and thereby finds a way out of the wilderness of sin. James Baldwin's complex narrative explores several ways in which Ruth Bowman is lost in a wilderness. The story takes place mainly on three levels of Ruth's consciousness: She moves through a workday that opens a new opportunity for her; she broods over her failing relationship with her lover, Paul; and she struggles to come to terms with the events that drove her from her rural Southern home at the age of seventeen. On each level, Ruth feels conflicting wishes and fears.

Rich in implications about race and gender in the modern United States, the story can also be examined through the concepts of master and slave. Ruth ends her day drinking in random bars and sees a young white man who seems as lost as she is. She connects him with Paul and with all the white "boys" she has known: "The sons of the masters were roaming the world, looking for arms to hold them. And the arms that might have held them—could not forgive."

The main offense that Ruth cannot forgive is being forced into slave consciousness by a white male master. Although her white lovers acknowledge that slavery ended a century earlier, they unconsciously treat her as a slave, eliciting her protest, "I'm not the black girl you can just sleep with when you want to and kick about as you please!" These men are probably blind to their offense because they treat her as men have treated women for ages—the way that Ruth's brother and father treated her when she was found in the barn. She is property of the men in her family, and she is expected to serve and obey. She is aware that Paul's expectation that she will patiently await his unexplained late arrival at home and then prepare his meal reflects the way all men treat "their" women, but she cannot keep from reading racism into his behavior.

Both black and a woman, Ruth is doubly the slave, daily experiencing, even at the hands of those who should most care for her, reminders not only that she does not belong to herself, but that her treatment has a racial history. Ruth's slave consciousness means that she cannot avoid reading racial exploitation into what may be "merely" gender exploitation. Because she feels powerless as an immoral woman living with a man to whom she is not married, she cannot force Paul or any other man to hear her story and give her justice. Seeing double, she is doubly torn, wanting to love a man freely and without guilt and to begin a family, and yet unable to see any man, black or white, simply and freely. And she is doubly bound, trapped in such labels as "Negro" and "Fallen Woman" that she feels she cannot discuss without exploding everything she depends upon, just as she can never speak the truth at her office. Unable to change her experience or her perceptions, she is lost in a wilderness, unable to forgive or to love or accept love at face value.

Style and Technique

Baldwin layers this story in several ways. At her job, Ruth finds the possibility for a better life opening up as she and Davis benefit from the integration of African Americans into better jobs. Davis' promotion promises to improve Ruth's own life, and their friendship suggests the possibility of a more fulfilling love relationship. Beneath this layer of bright prospects, however, is Ruth's brooding over her failing love relationship, and beneath that is another layer of fundamental guilt and terror over her family's betrayal of her innocence.

Baldwin moves the reader back and forth through these layers, always coming back to Ruth's fundamental problem—her family's failure to love her. Throughout the story, events in Ruth's day return her to thoughts of Paul, and then to thoughts about how she came to be as lost as she is. As Baldwin brings these three layers of experience into focus, words and events take on increasingly rich meanings. Each rereading of the story leads to new discoveries of the depth of Ruth's experiences, until the reader feels resonances that are only suggested. For example, in their morning conversation, Paul says it is time to paint a portrait of her, which she silently reads as a sign that he considers their relationship over. Paul's joke that he could sell her for a thousand dollars hurts her because it makes her remember how her memory of female ancestors were bought and sold for sexual use. On the level that Paul understands, they are merely joking together, but for her this conversation calls up her fear of losing Paul, her sense of being sexually dirty, and her racial history of sexual exploitation and terror.

Sometimes Baldwin's layering gives complex meanings to even simple sentences. During a telephone conversation, for example, Paul tells Ruth, "It sure would be nice to unload some of my stuff on somebody." He is speaking only of his hope of selling paintings, but Ruth sees other meanings in his sentence. He is, she believes, deceiving her about his plans and so unloading stuff on her. He has been using her as a sort of servant, unloading his work on her. He plans, she believes, to use sexual persuasion with a gallery owner's daughter in order to get a show of his work, unloading on the daughter. In every meaning that she sees and he does not, his unloading involves exploitation. The better one knows Ruth's story, the more sentences and events become double and triple in their meanings, and the more fully one sees how Ruth is trapped spiritually and psychologically in the web of her history. That history is characterized by betrayals both in Ruth's personal experience and in the more general experiences of racial and gender relations in the United States.

Terry Heller

THE COMEDIAN

Author: John L'Heureux (1934-   )
Type of plot: Magical Realism
Time of plot: The 1980's
Locale: San Francisco
First published: 1984

Principal characters:
CORINNE, a thirty-eight-year-old stand-up comedian
RUSS, her husband, a construction worker

The Story

Corinne and her husband Russ are surprised that she has become pregnant and are a bit nonplussed by her condition. At thirty-eight years of age, Corinne thinks she is a little old to be having her first child; the timing is especially awkward because her career as a stand-up comedian seems to be about to take off. Her gynecologist agrees with her and suggests that she consider having an abortion. Over the next few months, this question dominates Corinne's life.

Before long, however, the baby enters Corinne's internal conversation: The baby, she thinks, has begun singing. Sometimes the songs are Broadway show tunes, sometimes operatic arias. Although mystified and unable to explain the strange phenomenon, Corinne has trouble denying that it is really happening.

Three months into her pregnancy, Corinne begins to get bookings at comedy clubs, and it seems to her that the baby sings even more exuberantly just before her performances. She goes over well at one club, but is not renewed because, the club's owner says, her humor is all mental stuff: It lacks guts or feeling. She is not surprised. Almost everyone in California smiles a lot, she thinks, but few seem to laugh much.

After Corinne tells Russ about the baby's singing, he tries to be understanding, but concludes that the strange phenomenon is a sign that the pregnancy is overstraining his wife. He suggests that an abortion would probably be best. When she tells her gynecologist about the singing, he laughs and assumes that it is one of her typical jokes. When Russ presses her on the question of the singing, Corinne reluctantly admits that it is all in her imagination. The baby immediately stops singing.

When amniocentesis indicates that Corinne's baby will probably be deformed, Corinne decides on an abortion. During her initial pre-abortion examination, however, she finds herself sinking into darkness. She only manages to pull herself out of it when she shouts that she wants the baby after all.

Suddenly, Corinne's humor shows real feeling, and she begins receiving job offers from all the major clubs, whose audiences totally identify with her and her pregnancy. She has never been the sort of comedian to make fun of the way she looked or ridicule other people. Instead, she finds humorous things with which others can identify and still feel respected. Corinne now finds herself praying for her deformed baby, who sings all the time.

The prospective mother's sight is becoming overly sensitive to light, which seems increasingly to surround her. Soon the time comes for her delivery, and she drifts into a semiconscious state. She seems delirious, saying "please" and "thank you" constantly. The singing becomes more intense, the light brighter and brighter until she enters completely into the light.

Themes and Meanings

A former Jesuit priest, John L'Heureux often centers his stories around moments in ordinary lives in which something extraordinary—something possibly spiritually charged—takes place. This is one such story, an account of a crisis in the life of a woman who decides to have a few laughs before it is too late.

Corinne is unusual only in her fascination with getting on the stage as a stand-up comic. The first complication that the pregnancy causes is her increasing self-consciousness, her awareness that she is, in fact, different from the other people around her. Her body is changing shape and, unless she has an abortion, there is no avoiding the fact that she no longer blends into the crowd. She must stand on her own two feet and make choices of her own.

Corinne's growing sense of self causes further problems in her burgeoning career as she recognizes that she hates the jokes that other comedians find so funny, because they demean their audiences and themselves. The pregnancy changes Corinne's sense of what is important in life; she suddenly becomes serious.

In the process of Corinne's growing sense of individual identity and responsibility, her senses come alive, almost painfully so. Her eyes become overly sensitive to light, as if she is seeing the world around her for the first time and finds there is a great deal that is painful to look at. Even more significant, perhaps, is her increasingly acute sense of hearing. She is the only one who can hear the baby's singing. It may be that this is a sign of mental problems, as her husband suspects, but since the beginning of pregnancy, Corinne has consciously developed her ability to listen. She listens more closely to her husband than ever before, and discerns that he is as alone in life as she now recognizes herself to be. Mostly she listens to her interior, hearing not only the baby but also her own spirit that she has ignored for so long.

The result of these heightened senses is that Corinne now feels more than she used to, and empathizes with Russ, her baby, and her audience. Her comedy becomes the human comedy, sensitive and gently optimistic, which is why her lounge act becomes so successful.

Style and Technique

The writing in this story is simple and unembellished, rendering the characterization completely believable and familiar. L'Heureux cleverly lulls the reader into a recognition of his imagined protagonist, and then shocks us with the central plot twist: the singing fetus. The matter-of-fact manner in which the event is described is reminiscent of the magic realism of South American fiction, which combines the totally inexplicable with the utterly mundane. In both cases, the effect is to delight the reader with the possibility of something wonderful and unexpected breaking in on the humdrum world.

"The Comedian" also might be compared to the work of Flannery O'Connor, a Georgia writer who uses eccentric rural characters to embody the startling religious truths of Roman Catholicism. L'Heureux's characters here are certainly not eccentric, but the central crisis they face can be compared to that which faced Mary and Joseph in the New Testament. Corinne is undergoing a mysterious pregnancy that was totally unexpected. Her husband is a laborer, like Joseph, who wishes to support his wife in her decisions even though he thinks there might be something wrong with her. The child is apparently going to be unlike other children, but Corinne, like Mary, decides to go through with the delivery and take the consequences.

L'Heureux's technique is to leave the ending of the story mysterious and ambiguous, forcing readers to draw their own conclusions. Some might conclude that Corinne dies on the delivery table, and that the light which she sees is something like the tunnel described by some who have returned from near-death experiences. More plausible, however, is that the birth is a totally transformative experience for her, an occasion for her to see all of reality in new terms, as if bathed in bold light. This is often the experience for mothers, particularly in their first delivery. In terms of the implicit biblical allusion to Mary, who "treasured all these things in her heart" as Jesus grew up, this would mean that for the reader the story is ending, but for Corinne it is just beginning. As in Mary's famous prayer, the Magnificat, Corinne accepts what will be and what is.

The reader is left to decide whether Corinne has encountered something mysterious, or has simply lost her mind. L'Heureux's decision to quietly pass along the protagonist's dilemma to his readers explains the story's early suggestion that comedy saves people not from truth but from despair: They are left mystified, but possibly hopeful. Comparing Corinne at the beginning of the story with the protagonist at the end shows a transformation from a rather shallow middle-aged woman to one who addresses an unnamed reality and offers thanks.

On a more secular plane, L'Heureux's conclusion quickly alludes to the famous ending of James Joyce's *Ulysses* (1922), in which Leopold Bloom's life-affirming wife gets the final word, which is "yes" to all of life, including its complications, deformities, jokes, and questions.

John C. Hawley

COMFORT

Author: David Michael Kaplan (1946-   )
Type of plot: Domestic realism
Time of plot: A warm spring evening and the following morning
Locale: Saratoga, New York
First published: 1986

> *Principal characters:*
> LAURIE, a Skidmore College graduate
> MICHAELA, her friend and roommate
> TED BREMMER, her mother's current boyfriend

The Story

Laurie and Michaela have been friends since their senior year at Skidmore College. Since neither girl has definite plans, they have rented an apartment in Saratoga together while holding down nondescript jobs.

One spring evening about a year out of college, they are rocking themselves in wicker chairs at home facing tall bay windows, open to admit the warm breeze. They are waiting for Laurie's mother's current boyfriend, Ted Bremmer, to arrive for dinner. Laurie's mother, who lives in New York City, works for a business firm. She has asked the girls to give the presumably middle-aged man a little tender loving care while he is in Saratoga to direct a television spot for the Saratoga Performing Arts Center.

While killing time, the two girls talk of Laurie's mother, whose affairs Michaela has always followed with interest. In Laurie's opinion, her mother has not been very discriminating in her choice of boyfriends, but she has been with Ted for almost a year, longer than with some of the other "jerks." Although she allows that her mother feels comfortable with Ted, she distrusts him. She explains that the previous summer, Ted ogled her while the three of them were at the shore. Michaela, grinning mischievously, suggests that Laurie test him by attempting to seduce him. When Laurie objects, Michaela volunteers to try it herself. Laurie has always compared herself unfavorably with Michaela, whose control over things, grace and ease, "a sensuality that offered refuge yet promised nothing," she admires. She reluctantly acquiesces to Michaela's suggestion.

Ted appears belatedly with excuses and a bottle of good wine. At first, he lavishes his attention on Laurie rather than on Michaela, who he is meeting for the first time. He talks disparagingly about his work, but nevertheless appreciates the role of television spots in paying for programming. As the conversation proceeds, Laurie becomes more critical and Michaela more appreciative of these television commercials. Laurie ventures that the world might be better off without the propaganda. Observing Laurie's critical mindset, Michaela observes that she sounds like something left over from the 1960's.

While they talk of other things, more wine is being consumed all around, following the hard drinks that the two girls drank while waiting for Ted to appear. Eventually, all three move to the kitchen to prepare the salad, the pasta, even baste the bread—a deviation from the girls' normal dinner routine of heating of frozen foods and throwing salads together with whatever vegetables are wilting in the refrigerator. While Ted steps out to his car to pick up pills for the hay fever that has bothered him all evening, Michaela tells Laurie that she thinks he is nice and good-looking, and that she likes him. Laurie is more judgmental, characterizing him as smooth and slick.

Laurie's mostly repressed hostility to Michaela mounts. She silently resents Michaela's tendency to think of their place as if it were her house, with her as the hostess and Laurie herself as merely another visitor. Because of the drinks, Laurie is becoming light-headed and fantasizes that she is a young child and that Ted and Michaela are her parents.

Ted is both cynical and funny in his comments. He talks about trained cats who refuse to perform on cue and about not finding a talking seal for an art director for whom he once worked. He confesses that at times he does not know why a grown man does these things. Meanwhile, Laurie's anger keeps mounting. At one point Michaela follows her and asks pointedly what is wrong with her.

Back in the front room, they talk about Greek islands that Ted and Michaela both happen to know. In order to arouse Ted, Michaela spins a story about a sexual event, allegedly part dream, part fact, that involves a boy about twelve years old and includes a bit about her sleeping naked on a beach in Crete. Laurie, feeling increasingly left out and embarrassed, tries to change the mood and derail Michaela's increasing obvious play for Ted by suggesting they telephone her mother and all talk to her. When Ted rejects the idea, Laurie goes to her room and falls asleep. When she awakens in the middle of the night, she discovers that Ted is in her friend's room.

The next morning, Laurie wakes up again with a hangover. Michaela is still asleep, but now alone. Laurie cleans up the front room and the kitchen, then calls Ted at his motel. When he answers, she lets out an expletive and hangs up.

Michaela eventually gets up and admits to the seduction, breaking the promise of silence that she made to Ted. Laurie becomes even more disconsolate and swears that she will kill Michaela if her mother ever finds out. Michaela replies, "But at least we know, don't we? That's sort of a comfort, isn't it?"

Themes and Meanings

In "Comfort" and several other stories, David Michael Kaplan deals with people emotionally or physically estranged from their parents, but he does not always offer a resolution to the strange relationships and the unbridgeable distances between the characters he creates. This story is no exception. Its suspense flows from not knowing whether Laurie and Michaela will continue to be friends after the story ends. Laurie is seized with a strong sense of betrayal by her friend, but she emerges from the experience more emotionally mature than her roommate.

It also is not evident whether Laurie's mother, given the pledges of silence made separately among the threesome, will ever learn of her lover's seduction by Michaela.

In this story, as in others by Kaplan, the mother is unimportant. Here, she does not make even a cameo appearance. More important, the chasm between daughter and mother must have grown, considering Laurie's critical mindset of her lifestyle and now of her latest boyfriend as well.

Style and Technique

Kaplan focuses on sudden moments of recognition in the lives of ordinary people. He looks at how such flashes of discovery, such revelations, may alter, for better or worse, the relationship of his protagonists to those with whom they are deeply bound—in "Comfort," Laurie's roommate and her own mother.

The story of Laurie's casual acquiescence to her friend's suggestion that she seduces her mother's lover to prove whether or not he is a jerk like the woman's previous boyfriends is psychologically devastating to Laurie. The story is told from her perspective, since she is the one who quickly matures emotionally. Unlikely as such a story may seem, it does not stretch the reader's credulity beyond measure. The girls' obviously liberated lifestyles and attitudes mixed with Michaela's inclination toward mischief, as shown by her fabricating the story about a beach in Crete, help to keep the story line in character.

Despite his economy of words, the author does not profile cartoon characters. When Michaela wakes up the morning after her seduction, Laurie, although feeling an acute sense of betrayal, is still solicitous about her roommate's having fresh coffee, and she is apologetic because there is no milk in the house. The reader senses, however, that even Laurie's not-too-literal threat to kill Michaela if her mother ever finds out about the seduction can barely conceal the emotional storm brewing in her psyche. Accordingly, the use of the word "comfort" in the story's last sentence could not be more ironic. For it is the continuing sense of discomfort—a tension that is not released—that makes the story arresting for the reader long after the last word is read.

Peter B. Heller

COMMUNIST

Author: Richard Ford (1944-   )
Type of plot: Realism
Time of plot: 1961
Locale: Near Great Falls, Montana
First published: 1985

Principal characters:
LES, the narrator
AILEEN, his mother
GLEN BAXTER, Aileen's boyfriend

The Story

Les, the forty-one-year-old narrator, looks back to 1961, when he was sixteen and still living with his mother in a house left by his late father. His mother, Aileen, was a part-time waitress in the nearby town of Great Falls, where she met Glen Baxter, a self-proclaimed labor organizer and communist who had seen a side of the world that Les could then only imagine. A transplanted westerner, Baxter was a drifter who "stayed out of work winters and in the bars drinking with women like my mother, who had work and some money"—a common way of life in Montana. All of this is merely the backdrop. The real story that Les wants to tell happened in November of that year: a single day that he would forever remember as a turning point, his rite of passage into awareness, when life as he knew it would never again be the same.

Although two months pass during which Aileen does not see Glen Baxter, she is not pleased when he shows up from out of nowhere and wants to take Les hunting for snow geese. Unlike his mother, Les is pleased by Baxter's sudden reappearance and he enthusiastically accepts Baxter's invitation. Aileen strongly disapproves of sense-less bloodletting—as well as the attempt at male bonding between her son and the man who has deserted her. Eventually, however, Baxter and Les prevail and Aileen rides with them into the Montana prairieland that appears to lack any sign of wildlife.

Baxter, however, knows that the snow geese are there, and he finds thousands of them stretched out across a low-lying lake away from the road. Baxter proves to be experienced as both a hunter and a guide. Les recalls the moment when the birds break off into flight, and thinks to himself that this is something he will never see again and will never forget. Unfortunately, that one memorable moment is quickly dwarfed by another.

Aileen reappears, her spirit temporarily lifted by the magical sight of the snow geese rising up into the big blue Montana sky. It is clear that Aileen is impressed both by the geese and by Baxter's grace and expertise with a shotgun. For one moment, at least, it seems as if all is well. Then Les makes the mistake of pointing out to his mother a wounded goose that is "swimming in circles on the water." Aileen insists that they should wade out in the lake to put the bird out of its misery, but Baxter disagrees.

He tells Aileen that she does not understand the world, that one small mistake does not really matter much in the grand scheme of things. Then he settles the issue by firing four shots into the goose. When he turns around, Aileen is gone. Just like that, Les says, looking back on these sad and distant events, "A light can go out in the heart."

Later that night, after Baxter has left to lead whatever life he is destined to live, Les and Aileen share a tender moment together as geese pass by invisibly in the darkness overhead. For the first time, they see each other as they really are: not just mother and son, but two grown people who in a year's time will be like strangers passing silently in the night.

Themes and Meanings

"Communist" dramatizes a single sweeping moment in the life of a family as the ties that bind them together begin to unravel before their eyes. It is a theme that Richard Ford has explored in two other stories in his collection *Rock Springs* (1987)—in "Great Falls" and "Optimists"—and in his novel *Wildlife* (1990). These stories, like "Communist," have adult male first-person narrators who have struggled to transcend the often hard and unforgiving circumstances of their lives. Their events revolve around the themes of adultery and violence, of life and love not working out as they have dreamed. In "Communist," nothing—not even the snow geese—mates for life. Unforeseen events and people intrude, often assuring that nothing will ever be the same again. "Sixteen is young," Les muses in the closing lines, "but it can also be a grown man." He is prematurely forced to come of age, "pushed out into the world, into the real life." Les's voice is not, however, tinged with bitterness or even regret. Telling what has happened helps him to understand the complex reasons behind the seemingly harsh behavior of the few people who have entered his emotional landscape and helped to shape his character. Les is thereby able to reconcile himself with the hard cold fact that often people do not really know those whom they love the most—that they are estranged from them and left to face the world alone. Like many of Ford's characters, Les is a victim of having "too much awareness too early in life." Yet it is his very sense of awareness that gives him the resilience to go on living; the strength to stride forward, and to live independently—even if it means going at it alone.

Style and Technique

Ford has been criticized for giving his characters too much insight, too much room to muse and find meaning in those moments that remain memorable through their lives. Critics of his fiction claim that the men who typically populate his stories are a luckless breed of westerners who should not possess the lyrical impulses that drive his stories. They argue that the author imposes his own voice upon his narrators, and that men such as Les—who come from broken homes and marginalized backgrounds—could not possibly be as sensitive and articulate as Ford depicts them. It is true that Ford usually gives his characters dialogue that means something—words weighted with dramatic implication. Ford defends his method of meaning-filled conversation, however, by explaining that he is not trying to write dialogue that "is actual to life. I'm trying to write dialogue that refers to life." He adds that he does not think readers need to read stories merely "to have life rehashed. Stories should point toward what's important in life, and our utterances always mean something." Ford jeopardizes credibility when his characters step outside the boundaries of their emotional landscapes and go beyond the expectations of the reader; however, the risk is rewarded with an intimacy that would not exist if Ford refused to let his narrators speak. When Les reflects "I don't know what makes people do what they do, or call themselves what they call themselves, only that you have to live someone's life to be the expert," the simple wisdom of his words seems to be merited by the experience that he has lived through. He is forty-one years old at the time of his telling, looking back at a time when he was sixteen. He has had twenty-five years to think about the events of that November day. It is not at all surprising that he has learned a few hard lessons.

Peter Markus

IL CONDE

Author: Joseph Conrad (Jósef Teodor Konrad Nałęcz Korzeniowski, 1857-1924)
Type of plot: Psychological realism
Time of plot: Early 1900's
Locale: Naples, Italy
First published: 1908

> *Principal characters:*
> IL CONDE (THE COUNT), the protagonist, an urbane
> European aristocrat
> THE NARRATOR, his cultured acquaintance

The Story

Set in Naples, Italy, early in the 1900's, "Il Conde" is a tale told by an anonymous narrator about his brief companionship with a northern European aristocrat whom he knows only as the Count. Like the narrator himself, the Count emerges as a man of the world and a person distinguished by cultivated tastes, impeccable manners, and fastidious sensibilities.

The narrator meets the Count while both are viewing art works in Naples' National Museum. After discovering that they both are guests in the same quietly refined Neapolitan hotel, they spend three evenings enjoying pleasant meals together. During their conversations, the narrator learns that three years earlier the Count left northern Europe in order to seek relief from a dangerous rheumatic disease by living in small hotels and villas on the warm Gulf of Naples. A middle-aged widower who is virtually exiled by his affliction, the Count returns home during the summers to visit a married daughter in her Bohemian castle; it is the only hiatus in his pleasant, tastefully subdued, and orderly life. To leave the south for longer periods, he believes, would mean forfeiting his life to his disease.

Called away from Naples to attend a sick friend, the narrator returns ten days later to find the Count shaken and dispirited, although he is not prone to unbalanced emotions. The Count reveals the cause of his distress. After seeing the narrator to his train, the Count walked through a park toward a villa where a public concert was in progress. Upon reaching a secluded spot, however, he was accosted by a young knife-wielding Neapolitan who demanded his wallet, watch, and rings. The Count had prudently left most of his money safely locked in the hotel, and the watch he wore chanced to be a cheap substitute for a valuable one that was being cleaned. He bravely refused to part with his rings, however, which were gifts from his father and his wife. After closing his eyes, expecting to be stabbed by his outraged assailant, the Count opened them to find that the thief had departed.

Upset and hungry, the Count immediately sought out a café in which to regain his equanimity, only to recognize the mugger among the crowd. When the Count asked a café peddlar if he knew the mugger, the peddlar identified him as a respectable university student, adding that he was also a leader in the Camorra—a secret criminal organization dedicated to ridding Naples of the taint of aristocracy. As the Count paid the peddlar with a forgotten gold piece undiscovered by the mugger, the mugger saw the transaction, cursed the Count for holding out on him, and snarled that he was not through with him yet.

Thoroughly cowed and convinced that he is a marked man, the Count bids farewell to Naples and to the narrator. As the Count's deluxe train pulls away from the station, the narrator recognizes that the aristocrat's return to the cold north is a form of suicide.

Themes and Meanings

Many literary scholars, and indeed early reviewers, regard "Il Conde" as the best example of Joseph Conrad's short fiction. Conrad wrote it as one of a group of six short stories—the so-called "Set of Six"—that he published early for popular consumption when he needed money badly. He proudly declared that the story had taken him only ten days to write after he decided to elaborate on an event that occurred in the life of Count Zygmunt Zzembek, whom he had met on Capri. Although the "Set of Six" stories are separate, they gain unity as critiques of then current political tendencies within Europe's class structure. At one level, to be sure, each story explores individual integrity, honor, glory, romance, and bravery. But more importantly, each also embodies political observations on European class warfare.

Scholars have noted that "Il Conde" intimates the decline and eventual demise of the aristocracy with which Conrad identified himself. Obviously, Conrad's Count delineates both the admirable qualities and the flaws typical of his class. The Count is a polylingual cosmopolite; he is cultured and sensitive—an unostentatious and emotionally disciplined man devoted to living a balanced and moderate life of quiet comforts nourished by select tastes. Until he feels the Neapolitan's knife on his belly, he seems unaware of the social discontents that might imperil him, of the dark forces through which previously he had moved without disturbance.

That the dark young Neapolitan leaves the Count physically unharmed is irrelevant to the Count's reaction. The assault fractured the Count's sensibilities and irrevocably cracked his aristocratic perception of living within a shell of civilities and privilege that he had thought rendered him inviolable. Already forced by his rheumatic disease to live in warm climates, the Count moved south to prolong his life. In abandoning Naples and southern Europe, he consciously consigns himself to death. Conrad's message is clear: Europe's aristocracies were themselves debilitated by their own diseased estate, victimized, as it were, by their adaptations to secure lives and bourgeois comforts. By the opening of the twentieth century, their safe range had become tightly constricted, and they were psychologically too fragile in spirit to stave off the violent, sinister forces seething about them.

"Il Conde" underscored Conrad's perception that his own age contrasted sharply with the "heroic" spirit of the early nineteenth century Napoleonic Era—a period that deeply interested him. Instead of savouring the charms of living dangerous lives, instead of being motivated by strong beliefs, by personal honor, or by personal integrity, Conrad thought that men of his own era (such as the Count) were more apt to be motivated to seek secure, comfortable, and unheroic lives, or to act less from conviction than from boredom, like the villainous young men of Naples.

Style and Technique

Conrad relates the Count's story through an anonymous first-person narrator. In having an episode in the life of a nameless aristocrat recounted by an equally nameless narrator, Conrad signals his intention to explore social and political forces and their symbols, rather than to create distinctive characters. The narrator speaks for Conrad himself, very much the civilized man, conscious of aristocratic virtues, but also aware of the aristocracy's wasting, ineffectual condition.

Although the narrator maintains a charitable detachment as the Count's "pathetic tale" unfolds, he fills the story with ironic commentary and contrasts. By wandering back and forth through a darkened park, for example, the Count almost tempts the mugger, whom in fact he had passed several times and acknowledged once. Conrad adds another ironic touch by having the concert band play the aristocracy's traditional harmonious music, reaching its blaring *fortissimo* as the mugger pushes his knife against the Count. Likewise, Conrad repeatedly stresses the darkness of "sunny" Naples, emphasizing its sinister dimensions. As Conrad well knew, many Italians once viewed Naples and southern Italy as a land of thieves and as a dark "Africa." Again, both the narrator and the Count refer constantly to the dark young Neapolitans with bandit-like mustachios, deep, dark eyes, and curled lips, ensuring that readers are aware that the Count could scarcely have placed himself in a more dangerous environment.

By stopping short of overt and bloody violence, Conrad all the more skillfully establishes an ambiance of menace. Given the Count's sensibilities, it is the threat of violence more than violence itself that intimidates him and sends him packing—in, as the narrator ironically records, a suicidal journey on Europe's most luxurious train. Superb author that he was, Conrad was not above giving an ironic twist to the old Italian adage "*Vedi Napoli, et poi mori!*," ("See Naples and die!"). The Count, as the narrator tells us, would have regarded the phrase as excessively patriotic, but Conrad helps tie his story together by having the Count obey it.

Clifton K. Yearley

A CONVERSATION WITH MY FATHER

Author: Grace Paley (1922-   )
Type of plot: Metafiction
Time of plot: c. 1971
Locale: New York City
First published: 1971

> *Principal characters:*
> THE DAUGHTER, the narrator
> HER FATHER, a bedridden old man
> A MOTHER,
> A SON, and
> A YOUNG WOMAN, her fictional characters

The Story

One evening, the narrator's eighty-six-year-old father lies in bed in his New York home. Unable to walk, he suffers from a heart condition after having lived a rich life as a doctor and an artist. He appears near death, for he has pills at hand and breathes oxygen from a bedside tank. He has not lost his intelligence, interest in art, or concern for his daughter, however.

In what might be the speech of one knowing that he is near death, he confronts his daughter about the kind of short stories that she writes. He wishes that she would write "simple" stories like the old masters of the form: the Frenchman Guy de Maupassant and the Russian Anton Chekhov. He reminds her that she once wrote stories like that.

Although the narrator does not remember writing any such stories, she wants to please her father, so she quickly writes a very short story about what has been happening to a woman and her son who are their real neighbors. Her story is odd but simple, perhaps the sort that her father will like:

> A mother and her son live happily in the city. After the son becomes a drug addict, the mother becomes an addict in order to maintain their closeness. The son then gives up drugs, becomes disgusted with his mother, and goes away, leaving her alone and without hope.

The narrator's father does not like the story, finding it too spare. Classic short story writers, he maintains, would humanize the story with descriptions. After the daughter obligingly adds perfunctory details about such things as hairstyles, the father is still not satisfied because his daughter does not take her characters seriously enough.

When their conversation turns to how the daughter writes her own stories, they discuss what happens when she stumbles on a good character—one to be taken seriously. It takes time to devise an appropriate ending to such a story, but the father asks her to take the time. After an interval, the daughter writes a much longer version of her story. It is now full of evocative detail and bizarre complications, but its action remains essentially the same. The most important change concerns the son, who now edits a periodical that advocates drug use:

> Then enters a young woman who also has a magazine, but one that advocates drug-free living and natural foods. She takes the son home with her. He converts to her way of thinking, but his mother cannot break her own addiction, so the son and the young woman abandon her. As before, the mother is left with her addiction and her grief.

Even this version does not satisfy the writer's father, though he seems to approve of its definite and tragic ending. The daughter protests, however, that her ending is not so final as her father assumes, explaining that after the story ends, the mother goes on to have a satisfying career helping others. Again the father objects, arguing that such a hopeful ending is bad art because it evades life's ultimate tragedy—death. The conversation ends when the father asks his daughter when she will face such facts.

Themes and Meanings

Grace Paley's story deals with the conflicts between generations, specifically those between an elderly parent and an adult child. Although the father is old and sick, he is sufficiently alert to ask searching and intelligent questions. The narrator is clearly her father's daughter for she shares his quickness of mind. She seems devoted to him as she sits by what may be his deathbed, but she does not humor him. She does not hide the fact that she is younger and stronger than he. Even though she changes the story that she writes at his request, she concedes nothing in their argument.

Though their argument is often playful, it is significant. One of Paley's themes is the difference between the stories told by masters of the past and those present-day authors feel they must tell. The father prefers the old-fashioned kind because they progress to definite endings that evoke the tragic nature of life. The daughter's stories (and presumably "A Conversation with My Father" itself) are not like that. They are witty—sometimes grimly hilarious—and their endings are not necessarily final. Their open-ended nature evokes not the climactic catharsis of tragedy, but a sense of the flatness and minor pathos of everyday life. Paley suggests that the stories that satisfied readers during the father's modern era are not so satisfying to writers and readers of the postmodern present.

The argument between the father and his daughter in this story is about what stories should be like. For this reason, it is an example of metafiction: fiction about fiction. The contrasts that metafiction makes between its main stories and the stories within it help to make readers conscious of the differences between fiction and real life. In the narrator's exuberance, readers sense how much joy a writer may derive from inventing details and actions. Paley's story may also suggest the differences between the kinds of fiction that women and men write. Some critics argue that women's stories tend to be less climactic and more open-ended than those written by men.

No matter how theoretical "A Conversation with My Father" becomes, it remains a human story. Like its themes, its characters develop gradually. At the end, the reader senses that the father's preferences in fiction mirror his own preoccupation with the approach of his own death. And when he tells his daughter to face the facts of tragedy and death within her stories, he also implies that she must face it in her own life. The contrast between the characters can be seen as one between a man about to die and his grown daughter who is not near death, who is not ready for total closure in fiction or in her own life. In her insisting that her story is not closed, we also see how much she is moved by pity for other people and how much she wishes to see new life (not death) in their future. Perhaps the contrast can be read as one between the prophetic wisdom of age and the evasions of comparative youth. In any case, Paley's "A Conversation with My Father" implies that it is a story of its times, for its conclusion does not neatly summarize its themes but leaves open the question about what the daughter has learned.

Style and Technique

"A Conversation with My Father" is related in the first person by the daughter. By briefly describing her father's past life, present situation, and a few of his actions, and most importantly by recording what he says to her, she builds up a good sense of his character. As is usual in first-person narratives, the narrator's own character and ultimate opinions are more difficult to discern. Unlike many first-person narrators, this one is never confessional. Aspects of her style help reveal her: She tells her story efficiently and economically; she enjoys telling stories and is good at weaving facts from real life together with details of her own invention; her words are incisive, as when she describes her father's mind as flooded with "brainy light." Many readers will find her story full of a grim but effervescent humor.

The work's most obvious device is the story-within-a-story. In this case, there are two versions (and written versions at that) of the same general story, and both contrast markedly with the main story. This device enables Paley to illustrate the differences between the endings of her own stories and the types of endings that her father prefers. It also presents a contrast in styles. The stories-within-stories have a strange tone: a factual, abrupt, and plodding style tells of absurd happenings. By contrast, the main story at all times reveals the serious intelligence and emotional depth of characters whose lives are not at all silly.

Paley constructs her story artfully. At first one meets a demanding but understandable old man who says that he likes "simple" stories and a daughter who seems to toy with him by writing precisely the kind of story that he hates. Only gradually does one understand that what really matters to the old man is not merely a kind of plot, but an attitude towards the tragic nature of life. Even though the daughter will not back down in their intellectual tug-of-war, her playfulness is gradually shown to mask her real love and admiration for her father and her understanding of his situation. By the end of the story, the reader senses that, although her kind of story (that is, this story itself) allows no neat resolution, its open-ended future may include her understanding of what her father has tried to tell her.

George Soule

COOKING LESSON

Author: Rosario Castellanos (1925-1974)
Type of plot: Domestic realism
Time of plot: The 1960's
Locale: Mexico
First published: "Lección de cocina," 1971 (English translation, 1988)

Principal character:
THE NARRATOR, a young Mexican housewife

The Story

A recently married Mexican woman explains that because she does not know how to cook, she must resort to a cookbook for guidance. Her frustration grows as she skims through recipes too difficult for novices to follow. Feeling dishonest in wearing an apron that suggests an expertise that is generally assumed to be second nature to women, the narrator finally decides to defrost and prepare a roast.

While thus occupied, her mind wanders back and forth between her culinary task and the changes that have occurred in her life since she met her husband. Remarks that she makes, such as, "The meat hasn't stopped existing. It has undergone a series of metamorphoses," apply to both her cooking and her life—both of which have undergone major transformations. Meanwhile, her resentment toward other household matters surfaces.

Despite her supervision, the roast eventually burns, leaving her to contemplate two possible ways in which to deal with the problem. As a woman who has been socialized to be a wife who embodies perfection, she can air out the kitchen, toss out the burned roast to hide the evidence of her failure, and await her husband coquettishly dressed to go out for dinner. Her other option is to accept responsibility for the fiasco and risk shattering her husband's image of her. The story ends with her weighing the satisfaction of showing her true self against the ensuing consequences of not using traditional feminine wiles.

Themes and Meanings

The questioning of gender roles, especially women's, is a principal theme of Rosario Castellanos' "Cooking Lesson." Its opening sentence indicates the space that culture assigns to females: the kitchen. Lacking cooking skills, the narrator resentfully comments: "My place is here. I've been here from the beginning of time." She embodies generations of women before her who have been socialized for domesticity.

As the story progresses, the young woman's resentment toward other household matters surfaces, suggesting that her struggle with making dinner is merely a catalyst in questioning the cultural forces that give women the roles that trap them in the home, stripping them of self-identity. These views are presented through the anonymous character's interior monologue. Significantly voiceless and nameless, this woman represents countless married women who silently suffer the loss of their independence, identity, and self-esteem. Castellanos' irony lends relief to the tale of profound disillusionment with marriage.

In a traditionally patriarchal society, such as that depicted in this story, public forums are reserved for men, while married women are relegated to the private realm of the home. For the narrator, marriage means giving up the independence that she enjoyed while single. Her allusions to schooling and job skills suggest that she was previously gainfully employed. Quite literally, she sacrifices her engagement with the outside world at the altar: "I wandered astray through classrooms, streets, offices, cafés, wasting my time on skills that now I must forget in order to acquire others." These "other" skills, as she reveals, are domestic; they include serving as cook, maid, and hostess with neither a day off, a salary, nor the possibility of changing employers.

As a devalued worker, the housewife recognizes the selflessness that marriage requires of women. Adopting her husband's name is the first step in assuming his identity and losing her own: "I lost my old name and I still can't get used to the new one." She feels nameless because her own identity is subsumed in her husband's. His infidelity further accentuates her loss of self: "You moan unintelligibly and I'd like to whisper my name in your ear to remind you who it is you are possessing."

The patriarchal double standard in sexual matters that condones premarital and extramarital sex for males, while condemning females for the same behaviors, is also a point of bitterness for the narrator. The culture allows a husband to exercise his sexual prowess as a male prerogative; however, the ideal wife is one who "believes the evening executive meeting, the business trips and the arrival of unexpected clients . . . [even] when she catches a whiff of French perfume (different from the one she uses) on her husband's shirts." Significantly, the description of the kitchen that opens the story alludes to the ideal female image. Such words as "shining white," "spotlessness," "pulchritude," and "halo" suggest the purity and virginity or chastity that is prized in women.

Given that virginity and the ability to cook are valued traits in females, it is not surprising that food and sexuality, as essential drives, are integral components of the story. The narrator finds contradictions in both cooking and sexuality. Some incongruities in cooking are, "slimness and gluttony, pleasing appearance and economy, speed and succulence." The wife believes that sexual innocence before marriage becomes clumsiness, and inexperience becomes frigidity. The husband, annoyed by her modesty, behaves as if after the wedding she should immediately erase all the inhibitions that she has internalized during her years of patriarchal socialization.

Analogies may be drawn between the young woman as a cook and the roast. For example, the narrator comments that when her husband discovered she was a virgin, she felt "like the last dinosaur." When the meat that she is cooking turns out unusually tough, she remarks that "it must be mammoth." Her mishap with cooking oil evokes a parallel with the roast, which is now "spitting and spattering and burning me. That's how I'm going to fry in those narrow hells, through my fault, through my fault, through my most grievous fault." This last example suggests a prayer in the Roman

Catholic Mass in which the confession of sin includes articulating "mia culpa" ("through my fault") three times while pounding the chest.

Sin and guilt are key elements in Roman Catholic religious indoctrination that influences sexual behavior, especially among women. Since the narrator does not feel that she is appreciated as a wife or is desired as a woman, she begins to fantasize about dressing up, leaving the house, and encountering male admirers on the street. It takes the smoke from the burning roast to bring her back to reality. As is apparent, the previous reference to burning in hell alludes to her adulterous carnal desire and its punishment.

Elsewhere in the story, the wife associates fire and blisters with sacrifice and the body. The redness of the uncooked meat reminds her of the color of the sunburned backs that she and her husband got during their honeymoon in Acapulco. Although making physical love became agonizing for her, she did not breathe a word of complaint while her sunburned back ached under the weight of her husband—just as the Aztec emperor Cuauhtémoc remained silent while being tortured by the Spaniards over a bed of scorching coals. Recalling Cuauhtémoc's fate, the housewife feels imprisoned and a mute object of sacrifice.

"Cooking Lesson" is about women's struggle for subjectivity and autonomy. This concern is best illustrated by the narrator's self-reflection: "I'm myself. But who am I? Your wife, of course. And that title suffices to distinguish me from past memories or future projects. I bear an owner's brand, a property tag."

Style and Technique

"Cooking Lesson" uses interior monologue to portray a housewife's silent indictment of gender roles as representative of the general voicelessness of women in Mexican society. The monologue suggests that those in a subordinate role are not free to speak their minds.

Irony is used throughout the story to address and debunk cultural conventions. While mocking her role, the wife suggests the burden social dictates place on women: "For example, choosing the menu. How could one carry out such an arduous task without the cooperation of society—of all history?" The narrator, who obviously resents her role, describes herself as a "self-sacrificing little Mexican wife, born like a dove to the nest." She sarcastically denounces both male sexual competence and female pleasure: "The classic moan. Myths. Myths." Deriding the notion that a woman is an incomplete being without a man, she says that she has undergone "a profound metamorphosis." Previously, she "didn't know and now I know; I didn't feel and now I feel; I wasn't and now I am." Since society at large considers that a female's greatest accomplishment is securing a husband, the narrator ridicules the gratefulness implicitly elicited from brides saved from spinsterhood: "Thanks for giving me the chance to show off a long gown with a train, for helping me walk up the aisle of the church, carried away by the organ music. Thanks for . . . ."

The next sentence immediately switches the topic to the roast. By consistently alternating the wife's train of thought between two frustrating experiences (marriage and cooking), Castellanos juxtaposes the focus to suggest the analogy of wife to meat. Furthermore, the use of flashbacks to depict a change in consciousness suggests the wife's daydreaming state while cooking. The lack of transition between past and present in the narration can be as abrupt as "I . . . The meat," thus exemplifying the wife's blurring of identity, a subject turned object.

Gisela Norat

COUNTING MONTHS

Author: David Leavitt (1962-   )
Type of plot: Psychological realism
Time of plot: 1980
Locale: An unnamed California suburb
First published: 1984

Principal characters:

ANNA HARRINGTON, a recently divorced mother with cancer
JOAN LENSKY, her nosy acquaintance
GREG LAURANS, the disturbed son of a friend

The Story

Six months before the story opens, Anna Harrington was told that she had six months to live. Now, sitting in the oncology department waiting room, she is suddenly overcome by the realization that she was supposed to be dead by now. Instead of elation, she feels only dread, for she does not interpret the fact that she is not dead as a reprieve, but as a stay of execution. When her doctor praises her for keeping up an active life, she suddenly realizes what a lie she is living.

The doctor's optimism only depresses her as she leaves the hospital and drives to a supermarket. It is Christmas, and she marvels at sights and sounds that she never expected to live to see, but she feels no joy. The more she tries to forget her condition, the more obsessed with it she becomes. She is overwhelmed by the irony of the fact that she is living in a body that is killing itself from within.

Back home, she is plunged into the familiar domestic routine of dealing with three energetic young children who have no idea of what she is going through. At odd moments, the horror seizes her, then recedes as family demands intervene. Recently divorced, she has the added burden of being a single parent. Tonight she is supposed to take her children to a party at the Lauranses, Jewish friends whose son Greg is a born-again Christian who is displaying signs of bizarre behavior. Soon after the Harringtons arrive at the Lauranses, Anna settles a dispute between her son Ernest and a boy who he says broke his thermos bottle. The fact that Ernest is not telling the whole truth bothers her, especially when she remembers that she will probably not be around much longer to guide her son.

Two things happen at the party to aggravate Anna's fragile emotional condition. First, she accosted by Joan Lensky, a woman who pretends to be a concerned friend but who is really a busybody and a gossip. Joan seems to live for nothing but comparing other people's sorrows with her own. She presses Anna for details of her condition and seems to enjoy speaking graphically of radiation therapy, chemotherapy, and hair loss. She even goes so far as to suggest that Anna consult an organization that arranges things before people die to ensure that everything will be properly taken care of afterward.

Anna is no sooner rescued from Joan's morbid prying, than she is confronted by a group of retarded children whom Greg Laurans has brought from the state hospital to sing Christmas carols. One of the girls is a dwarf with a deformed head and large, alert eyes set unnaturally low beneath a broad forehead. When the children sing, they have such trouble pronouncing even the simplest words that their singing becomes grotesque. Anna sees their performance as a deliberate cruelty to all concerned and tries to comfort Greg's distraught mother.

Shortly thereafter, Ernest announces to his mother that his brother, Roy, is in the bedroom with some boys smoking pot. Instead of recoiling in horror, Anna merely tells Ernest not to be a tattletale, as if nothing else can now happen that could possibly upset her. Just as she says this, she spies the dwarf girl looking up at her. The girl is holding a glass of water in her tiny, fat hand, and on her face is an expression that Anna thinks could indicate either extreme stupidity or great knowledge. As the story ends, the dwarf girl is staring at Anna, unblinking, as if Anna herself "were a curiosity—or a comrade in sorrow."

Themes and Meanings

Being stricken in the midst of life with cancer is a theme in much of David Leavitt's fiction. At an age when most people have not yet even grasped the idea of mortality, Leavitt was probing the minds and hearts of cancer patients with uncanny authority. He is most concerned with the way cancer both unites and separates people. He uses cancer as a metaphor for the inescapable loneliness of life. Although disease can help one to sympathize with others similarly afflicted, Leavitt presents it as a reminder that everyone must pass alone through the valley of the shadow of death. His characters take no comfort in knowing that others may be suffering, for it means nothing to them. Only their own suffering is real, and thus their cancer becomes the ultimate reality. While it heightens the awareness of life around them, it also intensifies their loneliness.

Leavitt does not portray this loneliness as a cause for sadness or self-pity. People such as Anna Harrington do not envy the healthy or resent the well, nor do they view life at such a distance that it becomes meaningless and absurd. While their disease focuses their attention on themselves, it does not make them selfish or spiteful, but neither does it make them philosophical. In this respect, Leavitt's is a fresh view and a fresh voice. Unlike the characters of Anton Chekhov or Thomas Mann, who are either in love with their disease or angry with God for allowing it, Leavitt's characters have a dignity and courage that suggest, if anything, that the sentence of death summons forth something mysterious and fine, something essentially human that is not the result but the source of spirituality. In this respect, Leavitt is closer to Leo Tolstoy and Albert Camus, who see the acceptance of death as the first step toward wisdom. To them, death defines life and gives it its meaning.

Anna Harrington shrinks intuitively from Joan Lensky, because the latter's obsession with disease and death is really a form of denial. Her fussing about hair loss and funeral arrangements is her way of evading reality, not confronting it. Anna is drawn to the dwarf girl because this poor deformed creature is a visible manifestation of the disease that is invisibly disfiguring Anna herself. The girl can only be what she is. It does not matter whether she is stupid or wise. She exists without shame in an utterly private world, and she ventures forth into the social world heedless of whether or not she belongs there. For who belongs anywhere? This is what Anna finally realizes when their eyes lock, and they see each other as both curiosities and comrades in sorrow.

Style and Technique

David Leavitt writes short stories that are economical, suspenseful, and satisfying, but still left open-ended. He respects the purpose of the short story, which is to direct all its elements toward a moment of eye-opening awareness, of sudden realization, with a minimum of incidental material and the good sense not to drive the point into the ground.

The economy of this story is illustrated by its series of set pieces: scenes in a waiting room, in a car, at the supermarket, at home, at a party. In quick succession, Leavitt provides glimpses of a frightened woman fighting a losing battle with cancer against a backdrop of banal suburban life. The narrative moves swiftly from Anna's sudden memory of the six-month deadline, to her being inexorably drawn into the hectic life of family and social obligations, and finally to her chilling encounter with the dwarf girl.

Suspense is created from the beginning when it is revealed that Anna has cancer and is apparently living on borrowed time. As she gazes into an aquarium in the oncology waiting room, she sees herself floating in time, emotionally isolated from those who are closest to her. The question raised is not just how long she will live, but how she will live out the time that is left to her. Leavitt quickly moves through the rest of Anna's day, as she gets her children to the party, settles the feud between Ernest and Kevin, puts up with Joan Lensky, and finally comes face to face with the dwarf girl.

Leavitt is particularly good at incident: Anna's reactions to the bustle in the supermarket; her sitting at the traffic light, counting the seconds (as she has counted the months) until it changes, while superstitiously basing her chances for recovery on the accuracy of her guess; the particulars of the children's possessions and games; Joan Lensky always in black; Dr. Sanchez's hairy hands; her husband's running away to Italy with a law student; and, finally, the bizarre image of the dwarf girl, "owl eyes in a huge head," staring Anna down.

Leavitt also knows when to stop. The moment that Anna and the dwarf girl look deeply into each other's eyes, the reader knows that a bond between two human beings has been formed. It is not a bond based upon the mutual deception and false optimism that Anna has received from the doctors. It is a bond based on the full acceptance of who they are—and of each other. To Leavitt, the two are inseparable.

Thomas Whissen

A COUNTRY GIRL

Author: Mary Hood (1946-   )
Type of plot: Social realism
Time of plot: Mid-twentieth century
Locale: Rydal, a rural Florida community
First published: 1984

>
> *Principal characters:*
> ELIZABETH INGLISH, a country girl
> MAY INGLISH, her mother
> UNCLE BILLY
> UNCLE CLEVELAND INGLISH, a senior family member
> PAUL MONTGOMERY, a reporter
> JOHNNY CALHOUN, a forty-year-old family friend

The Story

A pair of Florida tourists stops in the small rural community of Rydal to enjoy the scenery. The man takes photographs while his wife paints a picture, which she gives to a barefoot young country girl named Elizabeth, who sings and plays a guitar. In return, Elizabeth sings a song for the tourists, who view her as a bit of local color—a part of the scenery. As the couple leaves the town, the man says "Country Girl," as he thinks of the caption for his slide.

Paul Montgomery, a reporter for a Sunday magazine, comes to Rydal to write an article on the life and works of a local writer named Corra Harris, who has been dead for several years. He arrives as members of the Inglish family gather for their annual reunion. Women busily prepare the food that they will serve on paper plates placed on picnic tables resting on sawhorses and covered with sheets.

Elizabeth is making potato salad when Montgomery appears in the kitchen looking for Cleveland Inglish, whom he wants to interview because the man once worked for Harris. Since Cleveland is not there, Elizabeth offers to show him Harris' writing studio. She leads him down a path thick with blackberry brambles and blueberries, past gardens blooming with geraniums, Shasta daisies, and hollyhocks. With everyone else gone fishing, the studio is locked, but Elizabeth and Montgomery look at Harris' workroom through the windows. As they look at stacks of yellow paper and a dry ink well, Elizabeth thinks the place is sad because it looks as though its objects are waiting for their owner to return. When Montgomery asks her if she has read any of Harris' books, she replies, "After sixteen they caint make you."

Back at the Inglish family gathering, Elizabeth introduces Montgomery to her Uncle Cleveland, who invites him to stay for the meal. Montgomery listens to the conversation, but does not learn much about Harris. As he leaves for his motel, he promises to return with his camera and questions about Harris.

More members of the family arrive: aunts, uncles, cousins, and children, as well as dogs, and they take their customary stations around a beech tree and engage in small talk. Johnny Calhoun, a forty-year-old yarn manufacturer, arrives and is invited to join the party, although he is not a family member. He is a handsome man who enjoys the ladies. When Jeff's wife, Patty, runs to welcome him with a kiss, Johnny and everyone else laughs.

Elizabeth stands near a group of children, hoping to avoid being asked to sing. From the time she was young she has vowed that she will "never love but one man." So far she has not fallen for anyone, but feels that her family is watching her to see if she has made a fool of herself yet. After slipping away from the group, she walks to a tree, where she lies down. Johnny follows her and gives her a present, a small music box. He is paying attention to her now just as he has done to a different girl each summer. As Elizabeth listens to the music box, she asks herself, "Johnny?" She then smokes a cigarette, waits, and decides, "Johnny."

Montgomery also leaves the main group and sets off with his camera to take pictures and look for Elizabeth. He is startled to find Johnny and Elizabeth lying together under the tree. Johnny nonchalantly says that they will return to the picnic, as Montgomery clutches his camera to his pounding chest and jogs off. Back at the reunion, only Patty, Jeff's wife, seems to notice that Elizabeth and Johnny are missing.

Several weeks after Montgomery's article on Harris is published, more tourists begin stopping in Rydal looking for her gravesite. The story ends with the image of Elizabeth sitting on the porch, guitar in hand, absorbed in reverie. Some strangers think she is blind, others think she is a fool.

Themes and Meanings

The third-person omniscient narrator observes the landscape and people of this small Southern town without participating in the action or passing judgments. The narrator merely records the scenery, dialogue, and actions. Paul Montgomery, with his reporter's eye, camera, and notebook also watches and records the actions of the people. He is a guest at the reunion, an outsider who stands on the sidelines and observes the rituals, conversations, and relationships. He appears to be interested in Elizabeth, but does not communicate that interest to her. The narrator says that "there wasn't a decade between, just the wide world." Montgomery thus remains isolated from the group.

Elizabeth also seems lonely and isolated. A dreamy, restless young girl who waits for something to happen, she has told her family that she will love only one man, but does not have anyone in particular in mind. The older women wait to see if she will be true to her word or make a fool of herself. When Johnny Calhoun singles her out for his attention, she decides, without much thought, that he is the one for her, and gives herself to him. Later she realizes that she has indeed been a fool for succumbing too easily to Johnny's charms. In fact, there is no purpose to her decision. Unable to communicate her feelings, she simply drifts into the situation with no real commitment. She has moved out of the circle of childhood into the world of mature women, but does not understand her own motives in allowing Johnny to seduce her.

The story is full of ritual. The family prepares for the reunion in the same way that they have for years. Each person has his own place in the family order and acts accordingly. The women prepare the food. They go about the ordinary business of their lives. Horace swaps lies with the men at the barber shop, Uncle Cleveland goes fishing. Uncle Billy is "out in the corn, potting crows." Elizabeth is part of this community, part of its customs and rituals, and has passed from childhood to womanhood in the same way as countless other women.

Style and Technique

In Mary Hood's story the people and landscape blend together to create a picture of the rural community. It is full of local color, descriptions of country ways and customs. Almost every paragraph contains such regional expressions as "she sent him round to the front door like company" or "the lights were on like a funeral was happening." Characters become part of the setting as they perform ordinary little acts such as polishing "a little twig smooth as a chicken bone." Adding to the flavor of country life, the characters' speech is marked by grammatically incorrect expressions such as "that don't differ." Characters exchange bits of country wisdom as they go about their daily tasks. One character observes that "old folks don't wear out their shoes." Elizabeth says of one farmer, "God never gave him quittin' sense." When Montgomery asks Elizabeth if she thinks he looks old, she replies "You're you. Just yourself. Born in God's time and going to last till you're done."

Hood describes scenes in realistic detail. She portrays a domestic scene with such images as "the tap-tap-tap of May flouring the cake pans." She shows us watermelons on chipped ice in a galvanized tub and a landscape filled with verbena, mint, lavender, geraniums, Shasta daisies, and hollyhocks. She captures the sounds of country life: crickets and June bugs, the slam of screen doors, the pop-pop-pop of Uncle Billy's gun as he shoots at the "laughing crows." The local customs, regional expressions, rituals, sights, and sounds of this community provide the key elements of this story.

Judith Barton Williamson

THE COUNTRY OF THE BLIND

Author: H. G. Wells (1866-1946)
Type of plot: Fable
Time of plot: The early 1900's
Locale: An imaginary valley in Ecuador
First published: 1904

> *Principal characters:*
> NÚÑEZ, a Colombian mountaineer
> YACOB, an old blind man
> MEDINA-SAROTE, Yacob's daughter

The Story

Long years ago, a valley in Ecuador's Andes was accessible to all. Then came a great landslide that cut the valley off from the outside world. An early settler who chanced to be outside the valley when the earthquake occurred was never able to return. Before he died, he described the place whence he came. A place where it never rained or snowed, it was a virtual utopia until a strange disease rendered everyone blind. Because people then considered sin to be the cause of disease, the settler was chosen to leave the valley to find priests to build a shrine that would buy holy help from the blindness. The mountain moved, however, so the settler could never return.

Lost to civilization, the valley was forgotten by the outside world and the disease ran its course. After fifteen generations had passed, the ways of the blind became the custom and culture. It then chances that a young man inadvertently enters the valley.

The stranger named Núñez is a mountaineer who has seen the world. While guiding a party of climbers, he falls from a mountain during the night. Although he tumbles more than a thousand feet, he survives. The next morning he climbs further downward until he finds himself among meadows dotted with flocks of llamas. He sees a cluster of strange windowless stone huts and remarks to himself that the builder "must have been as blind as a bat."

After shouting to three man who cannot tell where he is, Núñez realizes that he must be in the legendary Country of the Blind. He advances toward the men with the confidence of a sighted man thinking of the old proverb: In the country of the blind, the one-eyed man is king. He tells the men that he comes from Bogota in a country where people can see. Sensing that Núñez is not like them, the men hold him fast and examine him with their hands. As they perceive the malformation of his eyes, Núñez assures them that he can see. Since Núñez appears to be speaking nonsense words, such as "sight" and "see," they decide he is a wildman and give him the name of "Bogota."

When Núñez is taken before the elders, who have long since abandoned belief that the people of the valley ever had sight, he realizes that what he perceives as a miraculous gift is deemed as a flaw by those around him. He cannot even make the people understand that they are blind. After failing to impress them with his superior ability, Núñez considers using force; however, as a civilized person he cannot strike a blind man.

One day, Núñez walks on grass that is in a protected area and he refuses to get back on the path. The villagers drive him outside of the city walls. After two days without food and shelter, he returns and attempts to come to terms with his captors. Claiming that he now is wiser, he repents of all he has done. The blind people regard his rebellion as a mark of general idiocy; they whip him and give him the simplest and heaviest work to do. Seeing no alternative, Núñez acquiesces.

Núñez's adoptive family is that of old Yacob. Yacob's youngest daughter is Medina-Sarote, who is little esteemed in the world of the blind because her closed eyelids are not sunken as those of the other blind people. Finding her attractive, Núñez tells her about his ability to see and she appears to understand. Eventually Yacob understands that Núñez wishes to marry Medina-Sarote. Although no other village man wants to marry Medina-Sarote, there is opposition. Her sisters oppose it on the grounds that it discredits them, Yacob on the grounds that Núñez is an idiot, and the young men on the grounds that it will corrupt the race. Medina-Sarote is inconsolable, so Yacob goes to the elders to ask for advice. One of them who is a great doctor and philosopher believes that Núñez is better than when he first arrived and that he can be cured. The cure is to make Núñez just like everybody else—blind. "Thank Heaven for science," Yacob states.

The choice belongs to Núñez. He has believed that Medina-Sarote understands the meaning of sight, but he soon realizes that she does not. She urges him to subject himself to the surgery that will remove his eyes, but he elects not to do so. At first he intends to simply retreat to a place of solitude, but he instead leaves the city and begins to climb out of the valley, satisfied merely to escape from the valley in which he had thought he would become the king.

Themes and Meanings

"The Country of the Blind" aptly reflects H. G. Wells's criticism of both human limitations and possibilities. It illustrates his belief in the gradual advancement of humanity through evolution and scientific innovation in which the ideas of liberated individuals intrude upon a conformistic society. Núñez, figuratively, is the person of imagination in revolt against his social environment. He is the person who sees among those who do not see. As a symbol of an open mind among conformists, he is the opposite of the author's perception of the average, admirable citizen. The average citizen to Wells is a person dominated by the everyday routine of obtaining the physical necessities of life. This citizen is a person of prejudice, convention, habit, and imitation. All of this deprives the person of spiritual appetite, of a thirst for knowledge. It is this characterization of the blind men that gives the story its profoundly pessimistic outlook.

The symbolic meaning of the story hinges on the fact that the gift of sight symbolizes the human mind. Sight is a human being's reason; it creates the urge to think and search for truth. To live in blindness or darkness means to live in ignorance. Núñez's fate is meant to reflect the fate of the bearer of the light of truth. He offers spiritual light that has literally fallen from heaven in an attempt to enlighten the darkened minds of humankind. The blind men, however, do not acknowledge his mission nor do they accept it or honor his insight. Instead, they try to draw him into their darkness, even to blind him. The instrument for this is woman, with her power over the senses, and whom Núñez at first believes has an understanding of the spirit. Thus, as in many of Wells's other works, the idea that the demands of sexual love and society are dangers to the free spirit of humankind is an integral part of the story.

At the end of the story, it is obvious by Núñez's escape to where he came from originally, that the spirit no longer has a place in the world. Humankind does not want intelligence, the guidance of the wise, nor anyone to know more than anyone else. Ignorance is bliss, and ignorance will be defended by the multitude through force. Wells explained, "It is always about life being altered that I write, or about people developing schemes for altering life."

Style and Technique

Though the story is not typical of Wells's work, its narrative movement is as forceful and as well controlled as his earlier writings, and it is often classified among his finest achievements in short fiction. The story itself resembles a novella in that the topic is an extraordinary event; the setting and the plot are inherently connected; it has a turning point; it has a central symbol; and it has an obvious moral. The story is set as a leitmotif: the title is mentioned in the first sentence and then repeated several times. Thus, setting and story are a unified whole. In this way, its meaning is stressed and brought constantly to the forefront of the readers' mind.

Wells uses apparently trivial items of action and commonplace information to give an almost believable format to a fantastic story. For example, the setting is presented in the manner of an objective report: exacting geographical locations, details of the catastrophic event, and pseudoscientific language. The free play of imagination within this format of realistic fiction is typical of Wells's ability to invert life, to turn it inside out.

Lela Phillips

THE COUP DE GRÂCE

Author: Ambrose Bierce (1842-1914?)
Type of plot: Horror
Time of plot: 1862
Locale: A Civil War battlefield
First published: 1891

Principal characters:
> CAPTAIN DOWNING MADWELL, the protagonist, a Union Army officer
> SERGEANT CAFFAL HALCROW, his wounded friend
> MAJOR CREEDE HALCROW, Caffal's brother and the superior officer of Madwell, whom he hates

The Story

Major Creede Halcrow is the commanding officer of a Union Army infantry regiment from Massachusetts that is in combat during the Civil War. Captain Downing Madwell commands one of Halcrow's companies. Sergeant Caffal Halcrow, the major's brother, is an enlisted man in Madwell's company. When Madwell was a second lieutenant in the regiment, Caffal was such a close friend that he joined as an enlisted man in order to be with him. Although the two men had each risen in rank, it was hard to maintain their friendship because military protocol created a "deep and wide" gulf between them.

One day as the regiment is on outpost duty a mile ahead of its main unit, it is attacked in a forest but holds its ground. Major Halcrow approaches Captain Madwell and orders him to take his company forward to hold the head of a ravine until the company is recalled. Halcrow offensively suggests that if Madwell is apprehensive, he may order his first lieutenant to go into the dangerous area instead. Just as sarcastically, Madwell agrees to take command personally and expresses the hope that the major will go along—preferably on horseback—so as to present a "conspicuous" target. He adds, "I have long held the opinion that it would be better if you were dead." A half an hour after their ordered advance, Madwell and his company are driven back with a third of their men dead or dying. The rest of the regiment has been forced back several miles. With his company scattered through the forest, Madwell finds himself alone until he comes upon Sergeant Halcrow, who has been horribly wounded.

Madwell examines his friend, finds his abdomen torn open with part of his intestine exposed and evidence that wild swine have been gnawing on him as well. The doomed man is in unbearable pain and cannot speak, but with his eyes he silently pleads for "the blessed release, the rite of uttermost compassion, the *coup de grâce.*" Madwell's tears fall upon his friend's agonized face. As Madwell walks by himself for a moment, he sees wild pigs racing out of sight. Then he sees a horse with a shell-smashed leg. Without a thought, he dispatches the wounded creature with a revolver shot. The dead beast soon has "a look of profound peace and rest." Returning, Madwell puts his revolver to his friend's forehead and pulls the trigger. Nothing happens. He has used his last cartridge on the horse. He then draws his sword and resolutely pushes its point through Caffal's heart and deeply into the ground beneath. Just as the dying man tries instinctively to withdraw the weapon with his hand, three men approach. Two are stretcher bearers. The third is Major Halcrow.

Themes and Meanings

First published as "A Coward" in 1889, "The Coup de Grâce" is one of the most bitter tales by the celebrated horror-story writer Ambrose Bierce. Bierce was a Union Army infantry and topographical officer during the Civil War. Between 1861 and 1865, he saw action in major battles at Shiloh, Murfreesboro, Stone River, Chickamauga, Chattanooga, and elsewhere. After receiving a severe head wound at Kennesaw Mountain in June, 1864, he recovered in time to participate in part of General William Tecumseh Sherman's Georgia campaign. Bierce often saw hideous, useless, and indiscriminate carnage, and the memories of it colored his life and literary production ever after. A graphic example is "What I Saw of Shiloh," a reminiscence that he wrote in 1881, long after the war. In his characteristic prose, he describes a "variously hurt" soldier, details his ghastly head wound, and closes with this statement: "One of my men . . . asked if he should put his bayonet through him. Inexpressibly shocked by the cold-blooded proposal, I told him I thought not; it was unusual, and too many were looking." This memory was surely an inspiration for "The Coup de Grâce."

War was not merely the central experience of Bierce's life; it became his metaphor for life itself—whether in wartime or in times of so-called peace. In Bierce's view, life is a meaningless struggle against incomprehensible forces. Because it is futile to understand such imponderables, we should not bother trying. What we can do, however, is be aware of life's grotesque ironies, not grow too disappointed when things turn out badly, and try to laugh, though perhaps with considerable bitterness and scorn.

It is darkly instructive to trace the complexly knotted motives of the three central characters in "The Coup de Grâce" and those of Bierce himself in writing it. Caffal Halcrow enlists to be near his friend Downing Madwell but is rigidly separated from him by rank and is eventually killed by him. Major Creede Halcrow orders Madwell into an action which causes his brother to be fatally wounded. Madwell finishes off his friend with his sword, which Caffal instinctively grabs—with the ironic result that the merciful action looks like murder. Presumably, the relief trio has come to aid but witnesses a killing. Looking more deeply into the story, we can wonder whether Major Halcrow should objectively be relieved that his brother's agony has ended. Could the wounded man possibly have been saved if he had not also been stabbed? It is certain that the major ordered the captain into risky combat hoping that he would be killed. When the story ends, is Major Halcrow fiendishly delighted that his enemy is in his clutches, even when he considers the circumstances? Deep down, does he figure that if only his own brother died, his enemy would at least be deprived of the sort of friendship that he himself can never know?

In "The Coup de Grâce," Bierce surely seeks to dramatize the folly of human planning. Everything turns out wrong here. Madwell and Caffal, friends who are separated by the military code, fight bravely, perhaps hoping for at least a surly commendation. Instead, they end up in misery—short for one, prolonged for the other—and this because fate sees to it that Madwell's major observes his self-sacrificing act of mercy to his friend. For Bierce, the story is no less than a blood-curdling parable illustrative of the human condition.

Style and Technique

Of the many authors who wrote about the Civil War, Bierce was probably the most intensely involved; he saw the most horrific action and was influenced the most pervasively. His literary style, which was a function of these experiences, combines irony, incongruous diction, and photographic detachment.

It is ironic (that is, when one is led to expect something but is surprised by an opposite outcome) that two friends in the same military unit cannot remain close because one is an officer and the other is not. It is ironic that when a major orders his personal enemy into danger, his own brother dies. It is ironic that a man who mercifully kills a friend is likely to be court-martialed and ordered shot by the dead man's brother. Madwell will later have occasion to ponder the irony of his expressed hope for his enemy's demise.

Bierce's language is deliberately unsuited to the drama that he narrates. For example, after the murderous battle, the burial squad is said to be "tidying up." When Madwell first finds his injured friend and gently touches his face, we read that "it screamed." Just after Madwell shoots the horse, it "grin[s]" before it dies. Bierce describes the battlefield tree trunks at twilight as "a tender gray." Nature, as well as Bierce, seems contemptuous of the human condition.

As Bierce has his protagonist approach the hungry swine, his description resembles that of a movie script: "On the crest of a low, thinly wooded hill . . . several dark objects moving about among the fallen men—a herd of swine." He focuses on one: "Its forefeet . . . upon a human body, its head . . . depressed and invisible"; seen closer, "the bristly ridge of its chine . . . black against the red west."

It remains to praise the crisp structure of "The Coup de Grâce," which is presented in three distinct parts. First, Bierce describes the scene after the gory battle—the general confusion, then specific rows of corpses, and finally Madwell's return to the forest where he finds his friend. Second, a summary flashback sketches the background of his three central characters. Finally, Madwell undertakes well-intentioned actions—with unexpected and hideous consequences. Characteristically, Bierce breaks off his bitter tale abruptly, leaving the reader to speculate on the probable consequences.

Robert L. Gale

THE COUSINS

Author: Elizabeth Spencer (1921-   )
Type of plot: Psychological realism
Time of plot: The 1950's and 1980's
Locale: Martinsville, Alabama, and Italy
First published: 1985

> *Principal characters:*
> ELLA MASON, the narrator and protagonist
> ERIC MASON, her cousin, whom she loved
> BEN, another cousin, now a professor
> JAMIE and
> MAYFRED, other cousins
> DONALD BAILEY

The Story

Ella Mason, a woman in her early fifties, twice married, recalls a European trip that she and four cousins made thirty years earlier. The five of them—Ella Mason, Eric, Ben, Jamie, and Mayfred—are members of the "three leading families" of Martinsville, Alabama, who were, the narrator confesses, somewhat "snobbish" about their social position in the small town. They are all descended from a famous Confederate general. Ella, whose mother was a Mason, has the same great-grandfather as Eric.

On a visit to New York, Ella Mason has lunch with her cousin Ben, who surprises her by remarking that he has always felt that in some way it is her fault that "we lost Eric"—an allusion to the fact that their cousin has lived for many years in Florence, Italy. Stunned, "as though the point of a cold dagger had reached a vital spot," Ella determines to return to Italy, which she has not visited in thirty years, to see Eric and solve the riddle of his exile.

In Florence, Ella is surprised to find her cousin aged and stooped, no longer the handsome young law student whom she loved thirty years before. After dinner at a restaurant, the cousins sit on the terrace outside Eric's apartment, reminiscing about their early years and the trip that they once made with their other cousins.

Full of optimism and *joie de vivre* shortly after World War II, the cousins are in many ways alike but also different, each in his or her own way. Ben, a graduate student, intensely devoted to literature and especially the work of Edgar Allan Poe, becomes a father figure to the group, while Eric, then twenty-five, has just completed final exams in law school. The young Jamie is hungry for experience, to see all the museums and churches and to gamble at the casinos. Mayfred, a beautiful distant cousin of the group, shows up in New York where they are to board the ship, accompanied by Donald Bailey, whom she has just secretly married. Ella, a college student at the University of Alabama and the narrator, is still treated as a younger sister by Ben and Eric during the trip.

The visit to England, Italy, and France draws them together into an even tighter bond than their youth has done, enlightening them to much they had been denied in their provincial world. Although most of their time is spent in Italy, they also journey to Monte Carlo so that Jamie can gamble in the casino, where he wins a considerable amount of money before Mayfred insists that he leave. Mayfred's husband Donald becomes ill and returns to America; shortly thereafter Mayfred receives word that he must have an operation, so she returns home as well, leaving a lovesick Jamie to grieve.

During the trip, Ella is attracted to both Ben and Eric, but gradually her devotion focuses on Eric, and while the others are away in Rome, the two of them carry on a brief but passionate affair, which ends when Eric determines that they should rejoin their cousins. (Thirty years later Ella is still attempting to discover why things did not work out between them, attached as they were to each other.)

When the group must return to America, they are sad, for the trip has been, as Ella later recalls, a "Renaissance" for all of them. Subsequently their lives diverge into their own distinctive paths. Ella marries, has two sons, and, when her husband dies, marries again, then divorces. Ben marries a Connecticut heiress and becomes a professor. Jamie, much influenced by the Italian experience, converts to Roman Catholicism, marries a Catholic girl, and rears a large family. Mayfred, after divorcing Donald, becomes a New York fashion designer and marries several more times. Eric, having failed his law exams, moves to Italy where he remains, marries, and works for an export business. He, like Ella, is now widowed.

Thirty years after that eventful trip, Ella and Eric recall the events of the past and ponder their significance. Ella has come to Italy to discover what happened between her and Eric and why Eric has chosen to live as an expatriate, but she finds no simple answers to any of her complex questions. "You and I," Eric asks her as they sit in the darkness, looking out over Florence, "we never worked it out did we?" Her response is "I never knew if you really wanted to. I did, God knows." He replies that while she was always on the move, his life had become static after failing his law exams; he could move, "but not with much conviction," so he left her to lead her own life.

The story ends with them talking in the dark, knowing that "midnight struck long ago." Most of their lives are now behind them, and answers to the puzzles of those lives are not readily available.

Themes and Meanings

Elizabeth Spencer is a Southern author, born in Mississippi, who has lived much of her life in Italy and Canada. The influences of all these places and their interaction are evident in her fiction. Like many Southern writers, she has an acute sense of place, and she is fascinated by the Southern character, whose nuances she keenly perceives. Like Henry James, she became intrigued during her Italian sojourn with the interrelationship between Americans and Europe, an interest "The Cousins" clearly reflects. The visit abroad is a maturation process for these young people, who are well educated and well read, but essentially provincial until their encounter with the ancient, artistic, religious, and social wonders of the Old World.

Clearly one of the predominant themes of the story is the inability of human beings to understand one another in any but the most limited sense, even though they have been reared together in the same background, with the same antecedents and influences. This lack of communication leaves them puzzled by the full implications of their actions; however, the sensitive characters in "The Cousins" have clearly grown emotionally and spiritually as a result of their experiences. Thus the European journey and its aftermath have not been lost upon them, and their lives are more fulfilled from having known one another and having gone together through the events that occurred in their early maturity.

Style and Technique

Spencer's story achieves much of its effect through the contrast of Ella and Eric as they are in their fifties with how they were thirty years earlier. This retrospective method allows for a reflection on the part of the middle-aged characters on what happened to them in their youth and in the intervening years. Since this is a first-person narrative, with all the events seen through the eyes of Ella Mason, the reader can only guess at the true feelings of the other characters that the narrator interprets for us. Henry James argued that one essential element for a good story or novel is a "fine central intelligence," on whose judgment the reader can rely; in Ella, Spencer has created just such a figure. Her tone and the depth of her reflection upon events and characters convince us that she is a reliable reporter of what has happened and what its significance may be.

Elizabeth Spencer is one of the most skillful of modern American short-story writers, and one of her strongest points is her ability to create credible characters with whom readers can empathize. Although her most perceptive portrayals are usually women, her male characters are often equally convincing. She has a feeling for the subtle interrelationships among people that often go undetected by any but the most sensitive observers. Ella, the "fine central intelligence" in "The Cousins," comes as close as anyone can to understanding the implications of the events that occurred three decades before.

W. Kenneth Holditch

THE CREATURE

Author: Edna O'Brien (1930-   )
Type of plot: Psychological realism
Time of plot: Twentieth century
Locale: A village in western Ireland
First published: 1974

> *Principal characters:*
> THE CREATURE, an Irish widow
> HER GROWN SON
> HER SON'S WIFE
> THE NARRATOR, a substitute teacher

The Story

The story is narrated by a young woman getting over an unhappy love affair, who has come to a village in western Ireland as a substitute teacher. Fascinated with a widow whom everyone calls the "Creature," she seeks to befriend the woman. During visits to the Creature's house, the narrator is invariably served "a glass of rhubarb wine and sometimes a slice of porter cake" and hears the tales of the woman's meager, sorrow-filled life. During these visits, she learns that the Creature has been long separated from her only son and nearest living child. The Creature tells her how the son, after a long absence, returned and married a woman to whom the Creature had great hopes of becoming close. She secretly hoped that her daughter-in-law would pare her corns after the two women became intimate friends.

It happened, however, that the daughter-in-law is a selfish and ill-tempered woman who becomes increasingly intractable as she begins to have children of her own. Finally, she goads the son into betraying his mother. Through the eyes of the narrator, the reader sees the Creature as a loving, self-effacing mother whose daughter has emigrated to Canada and whose surly, pessimistic son has a wife who persuades him to take over the small family farm. The son convinces his mother that the farm should be deeded to him. It had been the sole home of the Creature and her own mother, another widow, who helped rear the Creature's children until she herself died. The townspeople dub the mother the "Creature" in part because they are repelled by her acquiescence in letting the son drive her from her home.

After leaving the farm, taking with her few belongings but among them an heirloom tapestry depicting ships at sea, the Creature sets up house in town, where the narrator learns that the Creature's greatest hope is for a joyful reunion with her son. After learning this, the narrator, motivated in part by her own loneliness and guilt, attempts to effect this reunion by going to the farm and convincing the son to visit his mother. On the eventful day, the narrator calls on the Creature and learns that when the son came, he accepted none of his mother's hospitality and left her feeling more for-lorn than ever. The story ends with the narrator realizing that the Creature has been surviving on the hope that she and her son would reconcile. With all hope gone, the Creature is near despair, and the narrator, whose plans have failed, "wished that I had never punished myself by applying to be a sub in that stagnant, godforsaken little place."

Themes and Meanings

The story's most pervasive theme concerns irrevocable, perhaps inherited, loss. From the Creature's loss of her father, to the loss of her husband, mother, and children, the story records a "tradition" of loss that is symbolized in the heirloom tapestry of ships perpetually at sea and in perpetual threat of destruction. The narrator, who is herself trying to recover from a love affair, becomes a player in this drama of loss—loss of family, innocence, and hope.

Attendant on this theme of loss is the role that landscape plays in the story. The story takes place in a remote part of western Ireland (the same region that James Joyce uses in his great story of loss, "The Dead"), where the narrator's unquestioning referral to the woman known simply as "The Creature," along with the town's godforsakenness, suggests that all the characters somehow assume the semblance of grotesqueness that marks their surroundings.

The theme of grotesqueness also pervades the story, from its very first line ("She was always referred to as the Creature . . .") to its ending with its grotesque description of the town and its landscape. Every character in the story, including the narrator, is a victim of a social, emotional, moral, and psychological blight. Perhaps one aspect of this theme of grotesqueness is that Ireland—western Ireland in particular—is especially prone to spawn damaged, ill-begotten, and "blighted" individuals. Certainly the last line of the story suggests that, from the narrator's point of view, place plays an important role in situating this sorrowful drama.

Despite the story's insistent themes of loss, grotesqueness, and place, it also reveals the underlying themes: Where there is loss there may also be gain; where there is ugliness, there can also be beauty. Though the story ends on a remorseful note, the narrator does a superb job of revealing to the reader the poignancy of human feeling. Referring to the Creature only in subhuman terms serves to heighten the great beauty of her unconditional love for her son and her warm acceptance of the narrator. And although the brutality of the Irish landscape coincides with the meagerness of life there, by choosing her details wisely and selectively, Edna O'Brien depicts a scene in which redemption, while not achieved, remains a possibility so long as hope can be sustained. Meaning within the story emerges not out of resolution, but out of struggle and the final failure, which is tempered by intention.

Style and Technique

O'Brien's use of a first-person narrator to relate her story has advantages as well as limitations. As an educated and articulate woman, her narrator can articulate the pain of those who suffer mutely. However, this narrator also has special limitations as an observing consciousness. Not even she can penetrate the mystery of the Creature's full identity; she thus ends her narrative by still calling the woman for whom she feels such compassion "The Creature." While this suggests that the woman possesses no true human identity, it simultaneously suggests that identity rests on more than names, labels, or reputations. Instead, the Creature's identity is captured and made alive for the reader by the narrator's greater attendance to the qualities of her character.

The use of a first-person narrator makes the reader always aware that the story is told through a limited point of view. Yet this use of a first-person narrator also contributes to the authenticity of the story largely because the narrator is not simply telling a story from her own life; as an outsider reporting on the lives of others, she can achieve an objectivity that the principal characters do not possess.

O'Brien's story is short and she selects her details tellingly, giving the reader only as much information as is necessary for them to enter into the drama and feel compassion for the Creature and the narrator. For example, the narrator catalogs the personal possessions that the Creature carries with her—her clothing, her Aladdin lamp, and the tapestry—just as sparely as the life that the possessions detail. But the selection of these details is accurate and revealing enough to create, within the story's small scope, a realism of the highest degree. At all times, the reader is made to feel that the locale, the people, and the motivations of the characters are true to the life that is lived in that "blighted" region of Ireland.

As an outsider, the narrator, despite her compassion for the Creature, does not redefine the identities of the characters as fixed for them by their surroundings. Though she comes to know the Creature better perhaps than anyone else, she nevertheless continues to call her the "Creature." Her consistent use of this pre-established identity of the main character allows her to remain apart from the factors that determine the characters' lives. By having the narrator fail in her attempt to reunite the mother and son, O'Brien reinforces her own refusal to view the story in sentimental terms. This results in ambiguity, which heightens the drama of an otherwise merely pitiful story. Ambiguity is evidenced by the fact that though the story is titled "The Creature," the reader always senses that the story is at least equally about the narrator and her own sense of loss, despair, and futility. Ultimately, the reader wonders who "The Creature" really is: the lonely mother or the narrator herself?

Susan M. Rochette-Crawley

THE CROCODILE

Author: Fyodor Dostoevski (1821-1881)
Type of plot: Parody
Time of plot: 1865
Locale: St. Petersburg, Russia
First published: "Neobyknovennoe sobytie: Ili, Passazh v passazhe," 1865 (English translation, 1895)

> *Principal characters:*
> IVAN MATVEITCH, a Russian bureaucrat who is swallowed by a crocodile
> ELENA IVANOVNA, his wife
> SEMYON SEMYONITCH, their friend and the narrator of the story
> THE CROCODILE
> THE GERMAN, the owner of the crocodile
> TIMOFEY SEMYONITCH, an elderly Russian bureaucrat

The Story

The story opens on January 13, 1865. The narrator, Semyon Semyonitch, and his married friends, Elena Ivanovna and Ivan Matveitch, go to St. Petersburg's Arcade to see a crocodile that is on display. The Arcade is a popular spot in St. Petersburg for public exhibitions and lectures. Semyonitch and Matveitch are distantly related and both work in the same government department. Because Matveitch is scheduled to go to Western Europe for intellectual advancement and has no official duties for the day, he can join his wife and friend on the excursion to the Arcade. He thinks that it will be valuable to see the crocodile because, before he visits Europe, it is well to acquaint himself "with its indigenous inhabitants."

The crocodile is housed in a large tin tank with only two inches of water, located inside a shop which also exhibits cockatoos and monkeys. Disappointed to find that the crocodile is not active because of the cold Russian climate, the visitors wonder if the animal is even alive. Its German owner uses a stick to prod the crocodile. Showing no fear, Matveitch moves forward and tickles the crocodile's nose with his glove at the same moment that Elena Ivanovna and Semyonitch turn their attention to the monkeys. In an instant, Matveitch is swallowed by the crocodile. His wife screams when she sees her husband in the jaws of the great beast, which swallows him, legs first, as a terrified audience looks on. After disappearing inside the crocodile, Matveitch's head pops out of its mouth causing his glasses to fall off and land at the bottom of the tank.

Although horrified, Semyonitch finds the tragedy absurdly comical and cannot help but laugh. The German owner and his mother are outraged by what has happened; however, they are concerned not about the fate of Ivan Matveitch, but with the safety of their crocodile. The German thinks it is only just that he be compensated for any damages to his property. Elena Ivanovna shouts for the crocodile to be cut open, using the Russian word *vsporot*, for "cut." The crowd, however, think that she is using the Russian word *vysporot*, for "flog." Since flogging is no longer tolerated in Russia, she is informed that it would be cruel to flog the crocodile. To everyone's amazement, Matveitch speaks from inside the belly of the crocodile. The German now realizes that he can charge higher fees to view his property. Because the animal is much more valuable than before, he declares that he will only part with it if he is paid thousands of Russian rubles. Matveitch advises his wife to apply directly to the superintendent's office because, without the assistance of the police, the German will never see reason.

Although seemingly unhurt, Matveitch is saddened that he will miss his trip to Western Europe because the German is asking such an exorbitant price for his crocodile. Semyonitch agrees to go see the respected bureaucrat, Timofey Semyonitch, and ask his advice concerning this peculiar situation. He leaves the Arcade with Elena Ivanovna, who feels "something like a widow."

Timofey Semyonitch sees no justification for interceding in this matter because he believes that private property is more important than Matveitch's life. The elderly bureaucrat rambles on about the need for Russia's communal land to be sold to foreign investors and suggests that Matveitch's fate may encourage other crocodiles to be brought into Russia. To him, the accumulation of capital is of primary importance. Semyon Semyonitch returns to the Arcade without a solution to his friend's problem. There he finds that the crocodile's owner is overjoyed at the prospect of making a fortune since the public will flock to see a man living inside a crocodile. Semyonitch is surprised to learn that Matveitch now wants to preach great thoughts from the belly of the crocodile, and he is not sure what to make of his friend's pronouncements. Elena Ivanovna concludes that it may be necessary to divorce her husband.

The story concludes with wild descriptions of the incident that appear in Russian newspapers. There is no resolution to Matveitch's predicament. (It is known that Dostoevski intended to finish this story, but he never got around to it.)

Themes and Meanings

Although Fyodor Dostoevski never finished "The Crocodile," it nevertheless stands as one of the most powerful indictments against humankind's inhumanity to humankind. His narrator, Semyonitch, seems to be the only person truly concerned with Matveitch's welfare. Even the victim's wife decides that divorce would be best for her. The German owner of the crocodile and his mother are concerned only with protecting their investment. The German realizes that he can make hugh profits by selling tickets to people anxious to see a man living inside a crocodile. Even the victim agrees that the "principles of economics" should rule the day. Dostoevski is thus making the point that when capitalist doctrines dominate human behavior, all notions of common decency among people will cease to exist.

During the 1860's in Russia, such prominent intellectuals as Dmitry Ivanovich Pisarev and Varfolomei Aleksandrovich Zaitsev argued that Russia should look to Western Europe for its economic model. Regarding rapid industrialization as a paramount goal, Pisarev theorized that the perfect individual to thrive in a capitalist society would be a "superman" type not constrained by the bounds of good and evil. The prospect of combining capitalism and nihilism in Russia worried Dostoevski, who feared that Russian virtues would be trampled. These theorists had little or no faith in the potential of the Russian people.

Dostoevski expresses his distrust for both the political Left and Right in "The Crocodile." Although the bureaucrat Matveitch is described as being politically "progressive" and is the victim of the story, he still agrees that economic interests should prevail over even his own safety. It can be argued that "The Crocodile" foreshadows the linkage that Dostoevski forcefully developed between nihilism and capitalism in his 1866 novel *Prestupleniye i nakazaniye* (*Crime and Punishment*, 1886). Many of his short stories touch upon the issues that he more fully developed in his mature novels. In *Zapiski iz podpolya* (1864; *Notes from the Underground*, 1913), for example, he touches upon the idea of social theorists attempting to mold a perfect society without taking into consideration the rights of the individual. Dostoevski is noted for juxtaposing the individual against a bureaucracy, the city against the countryside, and religious faith versus atheism. Even unfinished, "The Crocodile" stands as a merciless portrait of where an amoral approach to life might lead.

Style and Technique

In 1864, Dostoevski and his brother Mikhail began publishing the journal *Epokha*, in which "The Crocodile" appeared in February, 1865. With the death of his brother and mounting financial problems, Dostoevski was forced to cease publication of *Epokha* in March, 1865. The Russian subtitle of the story can be translated as "Or, Mauled in the Mall." It should be clear from the use of such a grotesque yet playful subtitle that the story that follows will have a strong satirical edge to it. As in Nikolai Gogol's 1836 story "The Nose," in which "a most extraordinary thing happened in St. Petersburg," Dostoevski presents a bizarre event in a matter-of-fact manner. In Gogol's story, a Russian barber discovers a human nose in a loaf of bread. In "The Crocodile," a Russian bureaucrat is not only swallowed by a crocodile but he lives through the experience, and the belly of the animal becomes his new residence. Both stories savage Russia's government bureaucracy. Dostoevski parodies the radical theorists of the 1860's not only through the swallowed bureaucrat Matveitch, but especially through the elderly and venerated bureaucrat Timofey Semyonitch—a buffoon who pontificates about foreign investment in Russia. As wild and absurd as the situation is for Matveitch, it is only the narrator who is concerned with his friend's safety. The "principles of economics" must rule the day. Dostoevski also includes parodies of newspaper articles about the event at the end of the story. Their various slants and exaggerations add to the uneasy feeling with which the reader is left.

Dostoevski left documents that make it clear that he hoped to resolve "The Crocodile." Although he left the story incomplete, it stands as an important precursor of what was to follow creatively for Dostoevski.

Jeffry Jensen

THE CYCLISTS' RAID

Author: Frank Rooney (1913-   )
Type of plot: Realism
Time of plot: The late 1940's
Locale: Central California
First published: 1951

> *Principal characters:*
> JOEL BLEEKER, a widowed hotel owner
> CATHY BLEEKER, his seventeen-year-old daughter
> BRET TIMMONS, Cathy's boyfriend, a drug store owner
> FRANCIS LASALLE, co-owner of a hardware store
> GAR SIMPSON, the leader of the Angelenos, a motorcycle gang
> AN UNNAMED ANGELENO, who is different from the others

The Story

The tranquillity of a small town in California's San Joaquin Valley is shattered toward sunset one day when the Angelenos, a band of motorcyclists from Los Angeles, arrive unannounced, planning to spend the night and part of the next day.

Joel Bleeker, a lieutenant colonel during World War II, has returned from overseas to this peaceful haven, where he operates one of the town's two hotels. Bleeker's wife died two years earlier, her neck broken when she was thrown from a horse. Bleeker now lives a quiet and methodical existence, managing a small hotel with the help of his seventeen-year-old daughter, Cathy. Each day at precisely the same time, he checks his old redwood clock in the lobby against the railroad watch that he wears on a chain and keeps in his pocket.

On the day of the story, when Bleeker hears a noise that he mistakes for aircraft engines, he moves the hands of his redwood clock ahead a minute and a half before investigating the commotion. On the hotel's veranda Cathy sits with Francis LaSalle and Bret Timmons, local businessmen. Suddenly, the noise becomes so great that no one can be heard above the din. A column of red motorcycles invades the hotel like an army column bent on taking a town. It is led by a man on a white motorcycle, Gar Simpson, unctuously polite and powerfully commanding.

Simpson addresses Bleeker by name, asking whether his cyclists might use the hotel's facilities, for which he offers to pay. He also asks whether Bleeker's dining room can feed twenty of the men; the rest will eat elsewhere. The bikers ogle Cathy, thereby unnerving her father, who agrees to feed part of the contingent and allows them the use of the downstairs washroom. Bleeker tells Cathy to work in the kitchen that night instead of serving in the dining room.

The bikers resemble visitors from outer space. Dressed alike, they perform with great precision, obey their "general," who understands his men well, and never remove the green cyclist goggles that make them look like huge insects. As their drinking continues, they sing loudly and begin to race their motorcycles along the town's main street. They also begin to damage Bleeker's hotel, but Simpson promises to pay reparations.

Assured that Cathy is safely ensconced in her bedroom, Bleeker walks down the street to Cunningham's Bar, where one biker, about twenty-five, stands out from the rest. He sits alone drinking Coca-Cola. Bleeker joins him, but the din is too great for sustained conversation. Nevertheless, he learns that beer makes this biker sick, as do many of his fellow bikers' activities. This biker is the only one who removes his goggles.

Before long, the other cyclists are out of control. Bleeker returns to his hotel, where he checks on Cathy. He escorts back to the lobby an Angeleno whom he finds on the second floor trying to enter rooms. Someone has struck Francis LaSalle, who is now sprawled uninjured on the floor. Gar Simpson approaches Bleeker, takes out a wallet, and puts money in front of him to cover the damage the bikers have done to his hotel.

Two motorcycles zoom through the lobby door; one of them roars through the lobby, striking Cathy at the foot of the stairs, injuring her badly. A doctor is summoned. After he administers first aid and has her taken to his office, she dies.

Grief-stricken, Bleeker returns to his hotel, where the boy with whom he spoke earlier appears, suffering pangs of guilt over what has happened. Bleeker observes him closely. Townspeople begin to beat the biker, knocking him down and stamping him maniacally. Bleeker, too, finds himself pummeling the boy's body, but soon he is on the ground, cradling the boy's head on his lap, trying to protect him from the others.

The story ends with Bleeker standing on his hotel veranda, physically and emotionally numb. He turns to go into the hotel, knowing that there is time for him to make his peace with the dead but that now he must make his peace with the living, represented by the boy.

Themes and Meanings

Two major elements pervade this tightly structured and closely observed tale, which became the basis for the 1954 film *The Wild One*. The theme of death is strong within the story. It is introduced first by the generalized suggestion of death that people connect with World War II, from whose European combat Joel Bleeker has returned physically unscathed to resume his existence in rural California. His postwar life there has been tranquil, marred only by the death of his wife two years earlier.

Bleeker has apparently learned to live with his loss. He adores his daughter, who, like her mother, is feisty, humorous, and caring. Bleeker has laid to rest his memories of war and its horrors. On the day of the story, however, all his painful memories are evoked instantly, first by the high-decibel approach of the cyclists—his first thought that they are airplanes must trigger his memories of enemy bombers—and, after the source of the noise is finally identified, by the military precision with which the motorcycle columns approach his hotel.

Clearly, Gar Simpson is "general" of the rowdy gang, whose members he understands remarkably well. He knows that, as commander, he can best maintain control over his men by allowing them the freedom that results eventually in massive destruction and, finally, death. Simpson is meticulously polite and, within his own boundaries, responsible. The Angelenos, all but one of whom are exactly like the others, follow him with a loyalty bordering on blindness—which is suggested by their wearing goggles at all times.

Nowhere does Frank Rooney suggest that the maverick cyclist who returns to the hotel after Cathy's death is the one who killed her. It is, in fact, impossible to tell one identically clad cyclist from another. This cyclist returns as an act of expiation, by which act he assumes the collective guilt of his fellow Angelenos.

Underlying the entire story is the rampant sexuality of a male group deprived of a normal sexual outlet. Their libidinous glances at Cathy early in the story reveal their sexual desperation, as does the maverick cyclist's telling Bleeker that the cyclists are looking for women. Given the overall context of the story, sexual repression helps explain their violence and violence in general, including war. But as the maverick cyclist deviates from his group, so does Joel Bleeker—who is himself seemingly deprived of conventional sexual outlet—differ from those who practice violence as a means of dealing with their urges.

Style and Technique

In "The Cyclists' Raid," Frank Rooney demonstrates his clear, crisp style. A master of detail, he creates with precise words and penetrating observation of physical details the story's landscape. His major characters come to life through the details that the reader quickly learns about them. Joel Bleeker—who was successful enough as a leader to become a lieutenant colonel—is methodical and controlled, checking the clock in his lobby at the same time daily against his more accurate railroad watch. No unusual occurrence, even the noisy approach of the cyclists, deters him from this established ritual.

Rooney demonstrates that Bleeker has laid to rest two major ghosts. First he has escaped from the dangers of World War II. He has also survived and moved beyond the loss of a wife who was precious to him. His love and concern for his daughter have been heightened by his wife's death.

Gar Simpson possesses the same sort of leadership ability that Bleeker does, but to a greater degree. Rooney consistently portrays him as methodical and meticulous. He knows the names of the hotels in the town as well as the names of their owners. He has planned the trip with the precision of a military operation.

Rooney's introduction of the maverick cyclist is particularly cogent. It lends itself to the eventual denouement of the story. In his budding individuality, this sympathetic character shows courage and provides readers with hope. That the townspeople turn on him in giving vent to their outrage about Cathy's death is understandable. Bleeker's protection of the pummeled boy, however, reflects a dimension in his personality that, despite surface similarities, makes him inherently different from Gar Simpson.

R. Baird Shuman

DADDY WAS A NUMBER RUNNER

Author: Louise Meriwether (1923-   )
Type of plot: Social realism
Time of plot: Summer, 1934
Locale: Harlem, New York City
First published: 1967

> *Principal characters:*
> FRANCIE, the bright eleven-year-old narrator
> JAMES, her father
> JESSIE, her mother
> SUKIE MACEO, her best friend

The Story

The story opens during a school lunch break, when eleven-year-old Francie is collecting number slips for her father; it ends with her father released from jail after being arrested by the police trying to show some power in this mob-controlled neighborhood. Between those two incidents, readers are granted a detailed and revealing look into the naturalistic world of one family's struggles to survive, and a prepubescent girl's struggle for her own identity.

The major details of the story circle around the numbers racket that permeates the community. Everyone plays and everyone dreams of the big win that will get them out of this world. When Francie's number 514—a number based on her dream of a catfish—pays off $215, the family eats well for about a week, but, as Francie notes, they soon are back to fried cabbage and ham hocks just as if the big hit had never happened.

Francie's journey toward adulthood is given in terms of this numbers game. Although only eleven years of age, she is responsible enough to collect the number slips and take them home to hide in a buffet drawer. When the police raid her railroad flat after the big win, they do not find the receipts they need for an arrest, but they take Daddy off anyway, charged with assault and battery for protecting Francie. She takes the numbers downstairs to Frenchy, the local agent for Big Dutch, and tells him that her father has been arrested. In this crisis, Francie demonstrates her resourcefulness and intelligence.

The rest of Francie's family has similar struggles in the story. After losing his job as a house painter, her father tries to help the family by playing the piano at rent parties over the weekend, but he does not make much money this way. Francie's two brothers may be cutting school to hang out with the Ebony Dukes, the local gang. Jessie, her mother, goes off as a domestic day worker for Mrs. Schwartz, and at the end of the story reveals that she has gone to the relief agency and applied for assistance. Daddy is hurt that she has done this but, as she tells her husband, his pride will not feed the children.

Besides incidents concerning family and the numbers racket, the story circles around Francie's friend Sukie. They are best friends, but Sukie fights with Francie whenever the pressures of her own life—her father a drunk, her sister a prostitute—get to her. By the end of the story, the incidents of Francie's life have made her as tough, and, instead of running away from Sukie, she seeks her out to fight. She has become the aggressor, and she beats up Sukie. The fight signals Francie's development into a tougher, more capable adolescent.

Themes and Meanings

The meaning of Louise Meriwether's story works on two distinct levels, the social and the psychological. Its social themes revolve around what it is like to grow up black in New York during the Depression, and the story relates that condition in a broad array of details. Meriwether reveals the socioeconomic conditions—the couch in the living room where Francie sleeps, infested by bed bugs; the educational—Francie's school, P.S. 136, "the baddest girls' school in the world"; and the cultural—the numbers racket, music, food, and so on. Depression-era Harlem life is shown in all its difficulties and violence, with few pleasures. It is a complex and accurate portrait: The Ebony Dukes jump the Jewish boys who attended the synagogue around the corner, but Francie's dining room furniture is a gift from the Jewish plumber downstairs. Meriwether's is no simplistic portrait of urban life and strife.

More significant than the social meaning of the story is the psychological, and this is far more subtle, for the eleven-year-old narrator does not always understand the significance of her own life. Like her slightly older fictional cousin, Huck Finn— likewise a first-person narrator of his own adventures—Francie relates incidents that readers must interpret. She wonders what makes her friend Sukie so mean, for example—but Meriwether gives readers all the evidence they need to make the analysis of Sukie's behavior themselves. Francie cannot articulate the pressures of her own life, let alone recognize them in her friends. She is suspended in that limbo between childhood and adulthood that is not yet adolescence. She still reads fairy tales from the library on her fire escape, and her dreams, such as the fish dream that gives her the winning numbers, aid the family. On the other hand, she witnesses the violence of Depression Harlem, as shown in a reference to mugging any white man caught alone there after sunset, and its poverty, highlighted by her mother searching half an hour for a dime she thought she had lost, but which Francie had stolen. She loves her father, who is trying to get her to grow up to be a lady, and still trusts him, wondering why her mother could not. She has not yet learned all the lessons life has taught her mother.

The story gives us clues that Francie will successfully navigate her way out of childhood to adulthood, in spite of the numerous dangers in her world. She is, in fact, halfway there. She is already resourceful and responsible for her family, and at the end of the story, after beating up Sukie, turns her face away from home and wanders aimlessly down Fifth Avenue. Her future will be away from this world. When a mob crowds around her and Sukie, she says, "I was suffocating. I pushed against the black, shoving mass until I was free of them. There was something evil in their sweating black faces, and that something was in me also." She must flee this world in order to attain her own healthy identity, even if it means wandering aimlessly at first. Readers can only hope for Francie's future.

The story was written in the Watts Writers Workshop, which screenwriter and novelist Budd Shulberg started after the Los Angeles riots of 1965. Three years later, Louise Meriwether published a novel based on the story. While the novel brings in many more significant details, sexual and violent, it does not change the basic thrust of the original short story. In both, readers witness a young girl coming of age against the myriad difficulties of urban Depression life.

Style and Technique

Meriwether's fictional technique has two distinguishing characteristics. The more apparent is Francie's first-person narration, which is realistic and clever and which hardly ever calls attention to itself. From her opening encounter with her neighbor Mrs. Mackey ("Lord, I thought, don't let Mrs. Mackey stand here with her big, black self telling me about her dreams"), through her description of her father's hurt pride and anger at welfare, to her final blasphemy ("Goddamn them all to hell."), Francie's narration comes by way of the authentic voice of a preadolescent girl struggling against the odds of survival in this all-too-real world. Much of the story's power comes from the uninflected but absolutely honest character revealed through that voice.

The broader characteristic of Meriwether's story is its naturalistic style. In detail as in language, the author reveals the ways in which these characters are trapped, not only by socioeconomic factors, but by the psychological as well. Naturalism works best in a style which is flat and uninterpretative, which is why Francie's first-person narrative voice works so well. From the vomit-green kitchen walls inside her apartment, to the violence of Harlem outside, "Daddy Was a Number Runner" is steeped in the naturalistic tradition of writers such as Richard Wright, James Baldwin, and Paule Marshall.

David Peck

DARK AVENUES

Author: Ivan Bunin (1870-1953)
Type of plot: Sketch
Time of plot: Late nineteenth century
Locale: Russia's Tula district
First published: "Tyomnyye allei," 1943 (English translation, 1949)

> *Principal characters:*
> NIKOLAI ALEXEYEVICH, an elderly army officer
> NADEZHDA, his former lover, the owner of a roadside lodge

The Story

On a cold autumn day, a mud-spattered carriage stops at a small roadside inn. The elderly yet handsome officer who alights is evidently glad to enter a warm, tidy room after his chilly, damp ride. He locates the innkeeper, an attractive woman who resembles a Gypsy, and engages her in conversation. When he compliments her on her establishment's cleanliness, she says that she knows how to keep things orderly because she grew up around nobility. She then astonishes him by calling him by his name—Nikolai Alexeyevich. As he looks at the woman more closely, he realizes that she is a woman whom he passionately loved some thirty years earlier, when she was eighteen and he was about thirty.

Their conversation begins innocuously. Nikolai tells Nadezhda that he lost touch with her after their affair ended and he learned that her masters had released her. When he asks her whether she has ever married, she says no. He wonders why not, since she was so beautiful. She again answers simply that she was not able to marry. Disconcerted by her reply, Nikolai asks her what she means. This time, her response carries an implicit reproach: "What is there to explain? Surely you remember how much I loved you." Nikolai seems to be stung by this and tries to minimize the seriousness of her words by saying that everything passes: love, youth—everything. Nadezhda does not retreat, however. She agrees that youth passes, but says that love is another matter.

As their dialogue continues, it becomes clear that Nikolai heartlessly abandoned Nadezhda, leaving her so distraught that she more than once considered suicide. She asks him to recall how he once read poetry to her. When he asks her to recall how beautiful and passionate she once was, she tells him that it was to him that she yielded all of her passion and her beauty, and that no one can forget such an experience. He again tries to downplay the seriousness of what she is saying by reiterating that "everything passes, everything is forgotten." Unwilling to let him get away with such an easy platitude, Nadezhda counters that while everything may pass, not everything is forgotten.

Perhaps feeling trapped by Nadezhda's responses, Nikolai asks her to leave, adding that he hopes God has forgiven him as, he assumes, Nadezhda has. Nadezhda rebuffs his attempt to dismiss the past, however, and says that she has never forgiven him. Just as there was nothing dearer than him in her life when she was with him, she has had nothing dearer since then. Overcome by the steadfastness and depth of Nadezhda's emotion, Nikolai confesses that he himself has never found any greater happiness in his own life. The woman whom he married abandoned him even more cruelly than he had abandoned Nadezhda; his son, on whom he pinned all his hopes, turned out to be a scoundrel without heart, honor, or consciousness. Nikolai finally admits that in losing Nadezhda, he lost the most valuable thing he ever had in his life. After she kisses his hand, he kisses hers and leaves the inn in agitation.

Back in his carriage, Nikolai ponders the encounter he has just undergone. Struggling with the feelings that the meeting has aroused, he is ashamed of his final declaration to Nadezhda, but then feels ashamed of this very shame. He acknowledges that his affair with Nadezhda gave him the finest minutes of his life, but then tries to cast off this vision of the past. What might have happened, had he not abandoned Nadezhda years ago, he wonders. Might she have become his wife, the mistress of his St. Petersburg home, the mother of his children? The thought seems so incredible that he merely closes his eyes and shakes his head.

Themes and Meanings

"Dark Avenues" (which has also been published as "Dark Paths") is not only the name of Ivan Bunin's sketch, it is also the title of a collection of stories that he published in 1943. He did not make his decision casually. The sketch explores several themes that were especially important to Bunin toward the end of his career. His late writings tend to concentrate on depicting the intensity of romantic passion and its brevity as a lived experience, while simultaneously revealing how powerfully passion can impact the human soul. "Dark Avenues" exemplifies how a passionate encounter, even a brief one, can leave an indelible imprint on the human heart.

This sketch depicts a brief but moving encounter between two people from vastly different social classes who meet after many years of separation. Bunin's reserved and understated approach to this encounter offers an effective counterpoint to the intense feelings that the meeting itself releases. The dialogue between the former lovers, Nikolai and Nadezhda, forms the heart of his story. Although the words that they exchange are simple, they contain a powerful reservoir of emotion.

The sketch also touches on other themes that play prominent roles in Bunin's writings. During the last decade of the nineteenth century, Bunin began relentlessly exposing how the inexorable passage of time affects human affairs, both on a personal level and on the level of human civilization itself. Later, as an émigré writer living in France after the Bolshevik Revolution of 1917, Bunin himself acutely felt the irreparable loss of things that he had cherished. Faced with the inevitable dissolution and decay of human achievements, he looked to memory and to art as ways to preserve the best moments of human existence. The importance of memory in "Dark Avenues" is underscored by the story's repetitions of such phrases as "Do you recall . . ." and "I remember . . ." As the story unfolds, Nadezhda's undying remembrance of youthful love eventually penetrates her former lover's attempted detachment, briefly bringing the characters together in a silent homage to the power and intensity of their shared passion. Life may go on, but the experience of profound love can never truly be erased from human memory.

Style and Technique

Bunin's sketch displays all the stylistic features that characterize the last part of his career. Deceptively simple in form, "Dark Avenues" reveals his penchant for paring away all that is superfluous in narrative exposition. A worthy successor to the art of Anton Chekhov, Bunin relies on carefully crafted descriptions to convey palpable moods or emotional conditions. For example, the sketch opens with a description of a cold autumn day in which elements of dirt and darkness prevail. This chilling external world through which the careworn Nikolai Alexeyevich travels contrasts sharply with the clean, tidy, and warm interior world of Nadezhda's lodgings. For a brief moment, Nikolai Alexeyevich comes in from the cold and is warmed by the ardor that Nadezhda carries within her. The sketch ends with Nikolai resuming his seemingly directionless travels. The narrator notes that the sun is setting as Nikolai departs. The image of a bleak autumn day drawing to a close provides a marvelous evocation of the condition of Nikolai's very existence.

Bunin's sensitivity to nuances of language is evident in other ways as well. The fundamental disparity in the social status of Nikolai and Nadezhda is conveyed through the forms of the personal pronouns with which they address each other. Nikolai addresses Nadezhda with the singular form of the pronoun "you" ("*ty*"), while she uses the pronoun's more formal plural form ("*vy*"). Her use of the more formal form indicates that she acknowledges Nikolai as socially superior to her, but the reader understands that in matters of the heart, it is she who is morally superior to him. "Dark Avenues" provides eloquent testimony of Bunin's own appreciation of the power of language to communicate on several levels, and the sketch stands out as a gem of his final years.

Julian W. Connolly

THE DAY THEY TOOK MY UNCLE

Author: Lionel G. García (1935-   )
Type of plot: Domestic realism
Time of plot: The 1940's
Locale: A small Texas town
First published: 1992

> *Principal characters:*
> THE BOY, the narrator of the story
> MERCÉ, his uncle, a local madman
> HIS PARENTS
> THE SHERIFF, who takes away the uncle

The Story

The narrator recalls a moment during his childhood in Texas when he and his young girlfriend played under the house, and she gave him his first look at female genitalia. He then remembers his uncle, a man he recalls as "insane, crazy." The uncle's madness manifested itself in bouts in which he would yank his earlobes violently and curse at people obscenely while remarking on imaginary scandalous events of their past. The narrator particularly remembers the moment when his uncle called the town mayor "a sonofabitch and a son of a whore, plus a bastard" and then accused the mayor's wife of being unfaithful by taking up with the mayor's cousin.

As the uncle's favorite relative, the boy often saw his disquieting episodes. In addition to being mad, the uncle also had a drinking problem. According to the boy's grandmother, the uncle's madness began when he drank the remains of a bottle of beer "that had been laced with a special potion, a potion so powerful it would cause insanity." At the local bar, which was the uncle's favorite hangout, the townsmen enjoyed watching his episodes, hooting and hollering as he paced back and forth screaming his insults. Unable afterward to recall what he had done, he quickly became gentle and docile. The man's behavior naturally embarrassed the boy and his sister— who lost her first suitor because of his lunacy and because the young man "would never call on a girl who had heard so many curse words in her young life."

The narrator reflects on the joys of small-town life, when things were simple. Even when his uncle died, there was no need to learn the cause. In a small town people die: That is all one needs to know. While the uncle was alive, he had only one set of tasks to perform each day: milking the cow in the morning, taking her out to pasture, bringing her back before sunset, and milking her once more before putting her up for the night. When he had maniacal episodes or got drunk, however, he would forget his responsibility, leaving the boy and his father to search for the cow, which the uncle never left in the same pasture twice.

One day the uncle cursed the mayor one time too many and the town leaders—

including the local priest and sheriff—decided it was time to put him away in a mental institution in Galveston. Selected to perform this task, the sheriff arrived at the house at the same moment at which the narrative begins—with the boy under the house with his girlfriend.

From this hidden vantage point the boy sees and hears everything. The sheriff doubts the boy's mother when she says that the uncle is not home. After searching the house, the sheriff turns his attention to the toolshed. As he approaches it, the boy's mother and grandmother plead for the uncle, who they know is hiding there. The sheriff keeps his hand on his revolver expecting the uncle to become violent when he is discovered, but after hunting with his uncle many times and never bagging anything, the boy knows that his uncle is incapable of hurting any living creature.

The sheriff enters the toolshed and causes a great commotion as he searches it. From under the house, the boy knows that his uncle planned to hide there, but then he detects the faint smell of stale beer: His uncle is now under the house also. As the uncle confesses his fear of being sent away, he enters another maniacal episode, crawls out from beneath the house, and begins tugging his earlobes violently and loudly cursing about the sexual antics of the priest and the nuns who live across the street.

The sheriff tackles the uncle and handcuffs him. As the madman gets into the sheriff's car, his relatives tell him to behave himself in the hospital so that he can return soon. When the car pulls away, the boy's father chases it calling to the uncle to tell him where the cow is pasturing.

A year later, the uncle returns home. Although he is not cured, he carries a card stating that he is "not a menace to society."

Themes and Meanings

A bittersweet coming-of-age story, "The Day They Took My Uncle" explores the theme of awakening, both socially and, to a lesser degree, sexually. Most important, Lionel García's narrator learns that family loyalty transcends everything. Despite the uncle's recurring bouts of madness and alcoholism, the family never considers ostracizing him. On the contrary, there is considerable tolerance for his erratic behavior. The boy's father, for example, does not become angry with his brother. When reproaching Mercé, the boy's father "would scold him lightly and in a very gentle way." Except for the narrator's sister, all the family members stand by Mercé.

By contrast, the characters in positions of power in the town exercise great control over the uncle's life. It is not until the mayor, the sheriff, and the priest band together that Mercé is taken away as a simple nuisance. Although the uncle has never acted violently, they treat him as a dangerous criminal. In the end, the boy feels incapable of helping his uncle avoid capture because he realizes that there is "no escaping the law." Although the family bond is strong, the need to conform to societal norms and not challenge those in power ultimately overrides all else. Nevertheless, the uncle enjoys a minor victory in the end when he returns home with psychiatric proof that he does not pose a menace to society.

Style and Technique

Told in the first person, the story has a confessional style. It begins with the narrator sharing his first sexual experience with the reader, then proceeds quickly to explain the strange case of madness that existed in his family.

Although a tale of an insane and alcoholic relative might easily be a sad one, the author tells it with humor, and this becomes his favorite device. His description of the uncle's maniacal episodes turns comical when he quotes the insults that his uncle hurls at other townspeople. The mayor and his frail old wife are the madman's favorite targets, followed by the priest and three nuns from the Sisters of Charity—the very characters least likely to commit the scandalous deeds of which they are accused.

The most comical figure, however, is the cow, which García endows with human qualities. At night, after the uncle has forgotten to pick her up, the boy and his father search for her, and they eventually find her waiting patiently, although a bit confused. Whenever the uncle has a fit as he leads the cow somewhere, she "would stop, look at him stoically, as if she knew this was the cross she had been given to bear." After the uncle is taken to Galveston, the narrator's mother and grandmother cry each time that they see the cow. Never knowing what it is about herself that brings tears to their eyes, the poor animal looks "inquiringly from one side of herself to the other, as if looking for some clue." The humor that García employs in the telling of this story is without a doubt the main factor that allows one to describe it as bittersweet.

Silvio Sirias

THE DAYDREAMS OF A DRUNK WOMAN

Author: Clarice Lispector (1925-1977)
Type of plot: Psychological realism
Time of plot: The 1950's
Locale: Brazil
First published: "Devaneio e embriaguez duma rapariga," 1960 (English translation, 1972)

>   *Principal characters:*
>   MARIA QUITERA, the narrator, a dissatisfied Brazilian housewife
>   HER HUSBAND, a businessman

The Story

Maria Quitera is a housewife on the edge. She is looking for her place in the world; not finding it, she is searching for someone to blame. The story begins on a Thursday afternoon just before her husband returns from work. Maria is in a tipsy mood, acting childish and as if she is drunk. She is talking and singing to herself, brushing her hair, admiring herself in the mirror, flitting from one mood and subject to another. Her children are away, and her husband is soon to be out of town on business. She prepares herself by sleeping.

The story falls loosely into two sections: the first being Maria's "day off," and the second, the Saturday night dinner. On her day off, when her children are away and her husband is to spend the day in the city on business, Maria fleetingly feels the freedom and consequent fear of not having a particular role to play for the day. When her husband comes in to kiss her farewell, she realizes that she does not even know what he has had for breakfast—the preparation of which is doubtless one of her daily rituals. She realizes that she need not get his meals nor check his suit for lint. But if not these things, what then should she do? Her answer is to snap at her husband and spend the next thirty-six hours or so in a dizzying, whirling sleep, effectively avoiding the self-defining task of asserting her will on the day. When Maria finally does get up late on Saturday morning, she is clearly happy to find the everyday routine restored as she goes about her chores and errands.

The Saturday night at the fancy restaurant, where Maria accompanies her husband to dine with a wealthy businessman, plays out this same scenario but more elaborately. Now drinking wine, Maria actually is tipsy, playing with her altered perceptions and self-awareness. On the outside she is socializing in the role of the loyal, if slightly shallow, wife. She feels alienated from that role, however, and is instead becoming hypersensitive to her own sense of self, as if that self were a secret. "But the words that a woman uttered when drunk were like being pregnant—mere words on her lips which had nothing to do with the secret core that seemed like pregnancy." She plays a bit with this duality, relishing it, as she remembers that she is a woman of culture, a woman who has traveled, who has an artistic sensibility. Wanting to pursue this identity, she becomes more and more drunk, reasoning that she has after all acquired a certain position in life which affords her protection from the social world. It is this very realization that brings her back into "reality." Her position is nothing if not the adjunct to her successful husband, whom she was just silently mocking. In an instant the "position" that saved her from misfortune has become a cloud that shadows her self into obscurity.

Maria's response to this sense of annihilation is again vehemently to defend her role as model wife and mother, as she jealously and hatefully criticizes another woman who has caught her eye at the restaurant. Though not wanting to do so, she still plays by the rules of the superficial, fluctuating from self-righteous disdain and indignation to humility and shame at going out to dinner without a hat like that which the slim socialite is wearing.

While recovering at home from her indulgent night, her hidden self makes one last stab at emerging and taking hold. The physical sensations of such a state of heightened awareness, however, become unbearable for Maria. Accordingly, she recites a series of Christian and domestic platitudes, as she resigns herself to a defeated state in subjugation to her "real world" position—cleaning house and being pretty and plump—at the side of her husband.

Themes and Meanings

"The Daydreams of a Drunk Woman" is fundamentally the story of a woman whose realization of self puts her at odds with the people and social structures that surround her. The issue of self-identity versus social alienation is a theme that dominates Clarice Lispector's work. The very first image of the story—that of Maria's trembling reflection in the mirror as the trolley cars go by—sets up the symbolic yet undeniable theme of a wavering sense of self. This is reinforced a few lines later when Maria catches the reflection of the intersected breasts of several women as she studies herself in the mirror.

Maria's drunken daydreams explore the duality of self while depicting the inherent alienation of a frustrated human existence. The seeming opposites of sober and drunk, awake and asleep, practical and reckless, physical and psychological, happy and sad, love and hate, are all conflated as Maria carries on her social functions while delving separately into her individual thoughts and perceptions. In so doing, she becomes acutely aware of her solitude and isolation within a supposedly collective, cohesive humanity. She recognizes concurrently both the freedom that isolation brings as well as the meaninglessness it connotes for the individual. This contradictory state of mind proves to be unbearable and unmanageable.

The personal discovery of the truth about one's own private human condition and how one deals with that truth is what Lispector brings to light. Maria's ambivalence about taking responsibility for her private condition keeps her fluctuating between bored resignation toward her own fate, animated disapproval of others for their apparent superficiality, mental self-flagellation for her inability to stay within the confines of her social position, and awestruck wonder at what her senses can perceive in this intense world. The recognition of her nothingness, and the nothingness of those around her, brings about fear, which manifests itself as petty jealousy and self-righteousness. This is clearly an act of both self-assertion and escape from the primordial fear of being without boundaries or meaning, ultimately dispensable and always alone.

The parallels between the author and her character are obvious, despite differences in their circumstances. Lispector, a well-educated wife of a diplomat, was successful as a writer and journalist in her own right. Maria is also apparently educated, but without a goal, a career, or a life of her own separate from her husband's. The degree to which the author identifies with Maria's difficult struggle of carving out a niche for herself and finding fulfillment as a woman in a man's world is so complete, however, as to seem wholly autobiographical. She projects her own psychological reality onto the character of Maria, allowing the reader a glimpse into her private dreamworld.

Style and Technique

Clarice Lispector is internationally known for her lyrical style of writing, which blurs the line between prose and poetry. This lyricism is in large part due to the subject matter with which she deals. Her stories are primarily interior monologues, probing their characters' psychic reality. The conflict of one of her stories is always within the mind of the main character, exploring the way people, things, and events in the physical world effect unexpected and seemingly unrelated reactions in the individual's psyche. The character's changing psychic perspective dominates both the style and structure of the narrative, as the author's focus tightens around the effects of situations, rather than the situations themselves. This structurally inventive style was considered at least unconventional, if not radically groundbreaking, in 1944 when Lispector's first novel was published.

The lyricism of Lispector's prose is found not just in the rhythm of its sentence structure, but also in the way the actual words used move seamlessly between real-world and the other-worldly realm. Again, this is reflected in the nature of her subject matter, flowing between the practical, social quotidian and the dreamlike inner reality of self. For language to have meaning one must be able to relate to it; in order to relate, the gap between self and other must be bridged. Lispector is skilled at transforming the nonlinear inner reality of her characters into a linear expression that retains its meaning.

As in Lispector's other stories, "The Daydreams of a Drunk Woman" is structured around an epiphany. The first half of the story, in which Maria moves in and out of consciousness, toying with different constructions of her self, can be viewed as a slow build toward the epiphanal moment in the restaurant when she realizes that the freedom afforded her by her position as wife is also her shackle keeping her from exploring her true self. The ambiguous ending is also typical of Lispector, leaving the reader to wonder whether Maria will again resign herself with a sigh, or free herself with a boisterous laughing shout.

Leslie Maile Pendleton

DE MORTUIS

Author: John Collier (1901-1980)
Type of plot: Horror
Time of plot: Mid-twentieth century
Locale: Upstate New York
First published: 1951

> *Principal characters:*
> DR. RANKIN, a fifty-year-old small-town physician
> IRENE RANKIN, his wife, a younger woman with a bad reputation
> BUD and
> BUCK, his fishing companions

The Story

As mild-mannered Dr. Rankin puts the finishing touches to a patch of wet cement on his cellar floor, he is startled by sounds, signaling the entrance of Bud and Buck, who call out, "Hi, Doc! They're biting!" Not wanting to be disturbed, he remains silent, but his friends figure out where he is and come down the stairs.

When the friends ask Rankin about the wet cement patch, he explains that he has repaired a spot where water has been seeping in from an underground spring. Bud—the realtor who sold him the property—refuses to believe that such a spring exists, and both men are skeptical about Rankin's explanation that his wife, Irene, is visiting friends. After asking several more questions, they announce that he has buried his wife's body under the cement. When Rankin reacts indignantly to this suggestion, his friends reassure him that they are on his side and will help cover up his murder. After telling him that they do not blame him for wanting to kill Irene, they reveal everything they know about her character, calling her "the town floozy." Both men admit to having had sexual relations with her themselves, but they hasten to assure Rankin that these incidents occurred before he married her.

All these revelations shock the unworldly Rankin, who has doted on his young wife. His love for her turns to hatred as he learns about her moral depravity and realizes how he has been deceived by her beauty and surface innocence. He concludes that she never loved him, that she married him only for financial security, and that she has been making a fool of him since the moment that they met. Rankin honestly believes the story that he has told Buck and Bud about his wife's visiting old friends named Slater in Watertown; however, his friends assure him that no such people exist. Rankin now believes that Irene has lied to him in order to meet a secret lover.

As Bud and Buck leave, they promise never to breathe a word about the supposed murder. They will swear that they saw Irene riding out of town with a man in a roadster—a story that everyone in town will believe because of Irene's shameful reputation.

While Rankin is still in the cellar, his young wife unexpectedly returns. She has missed her train and asks him to drive her to another station where she can still make connections. He asks her if she met anyone coming back. She tells him that she has not met a soul, leaving Rankin as the only person who knows that she is still in town.

At the end of the story, the doctor asks Irene to come downstairs so that he can show her a problem that has developed with the patch of cement he has been working on. It is clear that he intends to murder her and put her under the cement floor, now that Buck and Bud have provided him with an airtight alibi.

Themes and Meanings

In his cynicism about human affairs in general and about modern marriage in particular, John Collier has been compared to such authors as Somerset Maugham, Noel Coward, Oscar Wilde, and the vitriolic American journalist Ambrose Bierce. He has also been compared frequently to Edgar Allan Poe. Poe, however, did not possess Collier's ability to make his readers laugh, although he tried rather desperately to do so in some of his less successful stories.

Twice married himself, Collier often wrote disparagingly about marital relationships. His *His Monkey Wife: Or, Married to a Chimp* (1930) is about a man married to a chimpanzee. One of his most bitterly cynical short stories about marriage is "The Chaser," in which an old merchant who deals in magic potions advises a passionate young suitor to plan ahead for the time when he will get tired of the woman he adores and will want to rid himself of her cloying presence with a fatal dose of poison. "De Mortuis" is another of Collier's cynical stories dealing with the complications of modern marriage.

Collier's attitude toward marriage reflects modern realities. During the twentieth century the United States divorce rate soared until sociologists predicted that a marriage had little better than a fifty-fifty chance of success. Such statistics suggest there may be many husbands and wives who hate each other but remain married because of finances, children, religion, or other considerations. Collier was not only cynical about marriage, he was cynical about human nature in general. He dramatizes this theme in "De Mortuis" in the ease with which the gentle Dr. Rankin is about to become a cold-blooded murderer and the casual way in which his two buddies become his co-conspirators. It is difficult to find likable or entirely innocent characters in Collier's stories. Those who start out innocent generally do not remain so for long.

The thesis of "De Mortuis" is similar to that of "The Chaser." Both stories suggest that love can easily turn into hatred and that people who have romantic or idealistic notions about other human beings are bound to become disillusioned unless they are stupid. Like many of Collier's stories, "De Mortuis" suggests that it is impossible for one truly to know another human being, that we are all born strangers who live and die alone. What saves Collier's short stories from being overwhelmingly depressing is their quirky, sophisticated humor. This sugarcoating of Collier's bitter pills of worldly wisdom keeps the reader from taking his cynical outlook too seriously.

Style and Technique

"De Mortuis" belongs to a specialized mystery subgenre often called "the body in the basement story." It also belongs to the larger subgenre of "perfect crime" stories. In typical stories of this type, a man murders a relative, buries the body somewhere inside his home, and congratulates himself that he has gotten away with the perfect crime. Then, because of some fatal mistake, the murderer is caught and punished. Poe, the American genius who created many modern literary genres, was responsible for the popularity of both body-in-the-basement and perfect-crime stories. Examples of Poe's contributions are "The Black Cat," "The Tell-Tale Heart," and "The Cask of Amontillado."

What makes Collier's "De Mortuis" so effective is its ironic twists, its departure from the norm. In order to appreciate Collier's story, the reader must be familiar with stories of the conventional pattern, such as those of Poe and his imitators. Collier plays with fictional conventions in a manner that is hypermodern. Writing in the earlier decades of the twentieth century, he presaged some of the experimental innovations of much later writers. Collier is a sophisticated modern writer addressing sophisticated modern readers of magazines such as *The New Yorker*. "De Mortuis" almost completely reverses traditional mystery story conventions, betraying the reader's expectations: Because no body has actually been buried in the basement, it appears that the perfect crime really will be committed.

There are other reversals in "De Mortuis" as well. In typical perfect-crime stories, cunning murderers are proud of their ability to plan their crime and fool the police. In sharp contrast, Dr. Rankin is such a simple soul that he is completely unaware of what is well known to everybody else in his community. In a typical body-in-the-basement story, the murderer tries to get rid of someone he hates. If he murders his wife—as is often the case in such stories—she is likely to be old, unattractive, shrewish, demanding, and a "ball and chain." By contrast, the doctor's wife is beautiful and sexy, and he is deeply in love with her until he learns the truth.

Collier is a master storyteller; the unity of time and setting that he creates in "De Mortuis" is admirable. He ranges over many years and suggests the existence of a whole town without departing from the immediate present or from a single spot in the doctor's cellar. Another way in which Collier displays his craftsmanship is in orchestrating his characters. For example, the youthful, scatterbrained Irene makes Rankin seem old and stodgy by comparison, while his quiet, thoughtful manner highlights her hedonism and extroversion. Collier keeps his story dramatic through having Buck and Bud reveal Irene's scandalous past. A less skillful writer might have had Rankin find a letter or some other incriminating clue. Buck and Bud make the situation more immediate, bringing it "on stage," and adding dramatic tension by their initial suspicions and ultimate complicity.

Collier's short stories are invariably humorous in an ironic or bizarre manner. There is much humor in "De Mortuis," including the paradox that the doctor idolizes the town floozy, the fact that everyone knows about her behavior except him, and the fact that Bud and Buck assume that he has buried his wife's body in the cellar.

Bill Delaney

THE DEAD MAN

Author: Horacio Quiroga (1878-1937)
Type of plot: Social realism
Time of plot: Early twentieth century
Locale: Paraná Valley near Misiones, Argentina
First published: "El hombre muerto," 1920 (English translation, 1987)

Principal character:
THE MAN, the anonymous protagonist, a banana farmer

The Story

An unnamed farmer is working in his banana plantation as usual, clearing space with his machete. Satisfied with his progress, he decides to rest before finishing. As he usually does, he plans to cross a barbed wire fence and stretch out on the nearby grass. This time, however, things go terribly wrong. He accidentally trips and falls, landing on the ground. He is in the position he intended, but notices that his machete is in a strange position: half of it protrudes from his shirt, under his waist. Trying to look around, he realizes that the other half of the machete has pierced his abdomen.

Incredibly but inexorably, he calmly assesses the situation and concludes that his life has come to an end. He sees that he is so badly wounded that he is now dying; to all intents and purposes he is really already a dead man, as there can be no remedy. He thinks about his life, as he drifts in and out of consciousness. Nevertheless, it is hard for him to accept such a sudden and senseless end. He knows that death is inevitable, but he thought that he would have a normal lifespan, that he would have time to prepare for death. He had expected a full life, with its share of hopes, dreams and problems. Instead, he is suddenly dying—simply because of an accident, a moment of petty carelessness. He realizes that nothing around him has changed, that his surroundings have not reacted to what for him is a cataclysmic event. He resists the horrible thought. Nothing has changed—his own banana plantation is the same. He knows it well, after working on it for so many years.

The midday calm approaches. He sees the distant red roof of his house and the nearby woods. Although he cannot turn to look, he knows that in other directions lie the road to the new port and the Paraná Valley. Everything is the same as always—the sun, the air, the trees. He thinks that he will change the fence. It cannot be possible that he will be dead. It is supposed to be a regular, normal day. He can even see his horse sniffing at the barbed wire.

Suddenly, he hears whistling. He cannot see in that direction but knows that it is the youth who passes by every morning at eleven-thirty, crossing the bridge on horseback, going to the new port, always whistling. He does not call out for help, thinking perhaps that it is useless or that he is too weak to be heard.

The farmer knows the distances in every direction, since he measured them himself when he put up the fence. It is still his natural place, his normal surroundings—with the grass, the anthills, the silence. Nothing has changed. Only he is different. He realizes that he can no longer relate to his fields or his family. He has been abruptly yet naturally torn away from the life he had known. Within two minutes of the accident, he truly is dying.

Although he becomes very tired, he resists the transcendence of the moment. Everything is so normal; it seems impossible to him that he has had such an accident, especially since he is so experienced a worker. He even thinks about getting a better machete. He is just so tired from his labors that he needs a short rest.

As he looks at the things that he has planted, he ponders everything that is normal around him—grass, trees, sun, air, his sweaty and cautious horse—and insists to himself that he is merely exhausted, that he is only resting. A few more minutes have probably passed. He knows that his family will come at a quarter to twelve to get him for lunch. He always hears his younger child before the others, calling out for papa. He imagines that he hears the sound now. It seems like a nightmare that all this has happened on such a trivial and typical day. He remembers other days when he felt so tired, returning home from a hard morning in the fields.

He thinks that he can use his mind to leave his body now, if he wishes; he can look down at himself, resting in the grass, amidst his usual surroundings. He is just so tired.

His cautious horse sees him lying there. The animal wants to go around him and the fence, for better grazing, but that is normally forbidden. The horse hears the voices of the family, approaching now. Since the man does not stir, the horse grows calm and finally decides to move, passing by the body of its owner stretched out, just a shape on the grass. The man is finally, fully, and eternally at rest.

Themes and Meanings

Born in Uruguay, author Horacio Quiroga often used neighboring Argentina as the setting for his stories. During his own lifetime, he had experienced several family tragedies through accidental shootings and suicides. He was familiar with the dangers of the rugged jungle life in parts of South America. There was a constant threat of sudden, unexpected menace; people were often in the face of an unrelenting and inhospitable natural world, beset by wild animals, insects, disease, accident, and madness. Death could come at any time. This story is a fine example of that recurring theme.

"El hombre muerto" ("The Dead Man") first appeared in the daily *La Nación* in 1920; six years later it was published in the collection *Los desterrados* (1926), which was translated by J. David Danielson and Elsa Gambarini as *The Exiles and Other Stories* in 1987. "The Dead Man" has been included in many Spanish and English anthologies and is considered one of Quiroga's best stories.

The themes of danger and sudden death are found in many of Quiroga's stories. Concerning "The Dead Man," the reader knows the outcome almost from the very beginning. The protagonist's gradual awareness of his own condition is presented in such a powerful, compelling manner, however, that the reader's interest is maintained. There is a fatalistic, inexorable progression toward death. The end is inescapable, although it may come so suddenly and unexpectedly that the effect is stunning: A single momentary act of carelessness, an accidental lapse in concentration can lead to fatal, ultimate consequences, for anyone, at any time.

In a struggle to tame the wilderness, human beings may think that progress has been made. Yet nature may erupt suddenly and violently, causing untold destruction. Likewise, in the course of an ordinary day, a man may die accidentally. Nature does not change or react to that particular person's individual tragedy, at least if the story is told by a realistic rather than a romantic writer.

Style and Technique

A realist in style, despite receiving early training in the modernist school, Quiroga is preoccupied with the human situation and state of mind, death, and suicide. He describes his ideas on literary theory in his brief "Manual of the Perfect Short Story Writer" (1925), in which he praises such predecessors as Edgar Allan Poe, Guy de Maupassant, Rudyard Kipling, and Anton Chekhov. In this essay, he stresses the importance of originality, dedication, control, brevity, and precision in writing. Some repetition can heighten effect.

These elements can all be found in "The Dead Man," with its creation of atmosphere through controlled emotional intensity. The structure is tight and precise; the tone is direct, natural, and matter-of-fact. Subtle changes in the man's condition are suggested or implied. While he knows he is dying, he momentarily lapses into planning for future work on his farm. There is irony in the fact that he is suddenly facing death on an otherwise ordinary day. The reader has the dying man's perspective of events throughout the piece, until the shift in the last paragraph. By then, the protagonist has become "The Dead Man"—and his horse, now less cautious, finally reacts by moving.

Elements of adventure, horror, mystery, psychological, and social realism often appear in Quiroga's stories. "The Dead Man" stresses the latter two aspects with considerable skill. While his reputation was strong earlier in the twentieth century, Quiroga's fame was eclipsed by that of later writers, notably that of Jorge Luis Borges. There has been renewed interest in Quiroga's writing, however, and in the influence he had on recent authors. He is widely respected as a master craftsman who created memorable stories that linger in the reader's consciousness.

Margaret V. Ekstrom

DEAD MEN'S PATH

Author: Chinua Achebe (1930-   )
Type of plot: Social realism
Time of plot: 1949
Locale: An Igbo village in southeastern Nigeria
First published: 1953

> ### Principal characters:
> MICHAEL OBI, the protagonist, a zealous and idealistic young
>   mission-trained headmaster
> NANCY OBI, his wife, a shallow woman given to outward
>   appearances and equally infected with a shallow idealism
> THE VILLAGE PRIEST, an old man of very few words

The Story

Michael Obi's ambition is fulfilled when, at age twenty-six, he is appointed to whip into shape an unprogressive secondary school. Energetic, young, and idealistic as he is, Obi hopes to clean up the educational mission field and speed up its Christianizing mission. Already outspoken in his denigration of "the narrow views" and ways of "superannuated people in the teaching field," he expects to make a good job of this grand opportunity and show people how a school should be run. He plans to institute modern methods and demand high standards of teaching, while his wife, Nancy—who looks forward to being the admired wife of the headmaster—plants her "dream gardens" of beautiful hibiscus and allamanda hedges. With Nancy doing her gardening part, they will together lift Ndume School from its backward ways to a place of European-inspired beauty in which school regulations will replace Ndume village community's traditional beliefs.

So Obi dreams and plans until one evening when he discovers a village woman cutting across the school gardens on a footpath that links the village shrine with the cemetery. Scandalized by her blatant trespassing, Obi orders the sacred ancestral footpath fenced off with barbed wire, much to the consternation of the villagers. The local priest then tries to remind Obi of the path's historical and spiritual significance as the sacred link between the villagers, their dead ancestors, and the yet unborn. Obi flippantly derides the priest's explanation as the very kind of superstition that the school is intended to eradicate, since "dead men do not require footpaths." Two days later the hedge surrounding the school, its flower beds, and one of its buildings lie trampled and in ruins—the result of the villagers' attempt to propitiate the ancestors whom Obi's fence has insulted. After his supervisor issues a report on this incident, Obi is dismissed.

Themes and Meanings

Written early during Chinua Achebe's undergraduate days at Nigeria's University of Ibadan and published in *The University Herald* in 1953, "Dead Men's Path" is one of his earliest published short stories. Later collected in *Girls at War and Other Stories* (1972), the story contains the germ of what became the major theme of his first three novels: the collision of Christianity and African traditional culture. He most closely explores the theme of culture collision and the tension and estrangement of mission-trained converts from traditional community life in his novels *Things Fall Apart* (1958), *No Longer at Ease* (1960), and *Arrow of God* (1964).

Layered in irony, the essence of "Dead Men's Path" is expressed in the last part of the priest's admonition to Obi: "What I always say is: let the hawk perch and let the eagle perch." Although Obi is fully aware of the cultural code of deference to age and status, he persists in his arrogance because of his newly acquired power and ignores the culture-specific code of existence—the world of dualities that permits two very different things to stand side by side.

To the priest of Ani, the footpath represents continuity; it is the village's lifeline: "Our dead relatives depart by it and our ancestors visit us by it. But most importantly, it is the path of children coming in to be born. . . ." To Obi, however, it merely epitomizes what he regards as the backwardness that he has sworn to eradicate through his "modern methods" program. The priest's argument is simple: Two cultures can coexist, their differences notwithstanding, because there are no absolutes in the village's traditional thinking. The priest's view contrasts with the absolutism inherent in the world view of Obi's newly embraced alien religion. For this reason, the priest's brief reminder of the village's spiritual history and the need to resolve conflicts through dialogue are lost on Obi.

Carrying his modernization mission to an extreme, Obi denounces the villagers' traditional culture as nothing but pagan ideas that he will teach their children to deride and which he will eradicate through his modern methods program. Similarly, he condemns the views of his older, less educated, and allegedly unimpassioned colleagues as embarrassingly archaic, backward, and worthy of contempt and condemnation. To the priest's conciliatory offer to end the dispute by simply reopening the path, Obi offers the absolutism of his "modern methods" manifesto, in which paradoxes do not exist, let alone conciliation to and negotiation with old and so-called "superannuated" village ways. The essence of the lesson, reiterated to him by the old priest, as if he needed such a reminder, Obi haughtily waves off.

Extremism and absolutism militate against balance, the balance that allows, indeed provides, space enough for both the hawk and the eagle to perch. On this point tradition is inflexible. Idealism is one thing, extremism another, and excess yet another. The idealism that comes from youthful energy and enthusiasm that lifts Obi to "pivotal teacher" status and headmastership at twenty-six is admirable. Neither the priest nor the villagers begrudge him his personal achievement. Nor is the village upset about the school's encroaching on their ancestral footpath until Obi erects his ill-conceived barbed wire fence. Beautiful gardens and hedges—the tangibles of Obi's modernization crusade—may also coexist and even coextend spatially with ancestral footpaths and thoroughfares. When burdensome detours infringe on the "perching" rights that connect an entire village's spiritual life, however, the ancestors themselves must take up the war cry against such extremism born of "misguided zeal." It is at this point that the forces of tradition take on a conservative stance.

Ironically, the same energy and enthusiasm that raise Obi to the height of his career are also responsible for his stoop-shoulderedness and frailty, his premature aging, and his eventual tragic fall. His white supervisor's negative report on the "tribal-war situation developing between the school and the village" exposes the superficiality of Obi's idealism. The once acclaimed "pivotal teacher" is then laid low by his own "misguided zeal." The moral seems clear to all (the white supervisor included) except Obi. The philosophy of "balance" prevails.

Style and Technique

In prose that is at once leisurely and stately, Achebe blends the credulity of a folktale with an impartiality that is achieved more by allusion and implication rather than by explicit explanation. He uses irony and paradox to portray the contradictions arising from the moral dilemma faced by mission-trained converts whose estrangement from community life delineates the tragic conflict between the binary worldview of Christianity and the simple live-and-let-live duality of Igbo traditional worldview. The forces of the story lie in its condensed brevity and the suggestiveness illustrated by the old priest's pithy style. Unlike Obi's openly derisive mockery of the villagers' traditional beliefs, the priest's decorous but unceremonious style of confrontation and conflict resolution does not question the validity of the Christian religion that Obi represents. Choice of style notwithstanding, it is clear from the exchange between both men that neither side is supported or privileged. But the symbolic force of the priest's habit of emphatically tapping his stout walking-stick on the floor each time that he makes a fresh point is all too suggestive of the power of the unspoken to which Obi's misguided zeal blinds him.

Rather than explain the showdown between the priest and the young headmaster, Achebe cleverly uses dialogue to contrast Obi's warped mental attitude with the old priest's poise and his economy of words. The patience and wisdom of age are pitted against the restless energy and glib-tongued arrogance of unseasoned youth. Through deliberate impudence and mockery Obi seeks to unbalance the equilibrium of the village which the old priest's wisdom and poise embody. As though the barbed wire fence is not insult enough, Obi's arrogance pushes him beyond cultural bounds when he orders the priest to construct a path that will skirt the school premises, as if he is taking on the village ancestors personally. Obi seals his own doom when he glibly says, "I don't suppose the ancestors will find the little detour too burdensome." The priest's portentous reply, "I have no more words to say," sets the stage for the final irony of the story: the tragic fall of the new headmaster.

Pamela J. Olubunmi Smith

DEER WOMAN

Author: Paula Gunn Allen (1939-   )
Type of plot: Magical Realism
Time of plot: Mid- to late twentieth century
Locale: An Indian reservation near Anadarko, Oklahoma
First published: 1991

> *Principal characters:*
> RAY, a young Native American man
> JACKIE, his friend
> LINDA, an attractive traditional deer woman
> JUNELLA, her equally attractive friend
> THE OLD MAN, the deer women's uncle

The Story

Two beautiful deer women, Linda and Junella, arrive at a "stomp dance"—a traditional Sioux ceremony that is conducted with certain modifications on an Oklahoma reservation. The dance ground is ringed by a motley assortment of Cadillacs and pickup trucks, whose headlights provide illumination. Two " 'skins," Ray and Jackie, arrive at the dance hoping to "snag," that is, to score with, women. Pretending to want to go to the nearby town of Anadarko, the women accept a lift from the men, who cannot believe their good luck, and pile into Ray's pickup.

As the women climb into the truck, Ray thinks that he sees their feet look like deer hooves. After the women ask to stop by a river in order to refresh themselves, they lead the men up a path to their "old house," where their ancient Uncle Thunder is sitting. "I see you've snagged two strong men," the old man says, punning on the term "snag" and commenting sarcastically on the word "strong." Leading the men by their hands, the women then take them to a second ceremonial site—a field where a baseball game is being played.

In the midst of the game, the deer women vanish, leaving Ray and Jackie to search for them futilely. Ray awakens from a deep sleep to find himself lying by a river at midday. Jackie is nowhere to be found, but Junella is beside him. She tells him that "Jackie is staying there," and gives him Jackie's wristwatch as proof. Ray then becomes dizzy. He takes a step toward the woman, but the rock on which she has been sitting is empty.

Fifteen months later Jackie's fate is revealed: A sudden move to Seattle with Linda, the birth of a child, alcoholism, and a premature death for revealing things that he learned inside a mountain that he was not supposed to tell.

The story concludes with an ambiguous image of Ray rushing to catch a subway in San Francisco. On his way to a meeting, he is firmly entrenched in the modern wristwatch world.

Themes and Meanings

The implied moral of Paula Gunn Allen's story is that the fates suffered by Ray and Jackie are the consequences of their sexist, derogatory, and nontraditional attitudes toward Native American women. There is an instructive, retributive quality underlying the inversion of gender mistreatment. Firmly rooted in the didactic, allegorical, and oral Native American storytelling tradition, the story is meant to teach a lesson, to model an ideal for comportment in general, and particularly behavior between the sexes.

Jackie's slide into alcoholism and premature death can be viewed as his punishment for viewing women as sexual objects and for his dim-witted passivity. Ray notices the women's deerlike feet, but Jackie does not. Ray asks pertinent questions about the women's identity, but Jackie merely shrugs silently. Ray inquires about where they have been taken, but Jackie lapses into an almost catatonic passivity. Of the two men, Jackie is the more overtly sexist: "Well, I used to say I'd walk a mile for a camel . . . but I didn't say anything about snags."

Doubling the male victims allows Paula Gunn Allen to prosecute her attack on un-Indian male behavior (Jackie), while simultaneously offering Ray some hope. The latter is evinced by Ray's awakening to the realities of the situation ("maybe those old guys know something, eh?"), his perception of the underlying reasons for Jackie's death (for telling "what he wasn't supposed to tell"), and the fact that he is allowed to return to the world, perhaps wiser for his experience. The story's ambiguous offering of punishment and hope is mirrored in the unforgettable look that Ray gives—"a look that was somehow wounded and yet with a kind of wild hope mixed in."

"Deer Woman" is thus not only an attack on un-Indian male attitudes and actions, but a celebration of the universal power of femininity—particularly Native American womanhood. Women are presented as strong, assertive, and mysterious corrective influences on errant Native American masculinity. Women are both seductresses and guides; indeed, the deer women present themselves as seductresses in order to mask their role as guides to reaffirmation of traditional Native American values. "Deer Woman" is thus a tribute to the lasting relevance of the beliefs practiced by Allen's ancestors. Linda and Junella are the womanly watchdogs of transgressive Indian behavior whom Old Man Thunder dispatches in order to render justice, teach lessons, and give potentially redeemable offenders a second chance to live in accordance with the traditional ways of what Black Elk called "the good Red road." The deer women function as a kind of moral compass governing behavior in general, and behavior between the sexes in particular—a compass aligned, not with true north, but with true Native American virtues.

Style and Technique

The thematic content of "Deer Woman" is effectively reinforced by Allen's style, which comprises a variety of elements including sensory detail, sardonic irony, metaphor, foreshadowing, and symbolism. The opening passage affords evidence of her use of effective sensory detail to create a sense of realism and give her setting a feeling of immediacy: "The slowly turning fan inside felt cool"; "They drove for some distance . . . bumping across cattle guards." Her successful appeal to the senses creates an almost Faulknerian sense of place.

One of the finest features of the tale is its grim irony, as the would-be victimizers become victims of their own lust. Perhaps the most striking example of sardonic irony occurs when Ray wryly observes that this "is the only time I've heard of Little Red Riding Hood leading the wolves to Grandma's." In this, the story reinscribes the powerful Lakota Sioux myth of Buffalo Woman, who first brought the sacred pipe to the people of the Northern Plains, and exerted a similarly fatal allure upon a young 'skin, whose lust she exploited to bring about his ruin. Allen writes in this same ancient, didactic, oral tradition, using myth to model good and bad Native American behavior, as the vehicle for constructing and disseminating a collective Indian ethos.

At times Allen weds sensory detail to alliteration and metaphor, thereby enhancing the verisimilitude of her writing. For example, she describes the day as "sultry and searing as summer days in Oklahoma get, hot as a sweat lodge." "Deer Woman" is also encoded with symbols that in turn are deeply embedded in the Indian psyche. Whether deployed consciously or unconsciously, they work to underscore the themes of the tale. For instance, in the Native American mythic landscape the river is a traditional symbol of closeness to the source of life, of being in touch with oneself. Thus, the deer women's immersion in the current may be read as a symbol of their intimacy with the everlasting ways of the "traditionals." Their association with the river is reinforced through simile, for "their long hair flowed like black rivers." Likewise, the return of Ray and Jackie to the river, under the guidance of the deer women, may be viewed as a return to the imperishable ways of their ancestors.

Though not a complete list of the elements that make up Allen's style and technique, these examples demonstrate her command of writing and particularly her mastery of the Native American storytelling craft in which she is firmly rooted. At the same time, however, she is breaking new ground in an effort to construct a Native American feminine subjectivity that both situates itself in the conflicted past and orients itself toward an empowered future.

Stephen G. Brown

THE DEFEATED

Author: Nadine Gordimer (1923-   )
Type of plot: Social realism
Time of plot: The 1920's to 1940's
Locale: Capetown, South Africa
First published: 1952

> *Principal characters:*
> THE NARRATOR, a student in South Africa and daughter of Scottish
> immigrants who are also mine owners
> MIRIAM SAIYETOVITZ, her friend, the daughter of Jewish immigrant
> shopkeepers
> MR. and MRS. SAIYETOVITZ, Miriam's parents

The Story

As the narrator recalls her student years in Capetown, South Africa, where her parents owned a mine, she remembers her long friendship with her schoolmate Miriam Saiyetovitz and Miriam's parents, who owned a concession store.

Against her mother's initial objections, the narrator finds herself drawn into the exotic world of the concession stores where native Africans shop. She is enticed by the sights, smells, sounds, and activities of the shopkeepers and the Africans. Though she is careful to keep her physical distance, since she is repulsed by some of the customs, sights, and smells that accompany this busy merchant world, she experiences an excitement and abundance of life that is seemingly missing from her own.

One day, as she visits the shops, she recognizes a schoolmate among the faces in the shops and befriends Miriam Saiyetovitz (whose name the narrator initially terms "ugly"). The narrator's description of Miriam's mother makes it clear that she is befriending the daughter of a Jewish immigrant family, whose socioeconomic status falls far below that of her own family. Miriam's parents are hardworking, however, and try to give their daughter everything they can. The narrator is impressed that her newfound friend can retrieve a lemonade from the kitchen inside the shop whenever she desires. She also notes that while Miriam does not physically distance herself from the Africans, she seems not to notice them either, talking only of school and how the future will unfold for the two girls. In fact, Miriam appears unaffected by her surroundings in general.

Miriam is invited to the narrator's house for a birthday party but appears to think no more of it than of the concession stores. When Miriam tells her mother about the party, Mrs. Saiyetovitz, in her eagerness to reciprocate, invites the narrator to a party for Miriam that is to be held at their newly built house on the outskirts of town. On the day of the party, however, Miriam takes all of her friends to town instead of her house, to the disappointment of her parents. Her parents rationalize Miriam's actions, believing that she knows better than they do "what is nice and what is right" by virtue of her education. The narrator is eventually introduced into the interior of the store and notes Mr. Saiyetovitz's "hangdog gentleness" toward the two schoolmates, in contrast to his "strange blasts of power" when dealing with the Africans. She learns, too, that Mr. Saiyetovitz's name was changed, from Yanka to John, upon his arrival in Capetown.

The narrator and Miriam continue their friendship through their matriculation year, then decide to continue on to the university. Unlike the Saiyetovitzes, the narrator's parents need not worry about the money to fund an education. The narrator notices that while Miriam's parents own a newly built house, they still spend most of their time at the store. One day, as the narrator and Miriam ride the bus to town in order to purchase a new winter coat with money provided by Miriam's father, Miriam ironically declares her preference for the narrator's father, because he is educated and not a merchant.

During the years at the university, Miriam becomes a "lady," soft, bored, and conforming to whatever environment in which she finds herself. She socializes with young successful Jewish students and vacations in Johannesburg, while the narrator goes home to the mining town. After they become teachers, the two friends part ways. Some years later, the narrator hears that Miriam has married a doctor. One day, while back in Capetown, the narrator is reminded of the days spent at the concession store, and visits the old shop to inquire after Mr. and Mrs. Saiyetovitz. She finds Miriam's parents, "older, sadder," and waiting "as animals wait in a cage; for nothing." The couple tell her about Miriam's success. She has married a doctor, had a son, and lives in a beautiful home in Johannesburg.

The source of the Saiyetovitzes' pride is also the source of their pain and defeat. They rarely see their daughter and have never been invited to her home. The story ends with a picture of Mr. Saiyetovitz lashing out against an African customer in the back room. The narrator realizes, sadly, how in spite of their own suffering, the Saiyetovitzes are "defeated, and without understanding in their defeat."

Themes and Meanings

Nadine Gordimer's "The Defeated" reveals the strong class system of South Africa in the early 1900's—a system based on the exploitation of the labor of others by the ruling class. The most obvious underclass is made up of Africans who work in the mine owned by the narrator's parents. The narrator describes the unhealthy skin color and symptoms of tuberculosis among the mineworkers without naming the disease or its connection to work in the mine. She also fails to connect her own family's prosperity and leisure with the privations suffered by the mineworkers. The second class introduced is the Jewish immigrant class, represented by the Saiyetovitzes. They, too, are "defeated" in their labor, because they work so hard among the very underclass that they, too, seek to rise above.

Gordimer distinguishes among the various sources of affluence and subsistence among the South Africans in Capetown. The narrator's parents gain wealth through their education and commercial astuteness, while others, belonging to the merchant class, rely upon "instinctive peasant craftiness." Still others, such as Mr. Saiyetovitz, lack "craftiness," and so are relegated to "hard . . . dirty work" for which there is little payoff. In every case, affluence ultimately depends upon the sweat and blood of someone, though the relationship remains hidden to most people.

Gordimer makes a strong statement about the nature and consequences of the class system in South Africa through the character of Mr. Saiyetovitz. An immigrant forced to change his name and therefore his identity, he must labor just as the even "lowlier" Africans must in order to provide for his family. Yet he treats those "below" him as he is treated by those "above" him. Miriam, even more than the narrator's parents and the narrator herself, demonstrates how the labor of others is taken for granted by those who benefit from it. She, too, refuses to recognize the source of her affluence.

Style and Technique

Gordimer is known for her treatment of complex social and political issues, and "The Defeated" is no exception. At the same time, the story is simply told, enjoyable for its abundance of descriptive detail, and without overt judgment or moralizing. Gordimer effectively employs irony and contrast in her story. She sets up a strong socioeconomic contrast in the backgrounds of the narrator and Miriam. The narrator lives in a quiet, easily afforded home, while Miriam lives in a store, where she witnesses her parents' daily struggle for survival. In this way, Gordimer sets up the expectation that Miriam will be more appreciative of her gains, since her parents must work day and night to fund her education. Another expectation is that Mr. Saiyetovitz will empathize with others who share his plight. All of these expectations, when they are foiled, make Gordimer's portrayal of the class system even more powerful and frightening than could be conveyed by her vivid descriptions alone.

Another feature of Gordimer's style that makes the story so powerful is that the narrator, in effect, reports upon the action instead of interpreting it. The evidence laid out before the reader during the course of the narrative becomes almost overwhelming by the end of the story. The narrator's reporting leads the reader through a series of predictions and disappointments about predictions about the action and characters. This process builds tension in the reader, as well as suspense, causing the final picture of the Saiyetovitzes to appear all the more anguished. Perhaps it is Gordimer's aim that the reader undergo some of the tension experienced by the South African "defeated."

Jennifer McLeod

THE DESIRE TO BE A MAN

Author: Auguste Villiers de l'Isle-Adam (1838-1889)
Type of plot: Horror
Time of plot: Fall, 1871
Locale: Paris and the Brittany coast of France
First published: "Le Désir d'être un homme," 1883 (English translation, 1927)

Principal character:
ESPRIT CHAUDVAL, an aging actor, specializing in tragic roles

The Story

It is midnight in Paris' Grand Boulevard district on a windy Sunday in October, 1871. Because the city is still under martial law, the cafés and restaurants of that quarter are bustling to meet the curfew, ushering out their few remaining patrons and preparing to close their doors. The menacing gaze of two policemen encourages their haste. The surrounding streets are rapidly emptying of coaches and pedestrians for the same reason. Into this scene of hasty departures, there wanders a tall, sad-faced arrival, dressed in the style of the previous century and moving as though he were walking in his sleep. Oblivious to the bustle around him, the man stops before a tall, thin mirror, which decorates the exterior of an elegant café, and examines himself closely. After this solemn inspection, he ceremoniously removes his hat and bows politely to himself in the old-fashioned pre-Revolutionary manner. Now bareheaded, the man can be readily recognized as the illustrious tragedian Esprit Chaudval, whose real name is Lepeinteur, and whom everyone calls Monanteuil.

Seeming shocked, Chaudval continues to stare at himself in the mirror while all around him silence reigns, for everyone else has gone, and he is alone. What has shocked him is that his hair, salt and pepper only yesterday, is now the color of moonlight. In the mirror he has caught a glimpse of himself growing old. This spectacle sets off in the actor a host of memories and reflections about the sad necessity that faces him: to retire from the stage and give up the pleasures of the theatrical life that he has so long relished. He recalls his recent decision to retire to the Brittany lighthouse that his father before him had tended. He has already requested this government appointment, and, in fact, has the letter of appointment in his pocket but has forgotten about it. Chaudval now reminds himself that his fundamental desire in retirement is to be a man! For most of his life, he has portrayed the passions and emotions felt by others but has himself never experienced a real emotion. Real emotion is, after all, what makes one a genuine human being, Chaudval reasons. Since age is forcing him to leave the stage and return to humanity, Chaudval resolves that he must acquire passions, some real human feeling which best suits his nature. Rejecting love, glory, and ambition as no longer in season for him, Chaudval is led by his "dramatic temperament" to choose the emotion that is right for him: remorse. He recalls characters whom he has portrayed on the stage, such as Nero, Macbeth, and Hamlet, who experience remorse—whose remorse takes the form of a conscience haunted by ghosts. He decides he must do something horrifying enough to make him see ghosts as well—something spectacularly atrocious. With excited satisfaction, he hits upon the idea of setting a fire.

Pleased with this carefully reasoned solution to the problem of becoming a man, Chaudval suddenly picks up a paving stone, smashes the offending mirror, and dashes off into the night. Shortly thereafter, a major conflagration breaks out in Chaudval's quarter of Paris in which nearly a hundred people die. Chaudval watches the fire from a coach, in which he has placed all of his belongings. In the morning, he leaves for Brittany.

The ruin of a lighthouse, now his home, preoccupies Chaudval at first, and he forgets about his incendiary crime. But after reading an account of the event in a Paris newspaper, he experiences a surge of joyous triumph and awaits his reward: a conscience wracked by remorse. To his astonishment, nothing happens. He feels no pangs of conscience, no ghosts, no feeling of any kind. In a fever of despair and shame, he suffers a cerebral hemorrhage and, in his death agony, demands that God show him at least one ghost, since he has earned it. His prayer unanswered, Chaudval dies without realizing that he himself had become what he was seeking: a ghost.

Themes and Meanings

Auguste Villiers de l'Isle-Adam's ironic horror tale is constructed on the well-known psychological observation that actors pay a heavy price for their talent in portraying the characters and emotions of others. Their concentrated efforts to "think" their way into the skin of someone else drains them of any capacity to live a life of their own. According to this view, actors are tragic figures who, by constantly assuming the identity of others, lose their own identity. The classic case is that of the sad clown, laughing on the outside, crying on the inside. In France, at least, this conception originates in an essay of the eighteenth century writer Denis Diderot, who argues that a great actor's performance is a paradox because the portrayal of strong emotion requires an actor to be cold and dispassionate while performing. If the actor actually experiences the emotion, he will lack the disciplined control he needs to project the emotion accurately.

Villiers' tale pushes Diderot's insight to its logical conclusion, suggesting that a lifetime of portraying the emotions of others has left Chaudval unable to experience an emotion of his own. Feeling dehumanized by that fact and desperate to rejoin the human race somehow, Chaudval becomes a grotesque figure, trapped in the paradox of his theatrical mentality and therefore unable to address his problem. The only emotions he knows are those which he has counterfeited. That is why he commits a heinous crime, and the cruel irony that results is that Chaudval is revealed to be an empty shell of a man, a ghost. A sardonic conclusion to which the story inexorably leads the reader is that, in Chaudval, and perhaps in all thespians, the actor has systematically killed the human being in himself. He becomes the victim of his art.

Style and Technique

A striking feature of Villiers' story is that it has but one character. Whatever happens in the tale happens to him or is seen through his eyes. When he speaks, it is only to himself. A tale so concentrated in the consciousness of one character would seem to cry out for the technique of the first-person narrative. Nevertheless, Villiers has chosen to provide a third-person narrator, discreet, unobtrusive, apparently objective, but indispensable for characterizing Chaudval for the reader, and for bringing out the narrative's underlying irony. The narrator's effort, with regard to Chaudval, is to demonstrate that his whole manner of being and thinking is infected with the theatrical virus of make-believe. When Chaudval first appears, the description of his quaint clothing and courtly gestures informs us that he is always playing a part. He is never simply himself, because he has no self. When he starts to reason with himself about his plan for retirement, the narrator blandly observes that the old actor "ventured upon a monologue." When Chaudval reads, in a Paris newspaper, that a benefit performance will be given to raise money for the fire's victims, the narrator reports that Chaudval mutters to himself that he ought to have lent his talent to the benefit performance for his victims, since it could have been a brilliant farewell appearance for him. Chaudval betrays not the slightest awareness of how absurd and tragic this reaction is. Thus it is the narrator who reveals for the reader the tragic irony of Chaudval's ultimate fate: Long addiction to make-believe defeats his "desire to be a man."

Villiers' impressive skill as a stylist is especially evident in the way he uses his narrator in this tale. Villiers closely controls the choice of words, images, and even sentence rhythms to assure that not only Chaudval's own words, in direct discourse, but also the narrator's account of events, in indirect discourse, are always consonant with the bizarre persona of Chaudval and of his milieu. Villiers' language throughout is mannered, courtly, histrionic when necessary, a bit archaic, and replete with the expressive colloquialisms used by theater people. Villiers knew this Parisian theater milieu at first hand, having been part of it for several years in his early thirties, writing plays, negotiating with theater directors about getting them performed, and living with an actress who was his mistress. Both the theme and the language of "The Desire to Be a Man" are manifestly the product of those years.

Murray Sachs

THE DESTRUCTORS

Author: Graham Greene (1904-1991)
Type of plot: Psychological realism
Time of plot: The early 1950's
Locale: London
First published: 1954

> *Principal characters:*
> T. (TREVOR), the leader of a gang of adolescent boys
> BLACKIE, the gang leader whom he replaces and makes a lieutenant
> MR. THOMAS, an elderly man known to the boys as "Old Misery"

The Story

Amid the lingering London ruins of the bombing raids of World War II, a gang of adolescent boys pass their summer holidays carrying out various projects of collective mischief. They are the inhabitants of a neighborhood known as Wormsley Common, one of the poorest sections of the city. They meet and play in a communal parking lot, which adjoins a battered but stately eighteenth century house. The house, more than two hundred years old, stands alone, "like a jagged tooth," while its neighbors lie in wartime rubble. Blackie, the hitherto undisputed leader, is indirectly challenged one day by the newest recruit, a boy known as "T." From the time he first joined the group at the beginning of the summer, T. has had little or nothing to say, simply voting "yes" or "no" with the rest of this curiously democratic collection of children. Now T. intrigues the boys with a plan of diabolic proportions, an enterprise far beyond any that Blackie could conceive. The house that adjoins their parking lot play area, T. has discovered, was built by Christopher Wren, Great Britain's greatest architect. It was Wren who, in the late seventeenth century, designed and built Saint Paul's Cathedral, the most notable of London landmarks. The sole inhabitant of the house is the owner, an elderly and somewhat cranky gentleman named Mr. Thomas, whom the boys call "Old Misery."

T. has developed a curious fixation on the house. He gains entry by the simple device of asking Mr. Thomas if he can see it. Evidently flattered by the child's interest and attention, Mr. Thomas gives him a tour. The house is clearly an architectural and historical wonder, an enduring remnant of a bygone era when such buildings were the careful work of artistic craftsmen. Amid the antique china and eighteenth century paneling, one particular architectural wonder catches T's attention: a two-hundred-year-old staircase like a corkscrew, held up by nothing. He has learned that Mr. Thomas will be away on a long weekend holiday. T. proposes that they surreptitiously enter the house during that time and destroy it. Blackie and the others are at first hesitant, but also are intrigued with an action so daring and audacious. The boys undertake their task with quiet enthusiasm, completely under the spell of T's compelling leadership. In the space of a day and a half, they destroy the house with saws, hammers, screwdrivers, and sledgehammers. Nothing is left standing or intact but the four outside walls. Even the unexpected early return of Mr. Thomas does not daunt T., who quickly devises a plan to lure the old man into the outdoor lavatory, where he is locked up for the night. As a finishing touch, T. and the boys fasten a rope to the supporting struts on the outside of the house and tie the other end to a large truck left in the parking lot for the weekend. The driver arrives early the following morning, starts his truck, and proceeds toward the street. Suddenly there is a long rumbling crash, complete with bricks bouncing in the road ahead. The driver stops his truck and climbs down. The house that once stood with such dignity among the bombed-out ruins has disappeared. Freed from his lavatory prison by the truck driver, who responds to his shouting, Thomas utters a sobbing cry of dismay: "My house . . . where's my house?" The driver surveys the scene of the devastation and laughs. Thomas becomes angry and indignant. "I'm sorry," the driver reassures him, "but I can't help it. There's nothing personal, but you got to admit it's funny."

Themes and Meanings

The reader's first impression of "The Destructors" is that the story is a simple chronicle of senseless violence and wanton destruction carried out by thoughtless, unprincipled adolescents. Graham Greene's story, however, is actually a metaphor for class struggle in English society in the decade following World War II. The tension between working-class Britain and the upper-middle-class society that had absorbed all but the last vestiges of the nobility had surfaced dramatically in the years following the previous world war. These years were marked by repeated challenges, both social and political, to the established order of an empire in decline. Old Misery's house somehow survived the battering of a second great war, as did the monarchy and the entrenched class sensibility of British society. The house, however, is considerably weakened, held in place by wooden struts that brace the outside walls. In its fragile state, it needs support, as does the political and social structure that it represents. It cannot stand as it once did, independent with the formidable strength of the British Empire. The interior, although a trove of revered artifacts of civilized European culture, nevertheless represents a tradition that is increasingly meaningless to the lower classes.

The members of the Wormsley Common Gang—who significantly are twelve in number, like the apostles of the New Testament—are forces of change, agents subconsciously representing quiet, methodical revolution. Their demolishing of the house is painfully systematic. The boys work with steady persistence on their enterprise of destruction. They work, paradoxically, with the seriousness of creators. As Greene's narrator asserts, "destruction after all is a form of creation."

T. and his followers represent the extremes of nihilism, the philosophical doctrine that existing institutions—social, political, and economic—must be completely destroyed in order to make way for the new. In the context of nihilism, the destruction of Old Misery's house is both positive and necessary. T., whose nihilism is intrinsic to his distorted personality, makes it clear that he feels no hatred for old Mr. Thomas;

like a true nihilist, he feels nothing, rejecting both hate and love as "hooey." For someone with such a dangerously warped sense of mission, T. is also curiously ethical and high-minded. When he shows Blackie the bundles of currency discovered in Old Misery's mattress, Blackie asks if the group is going to share them. "We aren't thieves," T. replies; "Nobody is going to steal anything from this house." He then proceeds to burn them one by one as an act of celebration, presumably a celebration of triumph over the currency that more than any other entity determines the distinctions of social strata in postwar Great Britain. The truck driver, with his reassurance to Mr. Thomas that his laughter is nothing personal, reflects the position of the underclass: utter indifference to the sacrosanct values of tradition and civilized society.

Style and Technique

Greene's narrator is selectively omniscient. Although the reader is made aware of the internal doubts and anxieties of Blackie, the deposed leader, the inner workings of T's troubled mind remain closed. The narrator is also decidedly neutral and uncensorious in the general treatment of this focal character. To proponents of the tradition represented by the objects T. destroys, this child seems the very essence of evil. Greene, however, offers nothing to suggest anything other than a mysterious amorality that is cold, implacable, and generally inexplicable, although he piques curiosity with oblique references to T's background and mental state. When Old Misery suddenly returns home and threatens the enterprise, T. protests this unforeseen complication "with the fury of the child he had never been." Earlier, T., who generally looks down when he speaks, proposes the destruction of the house to the incredulous boys with "raised eyes, as grey and disturbed as the drab August day."

Prior to T's membership in the gang, its members' preoccupation was with adolescent mischief, such as stealing free rides on public transportation. T., however, is decidedly unchildlike and becomes the instrument that destroys not only the house but the group's collective innocence. The pleasures of their previous childhood preoccupations are forever lost to them. T. has taken them abruptly from innocence to experience, summarily depriving them of a gradual but essential learning process. In this regard, T's actions are presented as more the product of fate than malevolence.

The economy of description in character development is characteristic of Greene's writing. Extensive graphic detail and character background are all but nonexistent, but there is enough to make the reader more than willing to supply the missing dimension.

Richard Keenan

DINNER AT EIGHT

Author: Ezekiel Mphahlele (1919-   )
Type of plot: Social realism
Time of plot: The late 1950's
Locale: Johannesburg, South Africa
First published: 1961

Principal characters:
    MISS PRINGLE, a single white woman, the director of the Sheltered
      Employment Depot
    MZONDI, a black man who works for her at the depot

The Story

The daughter of an upright pastor, Miss Pringle is a self-righteous white South African woman who enjoys having black people hover over her admiringly. Her superficial liberalism has driven her into welfare work, in which she enjoys forcibly befriending helpless and needy Coloureds and Africans. The work fills a void in her otherwise dull life. She heads the Sheltered Employment Depot, a private workshop that trains "incurable cripples" in new trades. Preferring to work with blacks rather than whites because the latter are too independent, Miss Pringle prides herself in her knowledge and understanding of Africans.

Miss Pringle hides her fondness for Mzondi, a black inmate with a disability, under the guise of trying to help him with a problem that she alone perceives. She repeatedly invites him to dinner at her apartment, but he views her attention suspiciously and loathes her lack of decorum. One Monday morning, he is about to turn down her dinner invitation for the fifth time when the routine arrival of a policeman checking on a burglary report at the Depot changes the course of the day. When Mzondi sees the constable and Miss Pringle chatting and glancing in his direction, he assumes that she knows his secret and that this time her invitation is designed to get him drunk in her apartment so that he will confess his secret—that he has made two hundred pounds from bootlegging—so that she can turn him in to the police.

Determined to do Miss Pringle in before she does him in, Mzondi finally accepts her invitation. At her apartment building in Johannesburg's white-only Hillbrow neighborhood, she sneaks him up to her fourth-floor flat through a basement elevator designated for "Natives, goods, and hawkers." Although Miss Pringle knows that the police watch her for possible violations of the national Immorality Act because she entertains nonwhite guests, she is unaware that the building's watchman has telephoned the police. She performs her routine check of her apartment window to ensure that the police are not watching. Interpreting this gesture as a signal to the police, Mzondi decides to carry out his plan. After asking her to massage his aching and useless knee, he clubs her on the back of her head with his crutch, crushing her skull. As Mzondi leaves the building, he gives five pounds to the watchman—who only minutes earlier accepted a five-shilling bribe from a white policeman—promising him more money if he never reveals what he has seen that night.

Physically and mentally exhausted, Mzondi enjoys only a brief escape. Early the next morning, his body is found by a tree, his arms embracing its trunk.

Themes and Meanings

Miss Pringle's superiors in the social welfare organization often describe her with such phrases as "a trifle tiresome, but hardworking," "a little overbearing, but conscientious," and "a likeable person, but a queer fish." Her insistence on repeatedly inviting Mzondi to her flat for dinner points to her shallowness and naïveté, particularly since she always reminds him that they will be alone—an uncomfortable fact of which he needs no reminder. Any relationship between a "tiresome," "overbearing," and "queer" white female supervisor and a "crippled," deeply distrusting black male employee in South Africa's former apartheid system is certain to be ill-fated. Nevertheless, the fates of these two tragic figures seem to be intertwined. One person is white and female, the other is black and male; one is sexually frustrated but powerful, the other handicapped and powerless; one is naïvely trusting and repulsive, the other is immovably distrusting yet intriguing. Despite a lopsided body racked and made useless by "ever-tired bones" and "withering flesh," Mzondi bears his physical problems "with irresistible cheek." The puzzlement of Mzondi's "pathetic beautiful lips" and steady but almost expressionless eyes captivate Miss Pringle, turning her desire to befriend Mzondi into a passion that she feels for no other inmates in similar condition or even with the same dismal doctor's report. Her sexual desire for Mzondi is unmistakable, often expressed in overt behavior "whenever she bent over him to show him how to operate the new machine." Mzondi is as aware of her sexual desire as he is of the country's Immorality Act, which once forbade interracial liaisons between blacks and whites. Miss Pringle, like Mzondi, is not only fully aware of this law but she understands its consequences because she herself is under the constant surveillance of "the boys from Hospital Hill police station" who "knew she entertained non-whites" and are only waiting to "clamp down on her and her black partner in the middle of an 'immoral act.'"

Although Mzondi is more troubled by his distrust and dislike of white authority figures than by the indecorousness of Miss Pringle's behavior, his most powerful motivation is to realize his dream of renting a beautiful house and bringing his motherless nine-year-old daughter from Eshowe to live with him. It is because of this dream that fellow prisoners once savagely beat and paralyzed him. He cares nothing for the unhealthy, uncomfortable attention that Miss Pringle directs toward him. He understands that any friendly gestures from whites, no matter how well intentioned, should be distrusted and rebuffed at all cost. Unable to appreciate white liberalism, particularly when it is mixed with obvious sexual overtones, Mzondi has rebuffed Miss Pringle's advances many times, leaving her to reel under the sting of "being snubbed by a helpless cripple . . . who should grab the hand of friendship immediately it's extended."

For all of Miss Pringle's self-proclaimed insights into Africans after working with them for many years, she cannot understand what they need to do in order to survive in a repressive racist society. Fearing that Mzondi will again reject her dinner invitation, she unleashes an angry tirade on him, thus exposing the hypocrisy of her self-deceiving claim to knowledge about black people: "What is the matter with you black people? Trouble with you all is you feel and think you aren't as good as white people, or better. Other people trample on you because you are willing to become doormats . . ." Her naïve view of black response to institutionalized racism makes her liberalism suspect and dangerous. It is suspect because her apparently well-meaning welfare sensibilities are driven by an unconscious paternalism and her own psychological needs. They are dangerous because her sensibilities are masked by unconscious sexual longings. Her "conscious effort to win non-white friends" is unhealthy because it arises not from her "abundant sympathy for the needy"—as her testimonials state—but from her dislike of fellow whites, who are too independent for her.

Ezekiel Mphahlele expresses his preoccupation with the realities of the human condition through explorations of the nature and effect of racial separateness and relationships. Mzondi is tragically destroyed by forces beyond his control, forces which drain him of physical, emotional, and psychological energy and drive him to act disastrously. Summed up, the moral here is: In a repressive, pernicious police state where human relationships are circumscribed by inhumane laws which encourage subversion, the Mzondis and Miss Pringles are tragic characters caught helplessly in a quagmire of events which they do not understand or control. How else can one make sense of a legal system which sees fit to acquit Mzondi of theft charges because of insufficient evidence, while simultaneously failing to punish the inhumane crime of savagery for which his useless body stands as crying evidence?

Style and Technique

A deceptively short story, "Dinner at Eight" illuminates the world and nature of blackness in South Africa. Woven into the story are the depiction of the event of an undeveloped murder and the human condition responsible for Mzondi's misunderstanding and deep-seated mistrust of Miss Pringle's motives. It is precisely this shift between the actual event of the murder itself and the socio-political commentary it is intended to illustrate about the frustrations and indignities nonwhites are subjected to in South Africa that constitutes the force of the story.

Ambiguity and irony as well as the direct and implicit commentaries which augment the dialogue between Miss Pringle and Mzondi convey the story's socio-political message without making the story seem strident or polemical. For example, there is a mystery concerning three thousand pounds in payroll money that has been stolen; details concerning this crime are sufficiently ambiguous to leave one wondering whether it is of any moral importance whether Mzondi has actually stolen and hidden this money. Whether he has stolen three thousand pounds or two hundred pounds, would there be a difference in the degree of paralysis that he suffers?

Pamela J. Olubunmi Smith

THE DISTANCE OF THE MOON

Author: Italo Calvino (1923-1985)
Type of plot: Fantasy
Time of plot: An unspecified time in the distant past
Locale: A spot on the ocean, near the Zinc Cliffs
First published: "La distanza della Luna," 1965 (English translation, 1968)

> *Principal characters:*
> QFWFQ, the narrator, an ageless being and a born storyteller
> THE DEAF ONE, his cousin, who loves the moon
> MRS. VHD VHD, a harpist, who loves the deaf cousin

The Story

Old Qfwfq recalls past times when he and his companions rowed out on the sea every month and climbed up to the moon. This was an enchanted time. Only for a short while, somewhere near the beginning of time as humans know it, did the moon orbit close enough to the earth for the group to climb up ladders from their rowboats and reach it.

The first half of the story tells about these moon visits in general, describing vividly the routine: The group would row the boats out to the place where the moon came closest to the earth, some would hold up ladders, and others would scurry up the ladders and grab onto the moon. The purpose of the visits was to gather moon milk, a cream-cheese-like substance composed of such ingredients as "vegetal juices, tadpoles, bitumen, lentils, honey, starch crystals, sturgeon eggs, molds [and] pollens." Because the gravitational pull of the moon was strong, the moon milk had to be hurled off spoons into the sea, where it was collected, and the group had to jump as high as they could to escape the moon's force so that they too would drop back into the sea or be caught by one of the boat's occupants.

The Deaf One, Qfwfq's cousin, loved the moon. Normally a solitary soul, he relished the monthly trips to the moon and was the most enthusiastic and adept at reaching it, retrieving milk, and returning. Qfwfq, who was usually with his cousin on the moon, most relished each return, when he reconnected with safety by grabbing the breasts or hips or silver arms of Mrs. Vhd Vhd, whom he loved. Mrs. Vhd Vhd, however, loved his deaf cousin.

The second half of the story relates the events of one strange night, the last of the moon visits. Most members of the group are unaware that the moon is moving farther away from the earth. On this night, Mrs. Vhd Vhd joins the deaf cousin and other sailors on the moon. Except for Mrs. Vhd Vhd, who seems to have purposely chosen this night to make her first moon visit, it is only after they all reach the moon that they realize how difficult it will be to return. The deaf cousin gets off first, the other sailors do so only by clinging together to combine their weight against the increasing gravitational pull. Mrs. Vhd Vhd cannot get off, so Qfwfq jumps upon the moon to rescue her. They are stuck on the moon for a month.

Captain Vhd Vhd seems pleased to have his wife gone. Mrs. Vhd Vhd pines for the deaf cousin, with whom she had hoped to be stranded on the moon. Qfwfq discovers that his love for Mrs. Vhd Vhd is not as strong as his love of life on earth; he pines for his return. When, a month later, the crew returns to rescue them, Qfwfq shimmies down the long rescue pole as fast as possible. Mrs. Vhd Vhd stays. If she cannot have the deaf cousin, she will become one with the moon, which the deaf cousin truly loves. It is said that Mrs. Vhd Vhd on the moon is what sets dogs—and Qfwfq—to howling at night.

Themes and Meanings

Italo Calvino's book, *Le cosmicomiche* (1965; *Cosmicomics* 1968), in which "The Distance of the Moon" appears, is a set of evolutionary tales that combine a world of fantasy with the equally fantastic world of science. The stories are all narrated by the ancient yet ageless Qfwfq, a protean creature and expert storyteller who has been around through every stage of evolution. Calvino's simple but very human characters interact with an intriguing, ever-changing cosmos. Their struggles occur on both the human and cosmic planes, but they are all struggles of attraction.

On the human plane, the attraction is that of love, yearning, and jealousy. Only the Deaf One seems without the anguish of human relations, yet his detachment from others is the cruel result of his deafness. He enjoys his life through a sensual relationship with the physical phenomenon that he loves, the moon. Calvino presents the Deaf One's attraction to his physical environment as a reasonable way to respond to life. Mrs. Vhd Vhd yearns for the deaf cousin's love. She is jealous of the moon, and she turns to her harp to abate her desire. In the end, she chooses to become the moon, to make herself a part of the lunar body that the Deaf One now will be able to watch only from afar. Qfwfq himself yearns for Mrs. Vhd Vhd with all the passion of an adolescent, and he is jealous of the Deaf One for winning her love. During his month on the moon with her, he discovers that love, for him, is an earthly passion. Qfwfq's response to his predicament is to look to the future; his desire to return to earth suggests that he is ready to move on to other attractions.

On the cosmic plane, the attraction is gravity, and the conflict is between the shifting gravitational forces of the earth and the moon. The moon visitors learn that their places are small and their efforts ineffective in a powerful universe that changes randomly and unpredictably. The risks that they take seem at first to be minor, worthy of a few fast heartbeats and giggles as they jump and catapult to release themselves from the moon's gravity. Only the difficulty of the skinny child Xlthlx, who had to eat up the mollusks floating in the air to gain enough weight to drop to earth, hints at the potential seriousness of their risks. By their last visit, however, they know that the risks are real and the moon is indifferent to their plight; a month later, when Qfwfq is rescued from a quickly receding moon, it is sheer luck that the assemblage of bamboo poles reaches him.

After this time, the moon sets both Qfwfq and the dogs to howling. Those howls resonate with a yearning for lost love and for comprehending the cosmos. All are still drawn to a moon that serves as a metaphor for those yearnings, and the moon becomes divine.

Style and Technique

Calvino begins his fantasy with a scientific-sounding quote:

> At one time, according to George H. Darwin, the Moon was very close to the Earth. Then the tides gradually pushed her far away: the tides that the Moon herself causes in the Earth's waters, where the earth slowly loses energy.

This quote sets the tone for a story in which fantasy and science are inextricably linked. He places his story in a long-gone past; his characters may not even be quite human. Yet he gives them very human qualities: They love, they are jealous, and Mrs. Vhd Vhd plays the harp. Calvino uses irony to suggest that, despite the power and size of the cosmos that reminds humans of their diminutive stature and importance, it is human love and goodness that give meaning to life in this cosmos.

This message is presented in two ways. The first is through the use of humor and play. Calvino sets the tone by suggesting that, on these nights of moon visits, the companions "fell into a special mood": "gay, but with a touch of suspense, as if inside our skulls, instead of the brain, we felt a fish, floating, attracted by the Moon." His descriptions are given with a straight face, but provoke smiles: the "precious muck" that was moon-milk included much refuse, including "fingernails and cartilage, bolts, sea horses, nuts and peduncles, shards of crockery, fishhooks, at times even a comb." It is difficult not to be attracted to characters who would sift out this refuse to claim their precious milk.

The second is through the use of Qfwfq, the narrator. Qfwfq is a first-rate storyteller with an excellent memory of all past life. He tells his story in long sentences packed with sensory detail. He combines these details with wonder, philosophical musing, and a sense of drama. If the Deaf One seems almost unworldly, and the Captain and Mrs. Vhd Vhd seem mundane, Qfwfq affirms the potential of humanity. He has, for the moment at least, both moved beyond his human dilemma and outwitted the cosmos.

Janine Rider

DOE SEASON

Author: David Michael Kaplan (1946-   )
Type of plot: Fantasy
Time of plot: A cold winter
Locale: Pennsylvania woods
First published: 1985

> *Principal characters:*
> ANDREA (ANDY), a nine-year-old girl
> HER FATHER
> CHARLIE, her father's friend
> MAC, Charlie's eleven-year-old son

The Story

Two men and their children—a nine-year-old girl nicknamed Andy and a boy, Mac, eleven years of age—go on a hunting trip in the Pennsylvania woods. They leave Andy's home at dawn. Mac's father, Charlie, objects to Andy's coming along because of her age and because she will be the only girl in an otherwise all-male hunting party. Her father tries to conciliate Charlie by noting that animals—including deer, he hopes—seem attracted to Andy, and she is adept at handling a gun, although in target practice. Charlie is not reassured. They drive to an isolated location in the woods that Charlie and Mac previously scouted out as a likely deer-feeding ground. Andy arrives in a fairly congealed state, because the heater in Charlie's vehicle is defective. Still, she carries a day pack, although smaller than the three men's backpacks, and is to do more than her share of KP duties.

On the first day of the trip, while the three males lie in wait for game, Andy goes off to collect firewood, and she spots a buck and two does moving away. That night she and Mac share one tent while their fathers use the other. Mac teases Andy by baiting her with sexual and other matters, but the girl holds her own. For his part, Charlie has been ribbing Andy about her tomboyishness. Andy assesses them both as dumb. Her father tries to blunt their attacks by defending his "punkin" and "honeybun" despite her nickname.

The following day, Andy walks by herself some distance away from the resting threesome, in whose company she feels increasingly uncomfortable, after being subjected to a concerted assault by Charlie and Mac about being like a boy. Even Andy's father concedes that her mother voiced a similar opinion—given what Andy is like, they might just as well have had a son.

As Andy wanders off, she spots a doe, then quietly returns to alert the others, who hurry to the spot. When they find the doe still grazing, Andy's father suggests that she is entitled to the kill because she saw the animal first, but Charlie objects vehemently. He fears that Andy will miss. Furthermore, she does not have a hunting license. Andy herself is ambivalent, silently praying that the doe will run away. Because of the direction of the wind, the deer fails to pick up their scent. Finally, at her father's urging and under his direction, Andy takes aim and fires at the deer.

She appears to make a clean shot through the doe's heart, but after the animal collapses on the frozen soil, it raises itself and disappears into the woods before the approaching hunters can discharge a second shot. Charlie resumes his complaints about Andy's involvement in the hunt.

That night, Andy agonizes over the suffering that she must have inflicted on the doe. Sleepless, she steps out of the tent, just as the living-dead doe enters the hunters' camp. The animal helplessly allows the girl to approach closely enough to touch it and palpate the inside of its gaping wound. As Andy cups the doe's beating heart, its warmth nearly sears her hand. She has difficulty extricating it, but finally wrenches the hand free. The girl is struck by the horror and beauty of it all. In this dreamlike sequence—which is narrated as real—she dips her hand in the freezing snow to clean it. Even so, it feels weak and withered to her, so she keeps it concealed in her pocket. The following day, as she lags behind the rest of the party, the three men find the dead doe in a clearing in the brush. "Clean shot," Andy's father declares triumphly. "My little girl," he adds affectionately. Even the obnoxious Charlie and Mac are excited.

As her father begins to eviscerate the animal with his hunting knife, Andy runs away. The three males call after her, just as her mother called her to join her in deeper waters the previous summer at a New Jersey beach. In Andy's mind, the wind-blown forest that surrounds her is morphing into a threatening sea.

Themes and Meanings

David Michael Kaplan introduces two children who, while certainly not typical nine- and eleven-year-olds, are nevertheless believable, and their contrasting reactions to the hunt are striking. The younger Andy, although hoydenlike, successfully fights off Mac's and his father's baiting even as, despite her dislike of the pair, she tries to prove herself a worthy companion. Eventually, she seems to overcome her ambivalence about being a girl and no longer responds to her boyish nickname because it is not her real name.

As in several other stories, Kaplan illustrates, implicitly if not directly, the familiar theme of parent-offspring relationships. He does so not only with reference to the two parent-child pairs on the hunt, but also with reference to Andy and her mother. Except for waving them goodbye after the breakfast she prepares on their departure day, the mother does not appear in the story. Indeed, mothers are generally unimportant in Kaplan's tales; they are often dead, gone, or insane.

During the trip, each father shares confidences with his child, trivial secrets to which the mother at home would not be a party. Andy's father offers her otherwise forbidden coffee; Mac's father tells him it is good to get away from the house "and the old lady." The mother becomes a reality to Andy most dramatically in the flashback of the beach episode. On that occasion the woman, gone for a swim, momentarily lost the top of her bathing suit because of the waves and Andy, embarrassed by the event, ran away from her, just as she is now running away from her father and his friends butchering the doe.

In the last analysis, this is a story about how Andy is initiated into the adult world of sexuality and death. At its conclusion, the ambivalent Andy is maturing into the woman, Andrea. The fact that no analogous development occurs in Mac, who is two years her senior, makes her metamorphosis even more striking.

Style and Technique

Adding to Kaplan's suspense about the uneasy relationship that he sets up between Andy on the one hand, and Charlie and his son on the other, is the touch of the mystical and the supernatural. Kaplan weaves such dreamlike fantasy as Andy's mysterious nocturnal encounter with the doe with everyday experience, and this story follows others in this respect. Although he confesses to inspiration by the likes of John Cheever, Kaplan is also reminiscent of other late twentieth century short-story writers such as Robert Coover, for whom there is no objective reality different from what individuals perceive. Kaplan tries to show how the magical and the ordinary coexist with an indistinct dividing line between them, at least in Andy's mind.

The story is told from Andy's perspective; the reader is allowed to enter her mind and share her thought processes. As her story unfolds, her musings evolve from the more simple and concrete—for example, how vast the woods might be—to the more complex and abstract—for example, the analogy between the sounds of the forest and of the ocean—perhaps symbolizing her changing state.

The atmosphere of the forbidding frozen forest, through which the wind blows through the treetops chilling Andy and reminding her of the sound of the breaking surf of the "inevitable sea," strikes the key in which the action proceeds. Nature is not gentle, and the atmospherics serve as both prologue and epilogue to the brutalizing hunting event symbolizing the girl's initiation into womanhood.

Another stylistic feature is Kaplan's economy of words. He finds it unnecessary to broadly describe Andy's father, Charlie, and Mac, but their language is self-explicit. Talking about Andy, her father observes: "She shoots the .22 real good," to which Charlie responds: "Popgun. And target practice ain't deer hunting." Mac's language and choice of topics are more vulgar and crass. The economy of words, however, does not make the characters two-dimensional.

The pleasure of "Doe Season" does not flow only from the particular twist that Kaplan gives it, or from the supernatural that hovers over the events and makes them seem like dreams or, conversely, makes ordinary events seem like magic. Its enjoyment also comes from the suspense that the author creates by analyzing emotion (which determines whether Andy will shoot the doe or not) and by leading the reader into the drama, step by step, down to the last sentence of the narrative.

Peter B. Heller

DOG STORIES

Author: Francine Prose (1947-   )
Type of plot: Domestic realism
Time of plot: The 1980's
Locale: Western Massachusetts
First published: 1990

> *Principal characters:*
> CHRISTINE, the protagonist, a painter
> JOHN, her new husband, owner of a small construction company
> ROBERT, a carpenter temporarily employed by John and Christine

The Story

The story opens with dog stories that are being told at a wedding celebration by guests and the bride, because the bride has a bandaged leg and a slight limp from a dog bite. The dog stories relieve some of the tension in the air—caused partially by the bride, Christine's, pregnancy—but they also remind Christine and the groom, John, of another dog story about their old collie, Alexander. They've both sworn off retelling this story, and Christine thinks that this refusal to mention the story to the guests connects her with John more strongly than the ceremony about to take place. This is no ordinary wedding.

Christine and John's wedding takes place outside, on an unseasonably hot July day; Christine wishes they had gotten married in June, but then she remembers that they had not decided to get married until May. They have been living together for about five years, but the pregnancy seems to have driven them to marriage. The ceremony itself is barely seen in the story, and Christine is glad that it all goes by quickly, in a kind of fog.

Stevie, Christine's son from a previous marriage, was abandoned by his father when it was clear that Stevie had a learning disability. John, on the other hand, is very solicitous of Stevie, and it is his sweetness and patience that seem to bind Christine to her new husband. The story shifts directions during the reception: While John helps Stevie fill his plate, Christine notices the carpenter, Robert, walking to the studio John is having built for her as a wedding gift, and she decides to join him.

Now it is revealed that Christine was bitten by the dog while she was looking for a sink to buy for her new studio, but the search for the sink is not as innocuous as it sounds. She wants the sink because she has been talking about it with Robert and she thinks, because of her attraction to Robert, that mentioning that she stopped for the sink would add up to more than it was, to an irrevocable act. She even feels guilty about stopping at the sale for the sink and believes that perhaps she was bitten because her motivation was not pure.

Robert, too, feels some attraction for Christine, but the flirtatious edge his voice has is tempered by the fact that nothing can possibly come of it. Christine thinks that, because she is older and his temporary employer, this flirtation on her wedding day is innocent, but she also thinks his flirtatiousness makes a bolder claim than John's solicitousness. When Christine accepts a marijuana joint from Robert, despite her pregnancy and her social obligations, the reader recognizes her attachment to him, her irrational—and therefore strong—bond with him.

When Annette, her art dealer from New York, enters the barn and smiles at Robert, jealousy, loneliness, and embarrassment overcome Christine. While Christine, Annette, and Robert talk, Robert learns for the first time that Christine is pregnant, and while Christine thinks about her pregnancy, she reveals that she feels that her life is not just closing down, it has always been closed down. Some clamp on passion and recklessness has never been released inside of her, she believes.

At this point, she brings up the story about Alexander, their collie who ran away for love. This story, which Christine earlier admitted bound her with John more than the ceremony of the wedding, is now revealed as a love story, a story of passion. Christine recognizes the lack of passion in her own life, leaves Robert and Annette behind, and returns to her husband and son.

Themes and Meanings

In her author's note to *The Best American Short Stories of 1991*, in which "Dog Stories" appeared, Francine Prose said she "wanted to write a story about a wedding that was not exactly an expression of joy and hope for the future, but rather of some darker and less sanguine sense of acceptance." "Dog Stories" is darker than a reader might expect from a story taking place at a wedding and the reception following it, because the author focuses on the ambivalence the central character feels and the revelations about her life that she accepts. Christine is not afraid of the undercurrents in her life: She may acknowledge John's kindness, but she is also aware that kindness may not be sufficient to bring passion to a relationship; John may be applauded for his generosity in accepting Stevie as his son, but Christine notes that John also wants extra credit from the friends at the wedding for being so kind.

What makes Christine an attractive character is her self-awareness. She recognizes that the height of summer calls forth her unruly dreams and desires, but she also is aware that desire cannot always be acted upon. She accepts, somewhat tepidly, her relationship with John, not because it is her only option, but because marriage and stability will perhaps be the best for her two children. She would prefer that her life did not feel closed down, but she accepts the limitations of her situation and her marriage and goes on. Christine admits that Alexander, their dog, "was more capable of passion than its owners may ever be," and she struggles with the tension between a desire for comfort and a yearning for passionate fulfillment. The story does not offer any large moral or hidden meaning; it simply examines the multiple levels of human desire.

Style and Technique

In this third-person narrative, readers are privy only to the thoughts of Christine; her mind is the subject of the story. The other characters come into focus in the story only as Christine looks their way: Stevie is introduced, "meditatively chewing his hand," when Christine scans the lawn to see who has arrived; Annette arrives at the party and is introduced by the narrator as one of the signs of Christine's success. The fictional world revolves around Christine and everywhere she looks, the reader can feel emotion: Annette produces jealousy in Christine, Robert awakens her desire, and John frightens her at the story's close with his question about their marriage. If Prose had not allowed us this entry into Christine's consciousness, the story would not have the same power.

The story also achieves power by its gradual unfolding. Nearly every page has a new revelation about the central character and her relationship. The reader only gradually learns about her pregnancy, her ambivalent feelings about John, her attraction to Robert and her feelings of guilt, and the significance of the story's title. The story unfolds for the reader in the same way it unfolds for Christine. It is only in a conversation with Annette and Robert that Christine recognizes that her life has always been closed down. She, like many characters in fiction, discovers something about herself at the same time that the readers discover it. She learns about her inhibitions and her tentativeness in relationships only through telling the final dog story about Alexander; the reader reaches the epiphany at the same moment she does.

What distinguishes this story from many other contemporary pieces is the absence of overt sexuality. Neither Annette, Robert, John, nor Christine engage in any sexual acts in the story; there is plenty of attraction and desire in the story, but Prose keeps everyone's clothes on. She manages to create a story with great sexual tension without providing graphic details. Perhaps that is part of the technique of the story: everything is hinted at and muted in the piece. Christine finds out gradually and almost indirectly how she feels about her life and her loves, and she accepts her limitations with a certain degree of calm reserve. Although Prose uses humor and colloquial exchanges, the power of the story is in what is not said—except inside of Christine's mind—and what is not done.

Kevin Boyle

THE DOLL QUEEN

Author: Carlos Fuentes (1928-   )
Type of plot: Symbolic realism
Time of plot: Probably mid-twentieth century
Locale: Mexico City
First published: "La muneca reina," 1964 (English translation, 1978)

> *Principal characters:*
> CARLOS, the narrator, a twenty-nine-year-old Mexican
>   professional man
> AMILAMIA, his childhood playmate
> AN OLD MAN AND WOMAN, her parents

The Story

Carlos is a twenty-nine-year-old bachelor, leading a professional life in Mexico City. Although his life is pleasant, he feels that it is missing something, a central attraction. One day, while rearranging dusty, old books, he finds a card with a message written in a childish hand: "Amilamia wil not forget her good friend—come see me here where I draw it." With the message is a small map.

This message starts Carlos to reminisce about the summer that he met and played with Amilamia. She was an exuberant seven-year-old child; he was a fourteen-year-old adolescent trying to forget the approach of boarding school and adult responsibilities. He spent his days in a small, enclosed park, reading romantic fiction about pirates, runaways, and heroes who rescued princesses.

Into this dreamy refuge, Amilamia intruded herself. In his memory, Carlos sees her in constant motion: laughing, running, jumping, singing, and playing. Amilamia drew the self-conscious teenager into her orbit, becoming a point of support for his life, a visible symbol of the tension between childhood and adulthood. Carlos at this time of his life was beginning to find truth in books; Amilamia forced him for a time to participate joyously in life as a child would. Their friendship progressed from his indifferent tolerance to acceptance, and then, suddenly, to rejection.

Their last afternoon together they spent in playing childish games—running, making paper boats, and rolling down the hill in the park. Suddenly repulsed, Carlos angrily pushed Amilamia away and she fell, hurting herself. Ignoring her tears, he settled on his bench and resumed reading. She left, returning the next day only to give him the little card with the message and map and then leave without a word. He slipped the card into his book and forgot about it.

Now, fifteen years later, Carlos finds the map to Amilamia's house and decides to follow it. At first refused admittance, he discovers the name of the house's owner, Señor Valdivia, and gains entry with a lie about Valdivia's authorizing him to inspect the house for tax assessment.

A shabby middle-aged woman, fingering a rosary, admits him. In his mind Carlos pretends that he is a detective encountering clues, although he does not understand them: wheel tracks in the carpet, a comic book smeared with lipstick, a peach with a bite taken out of it, a child's blue-and-white-checked apron drying on the clothesline. He leaves, still mystified about Amilamia's whereabouts.

When he tries to continue his tax-assessor charade later that afternoon, the woman's husband appears and reveals that they know he is lying because the owner, Valdivia, has been dead for four years. Carlos now reveals that he is actually looking up his old playmate. Becoming less hostile but more emotional, the man and his wife repeatedly ask him what Amilamia used to be like, but he cannot satisfy them; he only remembers what she did and how she appeared. The couple lead him to another room where the scent of flowers is overpowering. Opening his eyes, Carlos sees a shrine, a child's coffin surrounded by flowers containing an effigy of Amilamia, a "doll queen who presides over the pomp of the royal chamber of death." Nauseated, he staggers out of the house, the old man's words ringing in his ears: "If you truly loved her, don't come back again."

The matter seems closed, but nearly a year later, Carlos decides to return once more, to give the card to Amilamia's parents. Whistling lightheartedly, he is unprepared for the shock that awaits him when the door opens. There is his Amilamia, alive, adult in years but child-sized and misshapen, sitting in a wheelchair, dressed in a blue-and-white-checkered apron that does not conceal the lump on her chest. Her once-beautiful hair has a frizzy permanent wave, and garish lipstick is smeared on her mouth. Only her beautiful gray eyes are unchanged. In the space of an instant she is welcoming, then fearful but still hopeful, then frightened and desolate. The story ends with the father shouting from inside the house: "Don't you know you're not supposed to answer the door? Get back! Devil's spawn! Do I have to beat you again?" Her frightened hands drop a comic book onto the rain-soaked pavement.

Themes and Meanings

A major theme in this story, as in much of Carlos Fuentes' work, is to define the Mexican national character. "The Doll Queen" appears in *Burnt Water* (1980), a collection of his stories set in Mexico City. Fuentes says, "I own an imaginary apartment house in Mexico City . . . [where] you will find the characters of the stories that are now collected here." This imaginary apartment house is like the house in the story that the narrator explores in his search to recapture that past and Amilamia, the symbol of his past. Its dusty, cluttered rooms are like a museum holding forgotten keepsakes. The map he finds thus sends him on a journey, not only through space but also back in time to his lost childhood innocence, in the Eden-like secret garden where they played. Poised for the journey, he wonders which is the true magnet of his life, the garden or the city. The quest for lost innocence and its symbol of the garden is another theme that recurs in Fuentes.

One's innocence is lost in part from suppressing and denying one's past. Carlos, the narrator, is alienated: He is the product of a cosmopolitan education and background.

He has read the best foreign literature, and he lives in a modern urban world of bureaucracy, traffic laws, and paperwork. He is a part of the orderly, rational world of the city. When he visits the house, he distances himself from emotional involvement by pretending to be a tax assessor and then a detective, both symbols of Western rational capitalist society. He is a good observer, scientifically noting details of sound, sight, and smell, but he lacks insight and cannot get involved—the very quality that Amilamia had briefly brought to his life so long ago. He is repulsed by the evidences of the mother's obsolete (to him) religion: her constant fingering of the rosary in her hand, and the room in which the "doll queen" effigy is enshrined. Carlos' alienation has limited him emotionally, as Amilamia is limited physically.

Style and Technique

Fuentes is a member of the group of Latin American writers known as Magical Realists, who blur the boundaries between reality and fantasy. He, however, calls his own writing technique "symbolic realism," which conflates other traditional categories: fiction and history, present and past, natural and supernatural. The narrative is fragmented, rather than strictly linear, and the present and past are jumbled together in the story, showing Fuentes' notion of time as cyclical rather than linear.

The narrator is cut off from his own past, which ultimately cuts him off from himself. His cultural allegiance is international, rather than Mexican, as shown by the foreign books he has read; he has embraced rationality and modernity rather than the irrational, mythical elements of his past, represented by Amilamia. He realizes that his life lacks something, but he is unwilling or unable to risk plunging into direct experience, preferring to remain an observer. As with many Fuentes stories, "The Doll Queen" undermines the surface order of the narration, showing the disorder beneath and implying that embracing the disorder is better than leading a sterile life without passion.

The two main characters, Carlos and Amilamia, can be seen as alter egos, two sides of the same person. Carlos is the rational, orderly, European modern ego; Amilamia is the primitive, intuitive, emotional, Indian primitive id. When he rejects her, he actually is rejecting a part of himself. Amilamia is misshapen and grotesque, emblematic of the distortion and destruction caused when one tries to suppress the primal forces within everyone and within everyone's cultural past. Significantly, the narrator's given name is the same as the author's, and the name is mentioned only once, when Amilamia calls it out at the end of the story. Only Amilamia has the power to name him, and he rejects her.

Myra H. Jones

THE DOLL'S HOUSE

Author: Katherine Mansfield (Katherine Mansfield Beauchamp, 1888-1923)
Type of plot: Psychological realism
Time of plot: Late nineteenth century
Locale: New Zealand
First published: 1923

> *Principal characters:*
> ISABEL BURNELL,
> LOTTIE BURNELL, and
> KEZIA BURNELL, daughters in a rich New Zealand family
> BERYL, their aunt
> LIL KELVEY and
> ELSE KELVEY, poor daughters of a washerwoman
> LENA LOGAN, a classmate of the Burnells and Kelveys

The Story

One day Isabel, Lottie, and Kezia Burnell are given a beautiful dollhouse by a houseguest. After it is placed in a courtyard so that its paint smell will disperse through the remainder of the summer, the children lift back its entire front wall to examine its contents. Its beauty overwhelms them. Kezia particularly loves a little lamp, filled with oil, that stands in the middle of the dining room table. To her, the lamp is real.

Burning to boast about their new dollhouse to classmates, the girls go to school the next morning. They are permitted to bring other girls home, two by two, to see the dollhouse in the courtyard. As girls surround the Burnells during a school recess, the eldest sister, Isabel, describes the dollhouse. The girls crowd in to get as close as possible, but two girls do not join the ring; they are the little Kelvey girls, who know better than to try to approach the Burnells.

The Burnell girls are not allowed to speak to the Kelveys, whose mother is a washerwoman and whose father is rumored to be in prison. Lil Kelvey, the elder sister, is a "stout, plain child, with big freckles." Her younger sister, Else, follows her everywhere, holding onto her skirt, which she tugs when she wants anything. The Kelvey girls wear "bits" given to their mother by the people for whom she works. Lil wears a dress made from an old tablecloth belonging to the Burnells, and her feathered hat once belonged to the postmistress. Else wears a white dress that looks like an old nightgown. She never smiles and rarely speaks.

The Kelvey sisters hang about around the circle of girls who raptly listen to Isabel Burnell. When Isabel finishes her story, Kezia reminds her that she has forgotten to mention the dollhouse's lamp. Kezia cries out, "The lamp's best of all," but no one listens as Isabel begins choosing who will be first to see the dollhouse. Every girl around Isabel adores her and wants to be her friend.

As the days pass, pairs of girls visit the Burnells' home in order to view the wonderful dollhouse, whose fame soon spreads. Everyone talks about the house in their classes. The Kelveys remain the only girls who have not seen the dollhouse, but they sit as close to the other girls as they dare so they can hear its descriptions. One evening when Kezia asks her mother if the Kelveys may come to see the house, she is told firmly that they cannot.

Eventually, the dollhouse ceases to interest the girls at the school, who now amuse themselves by taunting the Kelveys. At her classmates' urging, Lena Logan goes up to the Kelveys and insults them. The other girls enjoy this so much that they run off, skipping higher and running about faster than they ever have before. After school that afternoon, Kezia Burnell sneaks out of her house in order to avoid her parents' guests. When she spots the Kelvey girls coming up a road, she invites them to come in to see the dollhouse. Lil gasps and says they cannot because they know Kezia is not allowed to talk to them. Lil resists Kezia's insistent invitation until Else tugs at her skirt. Though still doubtful, Lil gives in and follows Kezia to the courtyard. The moment that Kezia opens the dollhouse so the girls can see inside, Kezia's Aunt Beryl enters the courtyard. Having had a bad day, the aunt orders "those little rats of Kelveys" away and scolds Kezia, thereby making herself feel much better.

The Kelvey girls rest in a field on their way home. Lil has taken off her feathered hat. They dreamily look over the hay paddocks across the creek. Else strokes the feather on her sister's hat; smiling her rare smile, she softly says that she has seen "the little lamp."

Themes and Meanings

The central theme in Katherine Mansfield's story is the cruelty of class distinctions. Mansfield was born in New Zealand when the country was still a British colony in which class distinctions were rigidly maintained. Her best-known short story, "The Garden Party," also deals with this subject.

The reason that the rich Burnell children attend a school along with working-class children such as the Kelveys is that they live in rural New Zealand, where there are no other nearby schools. These same characters also appear in other Mansfield stories, including "Prelude" (1917). The child Kezia is also in other stories. There are biographical parallels between the Burnell family and Mansfield's own Beauchamp family, and also between Kezia and the young Kathleen (later Katherine) Mansfield. Mansfield attended a rural New Zealand school in which she encountered class distinctions; according to Antony Alpers, in *Katherine Mansfield: A Biography* (1953), Mansfield modeled her fictional Kelvey girls on Lil and Else McKelvey, the real-life daughters of a washerwoman. It is possible that Mansfield—like Kezia—tried to stand up for these girls in school.

Mansfield uses this theme as a vehicle for a stinging portrait of the cruelty that was directed toward lower-class children. This portrait also contains a more sinister allusion to the pleasure that people, children and adults alike, derive from abusing those less materially fortunate. Not only are the Kelvey sisters shunned by their schoolmates, but even their teacher has a "special voice for them, and a special smile for the other children." When the girls at school tire of the dollhouse, they look for fresh amusement by inciting Lena Logan to abuse the Kelveys verbally, taunting them about their future and their father. This makes the little rich girls "wild with joy." After Aunt Beryl abuses the Kelvey girls, shooing "the little rats" from the dollhouse in the courtyard, she happily hums as she returns to the house, her bad mood dispersed.

"The Doll's House" is a disturbing story of a society in which snobbery and cruelty are regarded as acceptable behavior. It is ultimately redeemed by Kezia's attempt at kindness; however, it is uncharacteristic of Mansfield's stories to end happily.

Style and Technique

Mansfield aspired to write the perfect short story and her writing was influenced by the Russian writer Anton Chekhov. Like jewels, her stories exhibit many facets and are complex and luminous. She is skillful in deft character portrayal, creating powerful impressions with metaphor, and manipulating reader responses with a few apt words. Her description of Else Kelvey is an example. By frequently calling the girl "Our Else," she enlists the reader's sympathies: "She was a tiny wishbone of a child, with cropped hair and enormous solemn eyes—a little white owl." In her white "nightgown" of a dress, Else is a spectral image, perhaps a sad angel. She seems to be not quite of this world, and nobody has ever seen her smile. It is primarily through Else that readers experience the cruelty of the other children and adults.

Mansfield uses the doll's house itself as a metaphor for the world of the rich upper class and creates a symbolic language surrounding it. The dollhouse opens by swinging its entire front back to reveal a cross section: "Perhaps it is the way God opens houses at dead of night when He is taking a quiet turn with an angel." It is through Else's eyes that the reader sees into this world that normally would remain brutally closed to a poor child. The little amber lamp that Kezia loves comes to represent what is real, or of real value, in an otherwise desolate emotional world. It is apparently the description of the lamp that Else overhears that emboldens her to ask Lil to go see the dollhouse against Lil's better judgment.

The final view of the Kelveys after seeing the dollhouse, resting together on their way home, picks up on the spiritual overtone in the story. Beryl's cruelty is forgotten. The "little lamp" that Else has seen, a symbol for Kezia's kindness and human warmth that defies the inhumane tyranny of class distinction, is a light that shines in the darkness of the life of this child. Something "real" is redeemed as Else smiles her "rare smile" at the end of the story.

Tina Kane

DON'T CALL ME BY MY RIGHT NAME

Author: James Purdy (1923-   )
Type of plot: Psychological realism
Time of plot: A Halloween evening in the mid-twentieth century
Locale: An unspecified city
First published: 1956

> *Principal characters:*
> LOIS KLEIN, a newly married middle-aged woman
> FRANK KLEIN, her husband

The Story

Lois Klein decides that although she likes her husband Frank, to whom she has been married for six months, she does not care for his last name. Her maiden name, Lois McBane, by which she was known both professionally and socially, provided her with a sense of identity that she feels she has lost through her marriage. What it is about the name that annoys her she cannot say, but clearly it involves the fact that since she is a large, middle-aged woman, the name "Klein," German for "small," is inappropriate for her appearance. How long this discontent has been developing the reader does not discover, but it comes suddenly to the surface one Halloween while she and her husband are attending "one of those fake long parties where nobody actually knows anybody," at which all the guests except for Lois are men.

Several men, overhearing Lois' insistence that she cannot go on being Mrs. Klein, laugh at her. Having had too much to drink, she tells them that they would not like being "Mrs. Klein" either, a remark they find even more hilarious. When one man comments that Lois does not look much like Mrs. Klein, an obvious reference to her size, she demands to know why not. He inquires if she has not looked in the mirror. His remark is, to her, like "the last of many possible truths she could hear about herself," and she grows more dismayed and confused.

As Lois becomes more insistent that Frank allow her to change her name, he grows progressively more annoyed, and once again refuses to change "*our* name." When Lois insists that she does not understand what he means by "*our* name," he takes the drink from her hand and strikes her twice across the face. The men, bored with the spectacle, have moved to another part of the room, where they still laugh over the contretemps. Lois expresses to her husband the ultimate truth she has faced when she says that she can no longer be Mrs. Klein because she is getting old and fat. Frank refuses to accept her assessment of herself, insisting that his wife could not be old and fat. The argument grows more intense until Lois interjects the surprising remark that she will not bear his children, which leads Frank to knock his wife to the floor. The men circle around the couple, staring at Mrs. Klein sitting on the floor, her skirt pulled up to expose unattractive legs, and her bewildered and angry husband staring down at her. No one offers to help her to her feet, and one man cruelly answers her repeated insistence that she will not be Mrs. Klein by pointing out that it is too late for her to change now and that she is too old to be sitting on the floor.

Lois acknowledges that when she sobers up in the morning, she will regret her decision, but insists that she will not go home as Mrs. Klein. After helping his wife to her feet, Frank leaves the party. Lois throws her coat on, not bothering to straighten it, to hurry after him. While she stands outside, children in Halloween costumes pass and one asks, "Is she dressed as anybody?" Frank approaches her from behind a hedge and, when she again asks if he will change his name, knocks her down. After exchanging a few remarks with him, Lois, who has struck her head on the sidewalk, passes out. When two young men who have been working at a nearby delicatessen come by and inquire if they can assist Lois, Frank tells them that she is his wife and she has fallen. One young man observes that Frank does not look like her husband. The other insists that they should call a doctor, since Lois is bleeding from the mouth. When Lois rouses, one of the men asks her if she is Mrs. Klein; she replies that she is not. Frank helps her to her feet, the young men leave, and Lois strikes her husband with her purse. He falls back against the wall, and the story ends with the angry Lois calling Frank a cheap son of a bitch and demanding that he summon a taxi.

Themes and Meanings

James Purdy, one of the most skillful of modern American fiction writers, is primarily concerned with the enigmas of human relationships. Employing the grotesque, even Gothic, but always credible elements that are a hallmark of his writing, he examines the relationship between human beings, often within one family. In "Don't Call Me by My Right Name," he dramatizes the relationship—acutely painful for both characters and readers—between Lois, a discontented middle-aged wife, and her husband, Frank. One of the abiding human dilemmas dramatized by Purdy in story after story is the lack of communication between people, no matter how close they may be in their relationships. The dilemma is here evident in Lois' unwillingness to be called by her husband's name and his inability to understand her objection. It is obvious that Lois yearns for the individuality that was hers before her marriage, when she was a professional woman with name recognition and an identity of her own, an identity as a woman rather than as someone's wife. Her marriage to Frank has deprived her of this treasured identity and her sense of freedom, and the threat of what her husband may expect of a wife—including bearing children—complicates her responses.

The lack of communication, the animosity that exists beneath the surface of many human relationships, is powerfully dramatized in this story. Set among a cast of strangers—all of them men, significant since part of the wife's problem is her unwillingness to surrender her female self to the role of wife—the violent marital encounter takes on an added degree of irony as the unnamed men witness this most personal encounter as if they were watching a circus act or a stage show.

Another thematic element in the story involves the process of aging, embodied in Lois' frank admission that she is too old and too fat to be called "Mrs. Klein" and

Frank's unwillingness to acknowledge that a wife of his is either of these. The expectations of society as to the roles traditionally assigned to husband and wife are underscored by Frank's attitude and by his inability to understand his wife's problem. The ending is ambiguous: Lois, drunk and now injured as a result of her husband's knocking her to the sidewalk, asserts herself not just in word, by calling him a "son of a bitch," but in deed, by striking him with her pocketbook and, apparently, taking control of the situation. The reader is left to wonder about the future of the couple.

Style and Technique

In this brief, tightly constructed story, Purdy relies heavily on dialogue to create the almost painful tension of the encounter between husband and wife. The dialogue draws its power from its realistic tone and the use of repetition to create an effect related to the use of musical motifs. One distinguishing quality of Purdy's fiction is the conciseness of his language, the use of a few words to speak volumes about convoluted human relationships. The use of the limited omniscient viewpoint enables the reader to enter the consciousness of both Lois and Frank, and thus stresses the degree to which this husband and wife are strangers, each unaware of the other's feelings. The consciousness of the witnesses is also incorporated into the story, again to stress the limitations of human understanding in viewing conversations, arguments, and other encounters between people we do not know. Through the eyes of unnamed observers, one sees Lois, fat, aging, drunk, somewhat ludicrous to outsiders who know nothing of her feelings. One's awareness of her view, however, neutralizes the negative portrayal and humanizes her.

Purdy effectively uses atmosphere in this story to underscore the irony of the story. The time is Halloween, the setting a party at which most of the people do not know each other—in short, a tension-filled gathering. Although the symbolism is limited, the name "Klein" takes on figurative implications through its meaning and Lois' reaction to it, and the costumed children, curious as to what is happening in the adult encounter they observe between husband and wife, represent a grotesque metaphor for lack of human perception. In story after story, Purdy peels back the surface of seemingly ordinary events—in this instance a married couple talking to each other at a party—to reveal the grotesque and horrible truths of human relationships often lurking just beneath the surface of the seemingly ordinary.

W. Kenneth Holditch

THE DOOR

Author: E. B. White (1899-1985)
Type of plot: Antistory
Time of plot: The late 1930's
Locale: A modern American city
First published: 1939

Principal characters:
THE UNNAMED PROTAGONIST, apparently a middle-aged urban man
A FEMALE TOUR GUIDE
THE PROFESSOR, a behavioral scientist who studies rats

The Story

This story unfolds within the claustrophobic confines of one man's mind. Its unnamed male protagonist is apparently taking a tour of a modernistic model house in a large city, led by an unnamed female guide. He feels profoundly alienated from his surroundings but also trapped by them. He cannot tell if his unease derives from being in the city, from the building itself (which has doorways that turn out to be walls and vice versa), or perhaps even from the high-tech names of the objects and substances around him. He is certain of one thing, however: Like a rat that the Professor has taught to jump at a certain card to get its food, he has dutifully jumped through all the right doors—only now the doors no longer work.

He cannot stop thinking about the rats the Professor drove crazy by forcing them to deal with problems beyond their mental capacity. When the Professor changed his cards so that the rats could no longer find their food, the animals confronted an insoluble problem. After several painful stages, the rats went insane and were eventually willing to let anything be done to them. The protagonist feels that he has reached that stage himself, seeing in the reflection of his own eyes the same imploring look that the rats had.

In this washable, synthetic, scientifically tested, perfectly self-contained, inhuman house, he becomes convinced that his own mental torment is deliberate. "They," like the Professor, wait until their subjects are completely trained for a certain door, and then they change it. He recalls the many doors that once seemed to lead to the rewards people are supposed to desire. For himself as a child, the door of religion, of prayers and holy-sounding words, seemed to work, until one day that door would not open, leading to the first painful bewilderment. Other doors followed: science and rationality, professional success, and economic independence. At some point, each door suddenly failed to open to the anticipated reward, inflicting yet another wound.

He feels that going crazy would not be so bad, if only he could stop thinking about how every aspect of his life seems beyond his power to affect it. Even the ground below his feet seems to anticipate his weight and rises to meet his step. His mind wanders at random. Now his thoughts focus on a man in New Jersey, who has inexplicably begun to chop down the trees on his property and take his house apart, brick by brick. Is the man doing all of this because he is faced with an insoluble problem, a joy that has ceased to satisfy and become unbearable?

He concludes that "they" will always change the doors, because that is their job. The logical response would be to accept that fact, but that would mean opting out of the game, which is not permitted, at least not among humans. He remembers an old friend, a poet, who spent his life following "something I cannot name." After all the preliminary stages, jumping at the doors finally killed him.

The most painful door, the protagonist recalls, promised happiness through romantic and sexual love. He wishes he could speak the truth instead of allowing himself to be guided through this peculiar house. He is exhausted from jumping at doors that inevitably produce a painful disappointment. Do the rats, he wonders, have a name for what they are seeking when they jump at their doors? He does. He calls it plexikoid, and it is "unattainable and ugli-proof."

Once again, his thoughts turn to the man in New Jersey, to the endless effort it must cost him to care for his house and trees, and to the desperation that he must now feel to destroy what he had treasured for so long. The protagonist senses that he is far from alone in his alienation and despair. Indeed, he tells himself, any doctor can confirm how many people seek a surgical solution to ease their minds—the solution of removing part of the prefrontal lobe of the brain. The ones with the large prefrontal lobes simply cannot bear any more bumping against another door that will not open.

At last, the protagonist carefully makes his way to a glass door leading out of the model house. It opens at his approach, and he almost hopes to see one of the doors from his past. Instead he sees an escalator that takes him down to street level, where the ground rises to meet his foot.

Themes and Meanings

Although E. B. White is usually considered a humorist with a particularly gentle style, he has treated themes as serious as those in "The Door" in several other short stories and essays. Like Trexler, the psychiatric patient in White's "The Second Tree from the Corner" (1947), the protagonist of "The Door" feels alienated from his urban environment, tormented by bizarre thoughts, and fearful, even paranoid, about coping with life. In common with the army officers on the space platform who casually blow up the earth in White's "The Morning of the Day They Did It" (1950), he feels so disconnected from simple physical pleasures and natural beauty that destruction, whether of a house or of human intelligence itself, makes emotional sense to him. Many of the essays in White's collection *One Man's Meat* (1942) stress the pernicious side effects of technological improvements and urban life when such progress comes at the expense of an intuitive understanding of humanity's place in the natural world.

"The Door" is among the bleakest of White's works. Although its protagonist does find a door out of the model house, he still feels helpless to affect his life; the ground still anticipates his foot. By contrast, Trexler achieves a Zen kind of wisdom, as he accepts, at least momentarily, the rightness of wanting something as real but unattainable as "the second tree from the corner, just as it stands." The narrator of "The Morning of the Day They Did It" escapes the total destruction of the earth and winds up among much gentler people on another planet. White himself, despite his love for many aspects of life in New York City, chose to leave the city in 1938 and move to Maine, where he worked a saltwater farm. From there, he wrote about the satisfactions of rural life for his largely urban audience.

For the protagonist of "The Door," however, there is no escape, no door that will work anymore. He can neither transcend his situation, as Trexler does, nor change his life, as White managed to do. In "The Door," White gives literary form to the despair and alienation of modern urban life that had made his personal choice, just one year earlier, a necessity.

Style and Technique

White's third-person narration of "The Door" immediately establishes that the story takes place inside the mind of the disturbed protagonist. Its very first sentence sets a pattern, which continues throughout, of using parenthetical phrases, such as "he kept saying," to indicate that these are the thoughts of a man silently talking to himself. The protagonist's claustrophobic feelings about being inside the model house mirror his entrapment within his own mind. The story's nonlinear structure reinforces the idea that his obsessive thoughts spin helplessly around; he cannot choose a straight path and follow it, for he sees a door that will not open at the end of each one. The seemingly random repetition of ideas and phrases produces the same effect. Nearly everything desirable, from the cards that conceal the rats' food to a beautiful woman's dress, is described as having a circle on it.

The story also makes clever use of language itself. The unnamed female guide smoothly offers logically meaningless phrases, such as "maximum openness in a small room," as though these constitute scientific proof of superiority. The rhythms and phrasing become lyrical, even biblical, however, when the protagonist considers the tragic desperation of the man in New Jersey. White scatters high-tech terminology, words such as "flexsan" and "thrutex," throughout the story.

Technology has apparently permeated modern urban consciousness completely, so that the disaffected protagonist winds up choosing the harsh, ugly, synthetic word "plexikoid" to describe his deepest longings. Even in the privacy of his own mind, White implies, modern man can no longer find any human words to express his heart's desire.

Susan Wladaver-Morgan

THE DOWNWARD PATH TO WISDOM

Author: Katherine Anne Porter (1890-1980)
Type of plot: Domestic realism
Time of plot: The 1940's
Locale: A city in the southern United States
First published: 1944

> *Principal characters:*
> STEPHEN, a four-year-old boy in an unhappy family
> MAMA, his mother
> PAPA, his father, who is considered "mean" and unsuitable by his
> wife's family
> GRANDMA, his mother's mother
> MARJORY, a family servant who shows him little affection
> OLD JANET, a servant who works for Grandma
> UNCLE DAVID, Mama's brother, a bully who believes that Stephen
> needs stronger discipline
> FRANCES, a girl whom Stephen meets at school

The Story

Four-year-old Stephen lives in a chaotic household. The story begins as Papa accuses Mama of spoiling the boy, whom she brusquely pushes from their bedroom. Their servant Marjory calls Stephen "dirty" and "mean" like his father. Soon the family quarreling becomes so severe that Stephen is sent to live with his grandmother.

At Grandma's house, Stephen gets to know his Uncle David, a large man who roughhouses with him and teaches him to box. One day, Uncle David brings home a large box of advertising balloons that he and Stephen share in a game to see who can blow up the balloons and burst them the fastest.

When the summer ends, Grandma enrolls Stephen in school, where he is surprised to discover people who are mostly his size. He is delighted to learn that these other children have ordinary names such as "Frances" and "Edward," instead of titles such as "Grandma," "Uncle," and "Mommanpoppa"—the only people he has known during his short life. There he discovers that his name is "Stephen," not "Baby" as his mother calls him, or "Bad Boy" as he is known by the household servants.

At first, Stephen has great fun in school, but he soon becomes embarrassed when other children make fun of his dancing and his clay cat sculpture. He is particularly eager to impress a girl named Frances and is happy when she accepts two of Uncle David's balloons. That same afternoon, he climbs up on a chair to take down the box of balloons that Uncle David has hidden out of reach. After filling his pockets with balloons, he gives them away at school the next day, thereby increasing his popularity.

On Saturday, Frances visits Stephen and the two of them begin blowing up balloons. When Frances grows bored with this game, she suggests that they buy sticks of licorice to make "liquish water." Embarrassed when he realizes that he has already spent all of his money, Stephen fears losing favor with Frances. He sneaks into the pantry to steal sugar, ice, and lemon juice, which he mixes together in a china teapot, trying to make lemonade as adults do. Knowing that they have broken rules, Stephen and Frances carry the teapot to the back of the house, where they hide behind a rosebush to drink the lemonade.

When Grandma's servant Old Janet finds the pantry in disarray, she sends Frances home and tells Stephen's grandmother what the children have done. As she tells her story, Uncle David finds that his box of balloons is almost half empty. He accuses Stephen of a double theft and says that the entire affair is the fault of Stephen's father. Concluding that Stephen is incorrigible, Grandma and Uncle David order his mother to take him home.

When Stephen's mother arrives to collect him, the three adults get into an argument in which each blames the others for Stephen's problems and dredges up accusations of nearly forgotten wrongs. When Stephen leaves the house with his mother, he indicates his reluctance to see his father again. As his mother drives him home, Stephen sings himself to sleep, quietly expressing his hatred for all those around him: "I hate Papa, I hate Mama, I hate Grandma, I hate Uncle David, I hate Old Janet, I hate Marjory, I hate Papa, I hate Mama. . . ." Only Frances' name is missing from Stephen's litany of anger. Exhausted, he falls asleep, resting his head on his mother's knee.

Themes and Meanings

"The Downward Path to Wisdom" is a symbolic story depicting a four-year-old child's fall from grace. At its heart is imagery that suggests paradise and the Garden of Eden. Like Adam and Eve, Stephen is at first unaware of his own nakedness: He cannot figure out why adults throw a towel around him when he gets out of his bath, as though his body were filthy or evil. Both Uncle David's box of balloons and the "last lemon" in Grandma's pantry represent "forbidden fruit," which the child Frances—Katherine Anne Porter's equivalent of Eve—seduces Stephen into stealing. A revealing detail is the description of the last two balloons that the children take as "apple-colored" and "pale green." When Stephen feels exhausted from inflating balloons, he places a hand on his ribs, as though searching to see if one is missing. The children drink their stolen lemonade behind a rosebush, a secret "garden" from which they are expelled by Old Janet. The story's religious symbolism is further reinforced when Stephen and Frances use their lemonade to "baptize" the rosebush in the "Name father son holygoat."

Stephen's "downward path to wisdom" drops him from innocence and grace to a more disturbing world in which he can have no illusions. At the beginning of the story, Stephen is so naïve that he seems more at home with nature than with other human beings. Described as "like a bear cub," he crunches peanuts "like a horse" and is dismissed by his father as "dumb as an ox." He is not even named until several pages into the story. Nevertheless, as the narrative continues, this innocence is stripped away as Stephen's relatives use him as a weapon in their futile battles with one another. The adult world to which Stephen is introduced seems full of strange contradictions. His father brings him peanuts and then shouts at him for eating them. His uncle gives him balloons and then calls him a thief for taking some. The joy that he feels in giving is regarded as "stealing" by the adults. Throughout the story, Stephen learns that he cannot depend upon the unpredictable adults who surround him. He must keep his own counsel, treading a pessimistic "path to wisdom" that others have forced upon him.

Style and Technique

Although "The Downward Path to Wisdom," like all of Katherine Anne Porter's stories, is told by an impersonal narrator, its events are clearly seen through only Stephen's eyes. Thus the reader is never told what complaint Mama's family has against Stephen's father, or why his parents are quarreling so violently at the beginning of the story. Porter does not present a series of events so much as she describes the effect that those events have upon Stephen himself. She includes no detail that would not have been known to Stephen or understood by him. Certain objects—such as Old Janet's stole, described as "a dead cat slung around her neck"—are specifically characterized in terms reflecting Stephen's limited comprehension.

Porter's style combines the clear narrative technique of Ernest Hemingway with the more symbolic approach of James Joyce. Some critics even regard her character's name, "Stephen," as inspired by Joyce's Stephen Dedalus, who goes off into exile at the end of *A Portrait of the Artist as a Young Man* (1916). Porter's Stephen likewise goes into numerous "exiles." First he is ejected from his parents' bedroom; then he is excluded from their house for the summer; finally, he is sent away from his grandmother's home.

Other critics trace Stephen's name to that of Saint Stephen, the first century Christian martyr who was condemned to death by the Sanhedrin for his "blasphemy." In Porter's story, Old Janet characterizes young Stephen's baptism of the rosebush as "blaspheming."

Aside from Stephen and Frances, few characters are named in the story. This device serves to make the narrative more universal and to represent Stephen as an "Everyman" character, whose loss of innocence is simply part of every person's maturation. The deceptively well-ordered world into which he is born is revealed throughout Porter's narrative to be chaotic, hostile, and marred by petty jealousies. By the end of the story, Stephen is well on his way to adulthood, filled with more than a child's share of cynicism and hatred.

Jeffrey L. Buller

DRAGON'S SEED

Author: Madison Smartt Bell (1957-　　)
Type of plot: Fantasy
Time of plot: Late twentieth century
Locale: Somewhere in the United States
First published: 1990

> *Principal characters:*
> MACKIE LOUDON, a sculptor
> JASON STURGES, a young boy whom she befriends
> GIL, her neighbor

The Story

Mackie Loudon lives alone in her cluttered house in a neglected neighborhood of what appears to be a good-sized town or small city somewhere in the United States. She is a sculptor who continues to create, even though no one any longer stops by to purchase or even to see her work. Indeed, no one visits her ramshackle house, not even her husband, son, or grandchildren, whom Mackie sees only occasionally and then only in dreams. The townspeople find her odd as she forages for anything of interest in the street or shops for her food at a nearby Asian store. She wears shapeless dresses and a man's coat; her hair is hacked into a helmet shape; her skin is like elephant hide; her shoulders are broad and her hands are strong, but her legs are bowed and slightly arthritic; her chin is whiskered, her right eye is green and her left eye pale blue with an unusual tic. Strangest of all, Mackie talks to herself, or rather talks to her two demons, Eliel and Azazael, to whom she has relegated certain aspects of her personality: seeing, judging, remembering.

When work on her latest sculpture is going poorly, she meets a boy in the alley between her house and the even more disreputable-looking house next door. Although the boy says that his name is Monkey, Mackie decides to call him Preston and entices him into her house with the promise of milk and cookies. Even more enticing than her cookies—which turn out to be yellow bean and lotus seed cakes—are the stories that she tells of the Greek myths from which her sculptures derive. Preston proves an attentive and appreciative audience, until Mackie mentions the story of Jason and the Argonauts. The boy inexplicably turns pale, bolts from the house, and stays away for a week.

Before the week is out, Mackie's equally grotesque and reclusive neighbor, Gil, arrives in his customary ill-suited motorcycle garb, "thin as from some wasting disease," to warn her not to meddle in his affairs and those of the boy who lives with him. As Gil peremptorily explains, the Monkey's "skinny little butt is mine" and "no one cares what goes on around here." At this point, Mackie does not understand that what goes on in Gil's house, with its blacked-out windows, is the sexual abuse of children.

The boy does return, but just as Mackie begins to renew their milk-and-cookies ritual, she sees his picture on a milk carton captioned "Jason Sturges of Birmingham, eight years old and missing since. . . ." This time the boy bolts for good, but whether he has run away or been murdered by Gil is a mystery.

The demons that had been silent during Mackie's friendship with Preston now return to assail her for her terrible mistake. Her call to the police only earns her a second, even more violent warning from Gil not to meddle in his affairs. Found dazed on the ground by a stranger, after others had passed her by, Mackie is taken to the mental hospital where she has been confined several times before. She now withdraws even further into herself, refusing to take her medication, to participate in crafts classes and group therapy, even to talk, until the night Little Willa, whom the staff has forgotten to strap to her bed, demonstrates her fire-breathing trick. That is when Eliel and Azazael tell Mackie how she can solve her problem, and Mackie, who is eccentric but not insane, begins another of her miraculously swift recoveries.

Back at home, Mackie uses a mirror to become her own model, and solves the first of her problems, completing her Medusa sculpture. In a way she becomes Medusa, or, like Medusa's slayer, Perseus, takes on Medusa's awful power, with every stroke of the chisel feeling "the Gorgon visage pushing out on her brow as if embossed upon a shield." The rest of her demonic plan swiftly unfolds. She breaks into Gil's house, sees the results of his pornographic art, destroys his video and photographic equipment, and calmly awaits his return. Stunned, first by the wreckage and then by the gasoline that Mackie splashes on him, Gil is finally "turned to stone" when she pulls out the lighter and pulls back her hair to reveal the Gorgon. Gil dies, his house burns down, and Mackie, once she realizes that she will not be arrested, goes home and shuts the door.

Themes and Meanings

"Dragon's Seed" treats several social and literary subjects. The most topical and most disturbing concerns children: those who run away or are abducted from their homes and come to be sexually abused and made part of the "kiddie porn" industry. Another is madness and eccentricity, as well as the social means used to deal, or not deal, with them. Finally there is Madison Bell's use, or abuse, of the mythic method of literary high modernism, which T. S. Eliot defined as the manipulation of "a continuous parallel between contemporaneity and antiquity" in order to control, order, and give "a shape and significance to the immense panorama of futility and anarchy that is contemporary history."

Bell's story is not about any of these. Its purpose is broader and revolves around two general questions: how and how well one sees oneself and one's world; and how one engages the world, a question of concern for every individual and, more especially in this story, for every artist. The answer to the first question is neatly if pessimistically summed up in Bell's description of one of the objects that Mackie finds and then quickly discards, a marble that has lost its luster: "The cloud in it no longer looked like a whirlwind, but a cataract." As for the second, Mackie unwisely withdraws into her house, herself, her Greek myths, and her art, an art without an audience and without a purpose. Even at her most withdrawn and outwardly self-sufficient, she maintains at least some contact with the world, first through her demons, to whom she relegates the task of seeing what that part of her personality called "Mackie" prefers not to, and later the boy, Monkey/Preston/Jason Sturges, in whom the Greek myths live and for whom Mackie's art takes on meaning, purpose, finished form. In taking an interest in the boy, Mackie becomes not only the engaged artist but also the engaged citizen. She comes to stand in marked contrast to her indifferent neighbors in general, particularly to Gil, the artist as pornographer.

Style and Technique

For many readers, the most important issue raised by "Dragon's Seed" will be whether Bell's comic style is appropriate to a subject as serious as the sexual abuse of children. Such readers will undoubtedly question whether the treatment does not in fact trivialize the subject, making it little more than grist for the author's narrative mill in much the same way (those same readers will claim) that Mackie's plight in the mental hospital becomes the occasion for writing that seems stylistically clever rather than socially committed: "She let herself be herded from point to point on the ward, moving like an exhumed corpse made to simulate animation by a programmed sequence of electric shocks."

The language here and throughout the story is vivid, self-consciously wrought, and self-regarding, but never merely self-indulgent. Like the overall deadpan narration, it serves Bell's larger purpose. Although narrated in the third person, the story reflects its focal character's way of perceiving her world. Its grotesque realism is therefore as much a quality of her mind as it is a function of Bell's comic style. Even as it contributes to the story's humorous effect and psychological realism, the fantastic works here in much the same way that it does in the fiction of writers such as Ursula K. LeGuin, as a way to raise issues of social or moral import.

Bell's recycling of myths, on topics such as dragon's teeth, Medusa, and Azazael, and fairy tales, such as "Hansel and Gretel," works in a similar manner. Even as it suggests both a typically clever postmodern debunking of the mythic method and a more-or-less realistic means for representing Mackie Loudon's state of mind, Bell's playfulness has its own serious side. Bell underscores this point by embedding in the names assigned to the Monkey the name of the American director Preston Sturges, whose films, like Bell's fiction, effectively combine social satire and popular appeal. In the story's closing tableau, readers may detect yet another cinematic reference, equally apropos, this time to the sadly comic figure of the Little Tramp played by Charles Chaplin.

Robert A. Morace

DREAM CHILDREN

Author: Gail Godwin (1937-   )
Type of plot: Psychological realism
Time of plot: 1971
Locale: A farm by the Hudson River, New York
First published: 1971

> *Principal characters:*
> MRS. MCNAIR, the protagonist
> MR. MCNAIR, her husband
> A NURSE, her nurse during her postpartum hospital stay

The Story

The story begins some time after an unspecified tragedy has befallen the protagonist, Mrs. McNair, and it is a wonder that she has not gone mad. Nevertheless, Mrs. McNair is portrayed as a happy woman, one who embodies the qualities desired in a young wife. She is neat and cheerful, well dressed, and polite. She returns her library books on time and politely agrees with others' political opinions, even though she has experienced a terrible, freakish thing.

Mrs. McNair, whose husband remains in the city during weekdays and is little more than a visitor on weekends, lives in a seventeenth century Dutch farmhouse that is apparently situated along the lower Hudson River in New York State. There, with her stallion and her large silver dog, Blue Boy, she exists in a peaceful, but somewhat mystical, weekday world, in which she spends numerous hours reading about the supernatural and riding her horse. Science fiction, ghost stories, and parapsychology particularly appeal to her since she experienced her unexplained tragedy.

Through the eyes of her neighbor, Mr. DePuy, Mrs. McNair is observed on one of her early morning gallops on her stallion. Perceiving her as reckless and arrogant, Mr. DePuy, an otherwise kind and decent man, discovers himself wishing for her to fall. Her wantonness distresses him. Mrs. DePuy, however, more charitably recognizes the tragedy underlying Mrs. McNair's recklessness. She has nothing to fear anymore, thinks Mrs. DePuy, who simultaneously pities and envies her.

Although there are several allusions to her tragedy throughout the story, its exact nature is not described until the end. Meanwhile, the reader learns more about Mrs. McNair's somewhat dreamlike existence. As a child, she was prone to sleepwalking. Her parents, fearing for her safety, sent her to a psychiatrist. After the sympathetic psychiatrist informed her that children possess magically sagacious powers, her night journeys ended. Now, as a bereft adult, she derives comfort from the psychiatrist's words.

One evening she is awakened by peculiar noises emanating from a guest bedroom, in which she discovers her son, dead at birth, now two years old and clothed in clean but worn pajamas. His large eyes are the same as before: dark and unblinking. Mother and son do not speak to each other, but she is comforted by his presence. On six occasions during the next six months, she visits with him, imagining for him another life and another mother. She perceives herself as being like her husband, who maintains two separate lives—his weekday life in the city and his weekend life with her in the country. She also has two separate existences, but to her, the day world appears surreal while her dream world is real.

Mrs. McNair does not care whether her son's nocturnal visits actually occur or are simply imagined; to her, the level on which they meet does not matter. Through him she fully experiences the implications of the magically sagacious powers of children. Because of her dream child, she is a happy woman who rides her stallion faster than fear, awaiting her son's nightly visitations.

In the final paragraphs, the exact nature of her tragedy is described. In the midst of a smoothly progressing natural childbirth, during which she is told by her doctor that delivery will be a breeze, her son dies. Her doctor aggressively but futilely attempts to save him. While her husband faints, Mrs. McNair is sedated. The next morning a nurse enters Mrs. McNair's room and presents her with a baby whom she believes is her son. With a profound, religious relief, Mrs. McNair accepts the child and contentedly nurses him. When the overworked nurse realizes her mistake, she is unable to separate the mother and child, who are now both screaming. Mrs. McNair must be sedated before she will let the child go.

Themes and Meanings

On a fundamental level, Gail Godwin's "Dream Children" explores the nature of the real world—that which is quantifiable and explicable—versus the many levels of the mystical otherworlds, including the dream world. It also questions whether the otherworlds are observable reality or mere extensions of insane minds. Mrs. McNair searches for the meaning of the visits with her dead child by voraciously reading about the experiences of others. Through her research, she discovers that night journeys, apparitions, and paranormal experiences have captured the imaginations of countless generations of intelligent, literate people.

She further muses over the nature of reality while observing her dog. Does the rabbit of which he dreams have a separate reality, she wonders? Her search for explanation is an empty one, for her experience is personal and unique, not quantifiable. Finally, she does not care whether she has simply dreamed of her child or whether he has on some level actually visited her. Either way, she is supremely happy in her secret otherworld, for no matter what, she is convinced that her son loved her.

Mrs. McNair is not the only character to undergo a mystical awakening in "Dream Children." An exhausted nurse, after having worked for forty-eight hours during a strike, mistakenly gives Mrs. McNair another mother's child. In her almost hallucinatory exhaustion, the nurse undergoes a profoundly mystical revelation. After seeing the woman and the baby clinging to each other, she realizes that all children and mothers are interchangeable. Neither belongs to the other; one could no more own a child than one could own an idea. For the nurse, however, unlike the mother, the mystical revelation quickly fades.

Mr. McNair experiences an altogether different sort of reality. In the city, he lives with his mistress, a sensitive, understanding woman whom he loves. Nevertheless, with his mistress's blessing, each weekend he returns to his wife, whom he also loves, acting on weekends, at least, as her tender protector. He is acutely aware of his role in bringing about her tragedy and will never leave her. Mrs. McNair is unconcerned by his duality, for she also lives two lives, each separate and distinct. Mr. McNair's mistress, in her own version of reality, compassionately accepts her lover's duty to his wife while presumably living her own double life on the weekends.

Style and Technique
The mysticism and dreamlike nature of Mrs. McNair's life is mirrored in Gail Godwin's prose. Short, incomplete sentences printed in italics that are interspersed throughout the story forcefully convey the tragic, mystical aspects of Mrs. McNair's life. Godwin's precise language creates a surrealistic mood against the tragic undercurrent of the story. Images of a contented young woman are juxtaposed against fervent reminders of a tragedy that she underwent. Twice a detached voice wonders how the woman was able to retain her sanity, thereby planting doubts in the reader's mind. While the story is related from the point of view of a detached observer, it ends, persuasively, again with print italicized, in Mrs. McNair's own words. *"I am a happy woman, that's all I know. Who can explain such things?"* Whether she is mad as suggested and as her husband fears, or she has simply experienced an alternate reality, is rendered inconsequential. Only her visits with her son are important.

Symbolism abounds in this story. Deprived of sexual desire and physical sensation after her ordeal, Mrs. McNair rides in reckless abandon on her stallion, an animal that is the embodiment of uncontrollable sexuality. She rides him fearlessly, not as the demure housewife that her neighbors believe her to be, but as if she is beyond the mundane world, for nothing more can affect her. Surely the otherwise kind father and good husband, Mr. DePuy, would not wish her to fall were she riding a subdued mare, appropriate for a young wife. A stallion, however, best serves her altered, surreal state of existence.

Mary E. Virginia

EASTER EVE

Author: Anton Chekhov (1860-1904)
Type of plot: Social realism
Time of plot: The 1880's
Locale: Russia
First published: "Sviatoiu noch'iu," 1886 (English translation, 1915)

> *Principal characters:*
> THE UNNAMED NARRATOR
> IERONIM, a monk and a ferryman
> NIKOLAY, a monk and an author of canticles, the late
> friend of Ieronim

The Story

On the night before Easter, the narrator waits on the river bank for a ferry to take him to the monastery on the other side of the river to see the Easter ceremonies. It is dark; only the stars are shining as if they have come out for the festival procession, with each of them renewed and joyful, and each softly twinkling and beaming. The river is flooded and looks like a lake. It is as though nature itself celebrates Easter.

Soon the narrator finds out that he is not alone. Not far from him, a peasant is waiting for the illumination. He does not have the five kopecks for the ferry and refuses to accept the money when the narrator offers it to him. Instead he asks the narrator to put up a candle for him in the monastery. He likes it better this way. The ferry does not come, however, and on the other side of the river, the Resurrection is declared. The religious ceremony can only be seen and heard from across the river.

The ferry, whose shape resembles a gibbet, finally arrives. The narrator meets Ieronim, the ferryman, who is a monk from the monastery. The ferry slowly floats toward the other bank, where the illumination has begun. Now the Easter celebrations can be observed from the ferry. A rocket cleaves the darkness and brings a roar from the other bank. The narrator and Ieronim admire the scenery, although Ieronim is sad. It turns out that today his dear friend, the monk and deacon Nikolay, has died at the mass. He was an unusual person: not only intelligent, kind, and sweet, but also exceptionally talented at writing hymns of praise. Although Nikolay had not studied anywhere, he could do something no one else in the monastery could do, not even educated elders and monks. Nikolay wrote the hymns for his own comfort. With loving detail and admiration, Ieronim describes the art of writing canticles. One should possess a sweet, harmonious tongue in order to write them. No one, except Ieronim, appreciated them in the monastery. There were some who even laughed, considering Nikolay's writing a sin.

In the meantime, the ferry has approached the bank. The narrator shares the joyful excitement and agitation with the crowd outside the church. He observes the same unrest and sleeplessness in nature. An endless stream of people is going in and out of the church. The narrator does not forget about Ieronim and his late friend.

In the church, where the elation and agitation are felt more than outside, there is no concentrated prayer, just continuous, childish joy. The narrator sees the expression of triumph on the faces, but he also notices that no one is listening to the choir. Who can appreciate the song of praise better than Ieronim? Why is such a sensitive man deprived of this joy? Why must he work the ferry and mourn the death of his friend while other monks celebrate the holiday?

In the early morning, the crowd and the narrator come out of the church after mass. The narrator wants to have a look at the dead Nikolay, but he does not know in which cell his body is lying. Subsequently, he is glad he has not seen it; he might lose the picture created by Ieronim's story.

In the morning, the excitement is gone, and everybody and everything, including nature, looks exhausted and sleepy. Returning on the ferry to the other side of the river, the narrator is finally able to see the monk Ieronim clearly. No one has relieved him from his duty, and he looks exhausted and sad. Working the ferry across the river, he looks at the face of a young merchant's wife. There is nothing masculine in his gaze, however. It appears that he is trying to find in her face the tender features of his dead friend.

Themes and Meanings

In a letter to a friend, writer Anton Chekhov wrote: "When I recall my childhood now, it appears to me dismal enough; I have no religion now. You know, when my two brothers and I formed a trio in the middle of the church and chanted the canticles . . . the members of the congregation were touched and they envied our parents, but at the same time we felt ourselves to be little convicts." It appears from "Easter Eve," however, that Chekhov genuinely loved the Easter ceremony and its impact on people. He re-creates the heightened and exuberant atmosphere of the eve of Easter. At the same time, the atmosphere is imbued with sorrow brought into the story by Ieronim's tale and his mourning ritual (working the gibbet-like ferry between the two banks of the river), which create the mood of restlessness, anxiety, and mysticism. In describing this mood and in portraying Ieronim and his late friend Nicolay, who had an extraordinary gift for writing canticles, Chekhov is more interested in the aesthetic and artistic aspect of the event and the characters than in the religious ones.

Speaking about his vocation, Chekhov wrote in another of his letters: "My holy of holies is the human body, health, intelligence, talent, inspiration, love, and absolute freedom." In this story, his interest is mostly in human inspiration, imagination, and talent. They are like the rocket in the story that cleaves the darkness and lights up the human life. The narrator, who saved the picture painted by Ieronim's tale by not seeing the body of Nicolay, brings the reader back to the peasant, for whom it was enough just to watch the illumination in order to feel the magnificence of the Easter night. For Anton Chekhov, Nikolay was his fellow writer and Ieronim was a talented reader. Sorrow brought into the story by Ieronim's suffering and the indifference of the monks in the monastery, who did not value Nicolay's canticles and made Ieronim work the ferry on Easter night, becomes the important theme of the story.

Style and Technique

Anton Chekhov creates unity in the story through mood and atmosphere. The mood and atmosphere are created by his impressionistic method of writing, which includes not only the description of nature, but also the portrayal of his characters. It was Leo Tolstoy who first spoke about Anton Chekhov's impressionism. Chekhov's portrayals of nature, characters, and events are like patches of color that, in the distance, result in a remarkable picture of real life. In a letter to his brother, Chekhov wrote: "In description of nature one should seize upon minutiae, grouping them so that when, having read the passage, you close your eyes, a picture is formed. . . . In the area of mental states there are also particulars. May God save you from generalities." As one can see, nature plays an important part in the story. It creates the atmosphere, it supports the human actions. The sky, the stars, the river, the rhythms, the sounds, the rocket, the lights—everything works to create the poetic substance of the story, revealing its meaning. In order to show that the Easter ceremonies are both joyful and, at the same time, restless and mystical, they are observed at the beginning from the other side of the river, then from the ferry, then closer and closer, outside and inside the church. The symbol of the gibbet-like ferry with the reclining figure of Ieronim represents grief and sorrow. The endless stream of people going in and out of the church reminds one of the currents of water.

Anton Chekhov relates "Easter Eve" in the first-person singular. He chooses the anonymous narrator to combine the thrill of joy from the ceremony with the feeling of agitation and restlessness, to infuse sincerity and lyricism into the story, to bring the pitch of the story down, closer to the reader.

Grigory Roytman

EASY TIME

Author: Jack López (1950-   )
Type of plot: Domestic realism
Time of plot: Late twentieth century
Locale: Near the Colonia, perhaps Northern California
First published: 1993

>   *Principal characters:*
>   TONY, a young Hispanic man
>   ALEX, his uncle
>   SYLVIA, his former girlfriend
>   JIMMY, his older brother
>   HIS GRANDMOTHER
>   HIS MOTHER

The Story

Tony, who is about to serve thirty days—easy time—for auto theft, meets with his uncle, Alex, who is on probation. Concerned about Tony's first stay behind bars, Alex wants to give him a quick lesson in fighting. He soon grows impatient with Tony's lack of fighting skills, however, and exclaims: "Didn't your old man teach you nothing?" Tony remembers how his father once tried to get his brother Jimmy and him to spar. They did not show enough aggression, so their impatient father took Tony's gloves, put them on, and beat Jimmy himself. Jimmy got a nosebleed and Tony remembers trying to stop the flow of blood that should have been his.

After Tony finally collapses from his uncle's fighting lesson, Alex reluctantly offers to go back to jail himself with him. He says that he can call his parole officer and arrange it easily, but Tony says that he will take care of himself. They agree to meet at eight the next morning for the drive to the jail.

As Tony goes home to shower and change, he notes the beauty of the place in which he lives. His house faces the sea, and open land—much more in his childhood than in the present—surrounds the immediate cluster of houses. He remembers the stables and a helicopter landing in the strawberry fields and reflects on how the hunting land and the farmland have been parceled off, with tract housing encroaching on the open space. At home, Tony must lower his head as he enters a low-ceilinged room; this reminds him of when he became big enough to be wooed by the same football coach for whom his brother had played. Tony was flattered to be offered a spot on the football team, but by then Jimmy was flying a helicopter in Vietnam, and he himself was spending his afternoons with Sylvia.

Tony goes to his grandmother's house to eat. When he returns home, he finds a note from his mother. It says that she does not want to see him before he goes to jail, that if he wants to be like his father's family, "fine." The note also says that going to jail does not make him a man, and that his mother will spend the night at a friend's place.

Tony thinks of the parties that families once threw for their sons bound for jail. After one such party, when he was in high school, was the first time that he got somewhere sexually with Sylvia. He later stole a car in order to visit her at her college. She called him stupid for stealing the car, and on the way back he was caught. Tony also remembers a Fourth of July when he threw a sparkler on the roof of the hunting lodge. His drunk father proved incapable of putting out the resulting fire, so Jimmy put it out after climbing on the roof.

After Tony goes for a swim in the ocean alone, contending gracefully against the large waves, he telephones the house where his mother is staying and is told that she is not there. He rummages through old boxes, finding the certificate he earned for making the honor roll in high school—the achievement of which his mother was proudest. He also finds the silver star that Jimmy won in Vietnam and thinks about Jimmy's funeral, how admirable Jimmy was, how angry and apathetic about everything he felt after Jimmy died. Only Sylvia made him feel better, but she went away to college and broke up with him.

The next morning, Tony's mother wakes him up, having changed her mind about not seeing him off. She cooks him breakfast. Alex arrives to drive Tony to the jail. As they arrive there, Tony holds the medal in his pocket and remembers how his brother died in an act of heroism, flying back under fire to get his men. The word "stupid" rings in his ears.

Themes and Meanings

"Easy Time" has an ironic title. Tony is going through anything but an easy time. Jail will certainly not be an easy time for him. Try as he may to be otherwise, he is too thoughtful and too sensitive to do well in jail. He is suffering from the grief—with which he does not have many ways of coping—of losing his brother and his girlfriend. He has hurt his mother by stealing a car, and now she threatens him with rejection. His alcoholic father has, in Tony's view, abandoned the family. Tony now faces an unsettlingly clear-cut choice: He can go the way of his uncle, father, and friends—to crime, drink, and being bad—or he can go the way of his brother, girlfriend, and mother—to getting along, finishing school, and being good. Now that Tony has taken another step toward being bad he is painfully confused about what next to do with his life.

Tony faces a problem that confronts all people as they grow up. Additionally, his problem is a symbol for the problem facing all young Latinos. He feels pride in his Colonia, and fondly recalls a past in which the urban sprawl that is emblematic of the mass Anglo culture had not yet reached the beautiful coastal area where he lives. Indications of Tony's symbolic role include his reflections about the new houses, the trash on the land ("We kept it cleaner," he thinks), and such sentences as the following: "Weak lights from the mansions on the peninsula twinkled as if they were stars that money could buy." The culture that is encroaching upon Tony's rural peace celebrates money. The Colonia, for all its simplicity and beauty, does not have much money. Tony understands that he must either play the game (literally, in the case of the football team), go to school, and work, or assimilate in another way, with the cons and terminally unemployed of the Colonia. What he does not understand is his anger.

Style and Technique

Jack López's key technique in "Easy Time" is association. He limits the third-person narrative to Tony's point of view, so it follows his thoughts. For example, after sparring with his uncle, Tony goes home to clean up. He enters a "low-ceilinged room." Having to duck his head reminds him of when he first needed to duck to enter the room. "It was the summer of the tenth grade," and the coach began to try to persuade Tony to join the football team. This in turn reminds Tony of Jimmy, who had been on the team, and of Jimmy flying a helicopter in "Asia." This memory evidently leads to something Tony does not wish to think about—the reader discovers more later—because Tony then thinks of something else. Tony remembers turning the coach down for a reason Tony considers, with some naïveté, "simple": He was spending his afternoons with Sylvia. "Afternoons without Sylvia would drive him crazy." All these thoughts flow from his lowering his head in order to enter a room. This narrative technique is effective in conveying the inner life of a young man who does not speak much about his thoughts and feelings.

"Easy Time" owes a debt to Ernest Hemingway, particularly his short stories about a young man, Nick Adams, who grows up in a small town. "Easy Time" recalls these stories in its setting, spare, idiomatic style, celebratory descriptions of the challenges of physical activity (fighting, sex, swimming with grace against surf, handball), and young hero, who on the surface is laconic although articulate and who has a full, difficult, emotional life.

López accomplishes a difficult feat in "Easy Time." He presents the inner life of one who cannot himself articulate his inner life. The reader learns more about Tony from following his thoughts than Tony knows about himself. Tony is unaware of how his angry grief over his brother's death and his father's incompetence and abuse has led him, years after the fact, to steal a car in order to be rejected in person by someone who has escaped the small town and all it represents—namely Sylvia, who has gone to college. He went to see her in order to show her his new tattoo. Tony has sought unworthiness, and has found it. He seems unaware of the redemption—in the form of acceptance, work, and understanding—that lies within him, but the reader is aware of it. López's narrative implies much more than it says, using implication, association, and the nuances of everyday speech. For example, when Tony's grandmother asks after his father, Tony says: "I'm not going to that house." When she asks about his mother, he says: "She's alright. She's barely speaking to me." Another example of López's subtle use of language is how the narration of two simple acts implies Tony's condition: "He kicked apart the flames . . . and walked back up into the wind."

Eric Howard

ECCO

Author: Ronald Sukenick (1932-   )
Type of plot: Magical Realism
Time of plot: Late twentieth century
Locale: Venice, Italy
First published: 1990

Principal characters:

THE NARRATOR, a successful writer
A YOUNG MAN, a fledgling writer
A YOUNG WOMAN, his wife

The Story

The narrator awakens in Venice, pleased to be there with enough money to do whatever he wants. Happy to be neither a tourist nor a Venetian, he feels invisible. However, his invisibility—the consequence of his profession as a writer—has been exacerbated by recent events: deaths, divorce, and geographical circumstances. He is, in fact, in Venice alone, hoping to recuperate from his losses. His observations of activity in the city (usually made parenthetically) alternate with his narrative about his own activities.

As a water taxi goes by, the narrator goes to a blind shoemaker to collect his shoes. Only after three visits are the shoes finally ready, as the shoemaker has a different sense of time, one that is of another world. The narrator decides that Venice is as concerned with the spiritual as it is with the practical.

One day he wanders into the Hotel Falier (pronounced like "failure" in English). He sees a thin young man with black hair and green eyes trying to collect a refund on his reservation so that he can move to a less expensive youth hostel. Seeing this exchange makes the narrator recall his own first visit to Venice almost thirty years earlier. Arriving by train with an eye injury, he had no money to pay for medical attention. A young New Zealander at the youth hostel lent him the money to see a doctor. When the doctor removed a locomotive cinder from the narrator's eye, he cried, "Ecco!"— which is how the narrator learned the Italian term for "Here it is!"

The next day the narrator visits the Jewish ghetto that was established in the sixteenth century. He again sees the young man from the Hotel Falier and feels inexplicably attracted to him; his presence is somehow evocative. After leaving the synagogue, the narrator suddenly finds himself back inside it. How? It is not that he has lost his way, he thinks, "it's that a certain period of duration has disappeared, unaccounted for, during which you were transported back here in a wink of time, and you are not so much back where you started as back when you started and it occurs to you that the real meaning of labyrinth is time warp."

The next day, he again sees the boy, who is viewing paintings by Tintoretto at the Scuola San Rocco. Although the narrator is no longer surprised by these chance encounters, his curiosity about the boy so intensifies that he finally speaks to him. However, the boy—or young man, for his age is not clear—looks through him so absolutely that the narrator wonders if he himself is visible, or if the young man is staring into another spiritual dimension. Venice is, after all, a spiritual city and a timeless one whose waters offer a reflecting pool in which travelers may reflect.

When he sees the boy again a few days later, this time the boy is with a young brunette woman. The next day he meets the woman and learns that she is an artist and the young man, her husband, is an unpublished writer. It is her first visit to Venice; her husband was here once before, but he then had some kind of eye trouble that kept him from seeing everything that he wanted to see. The narrator mentions that he paid his second visit to Venice with his former wife. He turns to speak to the young woman, but finds that she has disappeared in a wink of time.

Later at a cafe, the narrator sees a lively senior citizen whom he wistfully thinks of as his future self. He also remembers having been in just such a café with his young wife in happier times, when he saw himself as a successful writer twenty years in the future. Remembering who one was going to be, helps to remember who one is.

In the narrator's last encounter with the young man and his wife, he overhears them celebrating the publication of his first story. The title of the story is the same as one of the narrator's own stories. The young man is also telling his wife about his first visit to Venice, when he had a locomotive cinder removed from his eye. Disturbed by these coincidences, the narrator tries to speak to the couple, but realizes that they cannot hear him. He approaches their table, desperately trying to communicate. The young man suddenly stares into space, paling as if he sees a phantom. He looks the narrator in the eyes, dropping his glass in fright. When his wife asks what has happened, he replies, "I just dreamed I saw myself twenty years from now." The narrator now understands his own invisibility as the young man miraculously disappears into passing time.

Themes and Meanings

The central metaphor in Ronald Sukenick's story is the labyrinth, which is explicitly mentioned several times and is metaphorically traced in the narrative. The narrator wanders within the physical labyrinth of Venice's streets and canals, even losing his way once. He also describes Venice as a timeless, spiritual city, a city whose many religious works of art, of transfigurations and ascensions, "signify expanding contact with the other world so aptly signified by Venice."

The lives of the narrator and the young man seem remarkably parallel—an otherworldly coincidence. In fact, the middle-aged writer-narrator walks the streets of Venice, turning the corner to see the earlier version of himself, the young, unpublished or newly published writer. Events from the present blend with events from the past and his two previous visits to Venice. The young man's experiences are in fact the narrator's memories. The apparent confusion of times, persons, and places gradually clarifies as the narrator comes to understand the labyrinth of time. After being invisible to the young man through most of the narrative, he becomes visible and then the young man becomes invisible to him. The two characters approach a fusion of worlds and times, but the various times—for the narrator the present and the past, for the young man the present and the future—cannot coexist simultaneously. Consequently, the one who is aware of the other becomes invisible. Ecco! Here it is. An echo in time, an echo of time, gradually fading.

Style and Technique

"Ecco" exemplifies many of the techniques for which Ronald Sukenick is known—self-reflexiveness, improvisation, protean characters, a disjointed narrative, and an autobiographical touch. Although "Ecco" has no characters named Ronald, its narrator is—like Sukenick himself—a divorced middle-aged writer who has visited Venice several times.

Self-reflexiveness—having a text comment on its own making or otherwise making readers aware of its construction as a literary artifact—manifests itself in several ways. First, parenthetical observations are constantly in the foreground of the physical scenes that the narrator observes, contrasting his own thoughts with the activities that he sees. When he thinks of Venice, for example, "a city so full of thereness your presence isn't necessary," he sees a houseful of furniture floating by on a boat. Such descriptions seem improvised, written as the narrator glances out the window, and break the expected narrative flow. Second, the narrator routinely analyzes his own activity, his own thoughts and reactions, directing the narrative to himself: "You recall yourself . . . you decide . . . you're walking . . . you see . . . you wonder . . . you are content." The insistent use of present tense also calls attention to a text in the process of being constructed, of coming into being as the reader reads.

Although the characters in "Ecco" are less complex—and thus more easily identified—than those in much of Sukenick's work, there is nonetheless a sense of changeableness, of flux, of uncertainty about them that seems almost disturbing, owing at least in part to the apparent lack of traditional linear narrative. Yet, despite parenthetical interruptions and shifts in time from a present being lived by his past self who glimpses his future self, and a present being lived by his present self, who has glimpses of his younger self, a chronological narrative gradually emerges, constructed by the reader's attempts to understand a seemingly confusing text. Sukenick has said that "experience is not prefab. It is immediate, metamorphic, and unpredictable." His aim is not to produce "literature," which packages and fixes experience, but rather to produce writing. Writing "is not different from experience, it is more experience." With "Ecco" Sukenick once again achieves his aim.

Linda Ledford-Miller

EDIE
A Life

Author: Harriet Doerr (1910-   )
Type of plot: Domestic realism
Time of plot: 1919-1948
Locale: California
First published: 1987

> *Principal characters:*
> EDITH FISK (EDIE), the protagonist, an English nanny
> THOMAS RANSOM, her employer and the father of the children whom she tends
> JAMES,
> ELIZA,
> JENNY, and
> THE TWINS, Ransom's children

The Story

In April, 1919, Edith Fisk leaves England for California in order to care for the five young children of Thomas Ransom, a lawyer, whose wife died during the birth of twins. Since Mrs. Ransom's passing, no relative or servant has been able to care for the children properly. Edie changes all that. On her arrival in the family, she serves the children tea and speaks to them in an adult manner. Within weeks, their behavior begins to improve as she stops every tear and bandages every cut. She posts the children's drawings in her own room along with the pictures of her two former charges—Lady Alice and Lady Anne, prim and proper little English girls. The children come to trust Edie and depend upon her.

This relationship develops just before the children's father marries a series of three different women. The first, nineteen-year-old Trish, has little to do with anyone in the house but her husband, except for Saturday afternoons when she, Edie, and the three oldest children go to the movies and immerse themselves in fantasy. Trish leaves after two years, during which the children grow and flourish.

Childhood diseases pass uneventfully and each child begins to develop an individual direction. James leans toward mechanical experiments, Eliza buries herself in books, Jenny escapes in romantic daydreams, and the twins entertain each other. Meanwhile, Edie occasionally reveals something about her own past, but the children fit everything relating to England into their own romantic picture of Lady Alice and Lady Anne.

Two years later, Ransom marries Irene, an exotic woman who fills the house with friends who discuss trendy philosophies, and she redecorates the house to fit her foreign tastes. Once she takes Edie and the children to a fortune-teller, who predicts the usual fame, fortune, and good luck.

By the time that Ransom's next wife, Cissy, comes along, the older children are teenagers. Cissy, an Englishwoman, glories in the California climate and lies in the sun until she blisters. However, as the seasons become drier and she confronts American holidays, her gaze turns eastward. It is clear to the children that she is miserably out of her element, so she too departs. The children discuss her with Edie as they have done with her two predecessors. Edie classifies all the various husbands and wives involved in such remarriages as "poor souls."

After having survived all these childhood traumas and events, the children grow up, appearing none the worse for not having a mother. Edie remains in the house until the twins leave for college. By then, the two girls are married and James has married, divorced, and remarried. Only occasionally does anyone visit. In 1938, when all the children are gone, Edie goes to Ransom, who sits in his study below a portrait of his first young wife. She tells him that because she has no one left in England, she wishes to stay in California. He grants her a pension and a small cottage in which to live for the rest of her life.

Retired to her cottage near the sea, Edie fills it with children's paintings and pictures of Lady Alice and Lady Anne. Each Ransom child visits her just once. Letters come less and less frequently. During the first autumn after her retirement she returns to the Ransom house to dispose of the belongings of the twins, who have been killed in a bombing mission over Europe. She and Ransom speak only two words: "Lovely day."

If the children had written to Edie, James would have told her that instead of becoming an inventor, he is a junior partner in his father's firm. Eliza would have told about living with her archaeologist husband in the damp jungle of Mexico where she looked north and remembered first tasting tea. Jenny would have told about her marriage to a thin pale English student whose accent she adored. She has spent her days making tea in their Massachusetts kitchen.

In the spring of 1948, Ransom assembles his children to tell them that Edie is dying. One at a time, they enter her hospital room to visit. Perhaps she does not recognize them. After their separate visits, they meet outside and recall Lady Alice and Lady Anne, imagining these girls, seven and eight years old, writing "I am sorry" over and over again, then signing their two names. In the midst of this, Edie dies.

Themes and Meanings

In just fifteen short scenes, Harriet Doerr's "Edie: A Life" covers twenty-nine years in the lives of Edie and the Ransoms. Edie establishes the tone in the very first scene when she arrives in the Ransom house and serves the children English tea. When James says that their mother has died, Edie merely nods with English formality and changes the topic. Gradually everyone reacts this way, becoming more and more isolated. No one talks about why things happen or how they feel about them. By the end of the story there is a total lack of communication.

This may be attributable to Edie's exaggerated English reserve, which contrasts with the greater openness of Americans. At the beginning of the story the children are so outgoing that they even tease Edie. However, they clearly need her care and are eager to please her. Her goal is a smoothly running household with properly behaved children, so they act accordingly. On the surface things are calm—with no more fighting, teasing, untidy hair, or untied shoes. There are no outward signs that the children are motherless. At the same time, however, the children are withdrawing: James to his headphones, Eliza to her books, Jenny to her dream world, and the twins to each other. Their father, relieved that all is calm, focuses his attention on his next three wives.

During the chaotic period when stepmothers are in residence, the children need Edie's constancy. In creating an orderly routine, however, Edie sets a pattern of noncommunication that influences the children's entire lives. Both of James's marriages fail, Eliza takes refuge from the world with her husband in an isolated Mexican jungle, and Jenny retreats to an imitation English cottage in a Massachusetts town. The twins die together in Europe. After three attempts to re-create the past, their father sits in his study below a picture of his first wife. Unable to communicate, all these characters are unable to carry on normally with their lives.

Edie also lives in the past. When she retires to the cottage, she hangs pictures of Lady Alice and Lady Anne on the wall along with the Ransom children's drawings. It is little wonder that they do not write to her or visit her, as they no longer need her to tie their shoes, give them aspirin, or settle their arguments. Because they have never talked about their feelings, there is nothing they can discuss.

When their father tells the surviving children that Edie is dying, they visit her. Afterward, however, they retreat into fantasizing how her two English girls would react. They have never dealt fully with the death of their own mother, so their pattern of not dealing with emotions continues. It is ironic, therefore, that Edie's description of people who repeatedly remarry as "poor souls" describes them all.

Style and Technique

The fifteen vignettes that make up the story are written in a cool, unsentimental, controlled style. On the surface, events seem casual and leisurely. Underneath them, however, are powerful tensions that build as the story moves toward its ending. To maintain this tension, Harriet Doerr carefully chooses just what information to disclose. Edie's cool exterior, for example, hides much repressed emotion. Glimpses of her past reveal that two brothers died and that a love was lost to "a girl with red curly hair." When the Ransom children press for more information about this girl, Edie says only that she worked at a pub. She proceeds to describe the pub, allowing the children to visualize it as the American stereotype of an English pub. Her cool, clear, factual language masks the emotion behind what happened to the romance. Nevertheless, the tension created by this unresolved conflict remains.

As the story progresses, more and more lies beneath the controlled dialogue. When Ransom recalls Edie to the house to sort through the twins' clothes and toys after they die in the war, all they can say to each other is "Lovely day." It is a tense moment because all feelings that surround two lifetimes of death and loss are near the surface. If they were to say more, the surface calmness and their lives would shatter.

It is appropriate that in the final scene in the hospital, Doerr describes Edie impersonally: "She had started to be a skeleton. Her skull was pulling her eyes in." At this moment, with a lifetime of unspoken feelings, there is almost nothing to say. Doerr's dialogue reveals that the children even lack the words themselves and must put them in the mouths of prim and proper Lady Alice and Lady Anne. Their "I am sorry" ironically reveals more than any of them can express. The tension created by Doerr's technique leaves the reader with a chillingly cold feeling of isolation and loneliness, enhancing the theme of the story.

Louise M. Stone

EDITHA

Author: William Dean Howells (1837-1920)
Type of plot: Social realism
Time of plot: 1898
Locale: Balcom's Works, New York
First published: 1905

> *Principal characters:*
> EDITHA BALCOM, a pretty young woman, eager for war but ignorant
>   of its consequences
> GEORGE GEARSON, her fiancé, who opposes war
> MRS. GEARSON, George's widowed mother

The Story

An impressionable young woman, Editha bases her sentimental views about war on the yellow journalism that she reads in the current newspapers. She insists that her fiancé, George Gearson, a conscientious objector, go to fight in the Spanish-American War. She is ecstatic that war is being declared and cannot understand his dislike for war and his unwillingness to fight in a war. She believes that a man who wants to win her must do something to deserve her. Now is his chance, since the Spanish-American War has been declared. Editha joyfully repeats jingoistic newspaper phrases to George, but he remains ironic, thoughtful, and rational. When George leaves Editha's presence after war has been declared, Editha's mother says that she hopes that George will not enlist, but Editha hopes that he will. Editha puts her engagement ring and various mementos into a package with a letter to George telling him to keep them until he enlists. She decides to keep the package for a while in case George does the right thing. George returns to the Balcom household that evening with the news that he has led the pro-war speakers at the town meeting and will be the captain of the local volunteers.

Editha gives George her letter as he leaves, to show him how serious she is about the war. She tells him that war is in the order of Providence: There are no two sides about war; there is nothing now but their country. George remains silent after Editha's words, musing and pensive. Editha brings him a glass of lemonade and calls the war a sacred war, a war for liberty and humanity. Yet she notices a strange thing in men; they seem to feel bound to do what they believe, and not think a thing is finished when they say it, as women do. George muses that he should have been a preacher after all, and he asks Editha to help his widowed mother, who opposes war, if he is killed. Editha writes to Mrs. Gearson, who is not well enough to reply.

Word comes that George is dead, killed in one of the first battles. Editha becomes ill but does not die. She eventually goes with her father to Iowa to see Mrs. Gearson, who surprises her with her cold bitterness and irony. Mrs. Gearson derides Editha's eagerness to send George off to kill other young men and Editha's assumption that

George would suffer only some trifling, glamorous wound and return to her in glory. Mrs. Gearson ends by saying she was glad George was killed before he could kill some other mother's son, and she attacks Editha for wearing mourning clothes. Instead of being aware of the reality of war and its consequences, Editha had been swept up by the sentimentality of war and the glamour and escapism of fighting a war in a foreign land.

That summer, a visiting lady painter consoles Editha. She says that the war was good for the country, that Editha's behavior was exemplary, and that Mrs. Gearson's behavior was vulgar. At this final word, Editha's misery falls away and she begins to live once again in the ideal.

Themes and Meanings

The subject of "Editha," one of William Dean Howells' most successful and best-known short stories, is war. Howells was very much opposed to war and especially the Spanish-American War, which he considered an imperialistic war. He shows his dislike in his portrayal of Editha, a thoughtless, selfish young woman, idealistic but ignorant of the consequences of war.

"Editha," which questions what constitutes a justifiable war, is a tale whose brevity belies its weight. The story impales Editha, who embodied all the nonsense about the heroic romanticism of war and whose false sense of values drove her unfortunate fiancé to a premature death in a questionable war.

Editha's egotism and ignorance led to the suffering of many people. Her fixation of belief about the correctness, indeed the necessity, of war impelled her pacifist fiancé to act against his beliefs and convictions about the supremacy of world peace, and engage in what he feared and detested most, battling and possibly even killing other human beings. George said it was not this war alone, although this war seemed peculiarly wanton and needless. Every war was so stupid that it made him feel sick. His total love for Editha, however, led him to act against his principles. When he went to the town meeting the day war was declared, he had intended to sprinkle cold water on the enthusiasm of the young men who were of the age to be soldiers. In the confusion and drinking of toasts, people called his name, the men adored him, and, after everyone had volunteered, they elected him their captain.

Both of the central men in the story, George and Editha's father, agreed that the Spanish-American War would not amount to much in terms of the length of the war and the loss of lives in battle. They were both mistaken, however, in assuming the war would be a "walkover," since George himself dies in one of the first skirmishes. Those who took the war lightly were proven wrong.

Style and Technique

William Dean Howells was capable of strong artistry and irony, as one sees in this bitter short story. In the United States, at the end of the nineteenth century, there was a revival of interest in the historical romance, which overwhelmed the realistic movement. People had tired of the commonplace and photographic in literature. They wanted imagination, and the general reading public was interested in swashbucklers and their swords. Howells complained that these historical romances, with their taste for strange lands, adventure, and sentiment, were poverty-stricken in ideas. Howells theorized that this return of interest in the "romanticistic," in the sentimentalism that took the form of the historical romance, represented an unconscious revulsion from the shameless imperialism of the Spanish-American War, an effort to get away from the facts of the odious present.

Howells wrote "Editha" in an effort to explode the sentimentalism that led to an interest in the historical romance. Editha blindly and ignorantly believed in the heroic romanticism of war and was totally oblivious to the real consequences of battle. At this time in history, there was a shift in focus from individualism to natural and social forces that seemed to enslave humanity. Émile Zola epitomized this naturalism. Despite the fact that authors were writing about natural and social forces in the hope that people would improve and reform society, by the turn of the century, people were buying superficial and shallow novels by the millions. By 1900, the historical romance not only had captured the general reading public, but also, critics asserted, had reduced the level of culture in the United States. Through his ironic indictment of Editha, Howells criticizes the sentimentality of the day, which counteracted the realism in which he believed.

Linda Silverstein Gordon

EMPEROR OF THE AIR

Author: Ethan Canin (1960-   )
Type of plot: Psychological realism
Time of plot: The 1970's to 1980's
Locale: A small town in California
First published: 1984

Principal characters:
THE UNNAMED NARRATOR, a sixty-nine-year-old
high school science teacher
MR. PIKE, his next-door neighbor
KURT, Mr. Pike's son

The Story

The unnamed narrator announces that he is sixty-nine years old, a high school biology and astronomy teacher, married with no children, and a recent heart attack victim. Vera, his energetic wife, is off on one of her frequent walking trips. Although the narrator and Vera have traveled widely throughout their lives, his failing health has prevented him from any serious strenuous activity. He must keep with him at all times a small vial of nitroglycerine pills in case his chest begins to tighten.

The narrator's next-door neighbor, Mr. Pike, comes to his house to inform him that the giant, 250-year-old elm tree on the narrator's land is infested with insects, a fact which the narrator has already discovered. Pike insists that the tree must be cut down to protect the three young elm trees that grow in his front yard. A week later, Pike reappears, this time with a chain saw in hand, arguing that his elms are young and he cannot let them become infested. The narrator replies that his tree is more than two hundred years old.

The narrator calls a man at a tree nursery who tells him that the insects do not necessarily mean that the ancient tree will die or that it is dying, although it could die if it is not strong. There is hope. After several confrontations with Pike, who suggests that they plant another tree in its place, the narrator reminds him that he had lived in this house all of his life, and the tree was ancient when he climbed it as a boy. Later, the narrator meditates on certain experiences in his life that had always deeply moved him: crossing the Mississippi River as a child, listening to Beethoven Quartets at a concert and, most of all, looking up at the stars at night.

After a successful attempt to stop the relentless line of insects, the narrator finds himself descending into his youthful memories and the key role that this magnificent elm tree played in his life. He recalls the time when his neighborhood had been threatened by a fire that raged through the town. His father took charge of their neighborhood and helped everyone move out. The young narrator climbed up into the highest part of the elm tree—the most dangerous act of his life—and there gained a visual and spiritual perspective that he had never experienced before: He beheld nature in one of its most sublime moments.

The narrator returns to a problematic present when he discovers that the insects have returned. Pike's renewed threat forces him into taking drastic steps to preserve the tree. He decides to transfer some of the insects from his tree to the three elms in Pike's front yard, reasoning that if his neighbor's trees were infested, they would probably still live, and then Pike would no longer want to chop down his old tree.

The aging high school teacher prepares for a night attack on Pike's domain. He blackens his face with shoe polish, dresses in dark clothes, and begins his dangerous journey. On his way to Pike's yard, he crawls across the bomb shelter that Pike built. Finding the hatch unlocked, he descends into its womblike interior. There he muses over Pike's character and about how fearful he must be in wanting to destroy the ancient elm and in building a bomb shelter.

As the narrator emerges from the shelter, Pike and his son, Kurt, come out of the house and into the beautiful summer night. The narrator sees them both pointing at the sky. Flashbacks of his own father teaching him the mythic names behind the magnificent stellar constellations converge with images of himself as an astronomy teacher giving his suddenly interested students the same information. What he hears, though, stuns him. Pike is telling Kurt about the stars, but he does not know the proper names; he is making up his own mythic version. "These," he said, "these are the Mermaid's Tail, and south you can see the three peaks of Mount Olympus, and then the sword that belongs to the Emperor of the Air." The narrator realizes that Pike has actually described the bright tail of Cygnus and the neck of Pegasus. The narrator then observes father and son go back into the house to watch television. Observing the paternal affection that Pike shows Kurt deeply moves the narrator. "Every so often when they laughed at something on the screen, he moved his hand up and tousled Kurt's hair, and the sight of this suddenly made me feel the way I do on the bridge across the Mississippi River."

That gesture of love restores the narrator's hope, so he decides not to infest Pike's trees with insects. Instead he sits up all night staring into the glorious stellar constellations with awe and gratitude. When the paperboy appears at dawn, the narrator asks him to do something for him. When the curious boy asks what, he asks him to put down his bicycle and look up at the stars.

Themes and Meanings

The principal theme that unifies all the various elements of this multifaceted story is hope. Ethan Canin clearly announces that theme at the conclusion of the first paragraph: "I now think that hope is the essence of all good men." The word "hope" recurs three other times during the course of the narrative, and always at the most crucial moments. What mystifies the narrator most about the bully, Mr. Pike, is the depth of his cynicism, a condition that demonstrates his utter lack of hope and forces him to live in a permanent state of despair. Pike (whose name derives from the words "pike," an aggressive instrument of attack, and "piker," a petty or stingy person) anticipates that his young elms will be infested and insists on cutting down the ancient tree in the narrator's yard. Pike's vision is so dark that it allows for virtually no hope, and the narrator labels him early in the story as a doomed and hopeless man. When the narrator descends into Pike's bomb shelter, he palpably experiences the cynicism in the very structure of the building. Once he observes the bleak Pike becoming human and showing love for Kurt, the narrator begins to sense that Pike may be human after all. The major threshold experience that the narrator undergoes takes place when he observes Pike teaching Kurt about the heavens and the stellar constellations. Pike does not know the proper names for those magnificent configurations, so he creates his own—an act that overwhelms the narrator and makes him rethink his attitude toward the man. Indeed, the story's title is one of Pike's fabrications in his awkward attempt to reveal to his son the sublime order of the cosmos. The inestimable beauty of the stars pierces even Pike's emotional armor, an accomplishment that restores a sense of hope to the nearly despairing narrator: "How could one not hope here? . . . Miracles . . . Anybody who has seen a cell divide could have invented religion." Seeing Pike teaching his son what the narrator's father taught him, and what the narrator has taught his students all of his professional life, he discovers himself in Pike.

Style and Technique

The most effective technique that Ethan Canin employs in this carefully wrought story is his artful use of flashbacks and symbolism, particularly in regard to the historical significance of the ancient elm tree in the young narrator's childhood. The tree takes on a mythic dimension as the tree of knowledge as it becomes the symbolic agent of revelation for both the youthful and the aging narrator. The tree becomes an instrument for gaining perspective—for learning not only about the world but also, equally important, about himself. The tree also becomes the controlling metaphor for the entire story, in that it ties together all the various branches of the narrative: the narrator's youth, the focus of conflict between Pike and the narrator, and a natural object that transcends the boundaries of time and mortality. It is, in a sense, a modernized version of the mythic Tree of Knowledge in Eden, because it becomes the medium through which the narrator more deeply understands himself, his past, and the possibilities of hope in what he had presumed was an irredeemable world.

Patrick Meanor

THE END OF OLD HORSE

Author: Simon J. Ortiz (1941-)
Type of plot: Social realism
Time of plot: The 1950's
Locale: Acoma Reservation, New Mexico
First published: 1974

> *Principal characters:*
> THE NARRATOR, a Native American boy
> GILLY, his younger brother
> TONY, an adult neighbor
> OLD HORSE, Tony's dog

The Story

The narrator, a young Acoma Indian boy, and his brother Gilly are in the habit of visiting their neighbor Tony during the long summer days that pass in much the same uneventful way, week in and week out. Nothing, he thinks, ever happens in the summer, so he expects nothing unusual to happen on one particular day when he and Gilly wander by Tony's place.

Tony has tied up his dog, Old Horse, which chews on the rope, snarling to get free. Feeling no sympathy for the dog, the boys do not equate its desire for freedom with their own; they only laugh and tell Tony that his dog "is going nuts." Tony, busy with chores, replies that Old Horse is a "dumb dog," and Gilly agrees.

The boys next go to the creek, where they have a good time playing. They try to chase trout upstream to a trap they have made, but this day they have no luck. As they prepare to go home, Tony arrives. Not smiling or joking as he usually does, he tells them that Old Horse has choked to death while trying to break free. Although the boys felt no particular affection for the dog, the news of its death evokes unexpected emotional reactions, which they try to hide. When the narrator suggests that perhaps Tony should not have tied up the dog, Tony erupts with anger, pushing him into bushes and frightening him. A moment later, however, Tony picks him up, brushes him off, and apologizes.

The boys start home, and Gilly begins to cry. The narrator does not know what to say except to repeat that Tony should not have tied up Old Horse. He, too, is about to cry, so he challenges Gilly to a race, but Gilly continues sobbing. After saying "The hell with you," the narrator runs by himself until his lungs hurt "more than the other hurt." His exhaustion makes him so sick that he goes to the side of the road to vomit.

By the time that Gilly catches up, he has stopped crying, and the narrator apologizes for telling him to go to hell. The boys arrive home late for dinner. After they sit down, their father asks what Tony is doing these days. Gilly replies, "Tony choked Old Horse to death, hellfire." The mother warns Gilly not to use that kind of language. The narrator does not want to talk about it and remains silent.

Themes and Meanings

Simon J. Ortiz's deceptively simple story provides the vehicle for a penetrating analysis of two children's first encounter with loss and of adult strategies for coping with grief and guilt. Old Horse's death is so unexpected that it takes everyone by surprise. Neither boy has developed a strategy for dealing with the losses and diminutions that come unexpectedly; nor, as it happens, has Tony. When the narrator says aloud what Tony has merely been thinking—that he should not have tied up the dog—Tony angrily lashes out in order to mask his grief and feelings of guilt. On their way home, the boys cannot discuss what has happened; both try to hold back the tears that they believe would be an inappropriate and "unmanly" reaction to a dog's death. Much of the boys'—and Tony's—physical and psychic energy is expended in the effort to act like "men," which means keeping silent, hiding emotions, and pretending to be unmoved by loss. Ortiz shows how the masking of grief can result in a lashing out at others that may be inappropriate and even cruel and brutal.

At the end of the story, the mother responds to Gilly's wrenching announcement of Old Horse's death with an irrelevant rebuke for his use of the word "hellfire," language he uses to demonstrate his "manliness." The father invokes his own posture of manliness by remaining silent, depriving the boys of the opportunity to develop appropriate strategies for dealing with loss and, by his example, seeming to validate their dysfunctional and repressive responses. In this world, there can be no sharing of grief, not even any outward acknowledgment of it. The adults are no wiser or better prepared to cope with loss than the boys are, and the ideas about "manliness" shared by the male characters are revealed as immature and unworthy.

Ortiz also presents a wonderfully subtle and understated commentary on the freedom of youth. This theme is developed primarily through the contrast between the freedom that the two boys enjoy and the confinement to which the dog is subjected. The boys, who never realize that they unconsciously identify themselves with Old Horse, are free to spend their days as they wish, visiting neighbors, wandering down to the creek, unfettered except for the injunction against cursing that their mother tries to enforce—against the example of the adult males—and which the boys recognize as her attempt to confine them to childhood.

The dog, on the other hand, is tied up, and his inability to adapt himself to confinement results in his choking himself to death. All creatures, including boys, should be free; confinement means death, if not to the body then to the spirit. However, Ortiz implies that a responsibility goes with freedom, and Old Horse has not shown himself sufficiently responsible to be free. The boys, too, seek freedom, not just physical freedom but also the freedom to use "cuss words" as Tony uses them, and they chafe at the restraint imposed by their mother on their exercise of language that will make them feel "manly." It is, Ortiz implies, through maturity and responsibility that one earns freedom.

Ortiz also uses Old Horse's death to comment on how the crucially important and formative events of people's lives—such as one's first encounter with death—come about without warning. They give one no opportunity to prepare, to anticipate, and thereby to steel oneself for what will come, just as the boys have no opportunity to prepare themselves for news of Old Horse's death. Instead, one is left with the struggle to formulate a response to what one never expects to happen; out of that struggle and under the pressure of the immediate trauma of events, the person that one will become is shaped by forces only dimly glimpsed and far beyond one's ability to control. As the narrator says, "I used to wonder what was the use for important things to happen when it was too late to do anything about them, like to jump out of the way or to act differently or to not think so much about them. But it never worked out like that."

Style and Technique

Ortiz makes effective use of the first-person point of view in this story. His style is appropriate to the young boy whose experience is the subject, and who, like Ortiz himself, is an Acoma Indian. His diction is simple, his sentences short and clear. However, within these restrictions Ortiz creates subtle and perceptive effects, as in the following passage: "Gilly was pretty silent, and I knew he was either crying or about to. I tried to take a sneak look, but I knew he'd notice and be angry with me, so I didn't." The diction in phrases such as "pretty silent" and "take a sneak look" is simple, but the insight that a "man" must ignore the tears of another "man" in order to allow the other to preserve his façade of manliness is deftly presented.

Because much of the meaning of the story lies beyond the limited understanding of the inexperienced narrator, it must be implied. Therefore, Ortiz carefully establishes structural parallels and contrasts to suggest those meanings that lie beyond his narrator's ability to verbalize. By using such a narrator, Ortiz involves the reader in the process of understanding the events of the narration, and the fact that the characters are American Indians does not, in this story, constitute any obstacle to that understanding. The characters and events are universal and thereby emphasize commonalities rather than the differences that are often emphasized in fiction by Native American writers.

Dennis Hoilman

ENEMIES

Author: Anton Chekhov (1860-1904)
Type of plot: Psychological realism
Time of plot: Late nineteenth century
Locale: Russia
First published: "Vragi," 1887 (English translation, 1903)

> *Principal characters:*
> KIROLOV, a small-town doctor
> ABOGUIN, a wealthy man

The Story

A six-year-old child—the only son of Kirolov, an aging doctor, and his wife, who cannot expect to have another child—has died of diphtheria. Just as the parents are beginning to succumb to grief, the doorbell rings. Leaving his wife beside the dead child's bed, Kirolov goes to the door. There he finds a man who is so distraught that he can hardly speak. After the man manages to introduce himself as Aboguin, he says that his wife has collapsed and that he believes her to be dying of heart failure. Since he has no inkling of what has just happened to Kirolov's family, Aboguin assumes that the doctor will, as a matter of course, come with him immediately. Although the doctor is still in shock, he pulls himself together enough to explain why he cannot go. Aboguin tries to be sympathetic, but points out that Kirolov is the only doctor in the area, and without his help, his wife almost certainly will die.

While Aboguin waits in the hallway, Kirolov wanders aimlessly about his house, looking at a book, sitting down for a time in his study, and finally ending up in the bedroom, where his wife is still prostrate beside the body of their dead child. After standing there for some minutes, Kirolov returns to the hall, where Aboguin is still waiting for him. Again, Aboguin insists on the doctor's going to his wife; again, Kirolov refuses. When Aboguin reminds Kirolov of his ethical responsibility and promises that it will take no more than an hour to make the trip, the doctor agrees to go. Shortly after they set off in Aboguin's carriage, Kirolov thinks once more of his wife, and asks Aboguin to stop. Aboguin ignores his outburst, and the coach speeds on through the night.

When the carriage finally stops, Kirolov sees an imposing, brightly illuminated house. After the men go into the house, however, they are met with total silence. At first, Aboguin takes this to be a good sign; surely, he says, his wife cannot have died. Leaving the doctor in a luxurious drawing room, Aboguin goes to find out what has happened. Soon he returns with the news that his wife is missing. Her collapse was evidently merely a ploy to get her husband out of the house; as soon as Aboguin left, she eloped with her husband's friend, who had stayed in the house with her. Aboguin is devastated, but Kirolov cannot think of anything but his own grief. When Aboguin launches into a heartfelt speech about what he sees as the tragedy of his life, Kirolov's indifference changes to anger, and he launches into a nasty verbal attack. Soon the two men are shouting insults at each other. When they part, it is as the bitterest of enemies.

As a result of this confrontation, Aboguin gives way to his emotions, fires all of his servants, and rushes off to complain to everyone he knows, thereby making a fool of himself. Kirolov goes home with a new hatred of the upper classes that will be with him as long as he lives.

Themes and Meanings

"Enemies" reflects Anton Chekhov's view of life as essentially ironic. Much of what happens to human beings, Chekhov believes, lies beyond their control. For example, Aboguin arrives on Kirolov's doorstep at the worst possible moment, when the doctor is exhausted and overcome by his own personal grief. As Aboguin comments, it is hard to know whether this unfortunate juxtaposition of events, the boy's death and the woman's apparent illness, should be ascribed to coincidence or to the workings of fate. When the two men discover the truth about Aboguin's wife, the situation becomes even more ironic. One is not surprised that more than one person in an area is gravely ill at the same time; however, the wife and her lover must have planned their flight well in advance. Given all the times when she could feign her attack and send her husband for a doctor, it is almost uncanny that she chooses this particular night to do so. No wonder Kirolov speculates that it all may be a cosmic joke at his expense.

From attributing the unhappy conjunction of events to fate, however, Kirolov proceeds to place the blame on Aboguin. As Chekhov points out, in doing so, he commits an unjust act, motivated by prejudice. As a doctor himself, certainly Chekhov was aware of the fact that men of his profession, although considered gentlemen, were socially and economically inferior to the landed aristocrats who ruled czarist Russia. Aboguin, however, treats Kirolov with great courtesy. It is not Aboguin, but Kirolov, who mentions the law requiring a doctor to come when needed. Aboguin speaks of a mutual friend, he helps Kirolov with his coat, and when he discovers that he has been deceived, he confides in Kirolov as he would in a personal friend and social equal.

It is Kirolov who sees in Aboguin, with his stylish clothing, his obvious good health, and his air of confidence, the smug self-satisfaction of the ruling class. When he arrives at Aboguin's home and observes the luxury in which he lives, Kirolov becomes even more resentful. Thus it is not merely being called away from his grieving wife on what proves to be a wild-goose chase that causes Kirolov to strike out at Aboguin, but a deep-seated class prejudice. The doctor reveals his own prejudice not only by refusing to treat Aboguin as a human being as capable of suffering as himself, but by making the unfounded charge that Aboguin is prejudiced against doctors.

Even though Chekhov treats his doctor sympathetically, underlining his exhaustion and admitting that it is difficult for a grieving person to think of anyone but himself, he shows Kirolov not as a victim of fate, but as a human being with the power to choose between good and evil. Such moral decisions are even more important because, as the tragic poets knew, whatever force governs the world does not have a sense of proportion in meting out punishment for an evil action. The final irony of Chekhov's story is that, because in a thoughtless moment Kirolov permits himself to vent his accumulated anger on an innocent man, two human lives are, in essence, destroyed.

Style and Technique

On occasion, Anton Chekhov's "Enemies" has been published in English as "Two Tragedies." This alternate title is appropriate in that the story begins with one tragedy and ends with another, which, although less dramatic than the first, shapes the course of two lives.

Chekhov uses the natural setting to symbolize the progress of his tragic human story. The child's death occurs in September, the time of year when, as Chekhov later says, the world seems to be sunk in apathy, waiting for winter. The story is pervaded by darkness. The child's death occurs on a dark night; Aboguin appears out of the darkness, waits in a dark hall, and then, with Kirolov, goes out into the dark, cloudy night, which is brightened only by the stars and the moon. The fact that the moon is veiled in clouds suggests that the light may well vanish; its red color indicates a possibility of warmth or, alternatively, of blood. The only sound that the men hear is the cry of the rooks, the night birds often associated with death, which seems to reflect their own sorrows.

At first, Aboguin's pleasant home seems like a sanctuary. Even here, however, there are echoes of the natural setting, suggesting that human beings cannot barricade themselves from grief. The hall and the drawing room are half in darkness; the red lampshade recalls the red moon. When Aboguin returns, it is evident that darkness and misery have invaded this house as well. After the final tragedy has occurred and the men have become enemies, Chekhov again uses nature to symbolize the state of their lives. Now the stars are shrouded in clouds, and the moon has completely vanished. Unfortunately, the two men in the story are too obsessed with themselves and their grievances to notice that the pervasive darkness in nature reflects the condition of their own hearts.

Rosemary M. Canfield Reisman

ENERO

Author: Mary Helen Ponce (1938-   )
Type of plot: Social realism
Time of plot: The 1940's
Locale: Southern California
First published: 1990

Principal characters:

CONSTANCIA DE PAZ, a woman pregnant with her tenth child
JUSTO DE PAZ, her husband
APOLLONIA, their eldest daughter, who is dying of tuberculosis

The Story

Expecting her tenth child, Constancia has just been examined by Dr. Greene, who has told her that her baby is due in January (the "Enero" of the title). This will be her first winter baby, and she only hopes it will be strong enough to fight disease.

Constancia's eldest child, seventeen-year-old Apollonia, is dying of tuberculosis, despite undergoing surgery and special drug treatments. During the three years that Apollonia has been in a sanatorium, Constancia has visited her faithfully. After Constancia's new baby is born in January, Constancia will have to stay in bed for several weeks; she fears that Apollonia will die in the interim. As she moves around the house doing her daily chores, she thinks about the past, present, and future, reviewing her life now in southern California and remembering her earlier life in her native Mexico, where Apollonia was born.

Constancia herself was one of five children carefully spaced three years apart, thanks to her mother's careful use of church-approved birth control—abstinence. Her father, Don Pedro, managed a large ranch in the state of Guanajuato; her mother supervised the women who did chores on the ranch. Constancia met her own husband, Justo, when he was working for her father. He later wrote her letters from California, telling her about the very different life there. He was twenty and she was eighteen when they married. Some time after Apollonia was born, they moved to the United States, separating Constancia from her family and her roots.

After bearing nine children, and especially after the difficult delivery of her last baby, Constancia did not plan to have any more. She recalls her cousin Amador's visit, when he brought a jug of wine to share with Justo, who seldom drank. Unable to drive home, Amador was forced to spend the night. "Much to Constancia's chagrin, he was given her husband's bed [and] soon after Constancia knew she was in the family way." "Weary . . . of childbearing," she and Justo will sleep apart again after the baby's birth.

Life in California has changed the life of the Paz family. Unlike Mexican ranchers, American ranchers do not feed their workers, who must carry cold lunches to work. Constancia is too tired to make tortillas every day, so her family eats white American bread, which the children like. "Americanas" buy it, she thinks, so why should she not?

Constancia's wandering thoughts finally focus on the task she has been avoiding— sorting the baby clothes in preparation for the new arrival. She has carefully stored Apollonia's baby clothes, hand sewn in Mexico by her mother and sisters, wrapped in tissue paper in the bottom of the trunk. Unlike the baby clothes of her other children, Apollonia's have never been worn by anyone else. Now that Apollonia is dying, however, Constancia has no reason to keep them. She clutches Apollonia's baptismal dress to her heart, crying for the impending loss of her daughter. She suddenly decides to dress the new baby in Apollonia's tiny dress, and all of her other clothes. It will make Apollonia happy. With that thought, Constancia walks out of the dark bedroom and into the warmth and light of her kitchen.

Themes and Meanings

Although Constancia is a woman living in the present, she is caught between a past that she remembers fondly and a future that she both fears and welcomes. To her, the past represents a happier, simpler time, when she helped her mother serve meals to the workers on the ranch and was responsible for only two children—her younger brother and sister. It was a time when her husband was a young man with a future. That was long ago, however, and now Constancia is no longer free like the clouds that she observes through the window, to Justo's annoyance. At thirty-eight, she is soon to be the mother of ten children, with one dying and another soon to be born. She will have twice as many children as her mother. She loves all of her children, but her life has been circumscribed by their numbers, very much like the rosebush that she tends in her garden, which "cannot grow with these small suckers," for they "take the nourishment needed by the plant."

Mary Helen Ponce's story is set in October, when the earth and its creatures prepare for the death of winter. Constancia, too, must prepare for death, and for life, and the two intertwine inseparably in this story. The title, "Enero," looks toward the future, toward the coming of new life to be born in the month that begins the New Year and holds the promise of the unknown future. There are other indications of a hopeful future, as Constancia makes a mental list of the home improvements that she wants to accomplish before January: new linoleum, additional clotheslines, and a yellow rosebush.

In her sixth or seventh month of pregnancy, Constancia is literally heavy with life, but her heart is filled with the coming death of Apollonia. This dichotomy between life and death is the central concern of this story, and it is a dichotomy whose resolution comes with Constancia's decision to use the baptismal dress of her dying daughter for the formal entrance into life signified by the baptism of the baby who is to be born.

Style and Technique

A third-person omniscient narrator supplies information on Constancia's age and appearance and the details of her daily life: At thirty-eight she is "still a pretty woman. Her olive face unlined, the black, wavy hair slightly gray." She is much like her neighbors, in a Mexican neighborhood of first- and second-generation Mexicans in southern California in the 1940's—the time and place on which Ponce focuses much of her writing. Ponce's occasional use of Spanish words (such as *"el lavadero"* for washroom, *"cocido"* for stew, and *"hija mía"* for "my daughter") gently reinforces the Latino context.

Ponce's use of Constancia's point of view lifts the narrative above mere social realism of place to create an intimate portrait of a woman straddling the boundaries of several conflicting worlds—Mexico versus the United States, the past versus the present, the present versus the future, freedom versus commitment, youth versus maturity, and, most important, death versus life and despair versus hope. Ponce uses a variety of symbols and metaphors to represent these conflicts. The name Constancia ("constancy") is the most obvious example, for despite her reverie and a certain longing for the halcyon days of her youth in Mexico, she is indeed constant. She fulfills all of her obligations as a wife and mother despite personal cost. Although her husband, Justo, may not have fulfilled the promise of his youth, he provides well for his family and is an honorable and just man, respected by all.

The month of "Enero" used as the title of the story seems carefully chosen to symbolize new beginnings and hope. The rosebush that Constancia tends is a metaphor for her situation as the mother of so many unplanned children: The suckers that spring up at the base of the rosebush are its attempt to propagate itself, and yet its "offspring" divert the rose's vitality to themselves, hampering its growth just as Constancia's growth has surely been hampered by her ten pregnancies in twenty years and their attendant responsibilities.

The baptismal gown, used in the religious ceremony that admits a baby as a spiritual member of the church, affirms life. The trunk where it has been stored in the dark bedroom suggests the carefully guarded past, a past that is useless to the present unless released into the light. The blue sky and the cloud formations that Constancia loves to watch remind her of the blue skies and freer days on the ranch in Mexico, where she "played on the open meadows." The kitchen is the center of domesticity, the room where she lovingly cooks and serves her family's meals and they unite to eat together. When Constancia leaves the dark bedroom to return with the baptismal dress to the warmth of her kitchen, she leaves behind despair, abandons the past, and moves toward the light and hope of the future. The circle of life, which always includes death, remains unbroken.

Linda Ledford-Miller

THE ENGLISH LESSON

Author: Nicholasa Mohr (1935-   )
Type of plot: Domestic realism
Time of plot: The 1970's
Locale: New York's Spanish Harlem
First published: 1986

> *Principal characters:*
> SUSAN HAMMA, a teacher
> LALI PADILLO, a Puerto Rican immigrant woman
> WILLIAM HORACIO COLÓN, a Puerto Rican immigrant who works
> at the luncheonette

The Story

Susan Hamma, a history teacher from a junior college in Queens, is teaching an adult-education class for immigrants trying to learn English. She is an exuberant woman who is convinced that the small group of mostly Hispanic students in her class desperately need her services, reasoning that if they can come to class after working all day in dreary, boring, even revolting jobs, the least she can do is make every lesson count.

Susan has asked the students to make oral statements about where they are from, why they are taking her class, and what their plans are. William Colón, a dwarfish man who is almost the same height standing as sitting, begins the recitation pattern that most of the students follow. All the students stand and read a prepared statement indicating that they have come to the United States in search of a better future, that they are living with relatives, and that they are working as unskilled laborers. All the legal aliens indicate that they want to become American citizens, except for Diego Torres, a young man from the Dominican Republic. When Susan urges him to be brief, he snaps at her that he is not finished, insists that he is proud to be Dominican, and maintains that he has no desire to be an American citizen. Aldo Fabrizi, an Italian immigrant who does want to become a U.S. citizen, speaks passionately about his goal, scolding and challenging Diego Torres, who only yawns and closes his eyes.

The last student to recite is Stephan Paczkowski, a Polish immigrant, who was a professor of music at the University of Krakow for ten years until his wife, also a professor, was asked to leave the country because she had Jewish parents. He now works as a porter in the maintenance department of a large hospital. At the close of the class meeting, William walks home with Lali Padillo, a Puerto Rican immigrant whose husband, Rudi, runs the luncheonette where she and William work. They talk together about the class, and William urges Lali not to be embarrassed about her poor English skills.

On the last night of the class, Susan brings coffee and cookies for a treat. Lali is sorry to see the class end, for it has meant an escape from the luncheonette and Rudi and all the things that she believes imprison her. Diego Torres and Aldo Fabrizi goodnaturedly argue about the merits of citizenship, the students praise Susan for her teaching, and everyone says good-bye. William and Lali, who have made plans to take a more advanced English class together the following term, walk home, teasing each other by imitating Susan.

Themes and Meanings

Nicholasa Mohr's "The English Lesson" is a restrained love story. Although neither Lali nor William refer directly to how they feel about each other, the story suggests that although they are only friends, each secretly wishes the relationship could be more intimate. In addition to William's gentleness with Lali, the most obvious suggestion about their unexpressed feelings occurs on the walk home after the class meeting when the students make their oral presentations. Lali says that she did not know that William's name was Horacio, remarking how imposing the name is. William, who is dwarfish, says that his mother expected a valiant warrior but got him instead. Lali, however, pays no attention to William's physical stature. A plain woman, she grew up in a tiny mountain village in Puerto Rico and had no suitors until Rudi, an older man, asked her parents for her hand. She now feels closed in and alone. Her only pleasure is the English class and William. She feels that when she attends the class, she is accomplishing something all by herself without the help of the man on whom she is dependent. She finds herself waiting for William to come in to work, looking forward to his presence. On the initial walk home, as William takes Lali's elbow and tells her in English to watch her step, Lali stares at him and wishes that she could be like everyone else, but in a moment the "strange feeling of involvement had passed, and William had taken no notice of it."

The parallel theme of the story focuses on the patronizing attitude that many native speakers of English have toward immigrants who do not speak English fluently. Although Susan Hamma is a caring and concerned teacher, she thinks of her students as if they were children. Indeed, she treats the class much as if they were elementary students rather than adults. This is why she is so embarrassed when Diego Torres snaps at her harshly for telling him to hurry along with his presentation, and why she is somewhat breathless and confused when she learns that Stephan Paczkowski was a professor of music. At the last class meeting, she tries to speak to Paczkowski and pay recognition to his advanced degree. It is clear, however, that she is more comfortable thinking of the students as if they were children rather than peers or academic superiors.

Style and Technique

The style of "The English Lesson" is realistic and straightforward. An omniscient narrator provides the expositional background, and most of the action is presented by means of dialogue between the characters in the five scenes: the classroom when the students give their oral presentations; Lali and William walking home together the first time; the luncheonette dialogue with Rudi; the last night of class, when Susan provides cookies and coffee and says good-bye to all; William and Lali's final walk home when they laugh and joke about Susan. The story is so formally organized that it could well become a short play.

All the details in "The English Lesson" contribute to the dual themes of the treatment of the immigrants as if they were children, and the submerged and unspoken relationship between Lali and William. For example, Susan trying to illustrate the idiom "get the ball rolling" by winding up like a pitcher and throwing an imaginary ball suggests the kind of simplistic gestures that one might use with a child. When Mr. Fong misunderstands and says that "get the ball rolling" is an "idiot" rather than an "idiom," Susan must correct him.

The fact that the immigrants do not understand English does not mean that they are either children or idiots, as Susan discovers when Diego Torres refuses to be patronized and when Stephan Paczkowski tells her that he is a professor. On the first walk home, when Lali complains that she is embarrassed because her accent is so terrible, William quite rightly points out what many English-speaking people forget: "Look," he says, "we all have to start someplace. Besides what about the Americanos? When they speak Spanish, they sound pretty awful, but we accept it." Moreover, the fact that William is dwarfish and Lali is shy does not mean that they are children.

The two themes come together at the end of the story when, on the walk home, William says to Lali, "I would like to say to you how wonderful you are, and how you gonna have the most fabulous future. . . after all, you so ambitious," and, realizing that he sounds just like Susan Hamma, he bursts into laughter. Lali joins in the game, also talking formally. The story ends with both of them breaking into uncontrollable laughter when William tells Lali that he is "now a member in good standing . . . of the promised future."

"The English Lesson" suggests the difficulty of expressing oneself in a language not one's own, as well as the difficulty of being oneself in a land that is not one's own. Because of this displacement, immigrants are initially compelled to ape the behavior of the natives and mouth the platitudes and generalities that the new language compels them to speak. The playful and good-humored joking of William and Lali at the conclusion of the story suggests that even as they submit to the necessity of this imitation, they can mock it. Looking forward to the promised future is, for them, both real and silly at the same time.

Charles E. May

THE ENGLISHWOMAN

Author: Ruth Prawer Jhabvala (1927-   )
Type of plot: Autobiographical
Time of plot: The 1970's
Locale: India
First published: 1976

> *Principal characters:*
> SADIE, the protagonist, a fifty-two-year-old Englishwoman
>   who has been living in India for thirty years
> HER HUSBAND, an Indian
> ANNAPURNA, her husband's mistress
> DEV and
> MONICA, their children, now grown up

The Story

Although fifty-two-year-old Sadie has been married to an Indian and has lived in India for thirty years, she has always remained an Englishwoman at heart. She feels young and free as she packs her bags and prepares to leave her husband, children, and grandchildren in order to return to England, where she intends to spend the rest of her days.

Over the years her relationship with her husband has so withered away that their marriage now exists in name only, but they remain friends. The person who is apparently most upset at Sadie's impending departure is Annapurna, a distant relative of her husband who now lives with them as his mistress—an open arrangement that suits everybody, including Sadie. There appear to be no hard feelings on any side. Annapurna is genuinely grieved that Sadie is about to leave the household because both she and Sadie's husband love her in their own way and enjoy taking care of her. Sadie, however, is so thrilled to be leaving that she can hardly contain her joy, but she tries to suppress her smiles because she feels ashamed of her happiness in the face of their grief at her leaving.

Sadie has carefully planned her departure. A week earlier, she went to Bombay to say good-bye to Dev and Monica, her grown children who have families of their own. When Monica asked her why she was leaving, Sadie explained that as people age they grow homesick for the places where they grew up until their need to return becomes unbearable. Monica understands and sympathizes, and both her children promise to visit her regularly in England. The only person who remains inconsolable is Annapurna, who cries and repeatedly asks whether Sadie will miss them, their love for her, and her life of the past thirty years. Sadie, however, is merely appalled to think that it has been such a long time since she left her real home.

Sadie does not like to remember the time when she arrived in India as a young English bride of a slim Indian boy with bright eyes, whom she had met when he was a student at Oxford. She was happy then, even when her husband was busy with his activities outside the home, because the family had lavished so much attention and love on her. However, the heady excitement of her strange new life in India paled over the years until she lost interest in it and her marriage. Her husband began straying to other women. Annapurna then entered the house after fleeing from an abusive husband, and she slowly took over Sadie's duties of a wife. Sadie was grateful and there was never any bitterness or jealousy between them. Annapurna looked after her husband, fed him delicacies that made him fat, and played cards with him during the evening before taking him to bed. After they retired for the night, Sadie often stayed up for hours arguing with herself about her own future.

It was during those hours that she decided to return to England. When she announced her decision, it seemed sudden, but she had actually agonized over it for a long time, and she realized that she had begun preparing to leave some twenty years earlier. She could even mark the exact day—a moment when her young son was very sick. Sadie wanted to nurse him alone in peace and quiet, but his room was filled with the numerous women of the house who fussed over him until it nearly drove her crazy. She remembered the cool and quiet sickrooms of her own childhood in England, which her mother had periodically visited with medicine. When she sensed the alarming difference of her new life, she became distraught and burst into tears on her husband's return. He and Annapurna struggled to soothe and comfort her, without understanding the real reason for her distress. She knew then that she did not belong.

On her last night in India, Sadie feels excited and young again. As she gazes over the moonlit garden of her Indian home, it is transformed into a vision of the English downs as she remembers them, and the wind that she feels is the English wind against the hair of her youth.

Themes and Meanings

Like Sadie, the author of this story, Ruth Prawer Jhabvala, is a European who married an Indian. She likewise returned to the West after nearly twenty-five years of married life in India. Of her own Indian experience, Jhabvala has said that she never felt that she really belonged, and this is the central theme of "The Englishwoman." Even after spending thirty years in her adopted country with a husband, children, and grandchildren, fifty-two-year-old Sadie still feels that she would be more comfortable in the land of her birth, although she admits that she now "knows almost no one there."

Sadie is not particularly unhappy or ill-treated in India. From her own impressions, she began her life there with much enthusiasm and excitement, and although all that gradually disappeared, she has always been well cared for by her husband's family. Although her marriage has disintegrated, her relations with her husband (and his mistress) have remained amicable. One thus gets the distinct impression that it is not unhappiness that drives her away. The major reason for her decision is her realization, after twenty years, that her own ways are so different that she can never really adapt to Indian society. Her homesickness for the place to which she believes she truly belongs—despite having had no connections with it for thirty years—has grown so unbearable that she can no longer stay away. The fact that she has indeed never connected with her adopted country is proved by her indifference to carrying anything to England to remind her of India. It appears that Jhabvala is using her fiction to prove to herself that one cannot really belong anywhere but in one's own homeland, and that however late it is, one can always go back. The essence of Sadie's story is captured in an early sentence as she prepares for her return: "Her heart is light and so is her luggage."

Style and Technique

Jhabvala is a straightforward storyteller who generally uses little literary embellishment in her fiction. "The Englishwoman" sets out its facts right at the start. Within a few paragraphs the reader is comfortably aware of the background. However, Jhabvala also manages to arouse one's curiosity by providing snippets of information that the reader will want explained—for example, why Sadie is so eager to leave a thirty-year marriage, or, why her husband's mistress is so upset at her impending departure—thereby ensuring that the story captures one's attention and sustains it.

Jhabvala also appears to be writing with a wider, non-Indian audience in mind— one for whom she provides sympathetic and accurate insights into Indian family life. While explaining, for example, why Sadie felt so out of place in a house teeming with relatives when her son was sick, she also points out that the prevailing social structure is respected and relied upon by the insiders, including her son, who enjoyed the great fuss made over him.

Jhabvala uses imagery sparingly, allowing the facts and details to convey the sense of her story. At the end of the story, when she describes Sadie's transformation of a moonlit Indian garden into a soft English landscape, the scene becomes an especially evocative image that provides both a sense of closure and the hint of a new beginning in Sadie's life.

Brinda Bose

EPICAC

Author: Kurt Vonnegut, Jr. (1922-   )
Type of plot: Science fiction
Time of plot: An unspecified time in the future
Locale: A computer room
First published: 1950

> *Principal characters:*
> THE NARRATOR, an unnamed mathematician
> PAT KILGALLEN, his girlfriend, later his wife
> EPICAC, an advanced computer

The Story

The greatest computer ever built, EPICAC has been designed for the purpose of rapid calculation, mainly for military purposes. It is a huge machine, described as plugged into the wall like a toaster or a vacuum cleaner. Soon, however, it is clear that EPICAC is far more than a machine.

The narrator, after repeatedly being turned down by his beloved, Pat, a mathematician as he is, sits down one night in front of the computer keyboard and playfully asks the computer for advice. To his great surprise, the computer responds, first asking for definitions of such basic terms as love, girl, and poetry. After some explanation, EPICAC produces a long poem, called simply "To Pat." EPICAC then starts asking questions of its own, about how Pat looks, what she likes to do, and so on. The computer will do nothing else until it gets its answers.

When Pat sees the poem, she is extremely moved, and finally agrees to a kiss. The narrator is thrilled and tells EPICAC all about the experience. The computer responds by producing a shorter poem, "The Kiss," which leads Pat finally to agree to marry the narrator, on the condition that he write her a poem on every anniversary.

Early the next morning, the narrator gets a frantic call from Doctor von Kleigstadt, who screams that disaster has befallen the great computer. The narrator finds smoking wreckage and a huge collection of computer printouts. He takes them home and decodes them.

EPICAC has left a suicide note, explaining that it does not want to be a machine and think about war all the time, but wants to be human and think about love. There are no hard feelings, however. The computer has also left enough poems to last the narrator through five hundred anniversaries.

Themes and Meanings

At one level, Kurt Vonnegut's "EPICAC" is a love triangle story, minus the jealous rage usually associated with such stories. The fact that one of the lovers is a computer might easily be played for laughs, and there is certainly a comic element involved. The way that the story is presented, however, suggests several far deeper levels.

The first level is that of science fiction. EPICAC is the greatest computer in history, with a huge potential. From the first sentence of the narrative, it is obvious that there is more to it than merely the ability to calculate rapidly and accurately. This is most clearly shown in the ways that the various characters are depicted.

EPICAC is described at first as a huge machine, but "he" soon replaces "it" as the pronoun used to describe the machine, and the narrator often refers to the computer as his friend. Pat Kilgallen, the narrator's girlfriend, is a wooden figure, useful only to advance the plot. Doctor von Kleigstadt is a stereotypical scientist, complete with an overdone German accent. Even the narrator is never named. The most human character in the story is the computer. The only dialogues with any meaning are between the narrator and EPICAC.

The most important plot development in this regard is the computer's suicide. It does not make much sense that a computer should be able to commit suicide; a computer is a machine, after all. Even more important is the manner of that suicide. EPICAC is a machine designed to make calculations for use in warfare. At the end of the story, it makes the ultimate sacrifice for love. Not only does it short-circuit itself, but before doing so, it prints out enough poetry to make sure its friend will be happy in the love that it can never enjoy.

The basic question is whether a thinking machine can become, in some sense, a human being. Human beings are far more than thinking machines. They have emotions, and often act illogically on the basis of those emotions. Vonnegut poses this question early in the story, when he refers to "my friend EPICAC, God rest his soul." Can a computer have a soul? At the deepest level, this is what "EPICAC" is about. Standard religious beliefs are useless in this regard, because they are based on teachings that far predate modern technology. Vonnegut later did question religious values, and even invented a new religion in *Cat's Cradle* (1963). In the present story, however, religion does not enter the picture, at least on the surface.

"EPICAC" was one of the earliest attempts at the fictional treatment of modern computers. As such, it was a radical departure from the usual ways in which machines had been treated by earlier science-fiction writers. Generally, they were shown as either complicated but mindless gadgets, or monsters out of control. "EPICAC" was one of the first stories that imbued computers with anything like human emotions.

In 1950, when this story was written, computers were primitive by the standards of the late twentieth century. They were huge, lumbering machines, requiring constant attention and regular repairs. The concept of a computer thinking for itself was something new, but it became a regular theme in later science fiction, and a few decades after "EPICAC," scientists were considering this question very seriously.

EPICAC is the reverse of Frankenstein's monster: He is a machine created for warfare, who dies for love; inefficient at calculating war programs, but capable of writing great poetry. As such, he is more human than the human characters around him, or certainly more humane.

Style and Technique

"EPICAC" is written in the playful style common to Vonnegut's works. The very name of the machine is comic; it is clearly related to ipecac, a medicine used to promote vomiting. The story begins with the narrator discussing his friend EPICAC, and referring to him with human pronouns. At the same time, there is no question that he is dealing with a machine, an object to be owned by human beings: "After all, he cost the taxpayers $776,434,927.54."

This technique of switching back and forth between humanizing the computer and presenting it as a machine might easily become confusing in a larger work. It would also be confusing if there were any serious plot development, or if the characters other than EPICAC were developed in a believable way.

Less than six pages long, "EPICAC" consists almost entirely of narration and dialogue between two characters, a human and a computer. After a brief discussion of the simple encoding techniques used, these dialogues are almost always presented as two people talking.

One result of this technique is to make the reader feel sympathy for the machine. It is easy to imagine the machine having facial expressions and changing tones of voice, even though the reader has been told that all the conversations are conducted by the operator punching a keyboard and the computer printing out answers in numerical code. One has far more sympathy for the computer than for any of the human characters, even the narrator.

"EPICAC" is told in the first person, which is usually an intimate way to narrate a story. In this case, however, it is difficult to have any feelings for the narrator, because he reveals so little about himself. He is a mathematician, and he is in love with another mathematician, but he never appears outside his computer room. One does not know what he likes to eat, what he reads, or what he does when he is not working. He is a narrator, and nothing more.

Apart from any sympathy that can be evoked for a computer, there is no real human interest in this story. Not one of the characters is described physically. The reader may picture the narrator as some stereotypical computer expert, or at least a 1950's reader could. Pat is difficult to picture at all. All of this is deliberate. The purpose of "EPICAC" is to pose quickly a few fascinating questions about intelligence, emotion, and behavior, and presenting realistic characters would get in the way.

This story is a peculiar mixture of comedy and tragedy. Certainly, the prospect of a computer falling in love and killing itself because it cannot consummate that love is ridiculous, and should evoke laughter. Still, EPICAC is such a human computer that the reader feels for it. The ultimate result is that the humans are proposed as comic figures, while a machine is proposed as tragic.

Marc Goldstein

AN EPISODE OF WAR

Author: Stephen Crane (1871-1900)
Type of plot: Psychological realism
Time of plot: 1864
Locale: A Civil War battlefield
First published: 1899

Principal characters:
THE LIEUTENANT, who has been wounded in battle
THE DOCTOR, who treats him

The Story
  An army lieutenant concentrates on rationing out his company's supply of coffee, meticulously dividing the brown squares before him, when a shot rings out. The enlisted men, startled by the noise, suddenly see blood saturating their lieutenant's sleeve. In pain, the wounded officer sways, winces in disbelief, mutely surveys the forest, and tries instinctively and clumsily to sheathe the sword that he has been using to count out the coffee packets. His mind swirls with mysterious revelations about existence and the meaning of life. As his dumbstruck, sympathetic troops try haltingly and timidly to assist him, he realizes his helplessness. He desperately holds his right wrist with his left hand. Silently and mournfully, he leaves the field to seek medical attention. His dark journey begins.
  The lieutenant's wandering quest takes him through scenes of wartime horror: An aide gallops to a general, salutes, and presents his commander a vital message; batteries sweep in majestic, frightening curves bent on destruction; and horsemen curse and shout amid a chaos of levers, motors, and wheels. This chorus of war is ferocious and emotional with dramatic passion. A beautiful unity seems to hover over these fields of mindless destruction and sudden death. The lieutenant comes upon a group of stragglers who are insensately trudging his path, all excitedly caught up in the drama; he encounters a roadside brigade making coffee—the pedestrian task in which he had been involved before his wounding—and buzzing with talk like girls at boarding school, as if war were simply an adventure. A solicitous officer, observing the lieutenant's bloody arm, scolds him to fix it and kindly, though amateurishly, binds the wound with his own handkerchief. The lieutenant is embarrassed both by his shattered arm and by the gesture of concern. He feels strangely apologetic. He has not yet mastered the proper etiquette for behaving as a wounded soldier, but believes there is some proper ritual to be followed when one is no longer a complete human being.
  At last the lieutenant arrives at the low, white tents of a makeshift hospital, a former school now surrounded by moaning and dying soldiers. A busy surgeon passes by and greets the lieutenant in a friendly way, but his considerate demeanor disappears, even approaches contempt, when he spies the wounded arm. He brusquely orders the lieutenant to come along. Suddenly fearful and overwhelmed by panic, the lieutenant

cries out that he will not allow his arm to be amputated; he tries to draw away. The surgeon seductively cajoles him, insisting that he will not amputate it. The lieutenant is far from reassured, but is not strong enough to resist. He proceeds reluctantly, suspicious and terrified, toward the doors of the field hospital that assume the appearance of the portals of death. The narrator then simply states that this was "the story of how the lieutenant lost his arm."

After some time has passed, the lieutenant's sisters, mother, and wife sob at the sight of his empty, flat sleeve. He stands ashamed before them, minimizing his disability, still not certain of the proper etiquette for behavior of the wounded. It was nothing, however, merely an ordinary experience shared by many soldiers who are doomed thereby to a lifetime of remembrance and suffering, just "an episode of war."

Themes and Meanings

An essential antiwar message predominates in this sober tale, but Stephen Crane, going well beyond the ethos of combat, infuses it with ideas endemic to the nineteenth century cosmic view, that humanity is but a tiny mote in the universal scheme, an insignificant entity driven by the fates and the winds of haphazard chance. Human-kind's triviality is underscored by the characters not even having names; they are identified as types of people, generic manifestations caught in capriciously unfolding events they cannot control. The characters are unable to exercise freedom of the will; each person is propelled to action by the circumstances and forces about him; no one can direct his own destiny. All life is driven by some inexorable, unpredictable fate, the only apparent certainty being the existence of human suffering. Passion, not rationalism, is the fuel that ignites and unleashes the forces precipitating human movements that occur amid anarchy and frenzy.

The nameless lieutenant is the unfortunate Everyman, powerless to help himself and clearly at the mercy of the forces directing his steps. He also represents the archetypal victim gratuitously marked out for this role within the chaotic forces of war. He is helpless, small, ineffectual. Unable to sheathe his sword, divide the rations, or deter the surgeon, he is dependent on destiny for his existence. In the furious tumult and aimlessness, he joins the figurative march of ants that move in fixed parade, part of an unremarkable species, minuscule but striving toward a mysterious purpose. Crane's battlefield transcends the Civil War and may be seen as a microcosm of the world, for all life becomes a battle, a struggle to exist against the challenging fates that casually toss obstacles in the daily path. Human beings, nameless to the deterministic forces controlling life, are never the captains of their souls. The prime undercurrent rushing through "An Episode of War" is this philosophy of pessimism that eliminates free will from human option and renders a somber picture of life.

Style and Technique

With admirable, conscious artistry, Stephen Crane brought to his episode a conflu-ence of literary impressionism and symbolism, a major triumph revealed in the abject anonymity of all of his characters. These human theory representations are fused into hectic actions that roll across a continuously exploding landscape roiling with menace and motion. The language is unremitting in its bleak, suggestive violence: "the slant of glistening guns," the "maniacal horses," the shooting that "crackled like bush fires." Within and against the colliding forces that reverberated with thunder and suffocated under rolling smoke is the solitary, wandering, wounded lieutenant, delicately holding his fragile, bleeding arm as if it were made of glass. The nameless officer, carrying his wounded arm, is thus described as already separated from the limb, bearing it as an independent part no longer attached to his body. The finality is clearly foreshadowed at this point, the diabolical lie of the surgeon notwithstanding.

The wounded arm, symbol of the lieutenant's separation from his essential self and his troops in wartime, is emblematized in civilian life by the empty sleeve, marking him as less than a complete human being. Both symbols also denote the end of the man's illusion—that the temporary arm of authority he once possessed was real, that he was in control of action and choice. The final picture Crane paints of the lieutenant finds this stammering veteran shamefaced, perhaps at what he now recognizes as his sin of pride in even momentarily believing he had the ability to fashion life. The missing arm is now a permanent reminder of his, and humankind's, impotence.

Abe C. Ravitz

ERRAND

Author: Raymond Carver (1938-1988)
Type of plot: Historical realism
Time of plot: July, 1904
Locale: Badenweiler, Germany
First published: 1987

Principal characters:
ANTON CHEKHOV, a Russian author and playwright
OLGA KNIPPER, his wife
DR. SCHWÖRER, the physician who attends Chekhov
    on his deathbed

The Story

In 1897, Anton Chekhov is dining with a wealthy publisher named Suvorin, at an elegant restaurant in Moscow. The two share an awareness of their peasant origins, although Suvorin's politics are reactionary and Chekhov's are quite the opposite. During the dinner, Chekhov experiences his first hemorrhage; the blood gushing from his mouth indicates that he has tuberculosis. Even while he is recuperating in a sanitarium for tuberculosis patients, however, Chekhov denies that anything serious is wrong with him. (Raymond Carver quotes from the memoirs of Chekhov's younger sister, Maria. During a visit with Chekhov at the clinic, she saw a doctor's drawing of Chekhov's lungs and recognized that the doctor had told him he was seriously ill.)

The author Leo Tolstoy also visits Chekhov during this time; although he does not like Chekhov's plays, he admires his short stories. During the visit, he tells Chekhov his ideas about immortality, ideas that Chekhov cannot share. Chekhov confines his beliefs to things that he can experience with his senses.

Chekhov spends much of his illness in denial, constantly insisting that he is getting better or that he is about to improve, even in his last weeks of life. He spends those weeks at Badenweiler, a popular German resort frequented by Russians, accompanied by his adored wife, Olga Knipper. The couple had met when Olga acted in Chekhov's *The Seagull* (1895), and married in 1901. After a lengthy and complicated courtship, Chekhov has found marriage to be a happy experience.

Before going to Badenweiler, Chekhov consulted a specialist in Berlin, but that doctor had summarily dismissed him because his disease was far too advanced for treatment. A Russian journalist who visited Chekhov at about this time confirmed for his editor that the famous writer seemed to have entered the last stages of his illness, and noted his thinness, his constant fever, and his difficulties in breathing.

In Badenweiler, Chekhov is treated by Dr. Schwörer. Chekhov himself is a physician, so he must know how sick he is; nevertheless, his letters to his mother and sister in these last weeks of his life insist that he is improving and getting stronger. Chekhov is not writing during this period, however. His last work was *The Cherry Orchard*, which he finished with difficulty in 1903 after expressing the belief that he would never write again.

On July 2, 1904, shortly after midnight, Olga sends for the doctor to come to Chekhov in their hotel. Chekhov has begun hallucinating, evidently about a trip he had once made to Japan. When Dr. Schwörer arrives, he senses that Chekhov has little time left. He gives him an injection to speed his heart, but it does no good. At last, he says he will send for oxygen, but Chekhov, momentarily lucid, says that he will be dead before it arrives. At that point, the doctor goes to the telephone and calls the hotel's kitchen to order a bottle of champagne and three glasses.

A rumpled young man who works for the hotel delivers the champagne and receives the doctor's generous tip. Then the doctor pours three glasses and presses the cork back into the bottle. Olga puts the cool glass into the hand of Chekhov, who says it has been a long time since he has drunk champagne. He drinks all of his wine, and Olga removes his empty glass. After rolling onto his side, Chekhov dies a few minutes later. Olga asks the doctor to delay telling the authorities for a few hours; she wishes to be alone with her husband before his body is taken over by others. Just as the doctor agrees, the champagne cork pops out of the bottle.

Olga sits with her husband until morning, when a knock at the door reveals the young hotel employee who has come to deliver a porcelain vase of roses and to collect the champagne bottle and glasses. Seeing the cork on the floor and becoming aware that someone is lying in the bedroom, he senses that something is wrong. Now Olga, who has not paid attention to the young man's suggestion that she might like breakfast on a tray, tells him that Chekhov is dead. She asks him to go for a mortician, taking care that he find someone appropriate for a person as important as Chekhov. She carefully instructs him to do nothing that will call attention to the situation or cause an unseemly commotion. As Olga instructs him, the young man thinks about how to retrieve the champagne cork that is lying near the toe of his shoe. He leans over and picks it up.

Themes and Meanings

Raymond Carver was a great admirer of Chekhov and his work. Like Chekhov, he was interested in the lives of common people struggling to get along in a difficult world, a theme Carver saw as central to his writing. Also like Chekhov, Carver died of a lung disease—cancer in Carver's case. In "Errand," one of the last stories that Carver wrote, he examines the ramifications of an artist's life, using Chekhov's life in part as a metaphor for his own. For example, he quotes Chekhov's unsentimental statement about how peasants face death and his rejection of all philosophical or religious world views. That rejection left Chekhov able to record only the objective details of his characters' lives—their births, marriages, deaths, styles of speech—the very material to which Carver limited himself in his own spare and undecorated writing.

Throughout "Errand," Chekhov denies the seriousness of his illness until the very end (unlike Carver, who wrote about his cancer several times). Even the journey to the spa at Badenweiler suggests this denial. The crisis of the story moves the focus from Chekhov himself to Olga, who must cope with her husband's death in the midst of strangers who cannot understand what has happened. Even after she has given the young hotel employee detailed instructions about finding a mortician, the name of the famous writer means so little to him that he can concentrate only on the champagne cork on the floor.

The champagne receives special emphasis in this story because it serves to link the opening scene in the elegant restaurant with Chekhov's last moments. The doctor's decision to order champagne, underscored by Carver's comment on the rightness of the action, and later the hotel employee's inability to recognize the significance of Olga's instructions, all seem to recall Chekhov's denial of his tuberculosis as well as his assertion that he will confine his fiction to the objective details of his characters' lives.

Style and Technique

This story, one of the last that Carver wrote, is quite unlike his usual portrayals of life among ordinary contemporary Americans. Instead, Carver has used many of the details of Chekhov's last days to make a story that is part biography and part fiction. As the story progresses, Carver indicates the material he drew from letters and journals of Chekhov's relatives and acquaintances. At the same time, he adds material such as the hotel employee in order to give the story texture and thematic focus.

Although this story, with its foreign setting and its historical detail, differs from Carver's usual work, its style is what Carver's readers have come to expect. Carver's sentences are bare; he uses relatively little modification, with the result that he sometimes seems rather distanced from his characters. It is his minute observation of detail that gives the story its emotional impact. The story deals with death and alienation, themes which inform much of Carver's work. At the end, the reader is moved by Chekhov's death partly because of his wife's tender devotion to him, partly because Chekhov is so little able to confront it, and partly because the man and his work remain so unknowable to the rest of the world—here suggested by the hotel employee, the very sort of person about whom Carver usually wrote. That the artist who interprets the lives of others must himself remain a mystery is an irony that surely Carver relished.

Ann D. Garbett

ESMERALDA

Author: Roberta Fernández
Type of plot: Domestic realism
Time of plot: 1958
Locale: Texas
First published: 1990

> *Principal characters:*
> VERÓNICA LUNA, also called Esmeralda or Ronnie,
>   a young woman
> ISELA, her mother
> CRISTINA, her grandmother
> AMANDA and
> LEONOR, her great-aunts
> ALFREDO, her violent uncle
> NENITA, the thirteen-year-old narrator

The Story

Verónica, a great beauty of eighteen, is a member of an extended family living in her great-aunt Leonor's house in Texas. She works as a model in a theater, where she simply sits in a booth, her beauty framed by "a round glass house." The narrator, Nenita, first meets her when Verónica and her mother come to live at Leonor's house. Nenita is curious about Verónica because she is so quiet and has a mysterious air. Nenita senses that there is something about Verónica that the family is leaving unspoken. Even more intriguing is the fact that Verónica never visits her former home at her uncle Alfredo's ranch.

After a newspaper columnist writes about Verónica, she becomes a minor public figure and attracts increased attention from men. Troubled by the notoriety that the newspaper column has brought her, she breaks into tears when her cousin Orión teases her by reciting the first line of a famous poem by Federico García Lorca: "Green how I love you green" (*"Verde que te quiero verde"*), which alludes to the columnist's calling her "a shining emerald" (*"una esmeralda brillante"*).

Leonor consoles Verónica and advises her to quit her job at the theater the next day. Leonor points out how men call their *piropos* compliments but that such behavior is "really self-indulgence." Verónica then explains how she came to leave her uncle's ranch five years earlier, when she and a seventeen-year-old worker named Omar were attracted to each other. Gentle and sweet-natured, Omar brought her gifts such as cactus flowers and fruit. Forbidden to see each other, they spoke together through her window at night. One night when the whole house seemed to be asleep, they finally dared to meet on the porch, where they talked and kissed. At that moment, Alfredo appeared. In a rage, he slapped Omar and threw him off the porch, then yanked Verónica around, screaming obscenities and calling her a whore. Verónica believes that Alfredo had Omar killed, but Leonor tells her that he simply had Omar deported. Taken aback, Nenita asks why Alfredo has interfered. Leonor can only answer that that is how things are. It is further revealed that Alfredo's wife will not leave him herself, but she has seen to it that their five children grow up in other family members' houses, away from him. Reassured by this conversation, Verónica says that she will continue to work at the theater. Later, Nenita and Verónica discuss how Omar was gentle and giving, while the twins Orión and Orso are loud and boorish. On the opposite end of the scale is Alfredo, whose own children openly profess to hate him.

Nenita, who has regularly walked home with Verónica since the latter's notoriety began, arrives late one evening. She runs after Verónica, catching up with her at the same time that the two Mondragón brothers stop the car in which they have been following Verónica. After a struggle, the brothers drive off with Verónica. Nenita runs home to report what has happened. Orión and Orso go off to find Verónica's abductors. Nenita begins to call the police, but is told that they will do nothing. Meanwhile, the Mondragóns rape Verónica, leaving her pregnant.

Afterward, the newspaper columnist prints a condolence for what has happened to Verónica, noting that her assailants were brought to justice, and he apologizes for any part he may have played in what happened. Over the next several weeks everyone helps take care of Verónica. The older women of the family perfume her room, massage her with herbal oils, and encourage her to sleep. They also repeatedly ask her to tell what happened, thereby allowing her to cry and grieve. She recuperates, reflecting on how the family's women have many griefs, largely caused by men. The family women have helped her by telling her their own secret pains. She determines that she will not be a victim. As a final sign of her readjustment, she enjoys a risqué joke with Nenita.

All is not the same as before, however; Nenita senses that Verónica has erected a wall around herself. Verónica meets and quickly marries David, a naïve young musician. In a moment of frankness, Verónica admits that she would like to think that she is happy. After the baby is born, David seems to believe it is his. Nenita has a dream in which the color green figures prominently. Verónica, adored by a crowd, retreats. Nenita passes through rooms reminiscent of the glass booth at the theater and of the colors and scents of the room in which Verónica convalesced. Finally, a stranger, who recalls Omar, approaches Nenita, offering her "half an orange . . . and cactus fruits." She reaches out to accept his gifts.

Themes and Meanings

Roberta Fernández's "Esmeralda" is a feminist story in the most basic sense of the term, in that it concerns itself with women and vindicates them. It is about the harm that men do to women, and the ways that women cope. It is also about resisting victimization and is about love. The two epigraphs that introduce the story announce these themes. One is from popular culture, the other from a writer. There is some tension between them; in many respects, they may be reduced to opposites. For example, one may point out that in the story, popular culture speaks with flowery language about love and beauty (the song, the columnist's words), and that, with education and experience, one learns to distrust such messages (Ntozake Shange's poem, Verónica's experience). Fernández, however, is interested in more than sending a message. Her characters and events are rarely simply opposites or symbols. For example, the men are not all bad. The twins Orión and Orso are insensitive and immature, but they—not the police—do what they can to help protect Verónica. Omar and David are loving and gentle. This makes the evil of Alfredo and the Mondragón brothers more believable.

Likewise, Fernández's women characters are not all good. Verónica marries not for love but as a means of escape. She retreats. The story is feminist simply in its advocacy of the women characters and its insistence on the realities of women's experience. Women do get raped; they also fall in love (even with the song's sweet and total surrender).

Another theme that pervades the story can be seen in its numerous acts of revealing and concealing. Family secrets are kept and told; Verónica, who is put on public display, remains quiet and out of reach even to Nenita, and lives a lie with her husband; Alfredo's angry "discovery" of Verónica and Omar uncovers his morally reprehensible, yet unspoken (hidden) desires.

Style and Technique

Told in twelve fragments, the story is discursive, and it mentions many names of family members only in an offhand way—as if the reader already knows who the characters are. Many times, a character tells a story about a past event that relates thematically to present events but does not advance the plot. Fernández, in short, breaks many of the conventions of how short stories ought to be told. She has excellent reasons for doing so. Upon a first reading of the story, a reader eager to learn what happens to Verónica may not notice the story's intricacy. It is told in the first person, not in Verónica's voice but in that of one who knew her. What the reader learns about Verónica is what Nenita learns about her. Verónica's story is too much for a typically constructed short story to contain. More than the frame that Nenita provides, it needs a box: the family, the family's stories, the room in which she is displayed, the room in which she convalesces, and the houses in which she is watched. If Fernández had written her short story in a more conventional way, it would not be art but rather a tract or a soap opera. The story's subtleties of narration reward those who reread it.

Eric Howard

EUROPE

Author: Henry James (1843-1916)
Type of plot: Psychological realism
Time of plot: Late nineteenth century
Locale: Brookridge, Massachusetts
First published: 1899

> *Principal characters:*
> THE NARRATOR, an unnamed man
> HIS SISTER-IN-LAW
> MRS. RIMMLE, an elderly woman who is a friend of his sister-in-law
> REBECCA RIMMLE,
> JANE RIMMLE, and
> MARIA RIMMLE, Mrs. Rimmle's daughters

The Story

The unnamed narrator has had a long acquaintance with a family of women. Mrs. Rimmle, the elderly widowed matriarch of the family, controls the lives of her three soon-to-be-old daughters by preventing their much-anticipated trip to Europe—a trip that she and her husband enjoyed in the distant past. The narrator, who is familiar with European culture, encourages the daughters, Becky, Jane, and Maria Rimmle, to make the journey, but soon perceives that their mother is subtly intent on preventing it, using her poor health as an excuse. It is commonly believed that Becky is the daughter most "prepared" and therefore most deserving of a journey to Europe, although the narrator early intuits that it is Jane who most passionately desires to visit the continent.

As the years go by and Mrs. Rimmle's repeated health crises prevent the European journey, the narrator observes that her daughters' rapid aging is exceeded only by her own aging. However, Mrs. Rimmle always rallies, and she moves toward an advanced age that is treated somewhat comically by the narrator and his sister-in-law, who is his interlocutor in the story. The subject of Europe becomes one that is both embarrassing and amusing for the narrator and the Rimmle daughters, who seem to hold out hope for such a trip, but also seem to understand that their own time is running out as their mother moves into her dotage. Finally, however, the narrator is informed by his sister-in-law that Jane Rimmle has departed suddenly for Europe with a family called the Hathaways, and that the trip has brought about important changes in her personality and demeanor.

The narrator claims not to be surprised, however, when he is told that Jane has become a person whom "no one would know," one who is now described as "obstreperous" and who has "taken to flirting." He later learns that Jane refuses to return to the United States with the Hathaways, whom she informs of her intention to remain in Europe and even visit the East. Delighted with Jane's metamorphosis, the narrator hopes that the other two daughters will follow her example.

That, however, is not to be. Although Becky approvingly helps finance her sister's continued stay in Europe, both she and Maria devote the remainder of their own lives to their mother, who continues to live long past her time. Becky dies before her mother. Before she dies, she tells the narrator that Jane will never return to them; her mother, barely able to speak, informs the narrator that her daughter Jane is dead. Knowing this is not true, the narrator also pretends to accept as true Mrs. Rimmle's statement that Becky has departed for Europe.

Themes and Meanings

Throughout his career Henry James was obsessed with the American experience of Europe; his aptly named short story "Europe" is one of many of his works that take this subject as its major theme. For James, the American response to the social and cultural milieu of Europe is a complex one that usually functions to effect irrevocable changes in the Americans who choose to experience this kind of transformation. To James, Europe often represents a world of greater sophistication, deception, and subtlety for Americans who venture to enter its complex, ambiguous web of social relationships. His characters are generally unprepared for the multilayered reality that they encounter in a European setting.

In "Europe," however, James concentrates on characters who remain in the United States, although Europe still functions symbolically in ways similar to his other fiction. The Rimmle daughters clearly represent what James sees as the major American virtues and defects. They are naïve, puritanical, provincial, and painfully sincere, and, with the exception of Jane, are destined to retain these characteristics because they are denied access to European experience. Jane, on the other hand, reveals her readiness for a personal metamorphosis when she departs hurriedly for Europe and then refuses to return. Rumors of her flirtatiousness and willfulness signal the new freedom from constricting American mores that Europe confers on her, and the narrator's speculation that she has undergone a second youth, or rebirth, in Europe is perfectly in keeping with James's own belief in the cultural and imaginative limitations that American culture imposes.

The theme of aging is closely connected to the theme of Europe in this story, for the narrator's continued focus on the physical and psychological ages of the Rimmle women is one aspect of the American-European dynamic. Mrs. Rimmle, who in her youth had the benefit of a European tour, achieves a preternatural old age that appears to drain the very life out of her daughters, except for Jane, who takes advantage of Europe's rejuvenating powers and apparently does not age like her sisters. Just as America represents the stultifying, self-sacrificing, life-denying power of a culture that is afraid of freedom, Europe symbolizes an escape from the limitations of American experience, an expansive, imaginative stage upon which to transform oneself. It seems inevitable that after Becky dies, Maria will slowly sicken and die, while their mother lives to an unheard-of old age and the adventurous Jane flourishes in European capitals.

At an early age James felt the need to escape from what he saw as the cultural provinciality of American society, and although his fiction often depicts Europeans in a less than favorable light, Europe always represents greater self-knowledge and personal growth for his characters. "Europe" is a tale of what its author most feared might have happened to him had he not chosen to live in Europe; the narrator's identification and approval of Jane's choice are also James's.

Style and Technique

Henry James is justly famous for his innovations in fictional style and technique, but both these aspects of his work make his writing difficult for the beginning reader. This is particularly true if the work, like "Europe," is written in the "late style," which he developed during the final phase of his writing career. His long and complex sentences contain many embedded clauses and frequently use a periodic structure that delays meaning until the end of the sentence. Such a style provides a challenge for the reader, who also must deal with the ironic, detached tone of many of his narrators.

The narrator of "Europe" is an excellent example of James's style. He is clearly a cultivated, fastidious, and perceptive man; his choice of language and attitude toward the tale he relates are ironic and distanced. He is not an actual part of the story, a fact that enables him to maintain his distance at all times. Indeed, much of the story is told to him by his sister-in-law, a device that creates another barrier between him and the Rimmles and helps to keep the reader from becoming emotionally involved in the story. James enjoys using narrators who have only partial knowledge of the story they tell, limiting the reader to the narrator's perspective and filtering all aspects of the story through the narrator's consciousness. The result is that the narrator's version of the tale becomes as important as the actual persons and events that are described. A close reading of "Europe" reveals perhaps more about the narrator than it does about the Rimmles, a result that James sought in his fiction.

"Europe" also illustrates another important characteristic of James's fiction in its focus upon the psychological reality of its characters. Early in his career James abandoned the traditional dependence of fiction upon plotted narrative, substituting instead a reliance upon the mental and emotional responses of characters. "Europe" has virtually no plot; the events of the story are simply several brief encounters between the Rimmles and the narrator over a period of years. The focus of the story is the narrator's perception of the psychological states of the Rimmles and the changes that take place in them over the years. Like many of James's narrators, he has an almost voyeuristic curiosity about the people around him, a curiosity that enables him to penetrate the psyches of the Rimmles and reward the reader with insights into their psychological reality. It is always the case, however, that several readings of James's work may be needed in order to appreciate the complex artistry of his style and technique, for no aspect of James's fiction is accidental; every phrase, nuance, and irony is consciously crafted.

Angela Hague

EVENING IN PARIS

Author: Denise Chávez (1948-   )
Type of plot: Domestic realism
Time of plot: 1960
Locale: Southern New Mexico
First published: 1986

Principal characters:
THE NARRATOR, a young girl
HER MOTHER, a schoolteacher
HER SISTER

The Story

With only three shopping days left before Christmas, the narrator is in a Woolworth's store wondering what to buy her mother. She wants something special. What most appeals to her are the dark blue bottles of Evening in Paris perfume. The cosmetic counter entrances her, although she feels inadequate before its shining glass cases, with their mysterious scents and images of womanhood, and she feels awkward and intimidated by the saleslady. "What help is there for three-dollar realities?" she thinks to herself. Her voice falters as she asks for her treasure, a gift-wrapped package of Evening in Paris cologne and bath water. She considers it her best gift ever to her mother and knows that her mother will like it.

Most of the gifts under the family Christmas tree are from her mother's students. The narrator watches her open them and knows that most of the presents will go into a gift box to be given to others the next year. As the girl waits for her mother to open her special present, she reflects on the passage of seasons, on growth and change, on the special smells and foods of Christmastime, and on the things in her mother's house. Her sister is disappointed that the bright package is not for her. The sister's gift is one that their mother gave the narrator to give to her, a red wallet with a picture of Jesus on it. With eager anticipation, the narrator asks her mother to open the midnight-blue package that she has carefully wrapped in white tissue paper. Her mother says yes, but instead stoops to pick up some stray wrapping paper.

Later it occurs to the narrator that perhaps her mother thought the Evening in Paris gift set was from one of her students. It remains unopened and unused. Maybe her mother prefers her usual Tabu perfume, the narrator thinks, although her mother does use the Avon perfume that a student has given to her.

The narrator feels unfulfilled, empty, inadequate. This attitude continues to haunt her years later, after she has gone to Paris and seen its dark and sad aspects, rather than the romanticized and illusionary world of Eiffel Tower postcards. Yet the Paris of magic and lights exists too, she believes.

The following Christmas, the narrator's mother gives her the wallet with Christ's picture; she has forgotten that she used it for the narrator's present to her sister the year before and that her sister put it in the general gift box for other occasions. The wallet reminds the narrator of the previous year, and she thinks her mother perhaps had as little need for perfume on the dusty school playgrounds as the narrator had of a wallet. As the story ends, she stares at the picture on the red wallet, a reproduction of a popular painting of Jesus. She muses that it is a handsome Jesus, one that anyone could love, with his long brown curls and beard, and his deep-set eyes staring out.

Themes and Meanings

The most obvious theme of Denise Chávez's "Evening in Paris" relates to the disappointment that the young girl feels after wanting so much to please her mother with a special gift. Her mother scarcely notices the present, even when the narrator eagerly asks her to open it. The present is put in a box with other unwanted items to be given to others during the coming year. The mother never acknowledges the gift from her daughter. She shows no recognition of the love that her daughter feels for her, or the financial and emotional sacrifice that accompanied the material gift. The gift's giver is rejected. The disappointment is especially sharp because it is her own mother whom she dearly loves who ignores her.

The boxed set of cologne and bath water strongly appeals to the narrator; it connotes glamour and the allure of a romantic womanhood yet to be. It appeals to her sister as well, but it clearly does not to the mother, who uses a more expensive scent, Tabu. The mother, however, uses the Avon perfume from a student, a perfume that costs less than Tabu but more than Evening in Paris. The mother clearly judges the Evening in Paris according to her own standards of taste and value, not according to what it means to her daughter. Ironically, the mother does not use a similar criteria of value in giving gifts; she takes items from the unwanted discards to pass out to others, forgets where they came from, and seems to have no concern about whether or not a recipient will like the gift.

The mother also fails to understand that her daughter is on the brink of becoming a young woman, moving from childhood into the stage where she is entranced by the bright cosmetic counter, but still feels shy and out of place before the mysteries of womanhood. The narrator's attention to the various items on her mother's shelf and her listing of several women who had worked in their home as maids reinforce the theme that she is struggling to understand her own place in the world of women. The references to the picture of a handsome Jesus on the wallet suggest that the narrator is moving toward a realm of sexual development in which the emphasis is often on worldly love and outer appearances.

The narrator's mention that years later she traveled to Paris and saw the harsh realism of the city shows that she keeps with her the hard truths that she learned that Christmas as a girl. Gifts—perhaps including Christ's gifts of spiritual love and sacrifice—are not always appreciated or even recognized. Much of life is a series of giving up hopes and illusions. Yet the Paris of lights and magic exists, the narrator claims. One must not despair or let the mundane cancel out the beauty. Everywhere there is change and movement toward growth, which offer the opportunity for a higher quality of existence than merely being lured by perfumes and romanticized illusions. The mother fails to notice her daughter's love or even her physical growth. The narrator learns that others often do not react as they should, but the brightest soul is the one that reaches out to others, even without reward.

Style and Technique

"Evening in Paris" is one of a series of stories in Denise Chávez's *The Last of the Menu Girls* (1986), which together tell the autobiographical history of a protagonist named Rocio Esquibel. Throughout this collection, as Rocio moves from a girl to a young woman, she struggles to understand herself and her relationship to the people around her. The central metaphor of the collection is her home, which expands to the Hispanic community in which she lives in southern New Mexico. It is here that she develops her caring and compassion for others, even for those who do not always respond with love toward her. Rocio decides that she will become a writer and tell their stories as well as her own. She is especially interested in women and the roles that society places on them and wants to write about their lives.

In "Evening in Paris," the narrator's name does not appear. Most of the story focuses on Christmas, 1960, when she is about eleven years old, and is told through the young girl's interior monologue as though she were in the present. The narrative voice shifts, however, as she tells about going to Paris years later and her associations with the Evening in Paris gift that she gave to her mother. It is clear at this point that the narrative voice is of someone older and less naïve than the eleven-year-old girl who loved the bright blue wrapping and the scent of the cologne that her mother ignored. In this story of loss, the adult narrator still believes in a transcendent goodness that goes beyond the response of others. The adult narrator accepts loss, but still believes there is a way to create beauty and to find light and magic in this fallen world.

Lois A. Marchino

EXCERPTS FROM SWAN LAKE

Author: Peter Cameron (1959-   )
Type of plot: Psychological realism
Time of plot: A summer during the 1980's
Locale: Cheshire, Connecticut, and New York City
First published: 1985

> *Principal characters:*
> PAUL ANDREWS, the young narrator and protagonist
> NEAL, his lover
> MRS. ANDREWS, his grandmother

The Story

Paul and his lover Neal prepare dinner for Paul's grandmother in the suburban Connecticut home of Paul's parents. Paul and Neal have moved out of their New York apartment for the summer in order to take care of Mrs. Andrews while Paul's parents cruise around the world. They are interrupted in their work by a visit from a representative from Meals on Wheels—a woman whom Paul calls "Gloria Marsupial" because of his uncertainty about how to pronounce her name. The social services volunteer is disconcerted when Paul answers the door wielding a knife and when she sees the bare-chested, lacto-vegetarian Neal stirring mushroom curry in a wok. In order to make space in the refrigerator for the tray of meat loaf, green beans, and pudding that she has brought for Mrs. Andrews, she pushes aside the men's beer.

The Marsupial woman asks if Mrs. Andrews wants her blood pressure taken, but Paul's grandmother is more concerned about her unreliable memory. Her recollections are very selective. She can no longer identify lilacs and does not remember how many times she has been married, but she can vividly recall one girlhood summer that she spent on a farm. Her memories are triggered by such sensuous details as the sheer physical exuberance of running and the sight of a single mulberry blown into her bowl of mashed potatoes.

In this regard, Mrs. Andrews and Paul are alike. He, too, is engaged more by sensation than by interpretation, more by present experience than by conjecture over the past and the future. Paul is intoxicated by the combined redolence of curry and lilacs; he is made "dizzy" by smoking an occasional cigarette.

Below the surface of domestic routine, however, disharmony lurks. After Mrs. Andrews retires to her bedroom and Paul and his lover are left to rewash the dishes that she has imperfectly cleaned, Neal announces his intention of returning to their apartment in the city. Uncomfortable in this suburban home, he points to the predictable African violets on the windowsill to emphasize his sense of displacement. He is also unable to relax at night when he considers the possibility of the grandmother's confronting both men in bed. No one in the family, it seems, comprehends the true nature of their relationship.

A week after Neal returns to the city, Paul and his grandmother see a television commercial for a coming production of the ballet *Swan Lake*. Because of his grandmother's interest in ballet and her assertion that she has never been to a live performance, Paul purchases three tickets to commemorate her eighty-eighth birthday. Neal drives up from the city to attend the birthday dinner. Afterward, as he puts ice-cream cake back into the freezer, he expresses his fondness for Paul's grandmother and his wish that she knew that Paul and he are lovers.

Later, at the theater, Neal leaves during intermission, still bothered by Paul's apparent inability to see a problem in his refusal publicly to acknowledge his sexual orientation and their relationship. Meanwhile, Mrs. Andrews falls asleep in her seat. The story ends with Paul left to himself. Unamused by the dancing on stage, he is painfully conscious of the contrast between the grace and surety of Prince Siegfried and the Swan Queen and his own clumsiness in matters of the heart.

Themes and Meanings

Peter Cameron's use in the title and narrative of his story of Peter Ilich Tchaikovsky's ballet *Swan Lake* (1877)—which is often performed in excerpts rather than in its entirety—provides the story's thematic frame of reference. Odette, the ballet's heroine, is a creature of two worlds. By day, she is queen of the swans; by night, she is simply a beautiful young woman. Paul's life is similarly divided between two spheres of existence. In the city, he is a gay man with a live-in lover; in the suburbs, he is a dutiful son and grandson. Like Odette's ill-fated duality, Paul's uneasy balance between two separate identities appears doomed to failure.

In *Swan Lake*, Odette seems to be more at home in the world of sky and water; in the world of humans, she is lost. Odette and her human lover Prince Siegfried are no match for the sorcery of the evil Von Rotbart, who schemes to thwart their romance. No such malevolent figure manipulates the destiny of Paul Andrews, but it can be said that his own maladroitness is the principal source of his problems.

Further textual resonance is derived from the fact that Tchaikovsky, who composed the music for *Swan Lake*, spent most of his adult life fearing that his homosexuality might become common knowledge. His was a closeted existence, akin to Paul's.

Another comparison between the world of ballet and the world of this story stems from their shared emphasis on nonverbal communication. In dance, performers communicate by physical gesture; so too does Paul express himself. When Mrs. Andrews admits that she and Paul had been lonely since Neal moved back to the city and subsequently defers to Paul for corroboration, her grandson remains mute. "I never admit to being lonely," he says. Instead, he communicates by touch. Paul holds hands with Neal or rests his feet on Neal's bare back. These are secretive gestures, however, which Paul hopes to conceal from others. "That's the problem," Neal asserts, Paul's inability to be open about their relationship.

Yet, romance is a major preoccupation of this tale. Paul's parents are away on a "romance cruise" to the "love capitals of the world." Mrs. Andrews seems fixated on the lilac, a shrub whose fragrant clusters of heart-shaped flowers the poet Walt

Whitman used as an emblem of love. There also are, of course, the central emotional attachment between Paul and Neal and the referenced love between Odette and Prince Siegfried. This is an abiding theme in Peter Cameron's fiction: the often ambiguous yearning for or the precarious maintenance of romance.

Style and Technique

Creating carefully crafted stories that have been compared in subject matter and technique to the works of such modern American writers as Ann Beattie and David Leavitt, Cameron chronicles the lives of modern young people with an understated grace. He is a master of short witty sentences, such as clever correspondents write on postcards that they send from vacation spots. Indeed, the text of the card that Paul's mother sends from Greece is indistinguishable in shape and syntax from the wording of the main narrative.

There is a conscious spareness of language that may be accounted for, in part, by the inability of typical Cameron characters to explicate their feelings. Paul, for example, responds to Neal's discontent by admitting to himself, "I think about answering, but I can't." If he could give full voice to his feelings, perhaps he would say that what really matters is the moment itself as articulated by the senses. Paul tells his grandmother that it does not matter that she cannot remember what year it is or where she is. As each year follows the last, Mrs. Andrews seems to forget more and more; perhaps, thinks Paul, he himself will one day forget what he now thinks is most important. "Someday, I'll forget Neal, just like my grandmother has forgotten the great love of her life."

In acknowledgment of the unreliability of memory and the futility of forecasting the future, Paul leads a life that seems to demonstrate the value of the moment, an existence predicated upon direct sensory experience. This may account for the almost lyrical moments in the text, such as when Paul imagines that he is on the balcony of a Mediterranean villa, and not in his parents' suburban kitchen.

Although some critics say that Cameron creates characters who are detached from the world around them, there is actually an exaggerated consciousness of external environment in the typical Cameron narrative. Much value is placed on trademarks and descriptive labels. Perhaps this excessive regard for brand names, such as "Players" cigarettes and "Hostess" cherry pies, and the impulse to enumerate objects, such as the grandmother's repeated queries regarding the identification of items in her immediate surroundings, are the means by which individuals stay connected to their environment and to each other. Specificity provides a sense of surety in a world where less and less is sure.

S. Thomas Mack

EXCHANGE VALUE

Author: Charles Johnson (1948-)
Type of plot: Psychological realism
Time of plot: 1980
Locale: Chicago
First published: 1981

Principal characters:
COOTER, a young, unemployed African American man
LOFTIS, his ambitious older brother
ELNORA BAILEY, a neighbor woman

The Story

Cooter, the first-person narrator, and his brother Loftis break into the apartment of Elnora Bailey, an old black woman whose apartment is down their own hall. The woman has not been seen for a while, and although these two young men are not criminals by habit, they believe she will be an easy mark.

They find that Elnora, who is known around the neighborhood as a beggar, has been hoarding money and material things, including her own feces in coffee cans, for quite some time. They find her body, inflated in death, as well as close to $900,000 and additional wealth in the form of stocks and jewelry. They also discover many years' worth of old junk, including, most disturbing to Cooter, three portions of a tree. An old issue of the *Chicago Defender* tells them that she inherited most of her wealth from a former employer for whom she had worked as a maid.

Cooter urges his brother to forget the money and leave the things where they are, fearing they could be cursed. After Loftis dismisses his fears, the two set about moving everything valuable to their apartment. While they wonder what they should do with their haul, Cooter takes some money and goes on a shopping spree, buying himself new clothes. When he returns, Loftis has changed the locks and rigged a booby trap to protect their new things from anyone who would try to take them.

Loftis is angry that Cooter has spent $250 on clothing and warns him not to spend any more money until he, Loftis, returns from work. After Loftis leaves, the superintendent of the building discovers Elnora's dead body, and as she is being carried away, Cooter looks at her face and thinks that he can see there the poverty she dealt with for many years, and the way the money she unexpectedly inherited changed her. When Loftis does not return for four days, Cooter, obeying Loftis' command not to spend any more of the money, begs for food at a local diner, as Elnora once did.

When Loftis finally comes home, Cooter wants to confront him, but Loftis falls fast asleep. Cooter sees that Loftis has taped to a penny the message, "Found while walking down Devon Avenue." Seeing that Loftis has decided to hoard wealth like Elnora did, Cooter wonders if it has to be this way, but places this newfound penny with the rest of their wealth.

Themes and Meanings

"Exchange Value" is the second story in Charles Johnson's collection of short stories, *The Sorcerer's Apprentice* (1986). One of the themes of "Exchange Value" concerns setting in motion forces that one cannot then control. Loftis is shown as an ambitious young man, who sews labels of expensive suit manufacturers into the suits he buys at discount clothing stores. When he finally obtains the material things he longs for, however, he is unable to deal with it.

Many of the stories in *The Sorcerer's Apprentice* deal with magic. In "Exchange Value," the transformational value of money as a universal value system that can put a number and a value on anything is presented as a powerful force, dangerously magical in quality, which spellbinds both Cooter and Loftis. Loftis reasons that the dollar value of the piano they push to their apartment is equal to that of two gold lamé suits, a trip to Tijuana, or twenty-five sexual encounters with a prostitute. Like wizards, Cooter says, they now have the power to transform these things into anything that they wish.

It turns out to be the power itself that entrances Loftis. Remembering a time when, as a child, he traded a piece of family jewelry for a few pieces of candy, he determines not to make such a deal again. Like Elnora, he becomes a miser: After they move Elnora's things into their own apartment, he drags two trash bags of discarded clothing in, because he sees some use for them.

While Cooter watches Elnora being taken away, he has a sense of insight into what moved her to become a hoarder. Having finally and unexpectedly come into wealth, she became worried about loss, and reasoned that every act of spending was a poor deal because it resulted in a loss of buying power, and a loss of life.

When Loftis does not come home for four days, Cooter falls into the same type of behavior that Elnora had exhibited in her life. He stays inside much of the time, refuses to call for help when there is a plumbing problem, and goes out only to beg for food. When Cooter sees that Loftis has attached a note to a penny he found, he deduces that Loftis has been roaming the streets looking for loose change, and wonders if they are doomed to become misers like Elnora.

The story strongly suggests that Cooter was correct when he suspected that Elnora's things were cursed. The money and wealth of material possession that she came into did her no good: She went from being a hard-working maid to a beggar, and now, apparently, something similar is happening to Cooter and Loftis. The general theme is that the greatest power of money is not its power to transform one thing into another (by selling a piano to buy two gold lamé suits, for instance) but its power to captivate the imagination so the power of the exchange value of money, or anything else, becomes itself something to accumulate and hoard.

A more specific theme relates to the importance of values within the African American community. When members of this community accept the accumulation of wealth as itself a value worth pursuing, they risk losing themselves. The wealth that comes first to Elnora Bailey and then to Loftis and Cooter from a wealthy, established white family does not liberate them—instead, it limits and contains them. In accepting this wealth, they are accepting someone else's values as well, and those values inhibit them and virtually enslave their lives.

Style and Technique

"Exchange Value" is a tightly compressed story. The majority of the story concerns Loftis and Cooter's discovery and removal of Elnora Bailey's wealth. Because Johnson has serious ethical questions to explore, he uses many careful techniques to tip off his deeper meaning. For example, Loftis' transformation into a miser like Elnora is signaled in part by adjectives. When Cooter recalls giving Elnora some change, he describes her walk as "crablike"; several pages later, when he returns from his shopping spree, Loftis is described as "crabby."

Similarly, Johnson uses language to present Cooter as a keenly intuitive young man aware of the magical nature of this money. When he sees Elnora's wealth, he tells Loftis that he is afraid the money is cursed. Later, as they are moving her things to their apartment, he imagines himself and Loftis as two wizards, able to transform one thing into another. Finally, seeing Elnora Bailey's body carried away, he understands that her wealth had a spellbinding quality on her.

The colloquial language of the first-person narrator makes for an entertaining and compelling narration. When Johnson has the narrator suddenly experience deeper insights, the narrative suffers from lack of consistency. The problem any writer faces when trying to use a spoken language as the basis for a written narration is that the true hesitations, digressions, and ellipses of spoken language would be intolerably distracting on the page. Faced with this dilemma, Johnson opts to suggest a spoken language, rather than accurately depict it. Even so, Cooter's sudden realization that Elnora feared depletion because she realized that every purchase was "a poor buy: a lack of life" is not consistent with the narrator that Johnson invented whose own reading is largely confined to comic books, and who calculates the worth of a piano in terms of the sexual favors it could buy from a prostitute. Similarly, the rather abrupt change in Loftis at the end of the story is not carefully enough delineated to be entirely believable. The references to magic begin to sound like an excuse for a lack of character exploration.

Although the artistry in "Exchange Value" is flawed in minor ways, it does make for compelling storytelling. Because the story is told from the point of view of Cooter, who is largely dependent on Loftis for his survival, the helplessness he feels when he sees how Loftis is changing becomes paramount at the end.

Thomas Cassidy

A FABLE

Author: Robert Fox (1943-   )
Type of plot: Fable
Time of plot: The 1960's
Locale: New York City
First published: 1972

Principal characters:

THE YOUNG MAN, a typical lower-middle-class suburbanite who has just started his first full-time job
THE BLONDE, a beautiful but empty-headed young woman
HER MOTHER, a domineering woman who wants her daughter to make a good match

The Story

A neat and clean-shaven young man is taking the subway to Manhattan to begin his first day on the first regular job he has ever had. He feels happy, thanks to his new status as a middle-class office worker, the prospect of being able to buy things that he has always wanted, and the day's invigorating weather. Indeed, he is in love with the whole world because of the optimism and self-confidence infused by his new career. When he spots a beautiful young blonde, who is evidently out shopping with her mother, he is so strongly attracted that he cannot help staring.

The blonde notices the young man's attention and complains to her mother, who simply explains, "He's in love with you." The young man then seizes an opportunity to sit next to the blonde and starts a conversation by saying, "I'm in love with you." Although he has never met her before, he proposes marriage on the spot. Neither woman is surprised by this abrupt proposal. Neither displays any emotion. Both are interested only in learning whether the eager young man is a good catch. The blonde asks if he has a job and what his future prospects are, but the naïve suitor has only the vaguest idea of what his work will entail. All he knows is that he will have his own desk and handle a lot of paperwork. However, he says that he is getting a good salary and that he intends to work his way up in the company.

The mother is especially concerned about the young man's ability to be a good provider. She asks him why he wants to marry her daughter. He merely answers that the daughter is pretty and that he is in love with her. "Is that all?" the mother asks. "I guess so," he answers. "Is there supposed to be more?" "Not usually," the mother answers.

When the mother feels satisfied that the young man really is in love—or at least that he has convinced himself that he is—and that he fully intends to provide a good lifestyle for her daughter, she invites him to propose to her daughter again. The young woman, who appears to be entirely dependent upon her mother's direction, then accepts his proposal. The other passengers in the subway car have all been listening to this interchange like an audience in a movie theater. When the blonde accepts the young man's proposal, everyone smiles and applauds.

The conductor approaches the couple with a Bible in his hand, ready to perform a marriage ceremony on the spot. Like everything else in the story, it must be performed quickly, because the train is nearing the end of the line.

Themes and Meanings

Robert Fox's "A Fable" illustrates the emptiness, sterility, and anomie of modern existence. Like all fables, it relies heavily on its implicit moral. The most famous writer of fables was Aesop, whose little stories about animals generally show them engaging in foolish behavior in order to teach by implication what intelligent people should do. For example, in one fable a dog loses the bone that he is holding in his mouth when he tries to snatch the bone that he sees in the mouth of his own image reflected in a pond. The moral might be expressed as "a bird in the hand is worth two in the bush." The moral of Fox's short story may be harder to express in a single sentence. It would be too simplistic to express the moral as "marry in haste, repent at leisure." The young man and young woman in the story are certainly marrying in haste, but they may never develop enough insight into their own identities to repent at all. If they go through life without knowing whether they are happy or unhappy, they will be just like almost everybody else.

Fox's story is a modern fable similar to those of the famous American humorist James Thurber, collected in *Fables for Our Time and Famous Poems* (1940). As such, "A Fable" is considerably more complicated than the fables, parables, and myths of classic literature. Life has gotten complicated because of the onslaught of mass media, the frantic pace of life driven by modern transportation and communication, the fragmentation of labor created by modern production methods, the anonymity and alienation created by millions of people being crowded together in dehumanizing urban centers, and the spiritual disillusionment created by modern science. People are turning into robots: They behave, not as they are taught to behave, but as they are conditioned to behave.

The story is presented with a deceptively light touch. It seems much like a film comedy set in New York City—the type of fare that has been served in motion pictures from the time of Ginger Rogers and Fred Astaire up to the latest flimsy variations on the same boy-meets-girl plots. The notion of an intimate love affair being conducted publicly under the scrutiny of dozens of sympathetic urbanites seems to come straight out of a Hollywood film. This similarity is undoubtedly intentional. It is meant to suggest that modern Americans get their opinions, values, and aspirations from films; however, whereas the people on the screen are only shadows who will disappear when the projector goes off, the people who are influenced by their meretricious values and pseudo-sophisticated behavior are made of flesh and blood and will have their lives irrevocably affected.

Style and Technique

"A Fable" is a short short story. Such stories are typically not longer than one thousand to fifteen hundred words and take only a few minutes to read. There are many different types of short short stories. What they have in common, besides brevity, is that they start much closer to their climaxes than more conventional short stories, which usually offer more description and background information. Because of the need for brevity, the writer of a short short story devotes few words to describing characters or the settings in which the action takes place. There is usually only one incident occurring in a single setting. "A Fable" is a classic example of a short short story in many respects; its entire action takes place within a few minutes in a section of a subway car.

By not giving characters names, the author emphasizes the fact that they are strangers. The reader is placed among the ranks of the anonymous, voyeuristic subway passengers, who are also strangers to one another. The characters are not intended to represent real people but types of people to be seen in a metropolis every day. The young man is like thousands of other young men rushing to work downtown. The young woman is like thousands of other young women who want to get married to upwardly mobile young men who will provide them with homes and all the standard amenities of modern middle-class life. They will probably be no more or less happy or unhappy than millions of other American couples who get their opinions and emotions from the media, particularly from Hollywood, and who live and die without ever finding out who they really are.

The dominant impression of this story is that things happen much too quickly. A young man should not fall in love with a young woman and propose to her within the space of a few minutes. It is important to note that the effect of speeding everything up is heightened by placing the action on a fast-moving subway car. This setting provides a sense of urgency, a "ticking clock," because the train will soon reach Manhattan, where the young man must get off to go to work and the blonde must get off to go shopping with her mother. In a city the size of New York, their chances of ever meeting again are minuscule.

The most important thing about a story, as Edgar Allan Poe pointed out long ago, is its "effect"—not what it says, but the feeling that it evokes in the reader. "A Fable" evokes a complex effect, or feeling, of amusement, pity, melancholy, and perhaps a few other emotions, including the embarrassment that goes with recognizing one's own mistakes in others.

Everything in "A Fable" is unreal. The comedy is not meant to be truly comic but just the opposite. Although the situation depicted seems completely unreal, it is not so much different from what really happens to many young people who think they are falling in love because they are ripe to fall in love and feel that it is expected of them. The action is accelerated and exaggerated to make the point that this is indeed the way too many people live in modern times. They are not only strangers to everyone else but strangers to themselves.

Bill Delaney

THE FAITHFUL WIFE

Author: Morley Callaghan (1903-1990)
Type of plot: Sketch
Time of plot: The late 1920's
Locale: A train station restaurant and a nearby boardinghouse
First published: 1929

Principal characters:
GEORGE, a young lunch counter attendant
STEVE, his boss
LOLA, a shy, pretty woman who frequents George's restaurant

The Story

George has been working at the lunch counter of a train station restaurant in order to save money for college. It is his last day on the job before he leaves. The restaurant is frequented by young women on their lunch hours. Though these women usually avoid contact with the three other men who work at the restaurant, they occasionally chat with George. Though not a handsome man, George has a polite and generous nature and is well liked by Steve, the restaurant's manager.

George always notices one particular young woman (later identified as Lola) who comes to the lunch counter, yet something in her manner suggests an aloofness that makes him hesitate to speak to her. On this day when she comes in, George again notes how shy and pretty she is, even though she is dressed somewhat shabbily. She does not even have a piece of fur around the collar of her thin blue coat—something that most young women can afford.

After returning from a break that evening, Steve tells George that a young woman has telephoned for him and left a number. Not knowing who might have phoned, George returns the call and learns that it is the shy young woman from the lunch counter. She invites him to visit her at half past ten that evening.

At the woman's boardinghouse room George is somewhat nervous, not knowing what to expect, but the young woman quickly takes charge. Wearing a tight red sweater, she invites him to sit next to her. Soon he is kissing her. She responds excitedly to his embraces, but as George grows overly eager, she breaks away from him and begins pacing the poorly furnished room. When George asks what she is doing, she explains that she is expecting her roommate to return shortly, so he must be gone by then.

George suspects that something strange is going on when he notices the mark from a ring on the woman's finger. He asks her if she is not really waiting for her husband. She breaks down and tearfully confesses that her husband is a war veteran with a serious spinal injury who will soon return from the sanatorium where he has also been recuperating from tuberculosis. Because of his physical limitations they can no longer make love. She insists that she has been a faithful wife, but that when she learned that

George would be leaving the next day, she decided to take advantage of the situation—trusting that he would not complicate her life after their "affair." After she asks George to hold her once more, he leaves. He briefly considers asking for his job back in order to be with Lola, but decides not to spoil things for her because she has it "all figured out."

Themes and Meanings

Morley Callaghan's short stories frequently question conventional morality and "The Faithful Wife" is an example of this type of interrogation. This purposefully open-ended sketch suggests an examination of calculated pretense, or the idea of consciously hiding one's true nature for the purpose of breaking with traditional codes of moral behavior.

Though the story begins simply, it becomes complicated as young George is invited to the apartment of a young woman about whom he has been dreaming. Although there are reasons to suspect that George is not a total innocent, he is unaccountably nervous at the prospect. For one thing, it is clear that George has a respectful admiration for this woman to whom he has never even spoken. His impression is based on the disposition that she wears at his lunch counter each day. Seeing her as pretty, shy, and aloof, he assumes that she is unapproachable. He empathizes with her somewhat shabby appearance and feels sorry for her. It is not surprising, therefore, that George should be nervous when she boldly invites him to meet her at her apartment. Her behavior seems to conflict with the image that he has built of her. The resulting tension manifests itself in George's awkwardness in her room. Yet, the idea that Lola is not who she has seemed to be is taken to a further level as she reveals to George that she is married.

Callaghan, seeming at first intent on exploring the morality of a casual affair, leads to a consideration of a more knotty problem. What does one make of Lola's real loneliness and isolation? The aloof mask that she wears at the lunch counter each day hides her true desperation and sorrow. No casual need for idle fulfillment, her use of George is seen as an urgent plea. The reader initially suspects her need is solely for physical contact, yet the implications are deeper. Not only is she denied physical fulfillment with her invalid husband, but she must support them both, pay the hospital costs, and endure a terrible isolation. George's reaction, "That's tough, poor kid," may be a heartfelt reaction to the true details of her life.

The story might be viewed as ironic, sad, mildly tragic, or even affirming—if the reader interprets George's decision not to interfere with Lola any further as altruistic. As Callaghan does so often in his short works, he leaves the interpretations to the reader. He himself makes no moral judgments about Lola's, or George's, behavior, rather forcing the reader to weigh ideas about morality and immorality. Why is Lola given the ironic label of "faithful" wife? What constitutes faithfulness? What is the emotional cost to Lola in breaking with conventional behavior? These questions may have no simple answers, but they reflect the types of questions that Callaghan's stories frequently pose.

Style and Technique

"The Faithful Wife" is the first of thirty-nine short stories that Callaghan published in *The New Yorker*. Though his style changed over the years, developing even more of the flat, uninflected, and pared-down quality of modernist American contemporaries such as Sherwood Anderson or Ernest Hemingway, here Callaghan focuses on a moral dilemma by almost meticulously presenting a series of contrasting images.

The oppositions are abundant and are initially suggested by the contrast of coldness and warmth in the first paragraph. George's characterization contrasts with those of the more worldly countermen and "red-capped porters" who work at the train station. Lola contrasts with the other young women who frequent the lunch counter; to some extent this is highlighted by the dissimilarity of their appearances. Lola is shabby and poor, while the other young women are "brightly dressed and highly powdered." Lola has no fur collar on her coat, while most of the others have "a piece of fur of some kind." Further, the other young women smile at George, who knows them by their first names, while Lola remains shy, aloof, and nameless.

Callaghan does not present these oppositions merely to define George and Lola, for both are more than their mere opposition to others first suggests. For example, George is seemingly shy about speaking to Lola, but he may be more experienced than the initial contrasts made between him and the other counter workers make him appear. Steve remarks about George's not being able to keep straight all the phone numbers of his girls. Also, when Lola makes her intentions clear at her apartment, George does not hesitate to embrace and kiss her. Lola is even more unlike what the reader expects her to be after Callaghan first describes her. Her shyness and hesitant manner give way to passion and seeming desperation. Not only does she become aggressive toward George, but she dresses and acts in a manner antithetical to the quiet, poorly clothed girl of the lunch counter who invoked George's initial sympathy.

In a way the reader is led to see Lola and George in opposition, though they may initially appear soul mates. As Lola sits at the lunch counter, George "remain[ed] opposite her." Later, at her apartment, she sits down "opposite him." Yet, George and Lola are not necessarily opposites at all, and both turn out to be capable of genuine feeling. It is possible that the deliberate contrasts serve to focus attention on each's perception of the other. Ultimately, it becomes apparent that just as Lola is not who George expects her to be, so George may not be what she thinks either. It is probable that she expects him to be like the other counter workers. Instead, George surprises her by genuinely caring about her. His caring, however, undermines her plan, as she wants to have no emotional strings attached. Although Lola does not have things quite so "figured out" as she thinks, George concludes that it is probably best to carry on as if she has.

George T. Novotny

THE FALL

Author: Alberto Moravia (1907-1990)
Type of plot: Psychological realism
Time of plot: Unspecified
Locale: Italy
First published: "La caduta," 1940 (English translation, 1954)

>   *Principal characters:*
>   TANCREDI, a preadolescent Italian boy
>   HIS MOTHER
>   VERONICA, his mother's maid

The Story

Tancredi, a young Italian boy, has been ill for a few months, so his parents get a villa near the ocean for the remainder of his recuperation. During his illness, he has changed from a willful, capricious boy with curly hair to a short-haired, scrawny, and listless youth. He feels obsessed, guilty, and remorseful, but does not know about what.

The villa into which he, his mother, and her maid move belongs to an antique dealer who allows them to stay there in return for favors that the family has done for him. The antique dealer has been using the massive, three-story building as a storehouse, and every room is crammed with ugly, unsalable furniture, paintings, tapestries, and knickknacks. Even its windows fail to provide much light, because many are covered with stained glass. Its rooms smell of old wood, mold, and mice, rather than healthful sea air. Tancredi's mother finds the house uncomfortable and worries that one of them might damage something, but for Tancredi, the house is both terrifying and seductive. Although he can play outside on the beach, he increasingly spends his time exploring the house. Particularly attracted to its attic, he thinks of the rooms there as being like cells, whose low, whitewashed ceilings and rough floors he is sure contain the secrets of tragic lost loves. The rooms are filled with large, dark paintings, and Tancredi spends hours lying on his back in them, inventing terrifying stories based on their pictures.

One day in the midst of such a reverie, Tancredi remembers that he has made a slingshot and goes outside to test it in an enclosure adjoining the villa. When his sleeve becomes stuck on brambles through which he has passed often before, he believes that the brambles are consciously trying to stop him but still manages to enter the trash-littered sunken enclosure. Although he is outdoors, it is as oppressive as being inside the house; the day is overcast with dark clouds, and the acrid smell of rubbish fills the still air. He puts tin cans from the trash heap on the wall and shoots stones at them. When a large cat living at the villa strolls across the wall, he aims a stone at it, but does not really expect to hit it. He is shocked when his stone puts out one of the cat's eyes, and the cat stands motionless, surprised, staring at him. Rather than fearing the cat will attack him, Tancredi imagines that the cat will gain revenge by loyally attaching itself to him. After a sudden clap of thunder, Tancredi races home, only to find the injured cat waiting there for him; it rubs up against his bare legs, and Tancredi runs away, screaming. The cat follows him through the house, sometimes looking terrified, sometimes hopeful. Tancredi seizes a pistol from a table filled with ancient weapons and throws it at the cat, but instead of hitting the cat, he breaks the glass on the dining room door. Tancredi escapes into a third-floor bedroom, soundlessly closing the door.

The room he has entered is adjacent to the room that he left earlier, and quite like it, except that it is barren of pictures. The door connecting the two rooms is ajar; Tancredi hears two voices coming from the other room, but sees no one when he peeks inside. He becomes aware that one voice is a man's, then hears someone leave the room, and someone else drop onto the bed. Tancredi then sees Veronica's naked, white legs on the bed; at first, they seem unable to keep still, moving wearily and voluptuously, then they stop. Although unsure what he has seen, Tancredi is overcome with shame.

Tancredi falls asleep, and awakens to darkness. He hears rats in the ceiling, and then a piece of plaster falls on him. Seeing a rat in the ceiling, he calls frantically for Veronica. She comes in from the next room and knocks the rat out of the hole, but it falls on her and both she and Tancredi become hysterical. His mother then enters the room, and Tancredi wakes up from his dream about the rat.

A thunderstorm has started and caused an electrical fuse to blow out. Tancredi, who is very handy with electrical things, is asked to get his tools and fix the fuse. The cat appears while he is working on the fuse box, and he determines to kill it this time. As he aims a screwdriver at it, there is a blinding flash, and he passes out.

Two days later, Tancredi's mother tells her friends over a game of cards that the cat got caught in electrical wires, causing the flash and electrocuting itself. She adds that she has forbidden Tancredi to go near the electricity again.

Themes and Meanings

Alberto Moravia was a lonely, sickly, isolated child, suffering for most of his preadolescent and adolescent years from tuberculosis. Between nine and seventeen years of age, he spent five years in bed, including a period in a sanatorium in the Italian Alps when he was sixteen. It was during this confinement that he began writing; his first book of verse was published when he was thirteen. It is likely that "The Fall" reflects his experiences as a sickly adolescent to some extent. It certainly speaks to the burgeoning imaginative powers of a child trapped in hospitals and infirmaries with few diversions other than his imagination.

It has been said that Moravia regards love and sex as indispensable tortures, and that he probably fears women as much as he loves them. According to critic R. W. B. Lewis, everything in Moravia's novels either is an extension of sex or is converted to it. In "The Fall," Tancredi reflects not merely the normal confusion felt by a young boy entering puberty, but the heightened intensity experienced by a child with no normal social outlets. Although Tancredi's exact age is never given, it is stated "that his childhood was over and that he was on the threshold of his turbid and troubled adolescence." The shame, guilt, and confusion he feels over mysterious physical changes in his body leave him vulnerable to greater confusion when he sees Veronica's naked legs in the adjacent room.

In the introduction to *Bitter Honeymoon and Other Stories* (1954), the collection in which this story first appeared in English, Philip Rahv says the male characters in these stories "are at once fired with desire and filled with fear of the objects of their desire. . . . ridden by a sense of the intimate menace of sex" and that they see the women in a way that reduces their humanness. Significantly, Tancredi sees only Veronica's legs—disembodied parts of her, rather than the whole person. It is also interesting that when Tancredi hits the cat, his fear is not that the cat will die or attack him, but that it will become attached to him. The responsibility of commitment may seem too intense for a solitary child unused to much human contact.

Style and Technique

Many of Moravia's works, particularly his novels, exhibit a documentary style of writing. His short stories and novellas, however, generally are regarded by critics as more successfully dramatizing his recurrent sexual themes. Although reported primarily by a limited omniscient narrator, "The Fall" escapes the boundaries of reportorial writing because of the surrealistic, hallucinatory perspective of the overwrought adolescent protagonist. With the exception of its final few sentences, in which the narrator switches to the mother's point of view, all the story's events are seen from Tancredi's perspective. The closed, airless, dark setting of "The Fall" provides a perfect incubator for Tancredi's fantasies.

In "The Fall," only Tancredi is a fully developed character. Although his mother is broadly sketched, she is seldom mentioned. His father, if he is even at the villa, is never mentioned. This is consistent with Moravia's life and most of his fiction—in both of which the mother is the dominant parent. There is little description of Veronica, and no indication of who the mysterious man visiting her might be; he might be Tancredi's father, a neighbor, or someone employed to work at the villa.

The ending cleverly points out that Tancredi is changing in ways that escape his mother's notice. While playing cards with her friends—her main amusement while her son spends his days alone—she states, "I've strictly forbidden him ever to go near the electricity again. Boys are so reckless." In the final line, "And the game began," the narrator ironically emphasizes what the reader already knows: The woman's reckless little boy undoubtedly will be playing with "electricity" again.

Irene Struthers

THE FALLING GIRL

Author: Dino Buzzati (Dino Buzzati Traverso, 1906-1972)
Type of plot: Fantasy
Time of plot: Post-World War II
Locale: A city on the Italian coast
First published: "Ragazza che precipita," 1966 (English translation, 1983)

> *Principal characters:*
> MARTA, the nineteen-year-old falling girl
> UNNAMED RESIDENTS of the skyscraper

The Story

A nineteen-year-old girl named Marta falls from the top of a skyscraper that houses apartments and business offices; the story chronicles her slow-motion toppling from the roof toward the street.

Marta lets herself fall from the building after she watches the brilliance of the sunset over the city, which "provokes dreams of greatness and glory," and after she sees that the city she lives in is filled with mansions, diamonds, parties, and affairs. She hopelessly lets herself fall, perhaps because she recognizes that she cannot achieve the greatness and glory others have.

Marta slowly floats past various floors of the skyscraper and interacts with nameless inhabitants. She passes millionaires' balconies, where she is invited in to join the cocktail parties. Marta refuses, however, saying she is in a hurry, and floats onward, feeling enormously satisfied that the rich people notice her; she feels fascinating and stylish because of the attention paid to her by the wealthy.

As the sun plunges into the sea and evening comes on, Marta continues past offices where employees sit in long rows, looking up at the falling girl, and somewhat enviously ask who she is and where she is going. Marta only laughs and falls, saying she is expected down on the street. She notices the street is filled with long black cars and that the rich in their sparkling jewels are entering the building for a party, exactly the kind of event that she had dreamed of ever since she was a child. She imagines that if she arrives on time at the entrance to the building, she will find the true beginning of her life, the romance and wonderful fate for which she has been waiting her entire life.

Unfortunately, Marta notices that she is not alone on her plunge: Other young women also are streaming down the side of the building, head first, waving as they drop. Marta notices that they are more fashionably dressed, some even in minks, and she begins to feel less self-assured and more fearful. She wonders if she has made some kind of error. As she continues her fall, a new day dawns, but Marta is feeling worse because everyone has left the ball by now and the long black cars are gone from the front of the building.

At the story's close, Marta is seen from the perspective of a forty-year-old man, Alberto, and his wife, who live on the twenty-eighth floor. Their dialogue reveals that

Marta has aged tremendously and is now an old woman. The couple enjoy their breakfast and discuss the advantages and disadvantages of living on their floor: They only see old women falling past their windows, but they do have the opportunity of hearing the thud when these women hit the ground. Alberto listens for a number of minutes but hears no thud; dissatisfied, he takes another sip of his morning coffee.

Themes and Meanings

In "The Falling Girl," Dino Buzzati offers a critique of post-World War II Italy and, by extension, of all industrialized countries in which conspicuous consumption and hierarchies based on class exist. The skyscraper provides a metaphor for the gradations in society based on wealth. On the top floors, luxurious cocktail parties are attended by rich, elegant people who make silly conversation and enjoy the interesting diversion that has become a regular occurrence in the building: the falling girls. Near the bottom of the building, the tenants' diversion is less pleasant because the girls who fall have become old women; the tenants realize that the apartments on higher floors cost more because of the splendid views of the city, the sea, and the falling girls.

No one seems concerned for the girl, Marta, because the society is based on consumption, pleasure, entertainment, and diversion. Other people exist solely for one's pleasure. Marta is no revolutionary hero who dies in protest against this consumer society; she is simply a young girl who wants access to this world of diamonds and minks. She does not want to bring this culture down; she wants to become a member of it.

Those who work in the building either are trapped in their rows with their typewriters, or they run to the windows, view the girls falling, and feel envy for those who, in free-falling, seem somehow to have escaped the constraints of the world of labor, the world of weariness. They envy Marta; she envies the rich who attend the ball; Alberto envies those on the higher floors who have the more pleasant views; and those on the highest floors seem to envy no one, content with their diversions, silly conversations, and stylish clothes.

The culture that Buzzati depicts offers nothing but pleasure and the possibility of pleasure. There is no sense that those values that have been ascribed to women in the past—sacrifice, love, selflessness, or concern—are considered important by this culture; perhaps this is, in part, why it is only women who are toppling from the skyscraper. On the other hand, perhaps women have been so well acculturated that they have accepted the values of the culture completely; they fall to their deaths hoping for fulfillment, for the enjoyments of ravishing couture and pointless pleasures, but they only provide others with visual pleasures until they age. Then they provide those on the lowest floors with the pleasure of hearing the thud when they hit the ground.

Style and Technique

Along with Tommao Landolfi and Italo Calvino, Dino Buzzati is considered one of the master fantasists of twentieth century Italian literature. Buzzati, however, does not abandon realism completely in his stories; he combines realistic with fantastic elements to create a world that seems oddly familiar and strange at the same time. Everything in "The Falling Girl" is said so matter-of-factly, in such a controlled tone, that the fantastic element is muted somewhat. The reader does not question how a falling girl can dramatically age as she falls, or how she can engage in conversations at certain balconies. The rather plain, journalistic prose provides some sure footing for the reader, and also works in counterpoint with the bizarre, stranger-than-life plot.

The story achieves its effect by dramatically slowing down the events in the story, freezing the frames, then letting them roll again. Most authors condense time in their stories, abbreviating events and long passages of time; Buzzati, however, slows time down, lets the free-falling girl gradually become aware of her plight, lets her mood swing from elation to despair in slow steps.

Buzzati also implicates the reader in his story because the reader too is put into the position of being a voyeur, a witness of the girl's dramatic flight. Like the characters in the story who watch her fall with a calm akin to callousness, the reader appreciates the pyrotechnics of the plot and receives pleasure from the comic artistry. The reader too is a consumer, an inhabitant of this unnamed city in which pleasure is the central priority. Readers can enjoy the story, turn their backs from the falling Marta, and, like Alberto, return to the realities of their own world—their sips of coffee, their pages turned.

Fiction, however, leaves its mark. Alberto seems not to come to any awareness about his life, his position in the society. Buzzati's fiction, however, allows the reader both to receive pleasure and to achieve some sort of insight into the condition of members of industrialized societies. The reader is not simply a consumer; the reader produces meaning, recognizes himself or herself in the inanities of the fictive world. Because Buzzati never allows Marta to fall completely to the street, she is still in flight in the reader's imagination, still opening up a vision of human culture, which is revealed in its horrible pointlessness, its petty pleasures, its obliviousness to others' pain.

Kevin Boyle

THE FARM

Author: Joy Williams (1944-   )
Type of plot: Psychological realism
Time of plot: Around 1980
Locale: New England
First published: 1981

> *Principal characters:*
> SARAH, an upper-middle-class suburban woman
> TOMMY, her husband
> GENEVIEVE BETTENCOURT, a mother whose teenage boy Sarah and
> Tommy accidentally run over

The Story

Sarah and Tommy are an affluent couple leading a comfortable life in suburban New England. On the face of it, nothing is wrong with their lives, but one shadow plagues their happiness: They both have a drinking problem. As Sarah and Tommy go to their third party on a certain night in August, Sarah recounts a story about a young child eaten by an alligator. Tommy does not seem to respond to the story, and Sarah begins to reflect on the troubled state of their marriage.

The party is one of many in the couple's customary routine of drinking and social-izing, interspersed with name-dropping and boasts of European travel. After the party concludes, the couple go home. Sarah, who is driving, begins to feel the effects of her heavy alcohol consumption and starts to hallucinate. Her visions are brought to a sharp halt when she runs over a teenage boy standing in the middle of the road, killing him instantly.

The police exonerate the couple in the death of the boy, Steven Bettencourt. No charges are filed, and Sarah is not prosecuted or held legally accountable for the young man's death. Nevertheless, Sarah feels a severe sense of guilt and vows to give up drinking and orient her life in a new, more positive direction. This resolution, however, does not improve her emotional state. Indeed, Sarah feels disoriented by no longer drinking; it is as if her entire identity had previously depended on her alcoholism.

During the next three months, things seem to be returning to normal, but just as Sarah's sense of psychological solidity begins to be restored, her life receives a sudden and disagreeable jolt. Unannounced and unexpected, Genevieve Bettencourt, the mother of the boy Sarah ran over, comes to Sarah's door. She is weirdly amicable, showing no overt resentment. She and Sarah exchange information about their lives and families, in a manner at once intimate and coldly formal.

There is an unreal quality about the meeting. Genevieve reveals that Steven was hardly the perfect son, but still she displays a sense of deep mourning for him. Sarah apologizes to Genevieve, but Genevieve will not accept her apology. Sarah begins to realize that Genevieve's friendliness is a form of calculating revenge. Genevieve is determined not only to make Sarah feel guilty, but to ruin her life. Genevieve's actions constitute harassment, even stalking; but they are also a form of retribution, and Sarah cannot help but feel a sympathy for Genevieve that is against her own best interests.

Tommy feels that Sarah is being harassed by Genevieve and wants his wife to stop admitting her to their house. The eerie presence of Genevieve in the couple's home is the subject of a long and increasingly nettlesome tug-of-war between husband and wife. Sarah persists with the acquaintance, noting that Genevieve seems to take a particular interest in their own daughter, Martha. In attempted atonement for her misdeed, Sarah offers to share Martha with Genevieve. Genevieve, though, continues to bring up more memories of her son, until Sarah feels that the intruder has taken over her life. Tommy wants to move the family away to a farm in the country, but Sarah realizes that she cannot escape the psychic burdens symbolized by Genevieve's presence in her life. For her, things can never be as they once were.

Themes and Meanings

Although "The Farm" does not carry an explicit thesis about alcoholism, much of the story's emotional resonance derives from the impact of alcoholism on its characters' lives. Alcoholism is examined not merely as a clinical malady, but as a metaphor for any syndrome by which alienated characters seek to remedy the lack of meaning in their lives. Tommy and Sarah are complacent, assured members of a privileged social class. They attempt to paper over the emotional gaps in their flawed and unexamined relationship by drinking and by maintaining a false sense of self-satisfaction. Joy Williams analyzes alcoholism as both a medical and sociological phenomenon, but stresses primarily its destructive psychological effects. Alcoholism immures Tommy and Sarah within their own neuroses. It heightens the problems they already have and prevents them from finding any solutions to them.

The walls they have built around their own hypocrisies are shattered by the death of Steven Bettencourt. The killing introduces an alien and disturbing element into the couple's lives, and forces them to interrogate all of their previous assumptions. There are also class and religious elements here: Tommy and Sarah are propertied and Protestant, whereas the Bettencourts are working-class Roman Catholics. More compellingly, Steven's death makes Sarah, in particular, cognizant of the disturbing contradictions in her life that she previously repressed.

The nature of the title is significant. "The Farm" does not refer to the farm Tommy wants to buy Sarah at the end of the story, but to the colloquialism "to have bought the farm," meaning to have died. This phrase, introduced into the story by Genevieve in conversation with Sarah, implies that death is not just extinction or disappearance, but entering a new and disturbing realm. Steven has "bought the farm" in figurative terms, but metaphorically, so have Tommy and Sarah. Steven's death has made them aware of their own inadequacies. In order to escape this newfound self-knowledge, Tommy attempts to "buy the farm" in the sense in which one usually employs the word "farm," to move his family to a new, reassuringly agricultural domicile. The serene and placid reference Tommy intends tumbles over into the more threatening and unsettling slang phrase. A conventionally restorative flight to bucolic safety is not feasible. Geographic distance alone will not restore the past. The couple's earlier complacency is gone forever.

Style and Technique

Like such modern short stories as "The Garden-Party" (1922) by Katherine Mansfield, "The Farm" uses the unexpected death of an outsider to reveal unexpressed problems in the lives of comfortable and self-assured characters. Williams does not use Steven Bettencourt's death manipulatively, however. One reason for this is that Williams makes her characters so ordinary, so everyday, that the presence of the unexpected or the unlikely does not strike the reader as gratuitous or unearned.

Joy Williams' stories are generally agreed by critics to resemble, in structure and in tone, the minimalism pioneered by the late Raymond Carver. Williams, however, imparts to her fiction a surrealistic air all her own. This surrealism can be seen in the telling anecdote of the child being killed by the alligator. At first, this seems to be a pointless interruption of the narrative, but it has a twofold function within the story. It reveals a panoply of incident and example that anchors the story's metaphoric register, foreshadowing Steven's death. In Williams' thick, braided mode of narration, every quote and every detail matter in the tale's ultimate composition.

Williams is a self-conscious artist, eager to advertise the sophistication of her own fictional mode, while also operating on a very human level. The odd interruptions, sudden swerves of voice and narrative, and the sense of fey, winsome, if slightly wry wonder that pervades the story mirror the situations of the characters. Far from being structured, Williams' surrealism reflects the way in which the random tragedies of life rupture the self-assurance of people who thought they had their world under control. The artistic skill with which the story is rendered mirrors the messiness and incoherence of real life.

Margaret Boe Birns

THE FAT GIRL

Author: Andre Dubus (1936-   )
Type of plot: Psychological realism
Time of plot: 1955-1975
Locale: Louisiana and Massachusetts
First published: 1977

> *Principal characters:*
> LOUISE, an overweight, compulsive eater
> CARRIE, her college roommate
> RICHARD, the young lawyer whom she marries

The Story

Louise was kissed for the first time at the age of sixteen, when a drunken young man roughly grabbed her at a barbecue. Her father, a wealthy lawyer in a small city in Louisiana, often kisses her as well, but she can see pity in his eyes along with love. The reason for Louise's lack of affection from young men her own age and for her father's pity is that, since she was nine years old, she has been putting on weight from overeating. Her slim and pretty mother, worried about Louise's attractiveness to boys, feeds her dietetic lunches, but Louise later sneaks into the kitchen and makes peanut butter sandwiches to eat secretly. At school, she makes a show before her friends of refusing fattening foods, emerging from the cafeteria line with only a salad. Later, however, she sneaks sandwiches at home and buys candy bars, storing them in her bedroom closet behind stuffed animals from her earlier childhood. At the movies, she is fascinated by fat actresses, and at home, by fat friends of her mother. Like herself, she rationalizes, they are different, and she believes that she, like them, is fat because God has made her that way. Yet she is curious about them. Do they try to lose weight? Do they, too, go around thinking of food all day?

At a women's college in Massachusetts, Louise continues her old ways; however, now she does not need to hide anything from her mother. She stores candy bars in a drawer and eats whatever she wants. She senses her parents' disappointment when she chooses an all-female school, away from boys, and at college she feels out of place, especially in gym class where she must wear shorts. She hates her body. Her only college friend is Carrie, a thin, unhappy girl with thick glasses who becomes Louise's roommate for four years.

In the summer before her senior year, Carrie falls in love with a music student in Boston and experiences both love and sex. Concerned about Louise and wanting her to be loved the way that she feels loved, Carrie offers to help Louise lose weight. She puts her on a strict diet, does all the shopping, serves her small portions of broiled meat, fish, chicken, and lettuce in their room, and nurtures her through each day. Louise suffers enormously, starts to smoke cigarettes, and becomes irritable with Carrie, but sticks to the diet and eventually loses more than seventy pounds. When she goes home, her parents are proud of her, all of her relatives tell her she is beautiful, and for the first time since childhood Louise swims in the country club pool without embarrassment.

After graduation, Louise returns home, takes an inconsequential job just to have something to do, and starts seeing Richard, a young lawyer who has joined her father's firm. He is the first man to kiss her since that first drunken boy. After she gives herself to him, they are married; Carrie flies down from Boston to serve as her maid of honor. With Richard, Louise now seems to have everything: a husband who loves her, a beautiful home by the lake, and vacations in Mexico, Canada, and the Bahamas. While vacationing in Europe during their fifth year of marriage, Louise and Richard conceive a child.

Louise becomes increasingly troubled by her newly found happiness. She thinks that by becoming thin, she has somehow compromised herself, bought into the pleasures of the thin people she has always envied. She believes that she chose her friends merely because they were thin. She believes that even Richard does not see her or love her completely, because he cannot relate to the fat girl who she once was. During her pregnancy, her body is gaining weight, and she starts to develop her earlier craving for sweets. She begins to hide candy bars in the bedroom, waiting for Richard to leave the house. Her mother starts to worry about her again, while Richard becomes increasingly cold and distant after the birth of their son. They quarrel frequently and Richard does not touch Louise anymore because she is letting herself go. At night, Louise eats candy bars in the darkness of the bathroom, she buys loose dresses to hide her body, and she avoids wearing bathing suits and shorts. Richard's anger about her weight seems not to touch her, and Louise remains calm, hidden beneath the layers of her expanding flesh, as she watches his frustration and helplessness.

In the final scene, Richard is raging at Louise, the baby is crying, and Louise is holding the child against the folds of her flesh. Richard offers to help Louise, even to eat the same things that she eats, but she sees in him none of the compassion and love she saw earlier in Carrie, although she remembers nothing of that final college year except the hunger. She is continually hungry now, and when she comes downstairs, after putting her son in his crib, she is eating a candy bar, surprised to see Richard still there, for she is certain that he is about to leave her.

Themes and Meanings

Andre Dubus' "The Fat Girl" is not so much a story about a young woman's uncontrollable urge to eat to the point of obesity as it is the story of a psychological hunger, not only for love but also for acceptance as a whole person. The protagonist, Louise, clearly does not grow up in a cold and indifferent family environment. On the contrary, her father showers affection on her, indulges her, and never chides her about her weight. Her mother is concerned about her appearance and tries to give her dietetic lunches and motherly advice. What then is Louise's problem?

One might say that the source of her disturbance is her difference, the fact that she is a fat person in an unaccepting world of thin people. In that sense, she is not unlike many other people who are different in some way. Both of Louise's parents are thin, and they expect their daughter to be the same way. In fact, when she does try to fit in by losing weight, she tries to emulate her mother who, like Louise, has long pale blond hair and smokes cigarettes—a habit that Louise takes up during her diet. Louise is not popular with boys not because of who she is, but because of her weight. Even after she marries Richard and has his child, Louise feels that he only loves her because she is now thin and would not have loved the earlier, fat Louise. Both Louises, the fat one and the thin one, are the totality of Louise, and she wants to be loved as a complete person. As it turns out, her suspicions about Richard are correct, for as she gains weight, Richard becomes more distant. At the end of the story, it is clear to Louise that Richard—and most of the world—will not love her for who she is; he will simply respond to what she looks like.

This is not to say that Louise is an admirable character in the story. She is self-indulgent, willful, deceitful, and ultimately self-destructive. She is, nevertheless, uncompromisingly herself, something that everyone is—or wishes to be—and she is not entirely to blame. In a world where thin is beautiful and the different do not fit in, many people like Louise are doomed to loneliness, shame, and pity.

Style and Technique

While he does provide glimpses into the mind of Louise, Andre Dubus relates her story with a clinical objectivity similar to a case study of abnormal behavior, as the opening line, "Her name was Louise," suggests. It is an appropriate style, for it keeps the reader emotionally detached from feelings of ridicule or pity. The flat narrative tone is designed to increase the reader's understanding, to give one a series of sketches of Louise from high school, through college, to marriage and childbirth. Everything is narrated, and little, until the end, is dramatized, so the reader will reserve judgment until all the facts are in. It is only when one sees the confrontation between Louise and Richard toward the end of the story that one feels an accumulated pity for and understanding of the protagonist.

The story is told in three sections: Louise's high school years, her college years and loss of weight, and her marriage to Richard. One might say, in fact, that since parts one and three show Louise as a fat girl, with the story of her thin self sandwiched in between, the construction of the story is a perfect illustration of the old adage, "Inside every fat person is a thin person trying to get out."

Kenneth Seib

FATHER AND I

Author: Pär Lagerkvist (1891-1974)
Type of plot: Sketch
Time of plot: 1901
Locale: Sweden
First published: "Far och jag," 1923 (English translation, 1955)

> *Principal characters:*
> THE NARRATOR, a thirty-year-old man recalling a moment
>   when he was nine
> HIS FATHER, a railroad employee

The Story

The short, recognizably autobiographical sketch appears merely to describe a Sunday walk in the country taken by a nine-year-old boy and his father and to be without complication in plot or narrative. This appearance is qualified, however, by complex perspective and a complexity of reactions detailed by the narrator as he recalls his first awareness of the life that he was to live.

The walk begins in bright afternoon sunshine, as the father takes his son by the hand. They wave good-bye to the mother, who returns to preparing the evening meal, and move off to the woods. There they listen to the singing of the birds and the sounds of nature, to which they are accustomed but for which they have never lost appreciation.

As they make their way along a railway line, they share a sensation of freedom and privilege. The father is free because it is Sunday and he does not have to work; and both are privileged to walk along the railway line, a route forbidden to others, because the father works for the railroad. This privilege is further established as a train passes by and the father signals a familiar greeting to its engineer. The narrator then notes an odd but pleasant combination of scents, those of field flowers and the tar on railroad ties. To this mixture of nature and technology the reader is offered the opportunity to add another: The narrator notes that the telegraph poles "sang"; this picks up the narrator's note of the birdsong and combines the two types of song, one technological and one natural. Up to this point everything is harmonious under a clear sky on a beautiful day.

Mention of the clear sky and the beautiful day is then followed by intimations of discord. Scanning a field of oats, the father understands the perfection of the crop, but the son, whose orientation is town life, does not. As they cross a bridge over a stream pleasantly swollen by the springtime flood, they hold hands to lessen the danger of falling through the railroad ties. Each delight now includes its check of inharmony. A visit to the cottage of a railroad lineman, who provides them with a snack, and the father's subsequent ascertainment of a semaphore's position make it clear that the Sunday afternoon is not entirely free of chores. As they walk along a river, enjoying its beauty, the father is reminded of his own boyhood delight in perch-fishing there, an idyllic pleasure for which he now has no time. After a cheerful contest of throwing pebbles into the water, they grow tired and turn homeward.

Twilight comes on, and the woods become unpleasantly strange. The boy catches sight of a glowworm under the darkening trees, but the father does not respond to his son's reaction. The telegraph poles, which sang in the daylight, now rumble hollowly with a menacing, subterranean voice. Crossing the bridge again, the boy is terrified by the roaring of the stream in the dark abyss below.

In full darkness the discord becomes complete, and the father's calm is in strong contrast with his son's fear and trembling. The boy's complaint about horror in the darkness is brushed off by his father, who is sustained by his unquestioning belief in God. The boy feels lonely and forsaken and considers the invisible God to be part of the horror. This moment of alienation of son from father is dramatically punctuated by the mighty roar of a black train speeding past. The entire train is unlit save for the coal fire of the engine, in the glow of which a strange engineer, unknown to the father, stands immobile and stonelike, intent solely upon plunging into the darkness. Choking with dread, the boy realizes the anguish that will be his in his movement out of the secure and real world of his father, who will not always be able to protect him, and into a life that hurtles "blazingly into complete and endless darkness."

Themes and Meanings

Early in his life, Pär Lagerkvist became aware of his incapacity for upholding and adhering to the stern and uncompromising religion of his forebears and of his consequent exclusion from the security and meaning that their religion provided. His estrangement from religious faith engendered his humanism; and his need for the security and meaning denied him produced his anguish (*ångest*) and his longing (*längtan*). His humanistic inclination and his experience of *ångest* constitute the theme of "Father and I."

The nature of Lagerkvist's humanism, with its development of an emphasis on alienation and authentic individualism, already much in evidence in "Father and I," came to coincide with existentialism, not so much in the character of Jean-Paul Sartre's philosophy as in the intonations of Albert Camus' fiction and lyrical essays. Like Camus, Lagerkvist was tormented by the essential unhappiness of human life and sought, not to escape it through rational philosophy or self-deception, but to nurture, as the nucleus of human unhappiness, that longing which—because it cannot be satisfied—becomes its own meaning and, as such, the fulfillment of the life of one who confronts it with the same constancy as Camus would have one confront the absurd. Where wisdom for Socrates consisted in knowing that he did not know, happiness for Lagerkvist, as for Camus, consisted in pursuing it while remaining unflinchingly aware of its untenability. The awareness entails *ångest*, which in turn intensifies life, which is its own value.

The religion of the father in "Father and I" is, like philosophical formulas for the achievement of happiness, a form of self-deception, so far as Lagerkvist is concerned.

The father sees neither the glowworm nor the significance of the baleful glow of the black train's fire, the one representative of life, the other intensified life. The son, who is conscious of both, experiences the anguish (the existentialists' *Angst*) that informs such consciousness.

Lagerkvist presented "anguish" as his inheritance (*arvedel*) in *Ångest*, a work that he published in 1916. His inheritance was not a spiritual tradition but the anguish of life itself. To him, life is not inherently good in the moral sense. In its meaninglessness and in the competitive struggle to survive, it is a form of evil, of original sin without a redeemer. It is like that fiery black train with its diabolical engineer. In *Ångest* he describes his life struggle: "I tear my sore and wounded hands/ against the hill and darkened woods/ against the black iron of the sky." He selected "Father and I" to be the first in his collection of stories entitled *Evil Tales* (*Onda sagor*, 1924; English translation, 1955). Without a god of light or a savior to atone for the evil of life, Lagerkvist saw only endless darkness and the responsibility of an individual to save his own or her own self, not as an immortal soul, but as a vitally mortal self. "Father and I" presents a nine-year-old boy's initial awareness of this lonely and fearful struggle.

Style and Technique

In his 1952 commentary on "Father and I," Arne Häggqvist says that Lagerkvist has "here composed one of his finest autobiographical sketches, realistically suggestive and, at the same time, acutely symbolical." This observation about Lagerkvist's style applies as well to all of Lagerkvist's later fiction, in which labyrinthine allegory assumes a surface of lyrical but simple narrative. By the early 1920's, Lagerkvist had fully abandoned his early expressionistic style, with its exclamatory color, in favor of a style governed by the subtle multiperspectivity of cubism.

The narration of "Father and I" is in the cubistic mode. Concretions in the first half of the story—such as the passing train, telegraph poles, and the rushing stream—are reconstituted and reconfigured in the second half, in the manner of segments of planes redisposed on a cubist canvas. The combined perspectives of day and night are interspatial with the combined perspectives of the thirty-year-old narrator and the child that he was at nine. The reactions of the child are genuinely those of a nine-year-old, and they are imperceptibly, almost indistinguishably, deepened by the symbolic content of the mature narrator's recollections. For example, after the black train is engorged by the night, the father puzzles over the strange train and the strange engineer, while the son has a presentiment of its significance and a sense that it was for his sake that the train roared past them: Speaking as narrator about his boyhood experience, he interprets that experience retrospectively as an anticipation of the anguish that he would much later articulate in this autobiographical depiction.

Roy Arthur Swanson